Prentice Hall
CONSUMER MATHEMATICS

Francis G. French

Francis G. French, Mathematics Teacher
Baltimore City Public Schools, Baltimore, Maryland

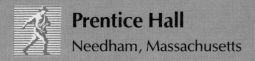

Prentice Hall

Needham, Massachusetts   Englewood Cliffs, New Jersey

EDITORIAL DEVELOPMENT
Linda Andrews
Terry Andrews
Suzanne Gentes
Deborah Sargent
Pauline Wright

DESIGN DIRECTION
L. Christopher Valente

DESIGN COORDINATION
Betty Fiora

PRODUCTION/MANUFACTURING
Bill Wood

PRODUCTION/DESIGN SERVICES
Daniel Ashton
Michael C. Burggren
Michael A. Granger
Dorothy Marshall
Sheaff Design, Inc.
Linda Dana Willis

PHOTOGRAPH RESEARCH
Susan Van Etten

PHOTO STYLIST
Elizabeth Willis

COVER DESIGN
John Martucci and L. Christopher Valente

FRONT MATTER DESIGN
Perspectives/Susan Gerould

REVIEWERS
Bettye C. Hall
Director of Mathematics, K-12
Houston Independent School District
Houston, Texas

Marvin Hartung
Classroom Teacher
Bloomington Kennedy High School
Bloomington, Minnesota

Clara P. Mathews
Math Teacher
Dreher High School
Columbia, South Carolina

CONSULTANTS AND WRITERS
For Critical Thinking and Decision Making:

Mary Ann Brearton
Science Specialist
Maryland Department of Education
Baltimore, Maryland

Sarah Dolde Duff
Educational Specialist
Baltimore City Public Schools
Baltimore, Maryland

Clarissa Brown Evans
Educational Specialist
Baltimore City Public Schools
Baltimore, Maryland

For Skill Development:

Marian B. DeLollis, Ph.D.
Principal
Saint Ursula Academy
Cincinnati, Ohio

1991 Printing
©Copyright 1989, by Prentice-Hall, Inc.

ISBN 0-13-166729-7

Printed in the United States of America

12 13 14 15 - 03 02 01 00

A Simon & Schuster Company

Table of Contents

CHAPTER 8

Buying a Car   254

CHAPTER 9

Public Transportation   290

CHAPTER 10

Renting an Apartment   320

CHAPTER 11

Buying a House   350

CHAPTER 12

Paying Taxes   384

CHAPTER 16

Probability, Statistics, and the Consumer   *508*

Reviewing the Basics

Rounding and Estimating
Whole Numbers and Decimals

Rounding and estimating are used when you do not need to know exact answers. For example, you can estimate the total amount of a purchase.

To round a number to a specified place, find the digit in that place. Then look at the number to the right of that place. If the number to the right is less than (<) 5, the number does not change. All the places to the right become zeros or are dropped. If the number to the right of the place is greater than or equal to (≥) 5, the number is replaced by the next higher number and all the places to the right become zeros or are dropped.

EXAMPLE 1
Rob bought three albums. One cost $9.75, one cost $12.39, and one cost $8.50. About how much did the three albums cost in all?

$$
\begin{array}{ll}
\$9.75 \rightarrow \$10 & \text{Round each} \\
\$12.39 \rightarrow \$12 & \text{number to the} \\
\$8.50 \rightarrow \underline{\$9} & \text{nearest dollar.} \\
\qquad\quad \$31
\end{array}
$$

ANSWER: The three albums cost about $31.

OTHER EXAMPLES

7,436.98 + 289.62

$$
\begin{array}{r}
7,436.98 \rightarrow 7,400 \\
+\ \ 289.62 \rightarrow +\ \ \ 300 \\
\hline
7,700
\end{array}
$$

$758.50 − $196.25

$$
\begin{array}{r}
\$758.50 \rightarrow \$800 \\
-\ 196.25 \rightarrow -\ 200 \\
\hline
\$600
\end{array}
$$

0.0642 + 0.0972

$$
\begin{array}{r}
0.0642 \rightarrow 0.06 \\
+0.0972 \rightarrow +0.10 \\
\hline
0.16
\end{array}
$$

EXAMPLE 2
Deborah purchased a bedroom set on the installment plan and must make 22 payments of $73.95 each. About how much will she pay in all?

$$
\begin{array}{r}
\$73.95 \rightarrow \$70 \quad \text{Round to nearest ten.} \\
\times \quad\ 22 \rightarrow \times 20 \\
\hline
\$1,400
\end{array}
$$

ANSWER: Deborah will pay about $1,400.

OTHER EXAMPLES

$13,455 \div 1,035$

$13,455 \rightarrow 13,000$
$1,035 \rightarrow 1,000$
$13,000 \div 1,000 = 13$

0.017×0.4892

$$\begin{array}{r} 0.017 \rightarrow 0.02 \\ \times\,0.4892 \rightarrow \times\ \ 0.5 \\ \hline 0.010 \end{array}$$

$\$2,061.50 \times 0.75$

$$\begin{array}{r} \$2,061.50 \rightarrow \$2,000 \\ \times\ \ \ \ \ \ \ 0.75 \rightarrow \times\ \ \ \ \ \ 0.8 \\ \hline \$1,600 \end{array}$$

EXERCISES

Round $36,258.168 to each of the following places.

1. Nearest 1¢

2. Nearest 10¢

3. Nearest $1

4. Nearest $10

5. Nearest $100

6. Nearest $1,000

7. Nearest $10,000

Estimate the answer to each of the following problems.

8. Maineville has a town budget of $13,472,816.43. Round this figure to the nearest hundred thousand for use in a newspaper headline.

9. Elaine has to drive 815 miles to a conference. If she drives 586 miles the first day, about how far must she drive the second day, rounded to the nearest hundred miles?

10. Ed earned $438.95 plus $98.50 overtime. About how much did he earn in all?

11. Roberto purchased 12 cans of juice for $1.49 a can. About how much did he spend?

12. Carolyn will pay her automobile insurance premium of $317.94 in 6 equal payments. About how much will each payment be?

13. Chris has $163.42 saved. About how much more does he need to buy a stereo that costs $249.95?

14. Rich and Karyn want to purchase a car that costs $9,863.58. They are going to add options costing $1,106.19. About how much will the car cost them with the options?

15. Ken purchased a wheelbarrow for $29.95, a garden hose for $14.75, a lawn mower for $315.20, and a rake for $4.50. About how much did his purchases total?

16. Cathy made six payments of $42.19, $45.58, $48.21, $40.91, $50.03, and $44 on her loan. About how much did she repay?

17. Tim took a job that paid $16,000 a year. If he was paid semimonthly, about how much was his salary each pay period?

Using Addition and Subtraction
Whole Numbers and Decimals

Addition and subtraction are used to keep track of the amount of money in a bank account. When you take money out of the account, you must subtract the value of the *withdrawal*. When you put money in the account, you must add the value of the *deposit*.

EXAMPLE 1

A deposit of $50 is put in a bank account. If there was $478.94 in the account already, what will the new amount be?

Add: $50 + $478.94   Check:

	Line up the decimal points.	
$50.00	**Write a decimal point and two zeros.**	$478.94
+ 478.94	**Regroup as necessary.**	+ 50.00
$528.94		$528.94✔

ANSWER: The new amount will be $528.94.

OTHER EXAMPLES

0.4 + 0.782	6.845 + 265	84.2 + 4.76	0.86 + 5.031 + 34.4
0.782	6.845	84.20	0.860
+0.400	+265.000	+ 4.76	5.031
1.182	271.845	88.96	+34.400
			40.291

EXAMPLE 2

A withdrawal of $33.85 is made from a bank account. If there was $563.40 in the account before the withdrawal, what will the new amount be?

Subtract: $563.40 − $33.85   Check:

12 13		
5 2 3 10	**Line up the decimal points.**	
$563.40	**Regroup as necessary.**	$33.85
− 33.85		+529.55
$529.55		$563.40✔

ANSWER: The new amount will be $529.55.

OTHER EXAMPLES

15.3 − 9.142	36.23 − 0.7	$80 − $5.35	731.46 − 5.6
15.300	36.23	$80.00	731.46
− 9.142	− 0.70	− 5.35	− 5.60
6.158	35.53	$74.65	725.86

EXERCISES

Add the value of the deposit to the present amount to find the new amount. Check by adding up.

Present Amount	Deposit	New Amount
$ 728.31	$348.72	1. ■
$ 35.72	$134.28	2. ■
$1,584.62	$491	3. ■
$ 375.95	$ 38.99	4. ■
$3,052	$ 76.37	5. ■

Subtract the value of the withdrawal from the present amount to find the new amount. Check by adding.

Present Amount	Withdrawal	New Amount
$ 263.83	$172.58	6. ■
$ 147.59	$ 9.89	7. ■
$ 360	$ 48.50	8. ■
$ 123.65	$ 55.79	9. ■

Add or subtract. Check your answers.

10. 0.9
 $+5.28$

11. 9.5
 0.33
 $+0.19$

12. 12
 $- 3.73$

13. 35.723
 4.27
 $+63.008$

14. 685.4
 $- 17.32$

15. 49.952
 -12.87

16. 0.25 + 0.3

17. $144.28 − $73.54

18. $12.45 + $3.38

19. 8.138 + 263.17

20. 15.86 − 4.7

21. $31.75 − $24.87

22. 218 + 67.3 + 35.493

23. $3.78 + $14 + $.63

24. $62.91 + $17.59

25. $15.41 + $138.37 − $56.93

26. 28.6 + 374 − 47.43

Solve.

27. Raymond has $476.25 in a savings account. He makes a deposit of $76.14. Find the new amount in the account.

28. Carol Lou's checking account contains $142.51. She writes a check for $37.69. Find the new balance of the account.

29. Salvatore deposited checks for $23.50 and $249.73 into his savings account. He already had $1,551.64 in the account. Find the new amount.

30. Nancy has $238.45 in her checking account. She deposits $65 and writes a check for $129.89. How much money is in the account now?

Using Multiplication and Division
Whole Numbers and Decimals

Multiplication and division are used to determine installment payments and the total amount paid for goods purchased on installment plans. When you know the amount of each installment payment and the number of payments you must make, you multiply to find the total amount of the purchase. When you know the total amount of the purchase and the number of payments you must make, you divide to find the amount of each installment payment.

EXAMPLE 1
The balance due on a bicycle may be paid in 12 payments of $15.90 each. What is the total of the monthly payments?

Multiply: $15.90 × 12

```
   $15.90    two decimal places
 ×     12
    31 80    $15.90 × 2
   159 0     $15.90 × 10
  $190.80    Mark 2 decimal places.
```

Check:
```
       12
   ×$15.90
     10 80
     60
     12
  $190.80✔
```

ANSWER: The total is $190.80.

OTHER EXAMPLES

| 480.62 × 3.5 | 68.31 × 0.02 | 783.002 × 5.004 | 0.2468 × 0.023 |

```
    480.62          68.31          783.002          0.2468
 ×     3.5        × 0.02         ×   5.004        × 0.023
   240 310         1.3662          3 132008           7404
 1 441 86                          3 915 01000         4936
 1,682.170                         3,918.142008     0.0056764
```

EXAMPLE 2
The total cost of a purchase is $97.80. This amount will be paid in 12 equal payments. How much is each payment?

Divide: $97.80 ÷ 12

```
      $ 8.15
 12)$97.80     Estimate and divide: 97 ÷ 12 = 8
     96        Multiply 8 × 12.
      1 8      Subtract, bring down, and divide.
      1 2      Multiply 1 × 12.
        60     Subtract, bring down, and divide.
        60     Multiply 5 × 12.
```

Check:
```
    $8.15
 ×     12
    16 30
    81 5
  $97.80✔
```

ANSWER: Each payment will be $8.15.

OTHER EXAMPLES

$36 \div 1.2$

$$\begin{array}{r} 3\,0 \\ 1.2\overline{\smash{)}3\,6\,0} \\ \underline{3\,6} \\ 0 \end{array}$$

$0.4963 \div 0.07$

$$\begin{array}{r} 7.09 \\ 0.07\overline{\smash{)}0.49\,63} \\ \underline{49} \\ 0\,63 \\ \underline{63} \\ 0 \end{array}$$

$0.2535 \div 5$

$$\begin{array}{r} 0.0507 \\ 5\overline{\smash{)}0.2535} \\ \underline{25} \\ 035 \\ \underline{35} \\ 0 \end{array}$$

$21.28 \div 3.8$

$$\begin{array}{r} 5.6 \\ 3.8\overline{\smash{)}21.2\,8} \\ \underline{19\,0} \\ 2\,2\,8 \\ \underline{2\,2\,8} \\ 0 \end{array}$$

EXERCISES

Multiply the amount of each payment by the number of payments to find the total cost. Check by multiplying the number of payments by the amount of each payment.

Amount of Payment	Number of Payments	Total Cost
$ 15.98	6	1. ■
$408.61	12	2. ■
$198.75	36	3. ■

Divide the total cost by the number of payments to find the amount of each payment. Check by multiplying the amount of each payment by the number of payments.

Total Cost	Number of Payments	Amount of Each Payment
$ 9,623.80	4	4. ■
$ 3,786	24	5. ■
$14,852.16	48	6. ■

Multiply or divide. Round to the nearest cent, if necessary.

7.
$$\begin{array}{r} 1.99 \\ \times\ 2.3 \\ \hline \end{array}$$

8.
$0.03\overline{\smash{)}96.3}$

9.
$$\begin{array}{r} 13.31 \\ \times\ 0.23 \\ \hline \end{array}$$

10.
$$\begin{array}{r} \$1,245.00 \\ \times\quad 0.667 \\ \hline \end{array}$$

11.
$2.5\overline{\smash{)}\$919.50}$

12. $128 \div 0.4$

13. $\$692.50 \times 7.75$

14. $0.1105 \div 3.25$

Solve. Round the answer to the nearest cent, if necessary.

15. Linda made 24 payments of $135.50 for her computer. What was the total cost of the computer?

16. Jill purchased 15.3 square yards of carpet for $260. What was the cost per square yard for the carpet?

17. Bob bought 7.35 pounds of ribs for a barbecue at a cost of $1.98 per pound. How much did he pay for the ribs?

18. Frank sold 60 magazines and received $149.40 in payment. What was the selling price of each magazine?

Using a Calculator

Examine the calculators in your class. Compare the position of the common keys, and note the major operating, arithmetic, and special function keys as well as the numerals.

Find the display on your calculator. This is the window in which a number or an answer is shown when you use your calculator. When a calculator is first turned on, the display will show ⟋0.⟍ . A zero will always be shown before the decimal point on your calculator if there is no whole number displayed.

Key: .632 ⟋0.632⟍

One limitation of calculators is that they all show a limited number of digits in the display, with a maximum of 8 digits being the most common. To discover what your calculator will do if there is an *overflow* in the answer, key 99999999 $+$ 1 $=$. Compare the result on your calculator to others in the class.

Find the following keys on your calculator.

Operating keys

On Off C_E^C

           correct error/clear

Before using a calculator, you should clear the display. Pressing C_E^C once clears the last entry; pressing it twice clears the display.

Arithmetic keys

$+$ $-$ $\times$ $\div$ $=$

Special keys

$\%$ percent $.$ decimal point $+/-$ change sign $\sqrt{}$ square root

Note: On some calculators the $=$ must be keyed after $\%$ to get a correct answer. See if your calculator requires $=$ to be keyed.

Key: 2550 $\times$ 2.5 $\%$

If the display shows ⟋63.75⟍ you do not need to key $=$ after $\%$. If the display shows ⟋0.025⟍ you must key $=$ after $\%$ to get the answer ⟋63.75⟍.

Memory keys

M+   add to memory

M−   subtract from memory

M_C^R 1 press recalls from; 2 pressses clear memory

The memory keys are particularly helpful in solving multistep problems.

EXAMPLE 1

Perry bought a set of tools for $178.95. He will pay for them in four equal payments. How much will each payment be?

You must first determine the operation that is needed. You must divide to find the answer to this problem.

Key: $\boxed{C^C_E}$ 178.95 $\boxed{\div}$ 4 $\boxed{=}$ ⟋⟋44.7375⟋⟋

To answer the question asked in the problem, you must round the number shown in the display to the nearest cent.

$$\$44.7375 \rightarrow \$44.74$$

ANSWER: Each payment will be $44.74.

EXAMPLE 2

Emily bought 3 gallons of paint at $15.98 per gallon, a paint roller kit for $9.98, 2 paint brushes at $3.59 each, and a clean-up kit for $6.50. How much change did she receive from $75?

The memory function is particularly helpful for solving problems such as this.

Key: $\boxed{C^C_E}$ 3 $\boxed{\times}$ 15.98 $\boxed{M+}$ cost of paint
Key: 9.98 $\boxed{M+}$ cost of roller kit
Key: 2 $\boxed{\times}$ 3.59 $\boxed{M+}$ cost of brushes
Key: 6.5 $\boxed{M+}$ cost of clean-up kit
Key: 75 $\boxed{-}$ $\boxed{M^R_C}$ $\boxed{=}$ ⟋⟋3.4⟋⟋ $75 - total cost = change

ANSWER: She received $3.40 in change.

EXERCISES

1. Find the sum: 687,231 + 5,469 + 382 + 4 + 58,926

2. Find the difference: 58.689325 − 9.00647

3. Find the product: 3,869.2 × 2.67

4. Find the quotient. Round to the nearest hundredth:
76,384.502 ÷ 25,968.24

Solve. Round to the nearest cent.

5. Sarah bought 28.75 square yards of carpet for $13.55 per square yard. How much did the carpet cost?

6. Dennis bought 12 bags of fertilizer for $191.40. How much did each bag cost?

7. Sylvia bought 2 pounds of steak at $4.19 per pound, 3 pounds of apples at $.49 per pound, a head of lettuce for $.99, and a carton of milk for $1.79. How much did she spend in all?

8. Karen bought 2 pairs of shoes for $24.98 each, 2 pairs of jeans for $29.95 each, a shirt for $13.50, a belt for $4.95, and 3 sweaters for $19.95 each. How much change did she get from $200?

Reviewing Problem Solving Skills
Four-Step Plan

Here is an easy step-by-step approach to problem solving.

1 **READ** the problem carefully.
   a. Find the question asked.
   b. Find the given facts.

2 **PLAN** the solution.
   a. Select a strategy.
   b. Think or write out your plan.
   c. Choose the method of computation you will use: calculator; paper and pencil; estimation; mental arithmetic.

3 **SOLVE** the problem.
   a. Estimate the answer.
   b. Compute the exact answer.

4 **CHECK.**
   a. Check the accuracy of the arithmetic.
   b. Compare the answer to the estimate.
   c. Look back at the problem to see if the answer is reasonable.

EXAMPLE

On a weekend trip, Anita traveled 325.5 miles. Her van used 17.5 gallons of gasoline. Find the average fuel mileage (miles per gallon).

1 **READ** the problem carefully.
   a. Find the question asked.   What is the fuel mileage?
   b. Find the given information.   17.5 gallons of gasoline
                                        325.5 miles traveled

2 **PLAN** the solution.
   a. Select a strategy.
      Choose the operation by looking for operation indicators. The words *find the average* and *miles per gallon* (rate per unit) indicate division.
   b. Think or write out your plan relating the given information to the question asked.
      The number of miles traveled divided by the number of gallons of gasoline used is equal to the fuel mileage.
   c. Choose the method of computation you will use.
      Because of the numbers used, a calculator would be a good choice for computing. If a calculator is not available, pencil and paper would be an appropriate method of computation.

3 SOLVE the problem.

a. Estimate the answer.

17.5 → 20 gallons
325.5 → 320 miles
320 ÷ 20 = 16 miles per gallon

b. Compute the exact answer.

```
        1 8.6
17.5 )325.5 0
      175
      150 5
      140 0
       10 5 0
       10 5 0
```

4 CHECK.

a. Check the accuracy of your arithmetic.

```
   18.6
 ×17.5
   9 30
 130 2
 186
 325.50 → 325.5✔
```

b. Compare the answer to the estimate. The answer 18.6 mi/gal is close to the estimate, 16 mi/gal.

c. Look back at the problem. 18.6 mi/gal is a reasonable value for the fuel mileage of a van.

ANSWER: The average fuel mileage is 18.6 mi/gal.

EXERCISES

Solve. Round to the nearest cent, if necessary.

1. Dean has set aside $25 to buy a birthday gift for his brother. He spends $17.63 on a basketball. How much money does he have left?

2. Belinda works 20 hours per week in a day-care center. She earns $147 each week. How much does Belinda earn per hour?

3. Cary had a jar full of change to deposit. He had $2.67 in pennies, $1.85 in nickels, $3.40 in dimes, and $6.75 in quarters. What was the total deposit?

4. A candidate for the state senate held a fund-raising dinner. Six hundred fifteen supporters paid $25 each to attend the dinner. How much money was raised?

5. Bruce types term papers for other students. He charges $1.25 per page and can type 5.25 pages per hour. How much can Bruce earn in one hour?

6. Phil drove 150 miles to see a baseball game. The combined cost of the gasoline and tolls was $7.90. What was the cost per mile for the trip?

Select the letter corresponding to the correct answer.

7. Carmen sells magazine subscriptions. In addition to a weekly wage, she is paid a bonus of $2.55 for each subscription sold. In one week she sells 23 subscriptions. What is her bonus?
a. $2.55 **b.** $25.55
c. $58.65 **d.** $81.65

8. Clint is following a cookie recipe that calls for walnuts, pecans, and almonds. The walnuts cost $1.49, the pecans $3.19, and the almonds cost $2.69. How much does he spend for these ingredients?
a. $4.68 **b.** $5.88
c. $7.27 **d.** $7.37

Problem Solving Strategy
Work Backward

Review the four-step plan for solving problems.

To plan the solution you must complete three steps:
a. Select a strategy.
b. Think or write out your plan.
c. Choose a method of computation.

Four-Step Plan

1 **READ**

2 **PLAN**

3 **SOLVE**

4 **CHECK**

Strategy: *Work backward.* Some problems are stated in such a way that working backward from the answer is easier and faster than starting from the beginning.

EXAMPLE 1

Susan bought 2 video tapes for $6.50 each and a cassette tape for $9.95. How much change did she get if she gave the clerk $30?

$30.00	**Start with amount given to the clerk.**
− 6.50	**Subtract amount of first video tape.**
$23.50	
− 6.50	**Subtract amount of second video tape.**
$17.00	
− 9.95	**Subtract amount of cassette tape.**
$7.05	**change**

ANSWER: Susan received $7.05 change.

With a calculator, you can work backward to solve the problem in Example 1.

Key: $\boxed{C_E^C}$ 30 $\boxed{-}$ 6.50 $\boxed{-}$ 6.50 $\boxed{-}$ 9.95 $\boxed{=}$ *7.05*

7.05 change received

EXAMPLE 2

Jackson bought 3 shirts, each at the same price, from a catalog. He had to pay a sales tax of $2.61 and a shipping charge of $2.98. His total purchase price was $49.09. How much did each shirt cost?

Think: Sales tax and shipping costs are added to the price of 3 shirts. If you *subtract* the sales tax and shipping costs from the total price, you will have the price of the 3 shirts. You can then divide by 3 to find the cost of each shirt.

total purchase price − sales tax − shipping costs = price of 3 shirts
  $49.09   −   2.61   −   2.98   = $43.50

price of 3 shirts ÷ 3 = cost per shirt
  $43.50   ÷ 3 = $14.50

ANSWER: Each shirt cost $14.50.

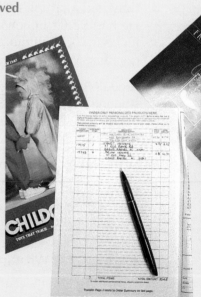

12   Reviewing the Basics

With a calculator, you can work backward to solve the problem in Example 2.

Key: $\boxed{C_E^C}$ 49.09 $\boxed{-}$ 2.61 $\boxed{-}$ 2.98 $\boxed{=}$ $\boxed{\div}$ 3 $\boxed{=}$ $\diagup\overline{14.50}\diagup$

$14.50 \quad$ **cost per shirt**

EXAMPLE 3

If you add 6 to 4 times a number, you get 58. Find the number.

Think: Reverse the operation. Start with 58.

$$\begin{array}{r} 58 \\ -\ 6 \\ \hline 52 \end{array}$$ Subtract the number that was added from the total.
52 **4 times the number**

$$\begin{array}{r} 13 \\ 4\overline{)52} \end{array}$$ Divide by 4.

ANSWER: The number is 13.

With a calculator, you can work backward to solve the problem in Example 3.

Key: $\boxed{C_E^C}$ 58 $\boxed{-}$ 6 $\boxed{=}$ $\boxed{\div}$ 4 $\boxed{=}$ $\diagup\overline{13}\diagup$

EXERCISES

Solve.

1. At the beginning of one month the balance in Rita's savings account was $1,674.52. She made a deposit during the month and her account earned $9.62. If her balance at the end of the month was $1,834.14, how much did she deposit that month?

2. Mike bought a lawnmower and a hose. The hose cost $9.98. He paid a sales tax of $21.60. If the total amount of his purchase was $380.58, how much did he pay for the lawnmower?

3. Sophie is 3 years older than her twin brothers. If all their ages add up to 36, how old are her twin brothers?

4. If you multiply 3 less than a number by 4, the product is 20. Find the number.

5. Katrina bought 2 pounds of stew meat for $2.50 per pound. She bought a head of lettuce for $.98 and a carton of milk for $1.70. She gave the clerk a $20 bill. How much change did she receive?

6. Joan bought a shirt and 2 pairs of running shoes. The shirt cost $14.95. She paid a sales tax of $4.95. How much did each pair of running shoes cost her if her total bill was $79.80?

7. Tina paid a $6 shipping charge for a catalog order of a sleeping bag. If she made two payments of $22.99 each, how much did the sleeping bag cost her?

8. Rodney's telephone bill one month was $15. His basic service costs him $12 and he pays $.15 for each call over 50 calls. How many calls did he make that month?

Using Fractions and Mixed Numbers
Addition and Subtraction

Addition and subtraction of fractions and mixed numbers are often used to solve problems related to units of measure.

EXAMPLE 1

A fashion designer made an outfit that required $3\frac{1}{2}$ yards of one fabric and $2\frac{2}{3}$ yards of a second fabric. How much fabric was used in all?

Estimate to the nearest half.

$$3\frac{1}{2} \rightarrow 3\frac{1}{2} \qquad 2\frac{2}{3} \rightarrow 3$$
$$3\frac{1}{2} + 3 = 6\frac{1}{2}$$

Add: $3\frac{1}{2} + 2\frac{2}{3}$

$$
\begin{array}{ll}
3\frac{1}{2} = \quad 3\frac{3}{6} & \text{Find the LCD (least common denominator).} \\
\underline{+2\frac{2}{3} = +2\frac{4}{6}} & \text{Write equivalent fractions using the LCD.} \\
5\frac{7}{6} = 6\frac{1}{6} & \text{Add fractions. Add mixed numbers. Simplify.}
\end{array}
$$

The answer $6\frac{1}{6}$ yards is close to the estimate $6\frac{1}{2}$ yards and is a reasonable answer.

ANSWER: $6\frac{1}{6}$ yards of fabric was used.

OTHER EXAMPLES

$\frac{3}{5} + \frac{1}{8}$

$$
\begin{array}{rl}
\frac{3}{5} = & \frac{24}{40} \\
\underline{+\frac{1}{8} = } & \underline{+\frac{5}{40}} \\
& \frac{29}{40}
\end{array}
$$

$6\frac{1}{5} + 2\frac{2}{5}$

$$
\begin{array}{l}
6\frac{1}{5} \\
\underline{+2\frac{2}{5}} \\
8\frac{3}{5}
\end{array}
$$

$15\frac{1}{8} + \frac{4}{9}$

$$
\begin{array}{rl}
15\frac{1}{8} = & 15\frac{9}{72} \\
\underline{+ \quad \frac{4}{9} = } & \underline{+ \quad \frac{32}{72}} \\
& 15\frac{41}{72}
\end{array}
$$

$3\frac{4}{5} + 7\frac{6}{7}$

$$
\begin{array}{rl}
3\frac{4}{5} = & 3\frac{28}{35} \\
\underline{+7\frac{6}{7} = } & \underline{+7\frac{30}{35}} \\
& 10\frac{58}{35} = 11\frac{23}{35}
\end{array}
$$

EXAMPLE 2

A plumber needed $3\frac{7}{8}$ feet of pipe for a repair. He had a length of pipe that measured $5\frac{1}{3}$ feet. How much was left after he cut the piece he needed?

Estimate to the nearest whole number.

$$3\frac{7}{8} \rightarrow 4 \qquad 5\frac{1}{3} \rightarrow 5$$
$$5 - 4 = 1$$

Subtract: $5\frac{1}{3} - 3\frac{7}{8}$

$$
\begin{array}{rcrcr}
5\frac{1}{3} &=& 5\frac{8}{24} &=& 4\frac{32}{24} \\
-3\frac{7}{8} &=& -3\frac{21}{24} &=& -3\frac{21}{24} \\
\hline
& & & & 1\frac{11}{24}
\end{array}
$$

Write each fraction as an equivalent fraction using the LCD. Regroup. Subtract.

The answer $1\frac{11}{24}$ feet is close to the estimate 1 foot and is a reasonable answer.

ANSWER: $1\frac{11}{24}$ feet of pipe were left.

OTHER EXAMPLES

$\frac{13}{15} - \frac{8}{15}$

$$
\begin{array}{r}
\frac{13}{15} \\
-\frac{8}{15} \\
\hline
\frac{5}{15} = \frac{1}{3}
\end{array}
$$

$8\frac{3}{4} - 6\frac{1}{4}$

$$
\begin{array}{r}
8\frac{3}{4} \\
-6\frac{1}{4} \\
\hline
2\frac{2}{4} = 2\frac{1}{2}
\end{array}
$$

$25\frac{4}{7} - 13\frac{2}{3}$

$$
\begin{array}{rcrcr}
25\frac{4}{7} &=& 25\frac{12}{21} &=& 24\frac{33}{21} \\
-13\frac{2}{3} &=& -13\frac{14}{21} &=& -13\frac{14}{21} \\
\hline
& & & & 11\frac{19}{21}
\end{array}
$$

$14 - 6\frac{3}{8}$

$$
\begin{array}{rcr}
14 &=& 13\frac{8}{8} \\
-6\frac{3}{8} &=& -6\frac{3}{8} \\
\hline
& & 7\frac{5}{8}
\end{array}
$$

EXERCISES

Add or subtract.

1. $\begin{array}{r}\frac{2}{7}\\+\frac{3}{7}\\\hline\end{array}$

2. $\begin{array}{r}\frac{8}{9}\\-\frac{5}{9}\\\hline\end{array}$

3. $\begin{array}{r}\frac{2}{3}\\+\frac{5}{6}\\\hline\end{array}$

4. $\begin{array}{r}\frac{7}{8}\\-\frac{1}{6}\\\hline\end{array}$

5. $\begin{array}{r}7\frac{4}{5}\\+9\frac{3}{4}\\\hline\end{array}$

6. $\begin{array}{r}15\\-12\frac{9}{10}\\\hline\end{array}$

Estimate the answer to each problem. Then find the solution.

7. Rainfall measured $5\frac{1}{2}$ inches in June, $4\frac{1}{8}$ inches in July, and $2\frac{3}{4}$ inches in August. What was the total rainfall during the three months?

8. A recipe calls for $4\frac{1}{2}$ cups of carrots. Jan only has $2\frac{2}{3}$ cups. How many more cups are needed?

9. Janice biked $15\frac{1}{3}$ miles on Monday, $9\frac{5}{8}$ miles on Tuesday, $12\frac{1}{4}$ miles on Wednesday, and $18\frac{5}{6}$ miles on Thursday. How far did she ride in all?

10. David cut $11\frac{3}{5}$ yards from a bolt of cloth that measured 20 yards. How many yards were left on the bolt?

Using Addition and Subtraction: Fractions **15**

Using Fractions and Mixed Numbers
Multiplication and Division

Multiplication and division of fractions and mixed numbers are often used to solve problems related to consumerism and home improvements.

EXAMPLE 1

Anne bought $\frac{3}{4}$ yard of lace and used $\frac{1}{2}$ of it to trim a dress. How much lace did she put on the dress?

Multiply: $\frac{1}{2} \times \frac{3}{4}$

$\frac{1}{2} \times \frac{3}{4} = \frac{3}{8}$ **Multiply the numerators.**
Multiply the denominators.

ANSWER: She put $\frac{3}{8}$ yard of lace on the dress.

OTHER EXAMPLES

$\frac{3}{5} \times \frac{2}{7}$ $\qquad$ $\frac{1}{3} \times \frac{5}{10}$ $\qquad$ $\frac{7}{9} \times \frac{5}{6}$ $\qquad$ $\frac{2}{3} \times \frac{4}{5} \times \frac{8}{9}$

$\frac{3}{5} \times \frac{2}{7} = \frac{6}{35}$ $\qquad$ $\frac{1}{3} \times \frac{5}{10} = \frac{5}{30} = \frac{1}{6}$ $\qquad$ $\frac{7}{9} \times \frac{5}{6} = \frac{35}{54}$ $\qquad$ $\frac{2}{3} \times \frac{4}{5} \times \frac{8}{9} = \frac{64}{135}$

EXAMPLE 2

Ed bought a length of rope that measured $5\frac{1}{3}$ feet. He used $\frac{1}{4}$ of it to repair a corral fence. How much rope did he use for the fence?

Multiply: $\frac{1}{4} \times 5\frac{1}{3}$

$\frac{1}{4} \times 5\frac{1}{3} = \frac{1}{4} \times \frac{16}{3}$ **Write $5\frac{1}{3}$ as an improper fraction.**

$\frac{1}{\cancel{4}} \times \frac{\cancel{16}^4}{3} = \frac{4}{3} = 1\frac{1}{3}$ **Whenever possible, divide any numerator and denominator by their greatest common factor before multiplying.**
Divide 4 and 16 by 4, their greatest common factor.
Simplify the answer.

ANSWER: Ed used $1\frac{1}{3}$ feet of rope for the fence.

OTHER EXAMPLES

$\frac{3}{4} \times 2\frac{5}{6}$ $\qquad$ $\frac{4}{5} \times 2,500$ $\qquad$ $3\frac{1}{4} \times 2\frac{1}{2}$ $\qquad$ $9 \times 6\frac{2}{3}$

$\frac{3}{\cancel{4}}^1 \times \frac{17}{\cancel{6}}_2 = \frac{17}{8} = 2\frac{1}{8}$ $\qquad$ $\frac{4}{\cancel{5}}_1 \times \frac{\cancel{2500}^{500}}{1} = \frac{2000}{1} = 2,000$ $\qquad$ $\frac{13}{4} \times \frac{5}{2} = \frac{65}{8} = 8\frac{1}{8}$ $\qquad$ $\frac{\cancel{9}^3}{1} \times \frac{20}{\cancel{3}}_1 = \frac{60}{1} = 60$

EXAMPLE 3

Paula had a piece of pipe $6\frac{1}{2}$ feet long. She cut it into pieces $\frac{1}{2}$ foot long. How many pieces of pipe did she get?

Divide: $6\frac{1}{2} \div \frac{1}{2}$

$6\frac{1}{2} \div \frac{1}{2} = \frac{13}{2} \div \frac{1}{2}$ Write $6\frac{1}{2}$ as an improper fraction.

reciprocals

$\frac{13}{2} \div \frac{1}{2} = \frac{13}{2} \times \frac{2}{1}$ To divide by a fraction, multiply by the reciprocal
of the divisor.

$\frac{13}{2} \times \frac{2}{1} = \frac{13}{1} = 13$

ANSWER: Paula had 13 pieces of $\frac{1}{2}$-foot pipe.

OTHER EXAMPLES

$\frac{3}{4} \div \frac{1}{2}$ $2\frac{1}{3} \div \frac{4}{5}$

$\frac{3}{4} \times \frac{2}{1} = \frac{3}{2} = 1\frac{1}{2}$ $\frac{7}{3} \times \frac{5}{4} = \frac{35}{12} = 2\frac{11}{12}$

$24 \div \frac{2}{3}$ $4\frac{1}{4} \div 2\frac{1}{3}$

$\frac{24}{1} \times \frac{3}{2} = \frac{36}{1} = 36$ $\frac{17}{4} \times \frac{3}{7} = \frac{51}{28} = 1\frac{23}{28}$

EXERCISES

Multiply or divide. Simplify the answer where possible.

1. $\frac{3}{4} \times \frac{2}{3}$ **2.** $3\frac{1}{2} \times \frac{7}{8}$ **3.** $\frac{5}{6} \div \frac{2}{3}$

4. $\frac{9}{10} \div 3$ **5.** $8\frac{1}{6} \times 3\frac{2}{5}$ **6.** $7\frac{2}{3} \div 5$

Solve.

7. Ted is buying a microwave for $280 and
has to pay $\frac{1}{4}$ of the amount as a down
payment. How much is the down
payment?

8. There was $\frac{1}{2}$ of a pizza left. Barbara ate $\frac{1}{3}$
of it. How much of the whole pizza did
she eat?

9. Dan spends $\frac{2}{5}$ of his time working in the
mail department. If he works a 40-hour
week, how many hours does he spend in
the mail department each week?

10. Marie plans to hike $12\frac{1}{2}$ miles. If she
hikes $3\frac{1}{8}$ miles each day, how many days
will the trip take her?

11. A train travels 180 km in $4\frac{1}{2}$ hours. What
is the average rate of speed?

12. How many strips $2\frac{1}{2}$ inches wide can be
cut from a piece of cardboard that is 15
inches wide?

Problem Solving Strategy
Solve a Simpler Problem

Review the four-step plan for solving problems.

To plan the solution you must complete three steps:
a. Select a strategy.
b. Think or write out your plan.
c. Choose a method of computation.

Strategy: *Solve a simpler problem.* Substitute small or whole numbers for large numbers or fractions in a problem. Determine the operation. Then replace the smaller numbers with the actual numbers and solve.

> **Four-Step Plan**
> **1 READ**
> **2 PLAN**
> **3 SOLVE**
> **4 CHECK**

EXAMPLE 1

Joanne had a $22\frac{3}{4}$-inch piece of paper. She wanted to cut strips $1\frac{3}{4}$ inches long. How many strips could she cut?

Think: 20-in. roll   Substitute whole numbers.
       2-in. strips
       How many pieces from the whole?   Indicates *division*.

total number ÷ length of each strip = number of strips
      20   ÷   2   = number of strips

You must divide to find the answer.

total number ÷ length of each strip = number of strips
    $22\frac{3}{4}$ ÷ $1\frac{3}{4}$ Use the given numbers.

reciprocals

$$22\frac{3}{4} \div 1\frac{3}{4} = \frac{91}{4} \div \frac{7}{4} = \frac{91}{4} \times \frac{4}{7} = \frac{13}{1} = 13 \qquad \text{Check:} \quad 13 \times 1\frac{3}{4} = \frac{91}{4} = 22\frac{3}{4}$$

ANSWER: Joanne could cut 13 strips.

EXAMPLE 2

A warehouse shipped 836 baseballs, 206 footballs, 419 basketballs, and 358 soccer balls. How many balls did it receive in all?

Think: 8 baseballs   Substitute smaller numbers.
       2 footballs
       4 basketballs
       3 soccer balls
       How many in all?   Indicates *addition*.

addends

$8 + 2 + 4 + 3 = $ sum

You must add to find the answer.

addends
$$836 + 206 + 419 + 358 = 1,819$$ Use the given numbers.

ANSWER: The warehouse received 1,819 balls.

EXERCISES

Solve.

1. Matt has to box 21,600 pencils. Each box holds 144 pencils. How many boxes does Matt need for all the pencils?

2. Martha had a bolt of material $20\frac{1}{2}$ yards long. She used $\frac{3}{4}$ of the bolt to make curtains. How much material did she use?

3. Paul has 24 disks. Each disk is 7.68 centimeters thick. If Paul stacks all the disks in one pile, how high will the pile be?

4. Jennifer drove 275.5 miles in 5.75 hours. What was her average rate of speed?

5. The Smiths bought a car that cost $11,976.42. They traded in their old car and used the amount they received for it as a down payment. If they still have to pay $8,481.42 for the new car, how much was the trade-in allowance on their old car?

6. A house on Third Street is for sale at $93,695. A house on River Street is selling for $89,500. How much less is the house on River Street?

7. Ellen bought $3\frac{2}{3}$ pounds of apples, $2\frac{1}{2}$ pounds of pears, and $1\frac{3}{4}$ pounds of grapes for a fruit salad for a party. How many pounds of fruit did she buy in all?

8. Connorstown had 3.052 inches of rain in 4 months. What was the average rainfall per month during this period?

9. Peter paid $58.95 for 25 pounds of fertilizer. What was the cost per pound?

10. Debbie purchased 21 gallons of gasoline at $1.29 per gallon. What was her total purchase?

11. Larry bought $2\frac{1}{8}$ pounds of beef at $4.39 per pound. How much did he pay for the beef?

12. Pam drove 938 miles at an average speed of 53 miles per hour. How long did the trip take her?

13. A carton contains 24 cans of vegetables. Each can weighs 0.375 kilograms. How much does the whole carton weigh?

14. Jim's leaky bathroom faucet wastes 14.25 quarts of water a week. How long would it take to waste 100 quarts of water?

Using Ratio and Proportion

A *ratio* is a comparison of two numbers by division. A *proportion* is a statement that two ratios are equal. Ratios and proportions are often used in solving problems related to shopping and unit pricing.

EXAMPLE 1

The ratio of the number of oranges sold to the number of apples sold is 2 to 4. For every 2 oranges sold, there are 4 apples sold. This ratio can be written in two ways:

2 to 4 $= \frac{2}{4} = \frac{1}{2}$ **Write a fraction. Use the number being compared as the *numerator* and the number to which it is being compared as the *denominator*. Simplify when possible.**

2 to 4 $= 2{:}4$ **Ratios may also be written with a colon.**

OTHER EXAMPLES

Write as ratios using a fraction bar. Simplify when possible.

6 to 10	450 km in 9 h	a dime to a dollar	5 eggs to a dozen
$\frac{6}{10} = \frac{3}{5}$	$\frac{450}{9} = \frac{50}{1} = 50$ km/h	$\frac{10}{100} = \frac{1}{10}$	$\frac{5}{12}$

Ratios must be expressed in the same units.

Write as ratios using a colon.

4 to 15	3 for 79¢	315 mi in 7 h	10 out of 2 dozen
4:15	3:79	315:7, or 45:1	10:24, or 5:12

EXAMPLE 2

Sheila paid $.69 for 3 cans of fruit. Manuel bought 5 cans of fruit for $1.15. Was one buy better than the other?

Compare the ratios.

$\frac{3}{69} \times \frac{5}{115}$ **Use cross multiplication:**

$3 \times 115 = 345$

$69 \times 5 = 345$

$\frac{3}{69} = \frac{5}{115}$ **The ratios are equivalent.**

ANSWER: One buy was not better than the other.

OTHER EXAMPLES

Are each pair of ratios equivalent? Write "yes" or "no."

$\frac{3}{4}, \frac{12}{16}$	$\frac{99}{3}, \frac{33}{9}$	$\frac{8}{3}, \frac{16}{7}$	$\frac{11}{12}, \frac{99}{108}$
$3 \times 16 = 48$	$99 \times 9 = 891$	$8 \times 7 = 56$	$11 \times 108 = 1{,}188$
$4 \times 12 = 48$ yes	$33 \times 3 = 99$ no	$3 \times 16 = 48$ no	$12 \times 99 = 1{,}188$ yes

EXAMPLE 3

Jen bought 2 cans of corn for $.87. How much will 6 cans cost?

$$\frac{2}{0.87} = \frac{6}{n}$$ Write a proportion.

$2 \times n = 0.87 \times 6$

$2 \times n = 5.22$

$n = 5.22 \div 2$

$n = 2.61$

$\frac{2}{0.87} = \frac{6}{2.61}$ Check by cross multiplying: $2 \times 2.61 = 5.22$

$0.87 \times 6 = 5.22$ ✔

ANSWER: Six cans of corn will cost $2.61.

EXERCISES

Write as ratios in two ways.

	With a fraction bar	With a colon
2 pencils for $.25	**1.** ■	**2.** ■
3 pounds for $4.59	**3.** ■	**4.** ■
35 miles per hour	**5.** ■	**6.** ■
1.75 gallons for $1.19	**7.** ■	**8.** ■

Solve.

9. $\frac{2}{5} = \frac{4}{n}$ **10.** $\frac{3}{7} = \frac{m}{28}$ **11.** $\frac{a}{8} = \frac{6}{16}$ **12.** $\frac{15}{b} = \frac{90}{180}$ **13.** $\frac{11}{13} = \frac{d}{91}$

14. $\frac{5}{1.50} = \frac{25}{n}$ **15.** $\frac{4}{5} = \frac{80}{f}$ **16.** $\frac{k}{12} = \frac{3.5}{7}$ **17.** $\frac{5.95}{1} = \frac{s}{6}$ **18.** $\frac{4}{0.06} = \frac{12}{t}$

Solve.

19. Sara bought 3 yards of material for $15.95. How much will 9 yards of the same material cost?

20. Craig paid $28.74 for a roast that weighed 6 pounds. Barbara paid $19.16 for a roast that weighed 4 pounds. Did they pay the same amount per pound?

21. Betty is averaging 45 miles per hour on her trip. If she keeps up this rate of speed, how long will it take her to travel 900 miles?

22. Ben bought 64 fluid ounces of detergent for $4.48. What is the price of 18 fluid ounces?

Using Percent

Percent is used to determine how much interest you must pay on a loan. The amount you borrow is called the *principal*. The *rate of interest* is the percent charged for use of the principal. The *interest* is the amount of money you must pay for borrowing the principal.

EXAMPLE 1

Jack borrowed $500 to buy a microwave oven. He agreed to pay the loan back in 1 year. He was charged 6% interest. How much interest did he pay?

For 1 year: **principal × rate = interest**
$500 × 6% = ■

6% means 6 hundredths, so 6% = $\frac{6}{100}$ = 0.06.

$500
×0.06   Write the percent as a decimal.
$30.00   Mark 2 decimal places.

ANSWER: The interest on the loan was $30.

OTHER EXAMPLES
Find the following.

8% of $1,295	7.5% of $950	3¼% of $1,500	125% of $400
$1,295	$950	$1,500	$400
×0.08	×0.075	×0.0325	×1.25
$103.60	4 750	7500	20 00
	66 50	3 000	80 0
	71.250	45 00	400
	$71.25	48.7500	$500.00
		$48.75	

EXAMPLE 2

Sandra paid $42 interest to borrow $600 for one year. What was the rate of interest?

You must answer the question, 42 is what percent of 600?

First write a ratio: $\dfrac{\$42}{\$600}$

Next, divide.

$$\begin{array}{r} 0.07 \rightarrow 7\% \\ \$600\overline{)\$42.00} \\ \underline{42\ 00} \\ 0 \end{array}$$

ANSWER: The rate of interest was 7%.

OTHER EXAMPLES
Find what percent one number is of another.

12 is of 48	$16.25 is of $250	$3 is of $400	$900 is of $600
$\begin{array}{r} 0.25 \to 25\% \\ 48\overline{)12.00} \end{array}$	$\begin{array}{r} 0.065 \to 6.5\% \\ \$250\overline{)\$16.250} \end{array}$	$\begin{array}{r} 0.0075 \to 0.75\% \\ 400\overline{)3.0000} \end{array}$	$\begin{array}{r} 1.5 \to 150\% \\ 600\overline{)900.0} \end{array}$
12 is 25% of 48	$16.25 is 6.5% of $250	$3 is 0.75% of $400	$900 is 150% of $600

EXAMPLE 3
Interest on a loan at 7.5% was $187.50. What was the principal?

You must answer the question, $187.50 is 7.5% of what number?

Write 7.5% as a decimal. Divide.

$$
\begin{array}{r}
\$\ \ 2,500 \\
0.075\overline{)\$187.500} \\
\underline{150\ \ \ \ } \\
37\ 5 \\
\underline{37\ 5} \\
0
\end{array}
$$

> **ANSWER:** The principal was $2,500.

OTHER EXAMPLES
Find the principal.

$50 is 25% of the principal.	$48.75 is 7.5% of the principal.	$24 is 0.3% of the principal.
$\begin{array}{r} \$\ \ 2\ 00 \\ 0.25\overline{)\$50.00} \end{array}$	$\begin{array}{r} \$\ \ \ 650 \\ 0.075\overline{)\$48.750} \end{array}$	$\begin{array}{r} \$\ \ 8,000 \\ 0.003\overline{)\$24.000} \end{array}$
Principal: $200	Principal: $650	Principal: $8,000

EXERCISES
Solve.

Principal	Rate	Interest
$900	12.25%	1. ■
$795	2. ■	$54.06
3. ■	75%	$5,452.50

Solve.

4. Helena borrowed $8,500 at a rate of interest of 13.5% for 1 year. How much interest did she pay?

5. Gene borrowed $950 for 1 year and paid $99.75 in interest. What was the rate of interest?

6. Roger paid $38.25 interest on a loan. If the rate of interest was 8.5%, what was the amount he borrowed?

7. Shari paid $3,875 interest on a loan. This was a rate of 15.5%. What was the principal of the loan?

Problem Solving Strategy
Solve Another Way

Review the four-step plan for solving problems.

To plan the solution you must complete three steps:
a. Select a strategy.
b. Think or write out your plan.
c. Choose a method of computation.

Strategy: *Solve another way.* Many problems can be solved in different ways. Each approach can sometimes give you a new or better understanding of the problem.

Four-Step Plan

1 READ

2 PLAN

3 SOLVE

4 CHECK

EXAMPLE 1
Richard has 25% of his gross pay withheld for deductions. If Richard earns $450 per week, what is his net pay each week?

Solution 1

Think: 25% = 0.25

$450   gross pay
×0.25
22 50
90 0
$112.50   amount withheld

$450.00   gross pay
− 112.50   amount withheld
$337.50   net pay

Solution 2

gross pay − deductions = net pay
100%   −   25%   =   75%

Think: 75% = 0.75

     gross pay   net pay
    $450 × 0.75 = $337.50

ANSWER: Richard's net pay each week is $337.50.

EXAMPLE 2
Julie bought a camera for $150. She had to pay a 6% sales tax on the purchase. What was the total purchase price of the camera?

Solution 1

Think: 6% = 0.06

$150   camera price
×0.06
$9.00   sales tax

$150   camera price
+   9   sales tax
$159   total purchase price

Solution 2

camera price + sales tax = total purchase price
  100%   +   6%   =   106%

Think: $106\% = 1.06$

$$\begin{array}{r} \$150 \quad \text{camera price} \\ \times 1.06 \\ \hline \$159.00 \quad \text{total purchase price} \end{array}$$

ANSWER: The total purchase price of the camera was $159.

EXAMPLE 3

The Columbus School band had to travel 600 miles to take part in a band competition. They traveled $\frac{2}{3}$ of the way the first day. How far did they have to go the second day?

Solution 1

$600 \times \frac{2}{3} = 400$ mi traveled

$$\begin{array}{r} 600 \text{ mi} \quad \text{total distance} \\ -400 \text{ mi} \quad \text{traveled} \\ \hline 200 \text{ mi} \quad \text{remaining distance} \end{array}$$

Solution 2

total distance − distance traveled = remaining distance

$$1 \qquad - \qquad \frac{2}{3} \qquad = \qquad \frac{1}{3}$$

$600 \times \frac{1}{3} = 200$ mi remaining distance

ANSWER: The band has 200 miles left to travel.

EXERCISES

Solve.

1. Cost of item: $435; Sales tax: 6%; Total purchase price: ■

2. A stereo sells for $750. What is its sale price if it is marked down 20%?

3. Susan bought furniture for $1,200. She made a down payment of 20%. How much more does she have to pay?

4. Derrin bought a truck for $15,500. He had to pay a sales tax of 6.25%. What is the total purchase price of the truck?

5. Jefferson High School won 80% of its basketball games one season. If it played 40 games, how many games did it lose?

6. Greg bought a video camera at a $\frac{1}{3}$-off sale. If the camera originally sold for $1,200, how much did he pay for it?

7. Ultan borrowed $1,500 for one year at 10% interest. How much did he have to repay in all at the end of the year?

8. Sandy budgets 25% of her income for housing. If her annual gross income is $14,500, how much does she have left to spend on all other items?

9. Cost of item: $1,350; down payment: 15%; left to pay: ■

10. Distance to go: 1,500 km; covered the first day: 35%; remaining distance: ■

11. Patricia had to travel 750 miles to a conference. She drove $\frac{3}{5}$ of the way the first day. How many miles did she have left to drive?

12. During the 2-week Thanksgiving food drive, 1,200 cans of food were collected. Of course, $\frac{3}{4}$ were collected the first week. How many cans were collected the second week?

Perimeter, Area, and Volume

In maintaining an apartment, a house, or a business, it is important to know how to determine the perimeter, area, or volume.

EXAMPLE 1

Perimeter is the distance around a geometric figure. To determine the perimeter, you must find the sum of the lengths of the sides.

Garry planted a garden on a rectangular plot 12 feet × 25 feet. He wants to rope off the area. How much rope will he need?

Think: 2 sides, 12 ft each; 2 sides, 25 ft each.

$$\text{perimeter} = \text{sum of sides}$$
$$P = 12 + 12 + 25 + 25 = 74 \text{ ft}$$

ANSWER: He needs 74 ft of rope.

OTHER EXAMPLES
Find the perimeter of each figure.

6 cm

$$P = 6 + 6 + 6 + 6$$
$$P = 24 \text{ cm}$$

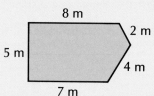

8 m
2 m
5 m
4 m
7 m

$$P = 8 + 5 + 7 + 4 + 2$$
$$P = 26 \text{ m}$$

EXAMPLE 2

Area refers to the number of square units contained in a region.

How many square feet are in a rectangular floor that measures 12 feet × 18 feet?

$$\text{Area (rectangle)} = \text{length} \times \text{width}$$
$$A = 12 \times 18 = 216 \text{ ft}^2$$

ANSWER: The floor is 216 square feet.

OTHER EXAMPLES
Find the area of each region.

5 cm

$h = 6$ m

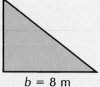

$b = 8$ m

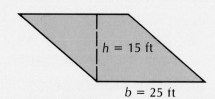

$h = 15$ ft

$b = 25$ ft

Square
$$A = s^2$$
$$A = 5 \times 5 = 25 \text{ cm}^2$$

Triangle
$$A = \tfrac{1}{2}bh$$
$$A = \tfrac{1}{2} \times 8 \times 6 = 24 \text{ m}^2$$

Parallelogram
$$A = bh$$
$$A = 25 \times 15 = 375 \text{ ft}^2$$

EXAMPLE 3

Volume is the measure of the interior of a three-dimensional figure. Volume is stated in cubic units.

Michelle is filling a new fish tank that is 30 centimeters high, 48 centimeters wide, and 60 centimeters long. How much water does she need to fill the tank?

$$\text{Volume (rectangular prism)} = \text{length} \times \text{width} \times \text{height}$$
$$V = 60 \times 48 \times 30$$
$$V = 86,400 \text{ cm}^3$$

ANSWER: She needs 86,400 cubic centimeters of water.

OTHER EXAMPLES

Find the volume of each of the following.

15 yd
15 yd
15 yd

$V = l \times w \times h$
$V = 15 \times 15 \times 15$
$V = 3,375 \text{ yd}^3$

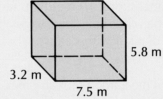

5.8 m
3.2 m
7.5 m

$V = l \times w \times h$
$V = 7.5 \times 3.2 \times 5.8$
$V = 139.2 \text{ m}^3$

EXERCISES

1. Find the perimeter.

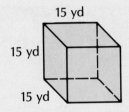

12 cm

2. Find the area.

12 cm
16 cm

3. Find the volume.

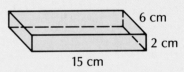

6 cm
2 cm
15 cm

Solve.

4. Dot wants to trim a tablecloth with fringe. The tablecloth is 2 meters wide and 3 meters long. How much fringe does she need?

5. Bill wants to carpet a room that measures 18 feet × 24 feet. How much carpet does he need?

6. Curtis is painting a mural and wants to paint one region red. The region is triangular and has a base of 4 feet and a height of 3 feet. How much area does he have to paint red?

7. Claire wants to mark off a no-parking zone in her office parking lot. The zone is a parallelogram with a base of 20 feet and a height of 8 feet. How large is the zone she will mark off?

8. What is the area of a triangular sail on Ann and Jack's boat if its base is 18 feet and its height is 27 feet?

9. How much water can a tank hold if its length is 3 meters, its width is 2 meters, and it is filled to a height of 1.5 meters?

Problem Solving Strategy
Make a Diagram or Model

Review the four-step plan for solving problems.

You must plan the solution carefully.
a. Select a strategy.
b. Think or write out your plan.
c. Choose the method of computation.

Strategy: *Make a diagram or model.* Use the information given in the problem to draw a diagram or make a model to help you find the solution.

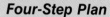

Four-Step Plan

1 **READ**
2 **PLAN**
3 **SOLVE**
4 **CHECK**

EXAMPLE 1

Eleanor has a garden plot measuring 10 feet by 6 feet. Half of the garden is for flowers and the other half is for vegetables. One-fifth of the vegetable garden is planted with beans. What is the area of the section used for beans?

Step 1. Draw a diagram of the garden plot and mark it off in square units. Shade in one-half of the total area. Label the shaded half "Flowers." Label the unshaded half "Vegetables."

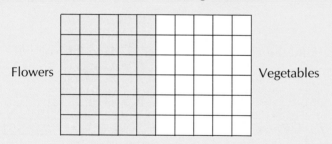

$A = l \times w = 6 \times 10 = 60$
Vegetables take one-half of the whole area. $\frac{1}{2} \times 60 = 30$ ft^2

Step 2. Mark off $\frac{1}{5}$ of the vegetable patch and label this section "Beans." Count the square units in the section labeled "Beans."

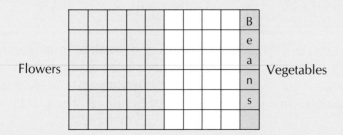

Beans take one-fifth of the vegetable area. $\frac{1}{5} \times 30 = 6$ ft^2

ANSWER: The area for beans is 6 ft^2.

EXAMPLE 2

Tom walked 0.5 kilometer from his house to the library, jogged
0.75 kilometer from the library to the post office, and walked
0.1 kilometer from the post office to the book store. Then he
jogged back to the library, using the same route. From there, he
jogged 0.25 kilometer to the market and then walked 0.4
kilometer home. How far did he jog?

Step 1. Draw a diagram showing Tom's route.

Step 2. Write in the distances between each
stop. Show whether Tom jogged or walked.

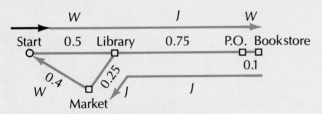

Step 3. Compute the distance he jogged.

$$0.75 + 0.85 + 0.25 = 1.85$$

ANSWER: Tom jogged 1.85 kilometers.

EXERCISES

Solve. Draw a diagram or a model.

1. Sam took a taxi ride of $1\frac{1}{10}$ mile. He was
   charged $.60 for the first $\frac{1}{5}$ mile and $.10
   for each $\frac{1}{10}$ mile thereafter. How much
   did the taxi ride cost?

2. Sheila ate half a pizza for lunch. She ate
   half of the pizza left for dinner. How
   much of the whole pizza was left?

3. Carole is preparing a wall for a mural.
   The wall is 12 feet long and 8 feet high.
   What is the total area of the wall?

4. You want to construct a 6-sided
   cardboard box that will be 6 inches by 4
   inches by 2 inches. How much
   cardboard will you need?

5. The peak of the Smith's house is 32 feet above ground level.
   A flagpole in the front yard is 18 feet high. The bottom of a
   bedroom window is halfway between the top of the flagpole
   and the peak of the house. How far above ground level is the
   bottom of the bedroom window?

Analyzing Data and Making Predictions
Mean, Mode, Median, Probability

When a teacher finds the class average for a test, the teacher is finding the *mean* of a set of data. Knowing only the mean, however, does not really tell much about all the scores on a test. In order to have a clearer picture of how the scores were distributed, or spread, throughout the class, three common measures can be used to analyze the data. These are *mean, mode,* and *median.*

EXAMPLE 1
The *mean* of a group of numbers is the sum of the numbers divided by the number of items. A mean is also called an *average.*
   Christy's grades on her science tests for one term are as follows:

$$80 \quad 78 \quad 87 \quad 79 \quad 90 \quad 75 \quad 82 \quad 83$$

What is the mean of her scores?

Step 1.   Find the sum of the scores.

$$80 + 78 + 87 + 79 + 90 + 75 + 82 + 83 = 654$$

Step 2.   Divide the sum by the number of scores.

$$654 \div 8 = 81.75$$

ANSWER: The mean of her scores, or her average, is 81.75.

OTHER EXAMPLE
Find the mean of 12, 10, 8, 10, 8

$$12 + 10 + 8 + 10 + 8 = 48$$
$$48 \div 5 = 9.6$$

The mean is 9.6.

EXAMPLE 2
The *mode* of a set of numbers is the number that occurs most often. What is the mode of this set of scores?

$$83 \quad 74 \quad 78 \quad 82 \quad 78 \quad 87 \quad 88 \quad 83 \quad 85 \quad 82 \quad 83$$

ANSWER: The mode is 83.

OTHER EXAMPLE
Find the mode of 3, 4, 8, 7, 4, 8, 3, 8

The mode is 8.

EXAMPLE 3

The *median* of a set of numbers is the middle number.
What is the median of this set of numbers?

$1,500 $1,575 $1,500 $1,550 $1,535 $1,575 $1,600

Write the numbers in order from least to greatest.

$1,500 $1,500 $1,535 $1,550 $1,575 $1,575 $1,600

ANSWER: The median, or middle number, is $1,550.

OTHER EXAMPLE

Find the median of 18, 12, 16, 14, 17, 21, 19, 15

The median of an even number of data is the average of the two middle numbers.

The median is $\dfrac{16 + 17}{2}$, or 16.5

To study the likelihood of an event when the size of the sample space is not known, it is possible to make a prediction based on part of the sample space.

EXAMPLE 4

Joe wants to find out how many students in his school favor the incumbent for mayor. He takes a sample of 75 students and learns that 45 favor the incumbent. What is the probability that any student favors this candidate?

$$P(\text{favors incumbent}) = \frac{\text{number of favorable outcomes}}{\text{sample size}} = \frac{45}{75} = \frac{3}{5}$$

ANSWER: The probability is $\frac{3}{5}$.

EXERCISES

One month Kate sold houses worth the following amounts:
       $78,000, $65,500, $72,500, $84,000, $78,000

1. Find the mode.

2. Find the mean price.

3. Find the median price.

Solve.

4. Karen earned $15, $12, $20, $14, $12, $10, $20, $25, $15, and $15. Find the mean, median, and mode.

5. Saul conducted a poll and found that 380 people out of a sample of 500 people were in favor of building a community center in his city. Give the probability that any person in the city would be in favor of the center.

Drawing and Interpreting Graphs
Bar Graphs, Circle Graphs, Line Graphs

Graphs are helpful for showing and comparing data and showing changes.

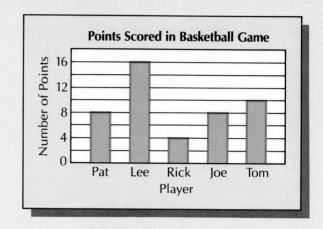

Points Scored in Basketball Game

EXAMPLE 1

Bar graphs are helpful for comparing data. Make a bar graph showing the number of points scored by each of five players in a basketball game. How many points were scored in all?

Points Scored in Basketball Game				
Lee	Rick	Pat	Joe	Tom
16	4	8	8	10

ANSWER: The five players together scored 46 points.

EXAMPLE 2

Circle graphs are often used to compare data when parts of a whole are given.

Make a circle graph to show how Kim spends her money if she spends 15% for lunches, 30% for clothing, 5% for transportation, 30% for recreation, and 20% for savings. On which budget item does she spend the least?

To draw a circle graph, you need to divide the circle into *central angles* representing each percent. The entire circle is 360°. To find the degrees in each central angle, you multiply:

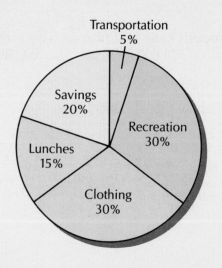

Item		Central Angle
Lunches,	15%	$0.15 \times 360° = 54°$
Clothing,	30%	$0.30 \times 360° = 108°$
Transportation,	5%	$0.05 \times 360° = 18°$
Recreation,	30%	$0.30 \times 360° = 108°$
Savings,	20%	$0.20 \times 360° = 72°$
Total:	100%	Total: 360°

Transportation 5%
Savings 20%
Recreation 30%
Lunches 15%
Clothing 30%

ANSWER: Kim spends the least on transportation.

EXAMPLE 3

Line graphs are useful for showing change. Make a line graph to show the number of cans collected for a recycling drive at one high school. The number of cans collected each month was as follows:

Jan., 300; Feb., 550; Mar., 500; Apr., 200; May, 525

In which month were the greatest number of cans collected?

ANSWER: The most cans were collected in February.

EXERCISES

Answer Questions 1–4 about this bar graph.

1. Which grade has the largest enrollment?

2. Which grade has the smallest enrollment?

3. Which two grades have the same enrollment?

4. What is the total enrollment of grades 7–12?

Answer Questions 5–9 about this line graph.

5. In which month were sales best?

6. In which month were sales worst?

7. In which two months were sales the same?

8. In which months did sales increase?

9. In which month did sales decrease?

10. Draw a circle graph to show how Helen spends a 24-hour weekday.

11. Draw a line graph depicting Snowfall in Granite.

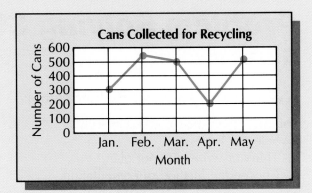

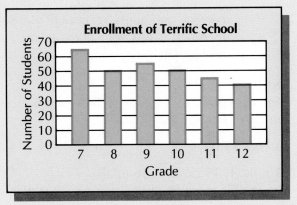

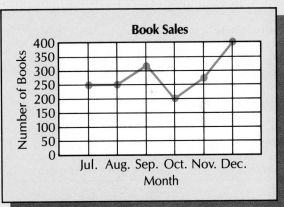

Helen's Weekday			
Working	8 h	Sleeping	8 h
Commuting	2 h	Relaxing	4 h
Eating	2 h		

Snowfall in Granite			
Dec.	16 in.	Feb.	16 in.
Jan.	10 in.	Mar.	12 in.

12. Make up and answer 3 questions about each of the graphs you drew.

Drawing and Interpreting Graphs **33**

Problem Solving Strategy
Guess and Test

Review the four-step plan for solving problems.

You must plan the solution carefully.
a. Select a strategy.
b. Think or write out your plan.
c. Choose the method of computation.

Strategy: *Guess and test.* Sometimes, the best way to solve a problem is to choose a reasonable answer, test to see if it is correct, and guess again until you solve the problem. Remember to test your guess to make sure the facts of the problem fit your solution.

Four-Step Plan

1 READ

2 PLAN

3 SOLVE

4 CHECK

EXAMPLE 1

A math class has 28 students. There are 6 more girls than boys in the class. How many boys are there?

Guess: 15 boys   Test: $15 + 6 = 21$ girls

21 girls + 15 boys = 36 total
The total is too high (there are only 28 students in the class). The guess was too great. Guess a lesser number.

Guess again: 12 boys   Test: $12 + 6 = 18$ girls

18 girls + 12 boys = 30 total
The total is still too high. Guess a number slightly less than 12.

Guess again: 11 boys   Test: $11 + 6 = 17$ girls

17 girls + 11 boys = 28 total
The total now agrees with the facts given in the problem.

ANSWER: There are 11 boys in the class.

EXAMPLE 2

What two consecutive numbers have a sum of 47?

Guess: 21 and 22   Test: $21 + 22 = 43$

The guess is too low. Guess greater numbers.

Guess again: 24 and 25   Test: $24 + 25 = 49$

The guess is too great. Try numbers slightly less than 24 and 25.

Guess again: 23 and 24   Test: $23 + 24 = 47$

The facts of the problem fit the solution.

ANSWER: Two consecutive numbers having a sum of 47 are 23 and 24.

EXERCISES

Use the guess and test strategy to solve these problems.

1. Sue is 4 years older than Jim. The sum of their ages is 42. How old is each?

2. What three consecutive odd numbers have a product of 3,315?

3. It cost Mary $1.25 to mail a first class letter. She had to pay $.25 for the first ounce and $.20 for each additional ounce. How much did the letter weigh?

4. Jim bought a dozen cookies and a loaf of bread for $1.82. Lee bought $1\frac{1}{2}$ dozen cookies and 2 loaves of bread for $3.22. How much did one loaf of bread cost?

5. John made a telephone call to a friend. It cost him a total of $3.65. If the first 3 minutes cost $2.15 and each additional minute cost $.30, how long did John talk?

6. At a dog show there are 65 heads and 190 feet in the show ring. How many people and how many dogs are in the ring?

7. Louise has seven coins. The sum of the value of the coins is $.53. Identify the seven coins.

8. Maria, Sue, and Pete have a total of $4.50. Sue has twice as much as Mary. Pete has the same amount as Mary and Sue together. How much does each have?

9. John bought 3 newspapers and 1 book. The newspapers each cost the same amount. The book cost 10 times as much as the total cost of the newspapers. How much did 1 newspaper cost if John's total purchase amounted to $8.25?

10. Colored computer ribbons cost twice as much as black ribbons. Sylvia paid $27.65 for 3 black ribbons and 2 colored ribbons. How much did she pay for each colored ribbon?

11. Kurt purchased a package of three cassettes. If the tax was $.99 and Kurt paid a total of $17.49, how much did each cassette cost?

12. Evonne saved $125 one month and $175 the second month. How much does she have to save in the third month to average $150 a month savings?

13. The total enrollment in grades 10, 11, and 12 is 80% of the total enrollment for grades 7, 8, and 9. If the total enrollment of grades 7 through 12 is 450, how many students are enrolled in grades 7, 8, and 9?

Problem Solving Strategy
Find Information

Review the four-step plan for solving problems.

You must read the problem carefully.
a. Find the question asked.
b. Find the given information.

Often extra information is included in a problem. You must choose only the information needed to solve a problem.

Four-Step Plan

1 READ

2 PLAN

3 SOLVE

4 CHECK

EXAMPLE 1
Karen drove 400 miles to a convention. She averaged 50 miles per hour and got 24 miles per gallon of gas. How long did it take her to make the trip?

Find the necessary information: distance and rate
Identify the extra information: gas consumption
Solve the problem: $400 \div 50 = 8$ h

ANSWER: It took Karen 8 hours to make the trip.

Sometimes you must find information in maps, tables, charts, menus, or other sources.

EXAMPLE 2
The following table lists some of the medal winners in the 1984 Summer Olympic Games. Look at the table and answer the questions.

23d Summer Olympics Los Angeles, CA, July 29–Aug. 12, 1984 Final Medal Standings				
Country	**Gold**	**Silver**	**Bronze**	**Total**
Canada	10	18	16	44
China	15	8	9	32
Germany, West	17	19	23	59
Great Britain	5	10	22	37
Japan	10	8	14	32
Romania	20	16	17	53
United States	83	61	30	174

(*Source: The World Almanac and Book of Facts*, 1987, p. 795)

Where were the 23d Summer Olympic Games held? <u>Los Angeles</u>
How many gold medals did the U.S. win? <u>83</u>
How many silver medals did Canada win? <u>18</u>
How many bronze medals did Great Britain win? <u>22</u>
How many medals did Romania win? <u>53</u>

EXERCISES

Identify the extra information in each problem. Solve the problem.

1. Len bought 2 pounds of apples for $.99 per pound and 3 pounds of pears for $.89 per pound. He gave the clerk a $20 bill. How much did the fruit cost him?

2. Marcia bought a house for $72,500. The real estate taxes on the house are $1,250 per year. She made a 15% down payment on the house. How much did she have to pay for the down payment?

3. The music store sells video tapes for $5.95 each and cassette tapes for $2.69 each. How much will Michael have to pay for 6 video tapes?

4. Cheri traveled 450 miles on a tank of gas. Her tank holds 20 gallons of gas. On her last trip she paid $1.29 per gallon for gas. How many miles does Cheri get on each gallon of gas?

Look at the table that lists the Olympic winners of the Men's 1,000-meter speed-skating contest. Answer the following questions using the information you find in the table.

5. Who won in 1976?

6. In what year did Eric Heiden win?

7. What country did Gaetan Boucher represent?

8. What was Eric Heiden's winning time?

9. What was Peter Mueller's winning time?

10. How much faster was Heiden than Mueller?

11. How much faster was Boucher than Mueller?

12. Who holds the fastest time?

Speed Skating: Men's 1,000 meters	Time
1976 Peter Mueller, U.S.	1:19.32
1980 Eric Heiden, U.S.	1:15.18
1984 Gaetan Boucher, Canada	1:15.80

(*Source: The World Almanac and Book of Facts,* 1987, p. 798)

Problem Solving Strategy
Organize Information

Review the four-step plan for solving problems.

To plan the solution you must complete three steps:
a. Select a strategy.
b. Think or write out your plan.
c. Choose the method of computation.

Strategy: *Organize Information.* Sometimes you can more easily recognize a pattern or find a solution by organizing the data.

EXAMPLE 1

Find the number of diagonals that can be drawn from any one vertex of a polygon. Organize information in a table and look for a pattern.

$3 - 0 = 3$ ⌐ ⌐$5 - 2 = 3$

No. of sides	3	4	5	6	7	8	9	10
No. of diagonals	0	1	2	3	4	5	6	7

$4 - 1 = 3$ ⌐ ⌐$6 - 3 = 3$

ANSWER: number of diagonals = number of sides − 3

EXAMPLE 2

Janice has 7 coins in her pocket. If their total value is $1.15 and none is worth more than $.25, what coins does she have?

Use the guess and test strategy. Organize your work in a table.

Quarters	Dimes	Nickels	Pennies	Total
2	2	3	0	$ .85
3	2	2	0	$1.05
3	3	1	0	$1.10
3	4	0	0	$1.15

ANSWER: She has three quarters and four dimes.

EXAMPLE 3

Mark's annual salary is $18,000. He spends 33% of his income on food, 25% on housing, 18% on transportation, 7% on medical, and 17% on miscellaneous. How much does he spend on each item?

Organize your information in a table.

Category	Calculation	Amount Spent
Food	$18,000 × 0.33 = $5,940	$5,940
Housing	$18,000 × 0.25 = $4,500	$4,500
Transp.	$18,000 × 0.18 = $3,240	$3,240
Medical	$18,000 × 0.07 = $1,260	$1,260
Misc.	$18,000 × 0.17 = $3,060	$3,060

ANSWER: Mark spends $5,940 on food, $4,500 on housing, $3,240 on transportation, $1,260 on medical, and $3,060 on miscellaneous.

EXERCISES

Solve.

1. Find the next three numbers: 5, 15, 25, 35, . . .

2. Jerry bought some trees for $15 each, some bushes at $8 each and some plants at $1 each. He bought 4 times as many bushes as trees and 2 times as many plants as bushes. If he spent a total of $110, how many of each did he buy?

3. Alicia has twice as many quarters as dimes and as many pennies as dimes and quarters together. If she has $3.15 in all, how many of each coin does she have?

4. Mario was 10 when Bill was born. Now, Mario is twice as old as Bill. How old are Bill and Mario now?

5. Roberto's income is $35,600. If he budgets 34% of his income for housing, 29% for food, 6% for medical, 12% for transportation, 8% for clothing, and 11% for miscellaneous, how much does he budget for each?

6. How many three-digit numbers can you make using the digits 4, 8, and 9 if repetitions are allowed?

7. Sally expects to receive $300 a month in her new job. If her employer has agreed to give her a 4% increase in pay each year, how much will she receive per month during the fourth year?

8. How many meals consisting of one sandwich, one salad, one drink, and one dessert can be made from a menu consisting of four sandwiches, two salads, three drinks, and five desserts?

Marla has four job interviews: one at a fast-food restaurant, one at an agency that provides temporary clerical positions, one at a restaurant that serves lunches and dinners, and one at a department store that needs sales clerks.

- How would you advise Marla to dress for the job interviews?

- What information about herself should Marla be prepared to give?

- What kinds of questions should Marla ask:
  1. the manager of the fast-food restaurant?
  2. the manager of the temporary placement service?
  3. the manager of the lunch and dinner restaurant?
  4. the personnel manager of the department store?

In considering a job, what kinds of factors are important to you?

1-1 Hourly Rates and Overtime

For some jobs, pay is based on an **hourly rate,** or a fixed amount per hour. Sometimes an employee works **overtime,** or more than the regular hours. The **overtime rate,** or amount per hour for overtime, is often $1\frac{1}{2}$ times the hourly rate (called time-and-a-half). Sometimes it is double time, or 2 times the hourly rate.

EXAMPLE

The Corner Bakery pays Yukio $7.45 per hour as a cashier. One week he worked 43 hours. He was paid for overtime at time-and-a-half for all hours over 40. Find his total weekly pay.

Step 1. Find regular weekly pay.

hourly rate	×	regular hours	=	regular pay
$7.45	×	40	=	$298

Step 2. Find overtime pay.

total number of hours	−	regular hours	=	overtime hours
43	−	40	=	3

hourly rate	×	1.5	=	overtime rate
$7.45	×	1.5	=	$11.175
				$11.18 Round to nearest cent.

overtime hours	×	overtime rate	=	overtime pay
3	×	$11.18	=	$33.54

Step 3. Find total pay.

regular pay	+	overtime pay	=	total pay
$298	+	$33.54	=	$331.54

Yukio's total pay for the week was $331.54.

With a calculator, the computation in the Example can be streamlined by using the memory functions.

Key: $\boxed{\text{C}^\text{C}_\text{E}}$ 7.45 $\boxed{\times}$ 40 $\boxed{\text{M+}}$ 7.45 $\boxed{\times}$ 1.5
$\boxed{\times}$ 3 $\boxed{\text{M+}}$ $\boxed{\text{M}^\text{R}_\text{C}}$ ⟋331.525⟋
$331.53 Round to nearest cent.

The $.01 difference between the two answers occurs because the rounding is done at different points.

Skill Review

To compute regular pay, you need to know how to multiply decimals.

Multiply. Round to the nearest cent if necessary.

1. $8 × 40
2. $6.30 × 29
3. 1.5 × $8.95
4. $13.75 × 35.5

(For additional help, see page 545.)

Class Exercises

Complete the chart. Overtime is time-and-a-half for all hours over 40.

Hourly Rate	Hours Worked	Regular Pay	Overtime Pay	Total Pay
$7.50	4	1. ■	2. ■	3. ■
$10.80	52	4. ■	5. ■	6. ■
$6.42	$45\frac{1}{2}$	7. ■	8. ■	9. ■
$4.17	$36\frac{1}{2}$	10. ■	11. ■	12. ■

13. Explain how mental arithmetic can be used to find the answer to Exercise 1.

14. Show how you would use a calculator to help streamline the computation for Exercise 9.

EXERCISES

Complete the chart. The overtime rate is time-and-a-half for all hours over 40.

Hourly Rate	Hours Worked	Regular Pay	Overtime Pay	Total Pay
$8.32	45	$332.80	$62.40	1. ■
$6.00	50	2. ■	3. ■	4. ■
$4.35	$45\frac{1}{2}$	5. ■	6. ■	7. ■
$5.70	$37\frac{1}{2}$	8. ■	9. ■	10. ■

Solve.

11. Job: Driver
Hours worked: 38
Hourly rate: $5.85
Weekly pay: ■

12. Job: Cook
Hours worked: 25
Total pay: $107.50
Hourly rate: ■

13. Job: Gardener
Hourly rate: $8.50
Overtime rate
(time-and-a-half): ■

14. To earn spending money, Julie works in the school cafeteria for 3 hours each day on Tuesday through Thursday afternoons. At $3.45 per hour, how much does she earn each week?

15. Edward operates a print shop press. He is paid $7.40 per hour with time-and-a-half for overtime. One week he worked $47\frac{1}{2}$ hours. Find his total pay for that week.

16. Marina earns $4.50 per hour as a lifeguard at the beach. On holidays, she is given a $100 bonus and is paid the time-and-a-half overtime rate. How much does Marina earn for working 8 hours on July 4?

17. Nestor is a bookkeeper and Rita is a driver for a delivery service. Nestor works $7\frac{1}{2}$ hours each weekday and one Saturday each month (at double time). Rita works 8 hours Monday through Friday with 3 hours overtime (at time-and-a-half) each week. If Nestor is paid $7.42 per hour and Rita is paid $7.64 per hour, what are their combined earnings for March, April, and May? Consider each month to have 4 weeks.

18. Robin worked 46 hours one week, of which 6 were overtime. She earned $392. How much did she earn per hour?

Critical Thinking: *Predicting*

You are considering two summer jobs:

Job A Hours: 4–12 P.M.
  Pay: $4.75/h
  Double pay for overtime

Job B Hours: 8 A.M.–4 P.M.
  Pay: $4.00/h
  No overtime

1. Predict how your life will change if you take Job A. Then predict for Job B.

2. Describe the thought processes you used to make your predictions.

3. How did you use math to help you make your predictions?

4. How important is accuracy in your calculations?

5. Write two questions you could ask that would help you increase the accuracy of your prediction.

6. Compare your thinking when predicting with the way another person in your class thinks when predicting.

7. How will making an accurate prediction in this case help you make a good decision about which job to take?

8. Describe another situation in which accurate predictions would help you make a good decision.

1-2 Unit Rates and Tips: Finding Average Income

Some workers are paid on the basis of the number of units they produce. The amount paid per unit is the **unit rate.** Such work is often called **piecework.**

EXAMPLE 1

Gregory cuts puzzles for a toy manufacturer and is paid by the puzzle, or unit. For each puzzle, he earns $.35. One week he cut 615 puzzles. What were his earnings?

number of units × unit rate = earnings
$$615 \qquad \times \quad \$.35 \quad = \quad \blacksquare$$

Estimate: $615 \times \$.35 = \blacksquare \rightarrow 600 \times \$.40 = \$240$

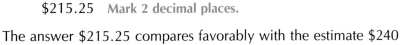

$$\begin{array}{r} 615 \\ \times\ \$.35 \\ \hline 30\ 75 \\ 184\ 5 \\ \hline \$215.25 \end{array}$$

615   number of units
× $.35   unit rate

$215.25   Mark 2 decimal places.

Key: $\boxed{C_E^C}$ 615 $\boxed{\times}$ .35 $\boxed{=}$ 215.25 $215.25

The answer $215.25 compares favorably with the estimate $240 and is a sensible answer.
Gregory's weekly earnings were $215.25.

Workers who depend upon unit rates do not have a constant income. Some workers receive an hourly wage plus **tips,** or money given by the customer for good service. Since the income of such workers varies from week to week, they often find it helpful to calculate an average weekly income so they can plan their spending.

EXAMPLE 2

Molly is paid $2.35 per hour for waiting on tables at the Country Inn. The first month on the job she kept a record of her weekly tips: $263.40, $314.10, $238.80, and $301.50. If she works 4 hours per evening on 6 evenings per week, what are her average weekly earnings?

Step 1. Find the weekly earnings from hourly wage.

$$4 \times 6 = 24 \text{ h/wk}$$

$$24 \times \$2.35 = \$56.40$$

Step 2. Find the average weekly tips.

$263.40 + $314.10 + $238.80 + $301.50 = $1,117.80   Find the sum.

$1,117.80 ÷ 4 = $279.45   Divide the sum by the number of weeks.

Step 3. Find the average weekly earnings.

$56.40 + $279.45 = $335.85   Add wages and average tips.

Molly's average weekly earnings for these four weeks are $335.85.

With a calculator, the computation in Example 2 can be streamlined.

Key: $\boxed{C_E^C}$ 4 $\boxed{\times}$ 6 $\boxed{\times}$ 2.35 $\boxed{M+}$ weekly wages (store in memory)
263.40 $\boxed{+}$ 314.10 $\boxed{+}$ 238.80 $\boxed{+}$ 301.50 $\boxed{=}$ $\boxed{÷}$ 4   average tips
$\boxed{+}$ $\boxed{M_C^R}$ $\boxed{=}$ 335.85
$335.85

Class Exercises

Find the earnings.

1. 26 units at $8.49 each

2. 150 units at $.32 each

3. $3.20 per hour; 40 h

4. $2.60 per hour; 33 h; $215.40 tips

Find the average weekly earnings.

5. Hourly rate: $3.45; Hours: 26; Weekly tips: $117.40, $123.75, $109.40, $114.65

6. 10 units in 3 h; Hours: 36; Unit rate: $2.50

EXERCISES

Find the unit earnings.

1. 84 units at $10.19 each

2. 1,153 units at $.78 each

3. 387 units at $2.86 each

Find the total weekly earnings.

4. $4.75 per hour; 37 h; $93.45 tips

5. $3 per hour; 30 h; $67.80 tips

6. $3.55 per hour; 21 h; $162.90 tips

7. $2.15 per hour; 39 h; $190 tips

Find the average weekly earnings.

8. Hours: 33; Hourly rate: $3.95; Weekly tips: $155, $137.85, $112, $128.55

9. Hours: 29; Hourly rate: $3.35; Weekly tips: $204.50, $218.35, $210, $198

10. Unit rate: $.67; Units per week: 438, 287, 354, 392

11. 3 perms at $24.50 each; 4 haircuts at $14 each; 26 sets at $9.50 each; $137.75 in tips

Solve.

12. Job: Packer
Units: 437
Total earnings: $353.97
Unit rate: ■

13. Job: Delivery person
Hourly rate: $2.85
Hours: 24
Tips: $119.65
Total earnings: ■

14. Job: Beautician
Units: 9 haircuts in 6 h
Unit rate: $7.65
Hours: 36
Estimated earnings: ■

15. Marty earns $28 for each perm plus an average tip of $9.50. What are his estimated earnings for four perms?

16. Lee worked 32 hours as a waitress and earned $314. If her hourly rate is $3.85, how much did she earn in tips?

17. The Speedy Messenger Service pays Miguel $2 for each package he delivers. In 3 days he delivers 30 packages. Use the average number of packages per day to predict his earnings for a 5-day week.

18. Explain how mental arithmetic can be used to find the answer to Problem 17.

19. Lorna earns $3.65 per hour as a taxi driver. In 8 days her tips are $35.60, $26.45, $31.80, $18.50, $37.60, $16.90, $19.55, and $23.90. Find Lorna's average daily tips and use them to predict her earnings for a 25-hour week in which she works 5 days.

20. Recently, there has been a shift from production to service jobs in the U.S. economy. Work independently or in small groups to find out why this has happened. Share your findings with the class.

You have eaten in a restaurant and would like to leave the server a tip. Here is a way to figure a tip mentally.

A typical tip is 15%. Suppose your bill was $48.75.

$$15\% = 10\% + 5\%$$

To make the computation easier, round $48.75 to $50.

$5.00	10% of $50; move the decimal point 1 place to the left.
+ 2.50	5% of $50; take half of 10%.
$7.50	total tip

Use this figure as a guideline—if your service was really good, you might decide to leave a larger tip. If you received poor service, you might leave a smaller tip.

Career
Payroll Clerk

Have you ever thought about the person who figures out your paycheck: the rate, the hours, and the deductions? That person is a **payroll clerk.**

Profile of a payroll clerk. A payroll clerk is probably a high school graduate. A person interested in working in the payroll department must be a careful, accurate worker. A payroll clerk should be trustworthy and respect confidential information. A payroll clerk should have good math skills and be able to compute percentage and use decimals and fractions.

The payroll department environment. Even in large firms, the department may not employ many people. After training, all payroll employees must be able to work by themselves with little supervision. They must be able to use adding machines and calculators; many are trained to use computer terminals. Work is done indoors and working hours are quite regular (for example, from 9 A.M. to 5 P.M. or 8 A.M. to 4 P.M.) with scheduled lunch periods.

All in a day's work. George is an experienced payroll clerk. He finds wages for the employees paid by the hour and for those paid by a unit rate.

1. Using the time and work record cards, help George find the gross pay for each employee.

TIMECARD							
Employee J. Thompson					Week Ending 6/7		
S.S. # 000-00-0000							
	Hours Worked	Hourly Rate	Amount Earned	Overtime Hours	Time-and-a-half	Overtime Amount Earned	Total Earned
Mon.	8	$7	■				■
Tue.	8	$7	■	2	■	■	■
Wed.	8	$7	■				■
Thu.	8	$7	■	2	■	■	■
Fri.	8	$7	■				■
Totals		■				■	■

WORK RECORD			
Employee C. Gonzales Week Ending 6/7			
S.S. # 000-00-0000			
	Item	Rate	Number Produced
Mon.	Brackets	$.40	260
Tue.	Brackets	$.40	198
Wed.	Brackets	$.40	203
Thu.	Brackets	$.40	220
Fri.	Brackets	$.40	218
			■

2. List some advantages and disadvantages of an hourly wage and being paid by the unit. Consider both the employer and employee.

1-3 Pay Periods and Salary

Many workers receive a regular paycheck for a fixed amount of money, or **salary.** This salary may be paid *monthly, semimonthly* (twice a month), *biweekly* (every two weeks), or *weekly.* The period of time between paychecks is called the **pay period.**

> **Part-Time**
> **Dental Assistant**
> ## Salary $7200
> **Call 555-8080**
> 9A.M.—5P.M.
> Regular hours.
> Weekly pay.

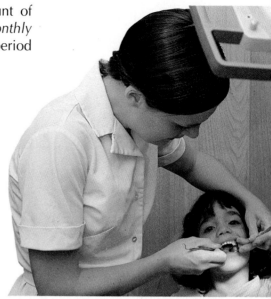

EXAMPLE 1

Ellie saw the above ad in the paper. If she gets the job, what will be her weekly pay if her salary is paid over 52 weeks each year?

annual salary ÷ number of pay periods = amount of pay
$7,200 ÷ 52 = ■

Estimate: $7,200 ÷ 52 = ■ → $7,000 ÷ 50 = $140

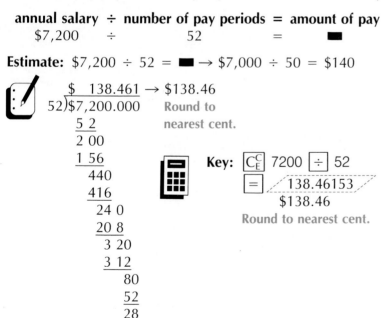

$$
\begin{array}{r}
\$\ \ 138.461 \rightarrow \$138.46 \\
52\overline{)\$7,200.000} \\
\underline{5\ 2} \\
2\ 00 \\
\underline{1\ 56} \\
440 \\
\underline{416} \\
24\ 0 \\
\underline{20\ 8} \\
3\ 20 \\
\underline{3\ 12} \\
80 \\
\underline{52} \\
28
\end{array}
$$

Round to nearest cent.

Key: C/CE 7200 ÷ 52
= *138.46153*
$138.46
Round to nearest cent.

The answer $138.46 is sensible and compares reasonably with the estimate $140. Ellie would receive $138.46 each week.

To find an annual salary, multiply the number of pay periods by the amount of each check.

EXAMPLE 2

Sam manages a convenience store. His biweekly pay is $678.50. What is his annual salary?

Hidden Question: How many biweekly pay periods (or 2-week periods) are there in a year?

$$52 \text{ wk in a year} \div 2 = 26$$

amount of paycheck × number of pay periods = annual salary

$$\$678.50 \quad \times \quad 26 \quad = \quad ■$$

Estimate: $\$678.50 \times 26 = ■ \rightarrow \$700 \times 30 = \$21,000$

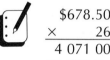

```
    $678.50
  ×      26
   4 071 00
  13 570 0
$17,641.00   Write $ and .
```

Key: $\boxed{\text{C}_\text{E}^\text{C}}$ 678.5 $\boxed{×}$ 26
$\boxed{=}$ _17641_
$17,641

The answer $17,641 is sensible and compares reasonably with the estimate $21,000.
Sam's annual salary is $17,641.

Class Exercises

Complete the chart.

Annual Salary	Pay Period	Number of Pay Periods	Amount of Paycheck
$24,000	Monthly	*1.* ■	*2.* ■
$28,647	Biweekly	*3.* ■	*4.* ■
$9,828	Weekly	*5.* ■	*6.* ■
$21,110	Twice a month	*7.* ■	*8.* ■
9. ■	Monthly	*10.* ■	$956.37
11. ■	*12.* ■	26	$539.16

Solve.

13. Rosita is a tax accountant. Her semimonthly pay is $850. What is her annual salary?

14. For the months of June, July, and August, Sandy is paid $4,200. How much is her semimonthly pay?

EXERCISES

Complete the chart.

Annual Salary	Pay Period	Number of Pay Periods	Amount of Pay
$10,552	Biweekly	1. ■	2. ■
$15,520	Semimonthly	3. ■	4. ■
$36,000	Monthly	5. ■	6. ■
7. ■	Weekly	8. ■	$394.22
9. ■	10. ■	24	$317.45

Solve.

11. Swimming coach
Annual salary: $18,000
Monthly pay: ■

12. Parking lot attendant
Weekly pay: $145.79
Annual salary: ■

13. Electronics technician
Annual salary: $22,100
Amount of pay: $850
Pay period: ■

14. Norma teaches skiing from November through March. She is paid $7,500 for the season. What is her monthly pay?

15. Raymond worked as a documents clerk in a county court last year. He received $9,260 for exactly half a year's work. What is his biweekly pay?

16. Jim receives an annual salary of $16,200 as a cook. Daphne makes $385.75 per week as a building inspector. Which one has the greater weekly pay? How much more is it?

17. Which of Exercises 14–16 could be done mentally? In which would pencil and paper be appropriate? Which could best be done using a calculator?

Reading in Math: Prefixes

To help learn the meaning of words such as *semimonthly* and *biweekly*, you can learn the meaning of the prefixes *semi-* (half) and *bi-* (two). In fact, the more prefixes you know, the more your vocabulary, both of math terms and other kinds of words, will expand.

State the meaning of each term. If you do not know the meaning of the prefix, look it up in the dictionary.

1. *semi*circle
2. *bi*annual
3. *pre*paid
4. *re*possessed

1-4 Commission

In some jobs, a person's pay depends upon the amount of goods or services the person sells. The salesperson receives a **commission,** or specified amount of money, for sales made during a pay period. Commission is usually expressed as a percentage of sales.

   A salesperson whose only pay is commission is said to work on a *straight commission.* The percent of total sales paid as commission is the **commission rate.**

EXAMPLE 1
Brenda sells the services of a home-improvement company. She receives a straight commission of 9% of her total sales. How much commission does she receive for sales of $2,556.50?

Think: 9% = 0.09

$$\text{total sales} \times \text{commission rate} = \text{commission}$$
$$\$2,556.50 \times \quad 0.09 \quad = \quad \blacksquare$$

Estimate: $2,556.50 × 0.09 = ■ → $2,600 × 0.1 = $260

$2,556.50	total sales
× 0.09	commission rate
230.0850	commission

$230.09   Round to nearest cent.

Key: $\boxed{\text{C}_{\text{E}}^{\text{C}}}$ 2556.50 $\boxed{\times}$ 9 $\boxed{\%}$ / 230.085 /
$230.09
Round to nearest cent.

The answer $230.09 is a sensible answer and is reasonably close to the estimate $260.
Brenda receives $230.09 as commission.

Problem Solving Strategy: Solving another way.

You can use mental arithmetic and pencil and paper to do this calculation another way.

Think: 9% = 10% − 1%

To find 10% of a number, move the decimal point one place to the left: 10% of $2,556.50 = $255.65

To find 1% of a number, move the decimal point two places to the left: 1% of $2,556.50 = $25.56.

$255.65	(10%)	Subtract the answer
− 25.56	(1%)	from the number you
$230.09	(9%)	wrote above.

Skill Review

To compute commission, you must be able to work with percents.

Express each percent as a decimal.
   1. 45%   **2.** 3%
   3. $4\frac{1}{4}$%   **4.** $0.6\frac{1}{2}$%
(For additional help, see page 550.)

Some people receive a fixed salary in addition to commission.

EXAMPLE 2
Lois sells auto parts. She receives a salary of $400 per month plus a commission of 5% of her total sales. What was her total pay for the month if she had sales totaling $4,396?

Think: 5% = 0.05

Step 1. Find the commission.
total sales × commission rate = commission
 $4,396 × 0.05 = $219.80

Step 2. Add the salary.
 $219.80 + $400 = $619.80

Lois' total pay for the month is $619.80.

With a calculator, you can streamline the computation in Example 2.

Key: $\boxed{\tfrac{C}{CE}}$ 4396 $\boxed{\times}$ 5 $\boxed{\%}$ $\boxed{+}$ 400 $\boxed{=}$ 619.80
$619.80

Class Exercises

Compute the amount of pay.

Commission Rate	Total Sales	Salary	Amount of Pay
8%	$956	0	1. ■
11%	$1,250	0	2. ■
$9\frac{1}{2}$%	$2,680	0	3. ■
6%	$5,150	$200	4. ■
$3\frac{1}{4}$%	$8,995	$300	5. ■

EXERCISES

Compute the amount of pay.

Commission Rate	Total Sales	Salary	Amount of Pay
5%	$8,500	0	1. ■
13%	$995	0	2. ■
$3\frac{1}{2}$%	$5,558	0	3. ■
14%	$5,150	$300	4. ■
$6\frac{3}{4}$%	$12,105	$125	5. ■

Solve.

6. Insurance sales
   Commission rate: 11%
   Month's sales: $54,000
   Monthly commission: ■

7. Computer sales
   Commission rate: 14%
   Month's sales: $4,298
   Monthly commission: ■

8. Vending machine sales
   Commission rate: 8.5%
   Month's sales: $9,572
   Monthly commission: ■

9. Clothing sales
   Commission rate: $4\frac{1}{2}$%
   Month's sales: $6,225
   Monthly salary: $400
   Monthly pay: ■

10. Appliance sales
    Commission rate: $8\frac{1}{2}$%
    Month's sales: $3,552
    Monthly salary: $350
    Monthly pay: ■

11. Furniture sales
    Commission rate: $3\frac{1}{2}$%
    Month's sales: $18,545
    Annual pay: $18,995.80
    Monthly pay: ■

12. Alexis sells season tickets to soccer games. The season tickets cost $225.75. She earns a commission of 16% on each sale. Last month she sold 42 season tickets. What did she earn for the month?

13. Jesse sells advertising. He is paid $13\frac{1}{2}$% commission for each page of advertising that he sells. A page sells for $1,350. He sold an average of 24 pages a month. What was his commission for the year?

14. Ron makes a straight commission of 11%. How much did he earn for sales of $14,927.65 and $9,882.75?

15. Explain how mental arithmetic can be used to find the answer to Exercise 6.

Using a Calculator: Computing Percents

You can use the percent key on your calculator to make computation with percents easier. Usually this key is labeled $\boxed{\%}$.

To find 28% of $91.50,

Key: $\boxed{\substack{C\\C_E}}$ 91.5 $\boxed{\times}$ 28 $\boxed{\%}$ ⟋ 25.62 ⟋

The answer 25.62 ($25.62) will be displayed.

Use the percent key of your calculator to find each value.

1. 18% of $47

2. 15% of $97.75

3. 9.15% of $475.38

Find the commission.

4. 5% on sales of $18,350

5. $3\frac{1}{4}$% on sales of $7,388

1-5 Daily Logs and Timecards

Employees who work on an hourly basis must keep track of the hours they work each day. A **daily log** is a record of the time the worker begins work (time in) and ends work (time out).

A **weekly timecard** is made up of the daily logs for each working day of the week. To use these logs, the worker records the times in and out and then subtracts to find the total hours worked.

Skill Review

To interpret a timecard, you need to be able to add fractions.

Find the sum.

1. $2\frac{3}{4} + 7\frac{1}{4}$

2. $3\frac{1}{2} + 2\frac{2}{3}$

3. $6\frac{1}{4} + 5$

4. $3\frac{5}{6} + 4\frac{1}{2}$

5. $5\frac{3}{4} + 3\frac{3}{4}$

(For additional help, see page 547.)

EXAMPLE 1

Amy logged the following hours on April 14.

NAME: Amy					
Date	In	Out	In	Out	Hours
4/14	8:30 A.M.	12:15 P.M.	12:50 P.M.	5:05 P.M.	■

How many hours did she work?

Step 1. Find the hours before lunch.

Problem Solving Strategy: Making a model.
You can make a model of a clock or use a clock in your classroom to help solve this problem.

$$
\begin{array}{ll}
8{:}30 \rightarrow 11{:}30 & 3 \text{ h} \\
11{:}30 \rightarrow 12{:}15 & = \frac{3}{4}\text{ h} \quad \frac{45}{60} = \frac{3}{4} \\
\hline
& 3\frac{3}{4}\text{ h}
\end{array}
$$

Step 2. Find the hours after lunch.

$$
\begin{array}{ll}
12{:}50 \rightarrow 4{:}50 & 4 \text{ h} \\
4{:}50 \rightarrow 5{:}05 & = \frac{1}{4}\text{ h} \quad \frac{15}{60} = \frac{1}{4} \\
\hline
& 4\frac{1}{4}\text{ h}
\end{array}
$$

Step 3. Find the total hours for the day.

$$
\begin{array}{l}
3\frac{3}{4}\text{ h} \\
+\ 4\frac{1}{4}\text{ h} \\
\hline
7\frac{4}{4}\text{ h} \quad \frac{4}{4} = 1 \\
8\phantom{\frac{4}{4}}\text{ h} \leftarrow 7 + 1 = 8
\end{array}
$$

Amy worked 8 hours.

Daily Logs and Timecards **55**

EXAMPLE 2

Rosa kept the timecard shown below. She earns $8.50 per hour and time-and-a-half for all hours over 40. Find her weekly pay.

Rainbow Musical Instruments					
Name: Rosa Morales			Department: Keyboard		
Date	In	Out	In	Out	Hours
1/29	8:30 A.M.	12:45 P.M.	1:45 P.M.	5:30 P.M.	8 h
1/30	8:30 A.M.	12:15 P.M.	1:00 P.M.	5:30 P.M.	$8\frac{1}{4}$ H
1/31	8:25 A.M.	11:55 A.M.	12:30 P.M.	4:45 P.M.	$7\frac{3}{4}$ h
2/1	8:15 A.M.	12:15 P.M.	1:00 P.M.	6:15 P.M.	$9\frac{1}{4}$ h
2/2	8:30 A.M.	12:20 P.M.	12:50 P.M.	5:30 P.M.	$8\frac{1}{2}$ h

Step 1. Find the total hours.

$$8 + 8\frac{1}{4} + 7\frac{3}{4} + 9\frac{1}{4} + 8\frac{1}{2}$$
$$= 8 + 8\frac{1}{4} + 7\frac{3}{4} + 9\frac{1}{4} + 8\frac{2}{4} = 40\frac{7}{4} \qquad \frac{7}{4} = 1\frac{3}{4}$$
$$= 41\frac{3}{4} \qquad 40 + 1\frac{3}{4} = 41\frac{3}{4}$$

Step 2. Find the regular pay.

hourly rate × regular hours = regular pay
$$\$8.50 \quad \times \quad 40\ h \quad = \quad \$340$$

Step 3. Find the overtime pay.

hourly rate × 1.5 = overtime rate
$$\$8.50 \quad \times 1.5 = \quad \$12.75$$

Think: $41\frac{3}{4}$ h $- 40$ h $= 1\frac{3}{4}$ h $= 1.75$ h

overtime rate × overtime hours = overtime pay
$$\$12.75 \quad \times \quad 1.75 \quad = \quad \$22.31$$

Step 4. Find the total pay.

regular pay + overtime pay = total pay
$$\$340 \quad + \quad \$22.31 \quad = \$362.31$$

Rosa's weekly pay is $362.31.

With a calculator and mental arithmetic, you can streamline the computation for Example 2.

Think: $41\frac{3}{4}$ h $- 40$ h $= 1\frac{3}{4}$ h $= 1.75$ h   overtime hours

Key: $\boxed{C_E^C}$ 8.5 $\boxed{\times}$ 1.5 $\boxed{\times}$ 1.75 $\boxed{M+}$ overtime pay in memory
8.5 $\boxed{\times}$ 40 $\boxed{+}$ $\boxed{M_C^R}$ $\boxed{=}$ 362.3125   regular + overtime pay
\$362.31   Round to nearest cent.

Class Exercises

Find the daily hours and total hours.

Empire Manufacturing Company					
Employee Timecard					
Name: Abe Roth			Department: Milling/Rolling		
Date	In	Out	In	Out	Hours
9/16	8:00 A.M.	12:00 P.M.	1:00 P.M.	5:15 P.M.	1. ■
9/17	8:00 A.M.	12:15 P.M.	1:15 P.M.	5:30 P.M.	2. ■
9/18	8:10 A.M.	11:55 A.M.	12:30 P.M.	5:45 P.M.	3. ■
9/19	7:45 A.M.	11:15 P.M.	12:00 P.M.	5:15 P.M.	4. ■
9/20	7:50 A.M.	12:10 P.M.	12:50 P.M.	5:30 P.M.	5. ■
				Total Hours	6. ■

Solve.

7. Use the timecard above. Abe earns $5.50 per hour and gets paid time-and-a-half for all hours over 40. What is his weekly pay?

EXERCISES

Find the daily hours and total hours.

Alpha National Bank and Trust Company					
Employee Timecard					
Name: Deidre St. Eves			Department: Bookkeeping		
Date	In	Out	In	Out	Hours
12/5	3:15 P.M.	6:30 P.M.	7:20 P.M.	11:50 P.M.	1. ■
12/6	3:00 P.M.	6:00 P.M.	6:40 P.M.	12:25 A.M.	2. ■
12/7	3:30 P.M.	7:15 P.M.	8:00 P.M.	12:30 A.M.	3. ■
12/8	2:55 P.M.	6:40 P.M.	7:25 P.M.	12:10 A.M.	4. ■
12/9	2:45 P.M.	7:15 P.M.	8:50 P.M.	11:50 P.M.	5. ■
				Total Hours	6. ■

Solve.

7. Use the timecard above. Deirdre earns $8.25 per hour. What is her weekly pay?

Find the total hours.

8. Kim Sung
   Mon: $5\frac{1}{2}$ h
   Wed: $8\frac{1}{4}$ h
   Thu: $6\frac{1}{4}$ h
   Fri: $8\frac{3}{4}$ h
   Total hours: ■

9. Raoul Diaz
   Mon: $7\frac{3}{4}$ h
   Tue: 8 h
   Wed: 8 h
   Thu: $8\frac{1}{4}$ h
   Fri: $7\frac{3}{4}$ h
   Total hours: ■

10. Elisabeth Moore
   Mon: $6\frac{5}{8}$ h
   Tue: $7\frac{5}{8}$ h
   Wed: 8 h
   Thu: $9\frac{1}{8}$ h
   Fri: $8\frac{1}{2}$ h
   Total hours: ■

Solve.

11. Sue works the evening shift five nights per week from 4:15 P.M. until 1:00 A.M. If she takes 45 minutes for supper each night, how many hours per week does she work?

12. Jin works five nights per week from 11:30 P.M. until 8:00 A.M. the next morning. If he gets 1 hour for a meal break, how many hours per week does he work?

13. Kim in Exercise 8 earns $9.25 per hour. How much did she make that week?

14. Elisabeth in Exercise 10 earns $8.60 per hour and gets time-and-a-half for any hours over 40. How much did she earn for the week?

Challenge

Roger is an appliance salesperson in a major department store. He gets paid $4.60 an hour for all hours up to 40 hours. He gets paid time-and-a-half for all hours over 40 hours. In addition Roger receives 2.25% commission on each appliance he sells.

During the store's clearance sale one week Roger worked 48.5 hours. He sold $6,750 worth of dishwashers, $7,040 worth of clothes washers, and $5,980 worth of dryers. What was Roger's average pay per hour for the one week of the clearance sale?

Calculator:
Using the Memory

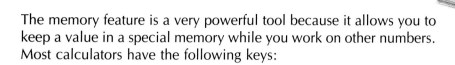

The memory feature is a very powerful tool because it allows you to keep a value in a special memory while you work on other numbers. Most calculators have the following keys:

| M+ | Adds the number currently displayed to any number stored in memory. |

| M− | Subtracts the number currently displayed from any number stored in memory. |

| MR/C | Displays the sum or difference of the numbers stored in memory if pressed once. Clears the memory if pressed twice. |

M+ and M− can be used in place of = if you want to find the result of a computation and store it.

In the expression $2.7 \times 9.3 + 8.5 \div 2.2$, the operations of multiplication and division must be done before the addition. This can be accomplished by using the memory keys.

Key: CE/C 2.7 × 9.3 M+ 8.5 ÷ 2.2 M+
MR/C   28.973636

Memory can be used to find the weekly pay for 36 hours at $3.25 per hour and 9% commission on sales of $956.25.

$$\text{wage} = \left(\begin{array}{c}\textbf{hours}\\\textbf{worked}\end{array} \times \begin{array}{c}\textbf{hourly}\\\textbf{rate}\end{array}\right) + \left(\begin{array}{c}\textbf{total}\\\textbf{sales}\end{array} \times \begin{array}{c}\textbf{rate of}\\\textbf{commission}\end{array}\right)$$

Key: CE/C 36 × 3.25 M+ 956.25 × .09 M+
MR/C   203.0625
$203.06

EXERCISES

Use the memory feature of your calculator to compute the following. Remember to clear the display and memory each time.

1. $9 \times 16 + 4 \times 7$

2. $3.7 \times 5.9 + 6.2 \times 2.7$

3. $9.1 + 5.4 + 8.2 \div 4.7$

4. $3.6 \times 9.9 - 5.2 \times 3.11$

5. $6.2 \times 6.4 + 12.5 \times 6.47 + 8.8 \times 10.1$

6. $27.81 \div 3.97 - 4.26 \div 1.48$

Find the total weekly pay.

7. Hourly rate: $4.38; number of hours: 32; commission: 12%; sales: $897.33

8. Hourly rate: $5.16; number of hours: 39; commission: 11.2%; sales: $1,016.95

Decision Making:
Getting a Job

A major turning point in a student's life is reached upon graduating from high school. With his graduation just a few months away, Li Sum was certain he wanted to continue his education. He had already registered at a nearby community college. He planned to attend college part time, in the evenings, and to work full time during the day. Li would use his income to pay the tuition and his living expenses.

However, the problem was that Li had not yet begun to look for a job. He just couldn't seem to make up his mind about the kind of job he wanted.

GETTING STARTED

One Sunday, with the newspaper employment ads at his side, Li began the process of making a decision. First, he stated the problem: What kind of job do I want? Then he began to list information related to the decision.

Li listed his personal goals:

GOALS
1. To continue my education.
2. To work with people.
3. To earn a good wage.
4. To live near my family.
5. To enjoy vacation travel.

Then, referring to the newspaper, he listed some facts about the job market. Li compared his qualifications—talents, abilities, and experience—and his goals with each major career field. Since professional positions usually require a college degree, he ruled out this field. Business was crossed out because Li did not think he would like working in an office. Manual labor did not appeal to him either, and he lacked the special training required for most jobs in the medical field. He thought sales was a field he might enjoy. Li did want to work with people. Also, he had liked selling magazine subscriptions in the past.

MAJOR CAREER FIELDS
Professional
Business
Manual Labor
Medical
Sales

Answer the following questions.

1. Could Li know with absolute certainty which jobs he would like and which he wouldn't? Why or why not?

2. How might going to college affect Li's ideas about what kind of job he wants?

3. Predict whether you would enjoy working at a job in sales.

4. Explain what you thought about in making a prediction about whether you would enjoy a job in sales.

5. Compare your answer to Question 4 with the answer of someone else in your class. List similarities and differences in your thinking.

6. Work with a partner to write at least two general statements about how people think when making predictions.

7. From what other sources besides the newspaper could Li have obtained information about the job market?

OPPORTUNITIES IN SALES

Once he had narrowed down his job choice to sales, Li again looked in the newspaper in order to obtain some additional information. He found that sales jobs pay in a variety of ways. He selected an example of each type that interested him.

RETAIL

F.T./P.T.
Salespersons

Men's Fashion Clothing. Retail experience pref'd. 37½ h/wk. $6.89/h.

20% store discount.

Telemarketing

Telephone Sales.

$10.71 per hour plus commission. Weekly earnings up to $500. 35 hours per week. Industrial Lighting Company.

SALES TRAINEE

No overnight travel.

Base salary of $8,500 per year, plus commission and bonus.

INSURANCE

Agency has opportunity for highly motivated individual with good communication skills. 35h/wk. Annual salary and commission.

SALES: OFFICE FURNITURE

Last year, the average earnings of all our salespeople exceeded $30,000. Will train. Straight commission. No overnight travel.

Answer the following questions.

8. Does Li have enough information about these five jobs to compare annual earnings for all of them? If not, what information is missing?

9. If Li did not want to travel on his job, which job(s) should he not consider?

10. Suppose Li did not want to sit at a desk all day. Which job(s) should he not consider?

COMPARING EARNINGS

Li wanted to find out what he could expect to earn in one year from each of these jobs. He called to get additional information. What he found out is listed below:

> TELEMARKETING: 9% commission.
> average weekly sales, $1,100.
> INSURANCE: $396.72 biweekly salary.
> average monthly sales, $16,500. commission 4½%.
> SALES—OFFICE FURNITURE: average
> weekly hours, 46. average pay, $30,000.
> SALES TRAINEE: 7% commission. average
> annual sales $250,000. bonus, 1% of all
> sales over $325,000.

Answer the following questions.

11. Li budgets about 8% of his earnings for clothing. If he took the retail job, how much could he save in one year if he purchased half his clothing in the men's department at that store?

12. List, from highest to lowest, the average annual earnings that Li could expect on each of the five jobs. (In the retail job earnings, be sure to include the savings calculated in Question 11.)

13. Which job pays the highest for the least number of hours worked?

14. Which job pays the least for the greatest number of hours worked?

15. Which job pays the highest *guaranteed* annual earnings?

16. For which job does the greatest percentage of annual earnings depend on the amount of sales?

LI'S DECISION

Before he could make a choice, Li thought he should interview for each of the jobs. In that way he could see for himself what the people and the working conditions were like. Also, he would find out if he were really qualified for the positions advertised.

Answer the following question.

17. How could predicting accurately help you have a successful job interview?

When he returned from his last interview, Li made two more lists. He rated the five jobs on the basis of both working conditions and the people he would be working with.

LIKE THE PEOPLE	LIKE THE WORKING CONDITIONS
1. Retail	1. Telemarketing
2. Telemarketing	2. Insurance
3. Insurance	3. Office Furniture
4. Office Furniture	4. Retail
5. Sales Trainee	5. Sales Trainee

Although he was qualified for all five jobs, Li chose the telemarketing position.

Answer the following questions.

18. What facts favored the telemarketing job?

19. What facts, if any, were not favorable to the telemarketing job?

20. Why do you think Li did not choose the office furniture sales job?

21. Why do you think Li did not choose the retail job?

DECIDE FOR YOURSELF

Suppose that you are faced with a decision about career choice. Collect information and use this information, together with your personal goals, to make a decision about a job. Try to go through all the steps that Li used. Then summarize how you, and Li, went about deciding what job to choose.

Chapter 1 Review

VOCABULARY

commission	hourly rate	pay period	tips
commission rate	overtime	piecework	unit rate
daily log	overtime rate	salary	weekly timecard

For Exercises 1–12, select the word or words that complete each statement.

1. The hourly rate for all overtime hours worked is called the _____ .

2. The amount paid per unit of work produced is called the _____ .

3. A record of the times a worker begins work and ends work is called a _____ .

4. Work paid for by the number of units produced is called _____ .

5. Some pay is based on a fixed amount per hour, or a(n) _____ .

6. A _____ consists of daily logs for each working day of the week.

7. A regular paycheck for a fixed amount of money is called a _____ .

8. The time worked over the number of regular hours is called _____ .

9. Pay earned that is dependent on sales is called _____ .

10. The money paid as a reward for good service is called _____ .

11. The percent of total sales paid as commission is called the _____ .

12. The period of time between paychecks is called the _____ .

SKILLS

Multiply or divide.

13. $7.50 × 40

14. $9.75 × 35

15. $19,533 ÷ 12

16. $13.50 × 1.5

17. $9,000 ÷ 24

18. $929.50 ÷ 26

Find the average.

19. 8; 12; 16; 20

20. $24.36; $38.96; $45.50; $31.60; $39.83

Find the number.

21. 4% of $345

22. 18% of $2,153

23. 7.6% of $9,328.50

Find the sum.

24. $3\frac{1}{2} + 5\frac{2}{3}$

25. $7\frac{3}{4} + 2\frac{1}{3}$

26. $4\frac{5}{6} + 2\frac{1}{2}$

CONSUMER TOPICS

Solve.

27. Carrie earns $7.34 per hour. What is her overtime pay at time-and-a-half?

28. Find Carrie's earnings (Problem 27) if she worked 45 hours one week.

29. Clare earns $4.10 per hour working as an attendant in a health spa. In 6 days, her tips were $26, $38.50, $46, $39.75, $32.25, and $43.25. Find Clare's average daily tips and use them to predict her earnings for a 35-hour workweek in which she works 4 days.

30. Sarah delivered 168 newspapers and received $.04 per paper. What were Sarah's earnings?

31. Melvin is paid $3.50 per hour plus tips. In one 4-week period he received $72.50, $86, $70.75, and $100.75 in tips. What was his average weekly wage for a 38-hour week?

32. Ani earns $.18 per unit for the work she does. For all units over 1,000 that she produces in a week she receives $.25. What were her weekly earnings if she produced 1,350 units?

33. Find the annual earnings if a worker is paid $843.75 semimonthly.

34. Raissa is paid $436.85 biweekly. What are her annual earnings?

35. Juan receives an annual salary of $23,827.68. What is the total amount of his paycheck each pay period if he is paid monthly?

36. Anne received a 5.5% commission on a house she sold for $98,750. How much commission did she receive?

37. Mario receives $5.40 per hour and 2% commission on sales. One week he worked 35 hours and sold $1,968 worth of goods. How much did he earn that week?

38. Joe takes 45 minutes each day for lunch. He does not get paid for the lunch break. How much does Joe earn in a 5-day workweek if he checks in at 9:00 A.M. and checks out at 5:30 P.M. each day and earns $4.80 per hour?

Chapter 1 Test

Find the weekly earnings. All hours over 40 hours are paid at time-and-a-half.

1. $5.25 per hour, 30 h
2. $4.38 per hour, 40 h
3. $9.50 per hour, 43 h

4. $2.80 per hour; 38 h; $135.50 tips
5. $3.40 per hour; 25 h; $89.75 tips

6. $3 per hour; 40 h; tips: $25; $35; $20; $25; $30

Compute the piecework earnings.

7. 250 units at $.15 per unit
8. 265 units at $1.10 per unit

9. Gwendolyn earns a commission of 8.5%. Find her commission on $1,200 worth of sales.

For an annual salary of $19,500, what are the earnings per pay period if the worker is paid at each indicated interval?

10. monthly
11. biweekly

Solve.

12. Patrick receives $4.50 per hour and 3% commission on sales. One week he worked 40 hours and sold $2,500 worth of goods. How much did he earn that week?

13. Miguel is paid $3.50 per hour plus tips. Over a 4-week period his weekly tips were $114.50, $115, $100.50, and $116. What was his average weekly wage for a 40-hour week?

14. John earns $2.80 per hour and $.25 for each unit produced. What were his weekly earnings if he worked a 40-hour week and produced 500 units?

15. Sally earns $603.95 each pay period. If she is paid semimonthly, how much is her annual salary?

16. Elaine is a hairdresser. What were her earnings for the day if she received $24.50 in tips and performed the following services: 2 haircuts at $12 each; 6 sets at $6.50 each; 2 perms at $25 each?

17. Kris's timecard is shown. What are her earnings for Monday if she is paid $4.80 per hour?

	A.M.	Lunch		P.M.
	In	Out	In	Out
M	8:15	12:00	12:45	4:30

Cumulative Mixed Review

Select the letter corresponding to the correct answer.

1. David worked 35 hours and received $5.50 per hour. What was his weekly wage?
   a. $220
   b. $192.50
   c. $1,925
   d. $19.25

2. Cathy worked 45 hours and received $6.50 per hour for regular pay. She received time-and-a-half for all hours over 40 hours. What were her weekly earnings?
   a. $308.75
   b. $292.50
   c. $269.75
   d. $260

3. Mark earns $.75 for each unit of work. One week he produced 450 units. How much did he earn that week?
   a. $337.50
   b. $256.50
   c. $733.50
   d. $33.70

4. Helen worked 40 hours at $2.80 per hour and made $75.50 in tips. What were her weekly earnings?
   a. $112
   b. $243.50
   c. $159.50
   d. $187.50

5. Samir worked 30 hours at $2.90 per hour. He made the following tips: $15; $18; $22; $20; $16. What was his hourly wage?
   a. $3.51
   b. $105.20
   c. $5.93
   d. $5.89

6. Eleanor earns $24,500 annually. What is the total amount of each paycheck if she is paid biweekly?
   a. $2,041.67
   b. $924.31
   c. $1,020.83
   d. $942.31

7. Kevin is paid $685.42 semimonthly. What is his annual salary?
   a. $16,450.08
   b. $15,450.08
   c. $17,820.12
   d. $8,225.04

8. Kate receives 7.5% commission on all her sales. One month she sold $12,500 worth of goods. How much was her commission for the month?
   a. $93.75
   b. $4,375
   c. $937.50
   d. $712.50

9. Jason earns $3.50 per hour plus 2.5% commission on all goods sold. One week he worked 40 hours and sold $5,750 worth of goods. What were his weekly earnings?
   a. $255
   b. $140
   c. $197.50
   d. $283.75

10. One week Kara earned a total of $325. Of that amount $225 was tips. If she worked a 40-hour week, what was her hourly rate of pay, not including tips?
    a. $2.50
    b. $8.13
    c. $13.75
    d. $4.62

Miguel has taken a job with a fast-food restaurant, starting at $3.75 per hour. He plans to work 35 hours a week and so he is looking forward to pay of $131.25 each week.

- Will Miguel actually receive a check for $131.25 each week? What are some factors that must be considered in deciding how much pay he will receive?

- How can Miguel find out what his take-home pay will be? Are there other sources of information he can use besides asking his employer?

About how much of a person's wages or salary do you think is likely to be withheld? What factors do you think affect the amount withheld? Compare your answers with those of others in your class.

2-1 Earnings Statements

An **earnings statement,** the record of earnings and deductions, is usually attached to your paycheck. It shows the **gross pay,** or total pay, the **net pay,** or take-home pay, and the amounts which have been withheld for taxes and personal deductions.

It is a good idea to check the amounts on your statement occasionally to be sure they are correct. By checking your earnings statement, you will also have a better idea of how much is being withheld for taxes and other **deductions,** or amounts withheld on a paycheck.

EXAMPLE

Vernon received the following earnings statement for one week. In addition to taxes withheld, Vernon had money taken out of his gross pay for personal deductions. Vernon decided to check the amounts on his earnings statement.

Skill Review

To check the accuracy of an earnings statement, you will need to know how to subtract decimals.

Subtract.

1. $257.95 − $134.72

2. $506.90 − $325.97

3. $452.25 − $79.68

4. $300 − $96.58

(For additional help, see page 544.)

Employee's Earnings Statement			Name: Vernon Abrams		
		Earnings			
Regular Pay	Overtime Pay	Gross Pay	Total Deductions	Net Pay	
214.29	0.00	214.29	82.97	131.32	
		Taxes Withheld			
Federal	State	Local	FICA	Other	
32.50	11.52	0.00	15.32	0.00	
		Personal Deductions			
Pension	Union Dues	Insurance	Charity Appeal	Savings	Other
10.19	3.16	7.28	1.00	2.00	0.00

Step 1. Find the total amount withheld for taxes.
Find the sum of the amounts in the row labeled "Taxes Withheld."

$$\$32.50 + \$11.52 + \$15.32 = \$59.34$$

Total taxes withheld: $59.34

Step 2. Find the total amount of personal deductions. Find the sum of the amounts in the row labeled "Personal Deductions."

$$\$10.19 + \$3.16 + \$7.28 + \$1.00 + \$2.00 = \$23.63$$

Total personal deductions: $23.63

Step 3. Verify that the amount under Total Deductions is correct. Find the sum of the total taxes and total personal deductions.

$$\$59.34 + \$23.63 = \$82.97$$

The amount under Total Deductions on the earnings statement is correct.

Step 4. Verify that gross pay minus net pay equals total deductions. Find the difference between gross pay and net pay.

$$
\begin{array}{rl}
\$214.29 & \text{gross pay} \\
-\ \ 131.32 & \text{net pay} \\
\hline
\$\ 82.97 & \text{total deductions}
\end{array}
$$

Class Exercises

Employee's Earnings Statement				Name: Darren Lamont	
		Earnings			
Regular Pay	Overtime Pay	Gross Pay	Total Deductions		Net Pay
472.67	0.00	472.67	■		288.62
		Taxes Withheld			
Federal	State	Local	FICA		Other
70.90	23.65	6.82	33.79		0.00
		Personal Deductions			
Pension	Dues	Insurance	Contributions	Savings	Other
22.31	6.22	10.15	5.21	5.00	0.00

Use the earnings statement above for Exercises 1–4.

1. How much was withheld for taxes?

2. What was the sum of personal deductions?

3. What amount should be under Total Deductions for this pay period?

4. How much less than gross pay was the net pay?

EXERCISES

Employee's Earnings Statement				Name: Martin Fischer
Earnings				
Regular Pay	Overtime Pay	Gross Pay	Total Deductions	Net Pay
225.86	88.90	314.76	107.95	206.81
Taxes Withheld				
Federal	State	Local	FICA	Other
48.20	6.88	4.55	23.64	0.00
Personal Deductions					
Pension	Union Dues	Insurance	Charity Appeals	Savings	Other
12.55	2.45	1.88	0.00	5.00	2.80

Use the earnings statement above for Exercises 1–6.

1. What is the total pay before deductions?

2. How much is withheld for taxes?

3. Find Martin's personal deductions.

4. Find the total deductions.

5. What is Martin's take-home pay?

6. If Martin is paid biweekly, how much is withheld in all for taxes for 1 year?

Solve.

7. Gina earns $16,250 per year. She pays 6% of her earnings to her pension fund. Her health insurance cost $81.50 per month and she had $55 taken from each monthly paycheck for savings. Calculate her total personal deductions.

Consumer Note: FICA

The original Social Security Act, also known as the Federal Insurance Contributions Act, or FICA, was passed in 1935. It has been amended several times since then. Practically everyone is covered by social security, and before you begin work you must apply for a social security number. It is important to give that number to all your employers.

Both you and your employers are required to make contributions in your name; self-employed people must pay both contributions. They make these payments along with their income tax. Your social security contribution gives four kinds of protection: retirement benefits, survivors' benefits, disability benefits, and Medicare benefits.

2-2 Federal Income Tax

Employers are required by law to *withhold,* or hold back, a portion of each employee's salary from every paycheck. This amount is applied toward the federal income tax the employee owes at the end of the year. In order to determine how much to withhold, employers use tax tables like those below.

WEEKLY PAYROLL PERIOD—SINGLE PERSONS

And the wages are—		And the number of withholding allowances claimed is—					
At least	But less than	0	1	2	3	4	5
		The amount of income tax to be withheld shall be—					
$170	$180	$23	$18	$12	$ 7	$ 2	
180	190	25	19	14	8	3	
190	200	26	21	15	10	4	
200	210	28	22	17	11	6	$ 1
210	220	29	24	18	13	7	2
220	230	31	25	20	14	9	3
230	240	32	27	21	16	10	5
240	250	34	28	23	17	12	6
250	260	35	30	24	19	13	8
260	270	37	31	26	20	15	9

WEEKLY PAYROLL PERIOD—MARRIED PERSONS

And the wages are—		And the number of withholding allowances claimed is—						
At least	But less than	0	1	2	3	4	5	6
		The amount of income tax to be withheld shall be—						
240	250	29	24	18	13	7	3	
250	260	31	25	20	14	9	4	
260	270	32	27	21	16	10	5	$ 1
270	280	34	28	23	17	12	6	2
280	290	35	30	24	19	13	8	3
290	300	37	31	26	20	15	9	4
300	310	38	33	27	22	16	11	6
310	320	40	34	29	23	18	12	7
320	330	41	36	30	25	19	14	8
330	340	43	37	32	26	21	15	10

The amount withheld from a paycheck depends upon factors such as whether the worker is married or not, how much the worker earns per pay period, and the number of **exemptions,** or amounts that can be deducted for dependents. An employee may claim exemptions for himself or herself, for his or her spouse, and for any children or other dependents (such as parents) that the employee supports.

Skill Review

To use federal withholding tables, you will need to decide if a given number is between two other numbers.

Tell whether the following statements are true or false.

1. $99.89 is between $80 and $90

2. $120.10 is between $120 and $130.

3. $236 is between $230 and $220.

4. $17 is between $1 and $70.

(For additional help, see page 539.)

Cecelia earns $214.31 weekly. She is not married and claims one exemption, or withholding allowance. How much federal income tax is withheld from her pay each week?

> **Problem Solving Strategy:** Finding information.
> To solve this problem, find information in the table for single persons on page 73.

Step 1. Locate her salary range.

Think: $214.31 is greater than $210 and less than $220.

Step 2. Locate the column with the number of exemptions, or withholding allowances, that she claims.

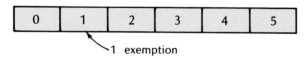

↳ 1 exemption

Step 3. Locate the dollar amount for 1 exemption for earnings between $210 and $220.

At least	But less than	0	1	2	3	4	5
210	220		24				

Each week, $24 is withheld from Cecelia's check for federal tax.

Class Exercises

Find the amount of federal taxes withheld for each of the following employees. Use the tables on page 73.

Name	Weekly Pay	Married?	Exemptions	Federal Tax
Giselle Reid	$262.50	No	1	**1.** ■
Billie Watsen	$264.89	Yes	2	**2.** ■
Myna Paar	$198.50	No	1	**3.** ■
Cicero Santini	$298.62	Yes	6	**4.** ■

EXERCISES

Find the federal tax withheld for each of the following employees.
Use the tables on page 73.

Name	Weekly Pay	Married?	Exemptions	Federal Tax
Ruth Demerrott	$259.89	Yes	2	**1.** ■
Faith Smeed	$318.36	Yes	0	**2.** ■
Perry Angston	$175.82	No	1	**3.** ■
Bruce Pace	$269.50	No	1	**4.** ■

Solve.

5. Rudi Holst
Weekly pay: $231.20
Not married
Exemptions: 2
Federal tax: ■

6. Brian Madison
Weekly pay: $301.22
Married
Exemptions: 1
Federal tax: ■

7. Albert Swift
Weekly pay: $195.32
Not married
Exemptions: 2
Federal tax: ■

8. Louise is paid $250.25 every week. She is not married and claims one allowance. How much federal tax should be withheld from her weekly pay?

9. Rosemary earns $269.80 per week. She is single but supports her elderly parents. How much federal tax should be withheld from her weekly pay?

10. John and Margaret have two dependent children. His weekly salary is $241.62 and her salary is $319.17. They decided that the person earning the greater salary would claim all permitted exemptions, and the other person would claim none. How much federal tax should be withheld from each person's weekly pay?

Using a Calculator: Comparing Numbers

You can use your calculator to compare numbers.

To find out if $229.95 is between $210 and $240,

Key: [C$_E^C$] 229.95 [−] 210 [=] ⟋ 19.95 ⟋
240 [−] 229.95 [=] ⟋ 10.05 ⟋

Since both answers are positive, $229.95 is between $210 and $240.

Use your calculator to decide if each statement is true or false.

1. $35.58 is between $35 and $35.50.

2. $4,834 is between $4,800 and $4,840.

3. $9,567.96 is between $9,600 and $10,000.

4. $46,523.49 is between $45,600 and $46,600.

Career
Teacher

There are many opportunities in teaching. You can teach at the elementary, junior high, high school, or college level. You can also be a teacher's aide, or helper, or an assistant in a workshop or library.

Profile of a teacher. Almost all teachers today have completed 4 years of college. Many high school teachers have earned a master's degree, and junior college and college teachers often have doctoral degrees. Teachers of mathematics and science must be highly skilled in mathematics, but all teachers need this skill for planning, scheduling, and grading.

Teaching environment. Teachers work indoors for the most part and spend most of their time with their students. Teachers take work home, must continue to study, and frequently go to school during summers and vacations.

All in a day's work. Sarah Benson and Richard Hampton have returned to their teaching jobs after summer vacation. Sarah has 15 university credits in addition to her master's degree. For this, she receives an extra 12% annually. The base salary for each is $18,000 a year. They receive 10 checks a year.

1. Calculate each person's net pay per paycheck, deducting 20% for federal tax, 2% for state tax, 7.25% for FICA, and 1.8% for pension.

2. A new contract states that all teachers with 1 year of teaching experience will receive an 8% annual increase and those with 5 or more years will receive a 9.5% annual increase to their base salaries. Sarah has taught 5 years and Richard has taught 3 years. How much will Sarah and Richard receive per paycheck if the percentages of their deductions do not change?

2-3 State and Local Income Taxes

In addition to federal taxes, employers are often required to withhold state and local income taxes from an employee's paycheck. The amount withheld is usually figured as a percent of the worker's taxable earnings.

Taxable earnings depend upon the number of exemptions claimed by the employee. To determine taxable earnings, multiply the number of exemptions by the amount allowed for each, and subtract the result from the annual earnings.

EXAMPLE

Paula earns $14,775 per year and claims 2 exemptions. Her local tax rate is 6.5%. The amount allowed for each exemption is $800. How much local income tax should be withheld each week?

Step 1. Calculate the taxable income.
Multiply the amount allowed for each exemption by the number of exemptions.

Think: $800 × 2 = $1,600

Subtract the total allowed for exemptions from the income.

$$\$14,775 - \$1,600 = \$13,175$$

Step 2. Calculate the tax.
Multiply the taxable earnings by the tax rate.

Think: 6.5% = 0.065

```
        $13,175
    ×    0.065
        65 875
       790 50
     $856.375   Mark 3 decimal places.
     $856.38    Round to nearest cent.
```

Step 3. Compute the amount withheld each pay period.

Hidden Question: How many pay periods?
Paula is paid weekly. There are 52 weeks in a year, so there are 52 pay periods.

$$\$856.38 \div 52 = \$16.468$$
$$\$16.47 \quad \text{Round to nearest cent.}$$

Paula should have $16.47 withheld from her pay for local taxes.

With a calculator and mental arithmetic, the computations for the example are made much easier.

Think: $800 × 2 = $1,600   total allowed for exemptions

Key: $\boxed{C_E^C}$ 14775 $\boxed{-}$ 1600 $\boxed{=}$ $\boxed{×}$ 6.5 $\boxed{\%}$

         $\boxed{÷}$ 52 $\boxed{=}$ ⟋ 16.46875 ⟋   weekly tax withheld

                    $16.47   Round to nearest cent.

Class Exercises

Find the amount of state or local income taxes withheld. Use $800 as the amount allowed for each exemption.

Name	Earnings	Number of Pay Periods	Exemptions	Tax Rate	Amount Withheld per Pay Period
P. Daltz	$12,145	52	3	3%	**1.** ■
A. Watson	$12,800	12	1	2%	**2.** ■
S. Rand	$15,600	24	2	4%	**3.** ■
N. Peters	$16,258	52	2	3.25%	**4.** ■
L. Cobb	$18,890	26	4	2.5%	**5.** ■
R. Speer	$23,620	24	3	5.75%	**6.** ■

EXERCISES

Find the amount of state or local income taxes withheld. Use $800 as the amount allowed for each exemption.

Name	Earnings	Number of Pay Periods	Exemptions	Tax Rate	Amount Withheld per Pay Period
W. Batz	$12,800	12	1	3%	**1.** ■
H. Feldman	$20,490	26	4	4%	**2.** ■
M. Farobi	$13,600	12	2	10%	**3.** ■
B. Laui	$14,260	24	1	3.5%	**4.** ■
B. Pittman	$12,558	52	2	4.2%	**5.** ■
K. Deitman	$24,862	24	5	4.6%	**6.** ■
P. Rendolf	$20,800	26	1	2.25%	**7.** ■
E. Pfaff	$28,920	12	4	4.75%	**8.** ■

Solve.

9. Lola Krist
Taxable earnings: $152.64
Tax rate: 6.2%
Tax withheld: ■

10. Leo Perkins
Annual salary: $18,450
Exemptions: 3 at $750 each
Taxable earnings: ■

11. Bill has a weekly taxable income of $240. His state tax rate is 3% and his local county adds tax at the rate of 2%. How much state and local tax should be withheld from his weekly pay?

12. Explain how mental arithmetic can be used to simplify the computation for Problem 11.

13. Which of Problems 9–11 could be done mentally? In which would paper and pencil be appropriate? Which could best be done by using a calculator?

14. Muriel's city imposes a tax that is 40% of the state tax she pays. Her taxable income is $198.50 per week. Her state imposes tax at a rate of 5%. How much state and local tax is withheld from her weekly pay?

Mental Math: *Multiplying by Powers of 10*

To find the amount you may deduct from your gross income if you have 4 deductions of $1,000 each, you need to find the product of 4 and $1,000. Multiplying by a power of 10 is easy to do mentally.

$$4 \times \$1,000 = \$4.000 = \$4,000$$

Move the decimal point 1 place
to the right for each zero.

Find each product mentally.

1. 23 × 100

2. 4.56 × 1,000

3. $9.76 × 10

4. 8 × $10,000

5. 243 × 100,000

6. $.72 × 10,000

2-4 Social Security (FICA) Tax

Employers are required to withhold employee contributions to the Federal Insurance Contributions Act (**FICA**) program, or social security. Social security provides retirement benefits and disability benefits for workers who have contributed to the system. To receive full benefits, a worker must have contributed payments to the fund for at least 10 (not necessarily consecutive) years. The amount withheld for social security is determined by law. Recently, social security was withheld at a rate of 7.51% on the first $43,800 of a worker's annual earnings. Employers must also contribute for each employee.

The following table shows FICA rates.

Year	FICA rate
1988–1989	7.51%
1990–after	7.65%

Skill Review

You will find it easier to find how much social security tax a person must pay if you know how to find a percent of a number.

Find the number.

1. 3% of $297.45

2. 15% of $28,950

3. 8.39% of $735.25

4. $9\frac{3}{4}$% of $39,684

(For additional help, see page 551.)

EXAMPLE

In 1988 Nick earned $792.15 per week designing stained glass windows. How much FICA tax was withheld from his earnings?

earnings × FICA rate = FICA tax
$$\$792.15 \times 7.51\% = \blacksquare$$

Think: 7.51% = 0.0751

Estimate: $792.15 × 7.51% = ■ → $800 × 0.08 = $64

```
      $792.15
   ×   0.0751
       79215
      3 96075
     55 4505
    $59.490465    Round to
    $59.49        nearest cent.
```

Key: $\boxed{C^C_E}$ 792.15 $\boxed{\times}$ 7.51 $\boxed{\%}$ 59.490465
$59.49
Round to
nearest cent.

The answer $59.49 is sensible and is reasonably close to the estimate $64.
FICA tax of $59.49 is withheld from Nick's check each week.

Self-employed workers must pay social security tax at a rate approximately double that of other workers, since they must pay not only their own contributions but also the contribution that would be paid by an employer.

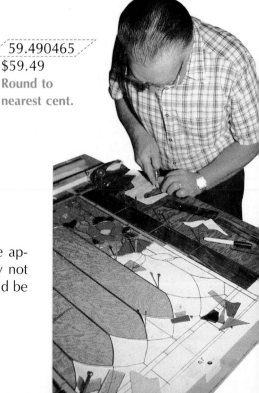

Class Exercises

Find the amount of FICA tax on the following earnings. Use 7.51% (12.3% for self-employed) as the FICA rate.

Name	Weekly Salary	Self-employed?	FICA Tax
Gina Broghatti	$419.22	No	1. ■
Nelson Agrath	$135.40	No	2. ■
Benji Alpert	$100.00	No	3. ■
Mareth Driscol	$297.56	Yes	4. ■
Zelda Smithson	$358.69	No	5. ■
Dale Bruce	$642.37	Yes	6. ■

Solve.

7. Show how you would use a calculator to streamline the computation for Exercise 6.

EXERCISES

Find the amount of FICA tax on the following earnings. Use 7.51% (12.3% for self-employed) as the FICA rate.

Name	Weekly Salary	Self-employed?	FICA Tax
Lois Sudenta	$381.56	No	1. ■
Brigette Muse	$465.31	Yes	2. ■
Tod Lupert	$198.00	No	3. ■
Beth Quinton	$551.72	Yes	4. ■
Pauline Thomas	$266.79	Yes	5. ■
Larry Sargent	$342.89	No	6. ■
Raoul Lopez	$350.47	Yes	7. ■

Solve.

8. Loman Smith
Weekly salary: $364.18
Not self-employed
Annual salary: ■
Annual FICA: ■

9. Violet Magins
Monthly salary: $3,908
Not self-employed
Annual salary: ■
Annual FICA: ■

10. Lileth Simmons
Annual salary: $22,380
Not self-employed
Monthly salary: ■
Monthly FICA: ■

11. Samuel is a self-employed landscaper. He charges $24 per hour for his landscaping services. He usually averages 22 hours of work per week. How much FICA tax should he pay per week at the self-employed rate of 12.3%?

12. Bracy is a self-employed writer who also works for a real-estate agent at $6.28 per hour. In one week Bracy earned $280 writing and worked 16 hours with the real-estate agency. How much FICA tax did Bracy owe for that week at a rate of 12.3%?

13. Patricia earns $4,175 per month working for an advertising agency. In what month of the year will she make her final FICA payment if she has been earning $4,175 per month since the beginning of the year and FICA tax is collected on the first $43,800?

14. Workers who retire at 62 may begin collecting social security retirement benefits if they accept a reduced amount. In the future early retirements will not be allowed. Try to find out the minimum age at which you may be eligible for full retirement benefits. Share your findings with the class.

Mixed Review

1. Pearl is a welder and gets paid $12.08 per hour with time-and-a-half for all hours over 40 hours. What was Pearl's gross pay for a week in which she worked $43\frac{1}{4}$ hours?

2. How much was withheld from Pearl's gross pay for taxes if she pays 19.6% of her gross for federal, state, and local taxes and 7.51% for FICA?

2-5 Take-Home Pay

Recall that take-home pay, or net pay, is the amount a worker received for a pay period after all taxes and deductions have been withheld from the gross pay.

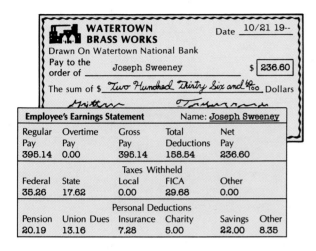

WATERTOWN BRASS WORKS

Date 10/21 19--

Drawn On Watertown National Bank

Pay to the order of _____ Joseph Sweeney _____ $ 236.60

The sum of $ _Two Hundred Thirty Six and 60/100_ Dollars

Employee's Earnings Statement   Name: Joseph Sweeney

Regular Pay	Overtime Pay	Gross Pay	Total Deductions	Net Pay
395.14	0.00	395.14	158.54	236.60

Taxes Withheld				
Federal	State	Local	FICA	Other
35.26	17.62	0.00	29.68	0.00

Personal Deductions					
Pension	Union Dues	Insurance	Charity	Savings	Other
20.19	13.16	7.28	5.00	22.00	8.35

EXAMPLE 1

Joe earned $395.14 one pay period. A total of $82.56 was withheld for taxes from his pay and $75.98 was withheld for personal deductions. What was his take-home pay?

Hidden Question: What were the total deductions?

taxes withheld	+	personal deductions	=	total deductions
$82.56	+	$75.98	=	$158.54

gross pay	−	total deductions	=	take-home pay
$395.14	−	$158.54	=	■

Estimate: $395.14 − $158.54 = ■ → $400 − $160 = $240

$$
\begin{array}{r}
\$395.14 \\
-\ 158.54 \\
\hline
\$236.60
\end{array}
$$

Key: [C^C_E] 395.14 [M+] 82.56 [+] 75.98
[M−] [M^R_C] _236.6_
$236.60

Skill Review

In order to find your take-home pay, it is helpful if you can add decimals.

Find each sum.

1. $4.67 + $19.75
2. $87.14 + $25.50 + $7.08
3. $18.80 + $10.75 + $.92
4. $61.58 + $9.84 + $1.09

(For additional help, see page 544.)

The answer $236.60 is sensible and is reasonably close to the estimate $240. Joe's net pay was $236.60.

EXAMPLE 2

Julio received the earnings statement below with his weekly paycheck. What was his net pay?

Employee's Earnings Statement		Name Julio Martinez		
		Earnings		
Regular Pay	Overtime Pay	Gross Pay	Total Deductions	Net Pay
214.29	38.45	■	■	■
		Taxes Withheld		
Federal	State	Local	FICA	Other
32.50	11.52	0.00	16.39	0.00

Personal Deductions					
Pension	Dues	Insurance	Contributions	Savings	Other
10.19	3.16	7.28	1.00	2.00	0.00

Step 1. Find the gross pay.

regular pay + overtime pay = gross pay
$214.29   + $38.45   = $252.74

Step 2. Find the total deductions.

Taxes: $32.50 + $11.52 + $16.39 = $60.41

Personal deductions: $10.19 + $3.16 + $7.28 + $1.00 + $2.00 = $23.63

taxes + personal deductions = total deductions
$60.41 + $23.63   = $84.04

Step 3. Find the net pay.

gross pay − total deductions = net pay
$252.74 − $84.04   = $168.70

Julio's net pay was $168.70.

With a calculator and the memory function, the computation for Example 2 can be streamlined.

Key: $\boxed{C_E^C}$ 32.5 $\boxed{+}$ 11.52 $\boxed{+}$ 16.39 $\boxed{+}$
10.19 $\boxed{+}$ 3.16 $\boxed{+}$ 7.28 $\boxed{+}$ 1 $\boxed{+}$ 2 $\boxed{M+}$
214.29 $\boxed{+}$ 38.45 $\boxed{-}$ $\boxed{M_C^R}$ $\boxed{=}$ ⟋ 168.7 ⟋
$168.70

Class Exercises

Use Willard's earnings statement below for Exercises 1–6.

1. How much was Willard's regular pay?

2. What were Willard's total taxes?

3. What were Willard's total deductions?

4. What was Willard's gross pay?

5. How much will be subtracted from his gross pay?

6. What was Willard's net pay?

Earnings				
Regular Pay	Overtime Pay	Gross Pay	Total Deductions	Net Pay
376.29	88.89	■	177.76	■

Taxes Withheld				
Federal	State	Local	FICA	Other
72.51	24.30	9.65	35.96	0.00

Personal Deductions					
Pension	Dues	Insurance	Contributions	Savings	Other
15.92	3.24	4.18	2.00	10.00	0.00

EXERCISES

Use Maria's earnings statement below for Exercises 1–6.

1. How much was Maria's regular pay?

2. What were Maria's total taxes?

3. What were Maria's total deductions?

4. What was Maria's net pay?

5. If Maria is paid weekly, how much is withheld each year for social security?

6. What percentage of Maria's gross pay is withheld for taxes?

Earnings				
Regular Pay	Overtime Pay	Gross Pay	Total Deductions	Net Pay
237.54	75.50	■	120.47	■

Taxes Withheld				
Federal	State	Local	FICA	Other
45.15	12.89	4.22	23.95	0.00

Personal Deductions					
Pension	Dues	Insurance	Contributions	Savings	Other
11.32	4.18	5.76	1.50	11.50	0.00

Solve.

7. Gross pay: $264.17
Total deductions: $108.94
Net pay: ■

8. Gross pay: $358.25
Total deductions: $128.98
Net pay: ■

9. Gross pay: ■
Total deductions: $130.62
Net pay: $279.45

10. Gross pay: $316.89
Total deductions: ■
Net pay: $196.89

11. Kareem worked 52 hours last week. His regular hourly rate is $7.23. If he works more than 40 hours he earns time-and-a-half for overtime. He had $63.50 withheld for taxes. Other deductions amounted to $37.98. Find his gross and net pay.

12. Laura received 12% commission on sales of $4,295 one week. She received additional pay of $55.12 for travel expenses. She had $125.30 withheld for taxes. Other deductions amounted to $175. Find her gross pay and net pay.

Critical Thinking: Analyzing Information

Analyzing information includes many separate thinking skills.

Your parents have given you permission to work 2 days a week after school and 1 day of the weekend. You are free to decide which days you will work and the number of hours you will work.

You have investigated employment possibilities and feel that the best opportunity is at a fast-food restaurant at $4.55 an hour.

1. If you work 15 hours a week, how much will you make?

2. How much of this will you actually take home? If you cannot give a dollar amount in answer to this question, what variables will affect your take-home pay?

3. Will any of the money that is withheld from your pay be returned to you? If so, are you required to take any action to have it returned?

4. To answer each of the preceding questions, what information did you have to use? Compare your analysis of information with another student's and then in a class discussion.

5. Why might you have decided to take a part-time job even though working makes doing well in school more difficult and takes time away from your social life? List these reasons to share in a class discussion.

6. Identify items from Question 5 that would require savings accumulated over a period of time. Write a plan for saving money that you would recommend for someone your age. List the information you considered in developing your plan for savings.

Computer:
Introduction

Mickie received a home computer as a birthday gift. It consisted of several components. One part of her computer was the *keyboard,* which is used to enter information into the computer. A second component was the *video monitor,* which looks very much like a TV screen. A third component was a *disk drive.* The disk drive is a rectangular box with a flat, horizontal slot in its front. When a disk is inserted into the slot and the computer is turned on, the disk begins to spin rapidly. A device called a *read-write head* rests gently on the surface of the spinning disk and reads information from it or writes information to it.

Mickie noticed that the keyboard is similar to that of a typewriter. In addition to the letters and digits, however, it contains several special keys that help to control the actions of the computer.

When Mickie wanted to start her computer, she placed a disk in the disk drive, shut the disk drive door, and turned the computer on. Information was taken from the disk and placed in the computer's memory. The information sent to the computer from the disk is called *input.* The keyboard can also be used for computer input. Information that the computer displays on the screen is called *output.* Information sent from the computer to the disk or to a printer is also called output. The monitor showed a small, flashing light called the *cursor,* which tells Mickie where she is on the screen.

The computer must be given a detailed set of instructions, called a *program,* before it can perform any operations. Programs must be coded into the computer's own special language. Many computers can accept languages other than their own, but they must translate instructions from these languages into their own before carrying them out. Two of the popular languages that many computers accept are BASIC and Logo. These languages allow use of familiar words such as GET, PRINT, and IF to communicate with the computer. In this book some of the commands in the BASIC language will be presented.

EXERCISES

1. What is meant by computer input?

2. What is meant by computer output?

3. What is a cursor?

4. How does information get from a disk to the computer's memory?

5. Name two sources of computer input.

6. Name three sources of computer output.

7. What is a disk drive?

8. What is a computer program?

Decision Making:
Adjusting Withholding

Tim and Darrell Black are brothers. After high school, they got similar jobs working for the Ace Manufacturing Company. In comparing notes, however, the brothers discovered that even though they were making the same amount, Darrell was bringing home more each week than Tim. Since Tim was having a hard time making ends meet, he was interested in deciding whether he could increase the amount in his weekly paycheck.

GETTING THE FACTS
Tim and Darrell are both married and each has two children. Tim and his wife, Theresa, have a son Scott, who is 4, and a daughter Sandy, who is 1. Darrell and his wife, Linda, have 8-month-old twins, Jason and Jessica.

Linda took a leave of absence from her job as a bank teller shortly before the twins were born. She hopes to go back to work when they are old enough for nursery school at age 2. Meanwhile, Darrell supports the family on his salary of $13,260 per year plus occasional overtime.

Tim also earns $13,260 per year plus occasional overtime from his job with Ace Manufacturing. In addition, Theresa contributes another $10,000 per year to the family's income from her job with a local insurance company.

The brothers live in adjoining apartments in the Pinewoods apartment complex. Linda and Darrell have a 2-bedroom apartment and Theresa and Tim have a 3-bedroom unit. Darrell's family has a 5-year-old compact car. Theresa and Tim have a 2-year-old 4-door sedan.

Answer the following questions.

1. Excluding overtime, how much does each brother earn in gross pay per week?

2. How much more does Tim's family earn per week due to Theresa's job?

3. Although Tim's family has more income, they probably also have additional expenses. What are some of the additional expenses that this family might have?

COMPARING WAGES

One Friday as the brothers rode home from work together, Tim said, "Darrell, I really don't know how you do it. It is all Theresa and I can do to make ends meet with both of us working."

"It isn't easy," Darrell replied. "But Linda does a really good job of managing the money I bring home. She really has to do some budgeting, though, to make the $207 a week I bring home stretch to pay all the bills."

"I didn't know you'd gotten a raise," Tim responded.

"What makes you think I got a raise?" Darrell asked.

"I thought we were making the same thing, but I bring home a little less than $195 per week," Tim said thoughtfully.

Later that evening, Tim and Darrell compared their earnings statements. The statements are shown below.

Employee's Earnings Statement		Name: **Tim Black**			
Earnings					
Regular Pay	Overtime Pay	Gross Pay	Total Deduct	Net Pay	
255.00	0.00	255.00	60.11	194.89	
Taxes Withheld					
Federal	State	Local	FICA	Other	
20.00	7.58	0.00	19.15	0.00	
Personal Deductions					
Pension	Union Dues	Insurance	Charity	Savings	Other
10.26	3.12	0.00	0.00	0.00	0.00

Employee's Earnings Statement		Name: **Darrell Black**			
Earnings					
Regular Pay	Overtime Pay	Gross Pay	Total Deduct	Net Pay	
255.00	0.00	255.00	47.76	207.24	
Taxes Withheld					
Federal	State	Local	FICA	Other	
9.00	6.23	0.00	19.15	0.00	
Personal Deductions					
Pension	Union Dues	Insurance	Charity	Savings	Other
10.26	3.12	0.00	0.00	0.00	0.00

Answer the following questions.

4. What deductions are the same on both checks? Why do you think these amounts are the same?

5. Check the arithmetic on both earnings statements. Did the payroll secretary make any errors in arithmetic?

6. What are the only differences between the earnings statements?

7. Why do you think these deductions are different?

COMPARING TAX RETURNS

After studying the statements carefully, the brothers realized that the difference in their take-home pay was the result of a difference in the amount of state and federal taxes they paid.

"Tim, how many exemptions do you claim for tax purposes?" Darrell asked.

"I'm not really sure," Tim replied. "I haven't changed any of that since I went to work at Ace. All I know is that since we've had Scott, we've gotten money back when we file our tax returns."

"I bet that's the difference. Shortly after Jason and Jessica were born, I increased my exemptions to 4 and that lowered my tax withholdings considerably," Darrell responded. "We don't usually get much money back at tax time, but so far I've never owed them anything."

"Together Theresa and I usually get about $1,100 back at tax time. I get back about $650 of what I pay in taxes and she gets back about $450 of what she pays. We use some of that money for the vacation trip we all take together in the spring."

"Linda and I usually take the vacation money out of our savings account," said Darrell.

"You mean you save that kind of money each year?" asked Tim.

"When she was working, Linda saved $40 a week, $20 from her pay and $20 from mine. Now she saves only the $20 from my pay. And it's great earning interest on your money," Darrell said.

"Earning interest on your money is fine, but first you have to have some money to save. Everything Theresa and I bring home goes to pay the bills."

Answer the following questions.

8. If Tim were to claim all the exemptions to which his family is entitled, about 3.53% of his gross pay would be withheld each pay period for federal taxes. How much would his federal withholding be each pay period?

9. The state in which the brothers live allows $1,000 for each exemption and then taxes the remaining income at a rate of 3.5%. How much state tax would Tim have to pay each week on his regular pay if he claimed all the exemptions to which he is entitled?

TIM'S DECISION

Before making a decision, Tim decided he should think about what he would do with the extra money. He knew he could put it in a savings account himself or that he could have some withheld each week and deposited in a savings plan. He decided to change his withholdings and have $20 automatically deposited in a savings plan each week.

Answer the following questions.

11. What facts do you think Tim used in making his decision?

12. If Tim had $20 deposited each week in the payroll savings plan offered by the company, how much could he save in a year? If the money earned 8% simple interest per year, how much would he have saved at the end of 1 year?

13. Compare your answer to Question 12 with the amount Tim normally got back in a tax refund each year.

14. What factors may make Darrell's tax situation somewhat different from his brother's?

10. Compare your answers to Questions 8 and 9 to Darrell's earnings statement on page 89. How do your answers compare?

15. In your opinion, which brother has the better way of saving the money needed for their spring vacation trip? Explain.

DECIDE FOR YOURSELF

Suppose you have to fill out a withholding form (W-4) at work that will affect how much is withheld from your pay. What facts will you need in order to make a decision? Summarize the way you, and Tim, made the decision about withholding.

Chapter 2 Review

VOCABULARY

| deductions | exemptions | gross pay |
| earnings statement | FICA | net pay |

For Exercises 1–6, select from the list above the word(s) that completes each statement.

1. Another name for *take-home* pay is _Net pay_ .

2. _____ are the withholding allowances claimed.

3. _____ is the total amount earned for a pay period.

4. Amounts withheld from a paycheck are called _deductions_

5. An _____ is a record of earnings and deductions.

6. *Social security* is a more common name for _____ .

SKILLS

Subtract.

7. $469.95 − $325.34 _144.61_ **8.** $310.69 − $98.89   **9.** $504.02 − $75.96

True or false?

10. $1,263.50 is between $1,100 and $1,200. _f_

11. $358.12 is between $300 and $360.

12. $4,297.86 is between $4,200 and $4,400.

Change to a decimal.

13. 18% _0.18_   **14.** 4.5%   **15.** $3\frac{1}{4}\%$

Find the percent.

16. 5% of $680.50 _$34.03_ **17.** $8\frac{1}{2}\%$ of $1,230   **18.** $10\frac{1}{4}\%$ of $896.50

Find the sum.

19. $5.89 + $6.30   **20.** $46.25 + $29.75 + $10.45

21. $9.50 + $15.89 + $20.76 + $7.50

CONSUMER TOPICS

Answer Questions 22–28 about Marcia's earnings statement, which is shown on the next page.

22. What are her regular earnings?   **23.** What is her gross pay?

24. How much was withheld for FICA?   **25.** How much was withheld for savings?

Regular Pay 298.50	Overtime Pay 24.25		Gross Pay ■	Total Deductions ■	Net Pay ■
Taxes Withheld					
Federal 32.15	State 22.10		Local 4.50	FICA 24.24	Other 0.00
Personal Deductions					
Savings Plan 25.00	Community Appeal 2.00		Insurance 3.50	Dental Plan 6.90	Other 0.00

26. What is the total amount withheld for all taxes, including FICA?

27. What are her total deductions?   **28.** What is her net pay?

Solve.

29. Use the tax table on page 73 to find Elaine's tax if she is single, earns $258.10 per week, and claims one exemption.

30. Leo earns $35,000 annually and pays $9\frac{3}{4}\%$ of his gross pay for state and local taxes. How much does he pay annually for these taxes?

31. Heather earns $25,750 annually and pays 8% of her gross pay for state and local taxes. If she is paid semimonthly, how much is withheld from each paycheck for these taxes?

How much FICA tax is withheld at a rate of 7.51% on these earnings?

32. $350   **33.** $2,589.75   **34.** $19,635

Solve.

35. Kevin owns his own electronic repair service, so he must pay FICA tax at the self-employed rate of 15.02%. How much must he pay on an annual income of $31,450?

36. Jon earns $496.85 weekly. He has $175.25 withheld weekly for taxes. He has $35.50 withheld weekly for personal deductions. What is his net pay each week?

37. Carolyn earns $22,500 a year. She pays 18% of her gross income for federal, state, and local taxes. She is taxed at the FICA rate of 7.65%. She has 5% of her income withheld for personal deductions. What is her net pay?

Chapter 2 Test

Answer the following questions about Sam's earnings statement, which is shown here.

Regular Pay 315.75	Overtime Pay 25.50		Gross Pay ■	Total Deductions ■	Net Pay ■
Taxes Withheld					
Federal 29.85	State 13.50		Local 3.90	FICA 26.10	Other 0.00
Personal Deductions					
Savings Plan 20.00	Community Appeal 1.00		Insurance 2.50	Dental Plan 7.00	Other 0.00

1. What is his regular pay? **2.** What is his overtime pay? **3.** What is his gross pay?

4. How much was withheld for FICA? **5.** How much was withheld for savings? **6.** What is the total amount withheld for all taxes?

7. What is the total withheld for personal deductions? **8.** What are his total deductions? **9.** What is his net pay?

10. Elizabeth is married, earns $327.50 per week and claims 3 exemptions. How much federal tax must she pay each week, according to the table shown on page 73?

11. Helen earned $23,500 annually; 6.5% of her gross pay was withheld for state and local taxes. How much were her taxes?

12. Ron is a writer, so he must pay FICA tax at the self-employed rate of 15.02%. How much must he pay on an annual income of $38,500?

13. Roberto earns $326.50 weekly. He has $105.25 withheld weekly for taxes. He has $25.50 withheld weekly for personal deductions. What is his net pay each week?

14. Sally's gross pay for one pay period was $275.75. Her withholdings for taxes amounted to $97.30. Her net pay was 153.95. How much did she have withheld for personal deductions?

15. Barbara earns $24,500 a year. She pays 15% of her gross income for federal, state, and local taxes. She is taxed at the FICA rate of 7.65%. She has 7% of her income withheld for personal deductions. She is paid semimonthly. What is her net pay for each pay period?

Cumulative Mixed Review

Select the letter corresponding to the correct answer.

1. Shelly earns $4.50 per hour and time-and-a-half for overtime for all hours over 40 hours. How much did she earn the week she worked 45 hours?
   a. $202.50   b. $184.52
   c. $213.75   d. $113.75

2. Garrick earns $3.50 per hour plus $2.50 for each lawn he mows. One day he worked 8 hours and mowed 5 lawns. How much did he earn?
   a. $40.50   b. $30.50
   c. $405   d. $305

3. Brandi works from 8:30 A.M. to 5:00 P.M. and has 1 hour each day for lunch. How much does she earn for each 5-day week if she gets paid $4.80 per hour?
   a. $174   b. $36
   c. $204   d. $180

4. One week Christopher earned $350.75 regular pay and $75.50 overtime. His net pay for the week was $290.30. How much did he have withheld for deductions?
   a. $15.05   b. $60.45
   c. $13.60   d. $135.95

5. Sheri earned $29,650 and paid a FICA tax of 7.65%. How much FICA tax did she pay?
   a. $2,268.23   b. $22.68
   c. $226.82   d. $4,453.43

6. Lowell earns $17,500 and has $3,685 withheld for taxes and $1,050 for personal deductions. What is his net pay?
   a. $13,815   b. $1,276.50
   c. $12,765   d. $14,865

7. Anne earns $29,750 and has $6,495 withheld for taxes and $1,500 withheld for personal deductions. If she is paid semimonthly, what is the net pay of each paycheck?
   a. $906.46   b. $1,812.92
   c. $836.73   d. $418.37

8. Mike works an average of 47 hours each week. He gets paid $4.50 per hour and time-and-a-half for all hours over 40 hours. What is his annual income?
   a. $9,711   b. $11,817
   c. $10,998   d. $227.25

9. Jennifer is a self-employed decorator. She averages a monthly income of $2,875. If the FICA rate is 15.02%, how much FICA tax must she pay each year?
   a. $5,181.90   b. $215.91
   c. $431.83   d. $2,639.25

10. Ralph works 40 hours a week at an hourly rate of $2.80. He averages $150 weekly in tips. What is his annual income?
    a. $6,288   b. $6,812
    c. $262   d. $13,624

CHAPTER 3
Personal Banking

Carla is planning to buy a refrigerator. It will cost $800. She can borrow the money from her credit union, from a bank, or from a financial service. She has some money in savings that she could use so that she would not have to borrow as much money.

- What kinds of information would you advise Carla to find out from the credit union, bank, and financial service before she decides where to borrow the money?

- Do you think it is a good idea for Carla to use her savings for the refrigerator? What are some of the pros and cons of using savings for a purchase like this?

- What are the advantages of repaying a loan in 24 payments instead of 12? What are the advantages of 12 payments instead of 24?

If you were planning a major purchase, how would you go about finding financing?

3-1 Checking Accounts

If you have a checking account, you can pay bills or expenses without carrying or mailing large amounts of cash. When you open a checking account, you receive a checkbook with a supply of checks and a *check register* in which to keep a record of your account. On each check is usually printed your name and address, the number of the check, the name of the bank where you have this account, and your account number. You also will receive deposit slips to be used when you put money into your account.

When you make a deposit, or put money into your account, the value of the cash or checks deposited is added to the *balance,* or existing amount, in your account. When you write a check to make a withdrawal, or take money out of your account, the amount indicated on the check is subtracted from the balance in the account. When you write a *check,* you are instructing your bank to transfer money from your account to the person or company you name on your check.

Skill Review

In order to write checks, it is helpful if you can write names for amounts of money.

Write the word names.
1. $47
2. $398
3. $503
4. $2,693

(For additional help, see page 538.)

EXAMPLE 1

Rebecca purchased license plates for her car on March 16. The plates cost $26.50. Write check 123 to the Iowa Motor Vehicle Department for this amount.

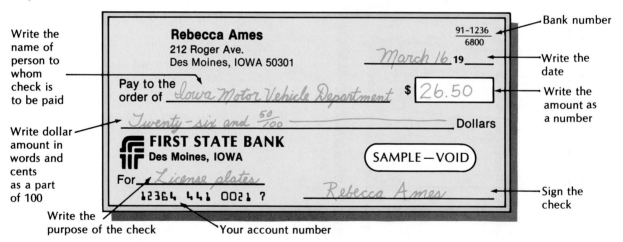

Write the name of person to whom check is to be paid

Write dollar amount in words and cents as a part of 100

Write the purpose of the check

Your account number

Bank number

Write the date

Write the amount as a number

Sign the check

In order to keep anyone from changing a check, you should:

- Write the numbers as close to the dollar sign as possible.

- Draw a line from the amount written as words to the word *dollars.*

EXAMPLE 2

Rebecca deposited some money in her checking account on April 28. She had a check for $121.83 plus $25 in cash and $.53 in coins. Fill in a deposit slip showing these amounts.

DEPOSIT TICKET				
REBECCA AMES 212 ROGER AVE. Des Moines, IOWA 50301	CASH	CURRENCY	$ 25	00
		COIN		53
	CHECKS		121	83
DATE _April 28_ 19___				
	TOTAL		147	36
SIGN HERE FOR LESS CASH IN TELLERS PRESENCE	NET DEPOSIT		$ 147	36

073

91-7070/3221

USE OTHER SIDE FOR ADDITIONAL LISTING

BE SURE EACH ITEM IS PROPERLY ENDORSED

FIRST STATE BANK
Des Moines, IOWA

⑆123⑃64 ⑈441 0021 7

EXAMPLE 3

Rebecca used a check register to keep a record of all deposits to and withdrawals from her account. She added deposits to the balance and subtracted from the balance the checks she had written. Enter these transactions in her check register.

April 13 Deposit $95.33
April 17 Check no. 217 to Germaine Banston, $16.54 for art supplies.
April 19 Check no. 218 to Pioneer Power, $71.32 for gas and electric.

Check	Date	Description	Amount (−)	Deposit (+)	Balance
					183.27
	4-13			95.33	+95.33
					278.60
217	4-17	Germaine Banston	16.54		−16.54
		(art supplies)			262.06
218	4-19	Pioneer Power Co.	71.32		−71.32
		(gas and elec.)			190.74

Class Exercises

Using a check form, write the following checks for your checking account.

1. Date: November 2; Amount: $11.82; Check no. 31; To: Amy Murphy; For: sports equipment

2. Date: September 13; Amount: $156.20; Check no. 2541; To: First National Bank; For: credit card bill

Using a deposit slip form, write deposit slips for the following.
Find the total deposit.

3. Checks for $20 and $80; Cash: $45

4. Cash: $132; Coins: $.75; Check: $172.81

Make the following entries in a check register form. Find the current balance.

5. Starting balance: $210.03; Deposit: $52.98 on March 27; Check no. 398, Date: March 20, Amount: $37.50, To: Ace Hardware, For: tools

6. Starting balance: $492.61; Deposit: $171.50 on August 13; Check no. 831, Date: August 15, Amount: $325.72, To: Frisby Credit Co., For: car payment; Check no. 832, Date: August 18, Amount: $64.13, To: Boswell Department Store, For: clothes

EXERCISES

Using a check form, write the following checks for your checking account.

1. Date: February 14; Amount: $15.99; Check no. 162; To: Silas Ephram; For: repairs to storm door

2. Date: April 22; Amount: $229.18; Check no. 18; To: Worthington's; For: stereo

Using a deposit slip form, write deposit slips for the following.
Find the total deposit.

3. Checks for $57.92 and $38.86; Cash: $19

4. Cash: $100; Coins: $.92; Check: $268

Make the following entries in a check register form.

5. Starting balance: $89.67; Deposit: $38.19 on June 12; Check no. 15, Date: June 20, Amount: $54.40, To: The Golf Shop, For: golf supplies

6. Starting balance: $326.45; Deposit: $118.13 on October 24; Check no. 132, Date: October 26, Amount: $22.50, To: Anderson's Discount, For: purchases; Check no. 133, Date: October 27, Amount $12.19, To: Towne Flower Shoppe, For: plant

Solve.

7. Deposit slip: W. Ashley
Checks: $16.20; $32.50
Cash: $31
Coin: $.38
Total: ■

8. Deposit slip: N. Perkins
Checks: $115.16; $29.47
Cash: ■
Coin: $1.55
Total: $161.18

9. Deposit slip: H. Epps
Checks: ■
Cash: $59
Coin: $2.35
Total: $131.72

10. Beginning balance: $100
Checks: $50 and $20
Deposit: $200
Ending balance: ▪

11. Beginning
balance: $172.18
Checks: $37.50; $91.20
Deposit: $58.36
Ending balance: ▪

12. Beginning
balance: $75.62
Checks: $21.13; $29.32
Deposit: ▪
Ending balance: $65.49

13. Find the current balance in this account.

Check	Date	Description	Amount (−)	Deposit (+)	Balance
					89.67
	6-12			38.19	a. ▪
					b. ▪
15	6-20	Golf Shop	54.40		c. ▪
		(Supplies)			d. ▪

14. Show how to key a calculator to complete Problem 13.

15. Abe made the following checking account transactions. Deposits: March 17; Cash: $40; Coins: $1.31; Checks: $71.50 and $32.18; Check written: Check no. 28 to General Auto Repairs on March 21; For: car repairs; Amount: $156.20. His beginning balance was $185.37. Fill in a deposit slip form, a check form for the check, and a check register form for the transactions. What is the ending balance in Abe's checking account after these transactions?

3-2 Reconciling a Bank Statement

If you have a checking account, once a month your bank will send you a *statement* showing all deposits, amounts paid for checks, and any bank charges. The statement also shows a beginning and an ending balance for your account each month. When you receive your statement, you need to reconcile your account, or show that your accounting agrees with the bank's.

Your bank statement includes a list of the checks you have written and the actual checks themselves. There is a form on the back of your statement to use in reconciling your account. To reconcile your account, follow these steps.

1. Check off all returned checks in the check register. Make a list of outstanding checks.

2. Write the ending balance shown on the statement.

3. Add to it any deposits not shown on your statement.

4. Subtract the total of outstanding checks.

5. From the balance in the check register, subtract all bank charges. This adjusted balance should agree with the adjusted balance in the statement.

EXAMPLE

Simon received the following bank statement. He compared it to his checkbook register to reconcile the two. In his checkbook register, there was an outstanding check for $35.74, an outstanding deposit for $28.39, and a balance of $288.57.

Skill Review

In order to reconcile your bank statement, it will be helpful if you can add and subtract money.

Compute in the order shown.

1. $27.50 + $36.95 − $15.72

2. $98.23 + $26.30 + $98.23

3. $654.35 + $450 − $789.30

4. $400.38 + $249.30 + $27.36

(For additional help, see page 544.)

THE FIRST NATIONAL BANK, Amarillo, TX				
Bank Statement				
Name: Simon Beck		Account No.: 44200338		
Period covered by this statement: 10/19 through 11/19				
		Beginning balance: 270.29		
Date	Check No.	Amount of Check	Deposit	Balance
11-08			64.56	334.85
11-13	143	16.98		317.87
11-19	142	21.95		295.92
Bank charges		4.75		291.17
		Ending balance:		291.17

Reconcile Simon's account and determine if the balances agree.

Check register:

Simon's balance:	$288.57
Bank charges:	− 4.75
Adjusted balance:	$283.82

Bank statement:

End balance:	$291.17
Outstanding deposits:	+ 28.39
	$319.56
Outstanding checks:	− 35.74
	$283.82

Simon's adjusted check register balance agrees with the adjusted bank statement balance, so the account is reconciled.

With a calculator, you can simplify the computation for the example.

Key: $\boxed{C_E^C}$ 288.57 $\boxed{-}$ 4.75 $\boxed{=}$ 283.82 register balance − bank charge

Key: $\boxed{C_E^C}$ 291.17 $\boxed{+}$ 28.39 $\boxed{-}$ 35.74 $\boxed{=}$ 283.82 ending balance + outstanding deposit − outstanding check

The balances agree.

Class Exercises

Reconcile the following accounts. Determine if the adjusted check register balance agrees with the adjusted bank balance.

Register Balance	Bank Charge	Adjusted Register Balance	Statement Balance	Outstanding Deposits	Outstanding Checks	Ending Balance
$184.32	$3.50	1. ■	$315.75	$113.80	$248.73	2. ■
$665.80	$6.75	3. ■	$709.53	$374.91	$425.39	4. ■
$212.04	$2	5. ■	$192.55	$ 72.45	$ 54.96	6. ■

EXERCISES

Reconcile the following accounts. Determine if the adjusted check register balance agrees with the adjusted bank balance.

Register Balance	Bank Charge	Adjusted Register Balance	Statement Balance	Outstanding Deposits	Outstanding Checks	Ending Balance
$763.44	$12.45	1. ■	$812.64	$487.95	$549.60	2. ■
$121	$ 3.75	3. ■	$100	$ 59	$ 34.25	4. ■
$582.08	$ 6.25	5. ■	$666.44	$137.95	$228.56	6. ■
$546.53	$ 7.50	7. ■	$515.69	$212.67	$189.33	8. ■

Solve.

9. Beginning balance: $189.56
Deposits: $85.13
Checks: $155.82
Bank charges: $7.55
Ending balance: ■

10. Beginning balance: $556.20
Deposits: $232.11
Checks: ■
Bank charges: $11.75
Ending balance: $614.72

Marie's Check Register					
			Amount	Deposit	Balance
Check	Date	Description	(−)	(+)	393.78
255	12/20	T. Abbottson	138.16		255.62
256	12/31	Murphy rugs	108.79		146.83
257	1/02	Baker's Foods	61.37		75.46
	1/10	deposit		105.00	180.46
258	1/12	Lola Peters	28.93		151.53

11. Marie received the following bank statement. She tried to reconcile her account using her check register, shown on page 104. Reconcile the account and determine why the adjusted balances do not agree.

12. If you cannot reconcile your account, where can you get help?

THE FIRST NATIONAL BANK, Cincinnati, OH				
Bank Statement				
Name: **Marie Rutter**			Account No.: **82801744**	
Period covered by this statement: 1/01 through 2/01				
		Beginning balance:		393.78
Date	Check No.	Amount of check	Deposit	Balance
1/04	255	138.16		255.62
1/10	258	28.93	105.00	331.69
1/18	257	61.37		270.32
	Bank charges	5.25		265.07
		Ending balance:		265.07

Using a Calculator: *Checking a Bank Statement*

Date	Check	Amount	Deposits
05/26			343.67
05/27	769	27.98	
05/28	797	86.39	
06/01	800	149.03	403.98
06/12	801	54.26	
06/17	802	18.50	
06/20			150.00
06/23	803	326.42	4.25 Int.

05/26	Balance	1,058.23
3	Deposits	897.65
6	Withdrawals	662.58
	Service Fee	0.00
	Interest Earned	4.25
06/26	Balance	1,297.55

Check this bank statement using $\boxed{M+}$, $\boxed{M-}$, and $\boxed{M_C^R}$.

Key: 1058.23 $\boxed{M+}$

Key: 343.67 $\boxed{+}$ 403.98 $\boxed{+}$ 150 $\boxed{=}$ *897.65* $\boxed{M+}$ Deposits agree.

Key: 4.25 $\boxed{M+}$ Add interest.

Key: 27.98 $\boxed{+}$ 86.39 $\boxed{+}$ 149.03 $\boxed{+}$ 54.26 $\boxed{+}$ Reconcile withdrawals.
18.50 $\boxed{+}$ 326.42 $\boxed{=}$ *662.58* $\boxed{M-}$ Subtract from memory.

Key: $\boxed{M_C^R}$ *1297.55*   Statement checks.

3-3 Savings Accounts

A savings account helps you to save money for later expenses or purchases or for emergencies. If you have a savings account, you may be given a passbook in order to keep track of your deposits, withdrawals, and interest payments. Most savings accounts do not allow you to write checks charged against the account.

EXAMPLE 1

The passbook for Frieda's savings account is shown below. To keep her record current, she must add all deposits and interest and subtract withdrawals. Complete her passbook.

THE STATE SAVINGS BANK

Savings Account No. 04-002-4

Name: **Frieda Haas**

Date	Deposit	Interest	Withdrawal	Balance
3/7				725.41
4/1	85.00			■
4/6		3.72		■
4/29			52.00	■

Step 1. Add the deposit to the beginning balance.

$725.41 + $85 = $810.41

Step 2. Add the interest.

$810.41 + $3.72 = $814.13

Step 3. Subtract the withdrawal.

$814.13 − $52 = $762.13

With a calculator, you can streamline the computation in Example 1.

Key: $\boxed{C_E^C}$ 725.41 $\boxed{+}$ 85 $\boxed{+}$ 3.72
$\boxed{-}$ 52 $\boxed{=}$ ⟨762.13⟩
$762.13

Balance + deposit + interest
− withdrawal

In order to deposit money to or withdraw money from savings accounts, you must fill out deposit or withdrawal slips.

EXAMPLE 2

Tom deposited $20 in cash and a check for $54.26 to his savings account. He had to fill in a deposit slip by writing his name and the date, listing the items to be deposited, and totaling the deposit slip.

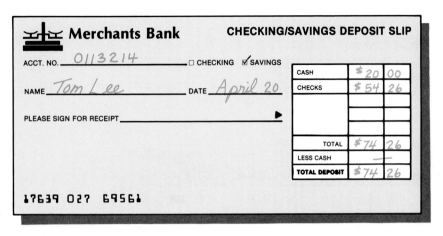

EXAMPLE 3

Rose needed to withdraw $57.20 from her savings account. She filled in a withdrawal slip by writing the date and the amount to be withdrawn in both words and numerals. Then she signed her name.

WITHDRAWAL TICKET   DATE *Feb. 16*

Account No. *62489321*

Account Name *Rose Neri*

Fifty-seven and 20/100 ——— Dollars *$57.20*

Rose Neri
signature

FARMERS BANK

Class Exercises

Compute the balances.

Beginning Balance	Deposits	Interest	Withdrawals	Final Balance
$138.56	$ 47.38	$1.22	$ 25	**1.** ■
$356.89	$128.45	$2.76	$101.37	**2.** ■
$700	$250	$6	$100	**3.** ■

Solve.

4. Explain why mental arithmetic is a more appropriate method of computation in Class Exercise 3 than a calculator.

5. Fill in a savings withdrawal form for $120. Use 5551212 as the account number.

6. Fill in a savings account deposit slip form for $45 in cash and checks for $62.69 and $118.70. Use 5551212 for the account number.

EXERCISES

Compute the balances.

Beginning Balance	Deposits	Interest	Withdrawals	Final Balance
$276.33	$101.54	$ 3.26	$ 75.00	1. ■
$ 98.26	$ 36.70	$ 1.01	$ 15.07	2. ■
$299.31	$ 15.87	$ 5.81	$105.50	3. ■
$725.06	$227.13	$15.62	$165.47	4. ■
$597.54	$362.71	$14.56	$216.37	5. ■
$943.65	$304.21	$23.71	$352.98	6. ■

Solve.

7. Fill in a savings account deposit slip form for $65 in cash and a check for $78.25 and another for $67.89. Use 12345645 for the account number.

8. Fill in a savings withdrawal form for $345. Use 12345645 for the account number.

9. Mary DePetri's account
   Beginning balance: $352.50
   Deposits: $172.50
   Interest: $12.10
   Withdrawals: $91.50
   Ending balance: ■

10. Vernon Abel's account
    Beginning balance: $128.60
    Deposits: $240.63
    Interest: $2.81
    Withdrawals: ■
    Ending balance: $257.77

11. Bart Simpson's account
    Beginning balance: $554.67
    Deposits: ■
    Interest: $7.90
    Withdrawals: $174.84
    Ending balance: $602.92

12. Leona Vale's account
    Beginning balance: ■
    Deposits: $307.10
    Interest: $14.36
    Withdrawals: $182.67
    Ending balance: $431.06

Use a savings account passbook form to update the following accounts.

13. Zoe Elexis
Account: 07-003-1
Balance: on 4/6, $625.87
Deposits: on 4/8, $52.54; on 4/19, $28.29
Interest: on 5/1, $2.20
Withdrawal: on 4/16, $71.30

14. Roland Amati
Account: 14-022-7
Balance: on 12/1, $195.83
Deposits: on 12/15, $100.00; on 12/26, $55.25
Interest: on 12/31, $5.46
Withdrawals: on 12/10, $25.50; on 12/21, $45.80

15. Reginald Noether
Account: 104-0022-1
Balance: on 3/16, $11,056.76
Deposits: on 3/17, $75.80; on 3/31, $85.20
Interest: on 4/1, $21.51
Withdrawal: on 4/4, $174.68

16. Audrey Lonetree
Account: 167-0011-0
Balance: on 6/12, $512.34
Deposits: on 6/16, $268.18; on 6/21, $152.18
Interest: on 6/18, $10.18
Withdrawal: on 6/20, $120

Use the following information to fill out a passbook form.

17. George places $650 of his monthly paycheck in his savings account on the 16th of every month. He withdraws $445.26 for a car payment on the 26th of the month. He will get one interest payment of $27.80 on June 1. His account had $852.37 on April 1. Record the above entries beginning with April 1, and determine his balance through June 26.

Reading in Mathematics: *Acronyms*

When you open a savings account, you may be told that your deposit is insured by the FSLIC or FDIC. When you deposit your paycheck, you may notice a deduction for FICA. All these letters do mean something! They are called *acronyms*—words formed from the first or first few letters of a series of words.

FICA   Federal Insurance Contributions Act

FSLIC   Federal Savings and Loan Insurance Corporation

FDIC   Federal Deposit Insurance Corporation

What do these acronyms stand for?

1. SCUBA

2. ZIP code

3. PC

4. CD

5. FHA

6. IRA

7. What are some other acronyms you hear in common use?

3-4 Simple Interest

A bank pays interest to an account holder in return for using the money that is deposited in the account. **Simple interest** is money paid only on the **principal,** or amount deposited, and not on any interest that may have accumulated on the principal. The percent used to determine the interest is called the *rate of interest* and is usually understood to be for a stated period of time. The rate paid when money is on deposit for 1 year is called the *annual rate of interest*. When the annual rate of interest is used, the time must also be given in years.

Skill Review

It will help you compute interest if you can multiply three numbers.

Multiply.

1. $25.2 \times 0.5 \times 3$

2. $\$8.50 \times 0.7 \times 4$

3. $\$395.50 \times 0.055 \times 2$

4. $\$535.24 \times 0.067 \times 0.5$

(For additional help, see page 545.)

EXAMPLE 1

Gina deposited $3,500 in a savings account for 3 years. How much simple interest did her money earn at 6%?

Think: $6\% = 0.06$

$$\text{interest} = \text{principal} \times \text{rate} \times \text{time}$$
$$i = p \times r \times t$$
$$i = \$3,500 \times 0.06 \times 3$$

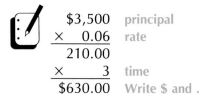

$$
\begin{array}{ll}
\$3,500 & \text{principal} \\
\times\ 0.06 & \text{rate} \\
\hline
210.00 & \\
\times\ \ \ \ \ 3 & \text{time} \\
\hline
\$630.00 & \text{Write \$ and .}
\end{array}
$$

Key: $\boxed{\text{C}^{\text{C}}_{\text{E}}}$ 3500 $\boxed{\times}$ 6 $\boxed{\%}$ $\boxed{\times}$ 3 $\boxed{=}$ 630
$\$630$

Gina's deposit earned $630 simple interest after 3 years.

EXAMPLE 2

Ira deposited $385 in a savings account for 1 year at $7\frac{1}{2}\%$ simple interest. What was the total amount in his savings account at the end of the year?

Think: $7\frac{1}{2}\% = 7.5\% = 0.075$

Step 1. Find the interest.

$$i = p \times r \times t$$
$$i = \$385 \times 0.075 \times 1$$
$$i = \$28.875 \rightarrow \$28.88 \quad \text{Round to nearest cent.}$$

Step 2. Add the amount of interest to the principal.

$$\text{principal} + \text{interest} = \text{new balance}$$
$$\$385 + \$28.88 = \$413.88$$

Ira has $413.88 in his account at the end of 1 year.

With a calculator, you can streamline the computation for Example 2.

Key: $\boxed{C_E^C}$ 385 $\boxed{\times}$ 7.5 $\boxed{\%}$ $\boxed{\times}$ 1 $\boxed{+}$ 385 $\boxed{=}$ 413.875 $p \times r \times t + p$

$413.88   Round to nearest cent.

Class Exercises

Find the interest. Remember: $i = p \times r \times t$.

Principal	Rate	Time	Interest
$ 200	7%	2 y	1. ■
$ 350	6%	$1\frac{1}{2}$ y	2. ■
$ 875	$4\frac{1}{2}$%	3 y	3. ■
$1,200	$8\frac{1}{2}$%	$\frac{1}{2}$ y	4. ■

Find the total amount. Remember to add the amount of principal to the amount earned as interest.

Principal	Rate	Time	Total Amount
$1,500	5%	3 y	5. ■
$ 280	$7\frac{1}{2}$%	$1\frac{1}{2}$ y	6. ■

7. Explain how using mental arithmetic can help simplify the computation for Exercise 1.

EXERCISES

Find the interest. Remember: $i = p \times r \times t$.

Principal	Rate	Time	Interest
$ 500	6%	2 y	1. ■
$ 425	7%	3 y	2. ■
$ 900	$6\frac{1}{2}$%	6 y	3. ■
$ 1,000	$9\frac{1}{2}$%	$\frac{1}{2}$ y	4. ■
$ 1,350	$8\frac{1}{4}$%	2 y	5. ■
$ 1,590	$6\frac{3}{4}$%	1 y 6 mo	6. ■
$ 216	$9\frac{1}{4}$%	9 mo	7. ■
$56,000	10%	24 mo	8. ■

Find the total amount. Remember to add the principal to the amount earned as interest.

Principal	Rate	Time	Total Amount
$ 200	7%	24 mo	9. ■
$ 500	$6\frac{1}{2}$%	3 y	10. ■
$1,300	$8\frac{1}{4}$%	30 mo	11. ■
$4,600	$6\frac{1}{4}$%	18 mo	12. ■

13. Which of Exercises 1–12 could be done mentally? In which would pencil and paper be appropriate? Which could best be done by using a calculator?

Solve.

14. Peter Ninji's account
Principal: $1,100
Rate: 8%
Time on deposit: 24 mo
Interest: ■

15. Les Moskva's account
Principal: $675
Rate: $10\frac{1}{2}$%
Time on deposit: 4 mo
Interest: ■

16. Naomi Westley's account
Principal: $1,680
Rate: $6\frac{1}{4}$%
Time on deposit: 18 mo
Interest: ■
Total amount: ■

17. Suki's bank pays an annual interest rate of $7\frac{1}{4}$%. The bank makes its interest payment on August 1 on money that has been on deposit at least 6 months. Use a passbook form and fill in Suki's passbook. She had a balance of $856.29 on January 1. She deposited $365 on January 3. What was her balance on August 1?

18. Mary had $2,585 in her account at the end of a year. The interest earned was $\frac{1}{10}$ of the principal that Mary deposited. How much interest did Mary earn?

Mental Math: *Changing Months to Years*

To change months to years, write a fraction with the number of months as the numerator and 12 as the denominator.

$$4 \text{ mo} = \frac{4}{12} = \frac{4 \div 4}{12 \div 4} = \frac{1}{3} \text{ y} \quad \text{Reduce the fraction to lowest terms.}$$

Write each number of months in terms of years.

1. 6 mo **2.** 9 mo **3.** 5 mo **4.** 18 mo

5. 24 mo **6.** 10 mo **7.** 36 mo **8.** 30 mo

Career
Travel Agent

You do not need college training to be a **travel agent,** but travel-related jobs are becoming competitive, so taking courses related to the field is a good idea. You will use a lot of math in figuring travel expenses.

Profile of a travel agent. A travel agent must enjoy working with people and be able to present and sell travel plans to prospective customers. Good organization is a must! The agent must be able to communicate with other travel representatives at home and abroad. The agent must manage information on schedules, accommodations, needs and wishes of travelers, foreign customs, and regulations—a host of details.

The travel agency environment. A travel agency is a colorful place to work. Agents generally have access to computer terminals that connect the agency with airlines, hotel groups, railroads, and a number of other specific information sources. The agent keys in information and very rapidly has answers to a number of questions about availability of accommodations and airline flights.

All in a day's work. Mary has just completed the on-the-job training program with the Rainbow Travel Agency. Today she has an appointment to make travel arrangements for Mr. and Mrs. Dirks.

1. Mr. and Mrs. Dirks would like to give their son, Peter, a present of a vacation trip to Washington, D.C., after his graduation from college. They placed $1,500 in a certificate of deposit a year ago in order to pay for the trip. The certificate of deposit pays $6\frac{1}{2}\%$ simple interest annually. How much money do the Dirks have available to spend on the trip? How much interest have they earned?

2. Visit a travel agency with a classmate and find what things you should plan for if your class were to make a 200-mile trip to attend a concert or the theater, visit the Federal Reserve Bank, or go to a ball game. What can a travel agent tell you about group rates, discounts, and inexpensive times to travel?

3-5 Compound Interest

Compound interest is interest paid not only on the principal but also on the accumulated interest. Compound interest can be paid once a year, twice a year, four times a year (quarterly), monthly, weekly, or daily. The time between interest payments is called the *interest period*.

To calculate compound interest, you compute it one period at a time by dividing the product of the principal and the rate by the number of interest periods per year.

EXAMPLE

Reginald deposited $1,000 in a savings account that compounds interest quarterly at the annual rate of 8%. Calculate the amount he will have in his account after two quarters. Compare this balance with the amount he would have in an account that paid 8% simple interest for the same amount of time.

Think: 8% = 0.08

Step 1. Find Reginald's balance after the first quarter.

principal + interest = new balance

Think: $1,000 × 0.08 ÷ 4 = $20   interest for first quarter
$1,000 + $20 = $1,020   principal after first quarter

Step 2. Find Reginald's new principal after the second quarter.

Think: $1,020 × 0.08 ÷ 4 = $20.40   interest for second quarter
$1,020 + $20.40 = $1,040.40   principal after second quarter

Step 3. Find Reginald's balance after two quarters if his account earns simple interest.

Think: $1,000 × 0.08 ÷ 4 = $20   interest for one quarter
$20 + $20 = $40   interest for two quarters
$1,000 + $40 = $1,040   new principal after two quarters

Step 4. Compare the two balances after two quarters.

$1040.40   balance with compound interest
− 1040.00   balance with simple interest
$.40   additional interest earned by compounding

Reginald's account with compound interest would earn $.40 more than a similar account with simple interest.

With a calculator and the memory function, the computation for the example can be shortened.

CHECKING ACCOUNT

Interest Compounded Monthly

Step 1. Find the balance after two quarters with compound interest.

Key: $\boxed{\text{C}^{\text{C}}_{\text{E}}}$ 1000 $\boxed{\text{M}+}$ $\boxed{\times}$ 8 $\boxed{\%}$ $\boxed{\div}$ 4 $\boxed{\text{M}+}$ *principal after first quarter*
      $\boxed{\text{M}^{\text{R}}_{\text{C}}}$ $\boxed{\times}$ 8 $\boxed{\%}$ $\boxed{\div}$ 4 $\boxed{\text{M}+}$ *second-quarter interest added*
      $\boxed{\text{M}^{\text{R}}_{\text{C}}}$ ⟋ 1040.4 ⟍   *principal after second quarter*
           $1,040.40

Step 2. Find the balance after two quarters with simple interest. Store in $\boxed{\text{M}-}$.

Key: 1000 $\boxed{\times}$ 8 $\boxed{\%}$ $\boxed{\times}$ .5 $\boxed{+}$ 1000 $\boxed{\text{M}-}$ ⟋ 1040 ⟍
                                     $1,040   *principal after second quarter*

Step 3. Compare the two balances by recalling the memory.

Key: $\boxed{\text{M}^{\text{R}}_{\text{C}}}$ ⟋ 0.4 ⟍
          $.40   *additional interest earned*

Class Exercises

Find the interest compounded for each quarter and the new principal at the end of each quarter.

Starting Principal	Rate	First-Quarter Interest	Principal End of 1st Qtr.	Second-Quarter Interest	Principal End of 2nd Qtr.
$ 800	6%	$12	$812	$12.18	**1.** ■
$2,000	8%	**2.** ■	**3.** ■	**4.** ■	**5.** ■
$ 680	5%	**6.** ■	**7.** ■	**8.** ■	**9.** ■
$2,180	$10\frac{1}{4}$%	**10.** ■	**11.** ■	**12.** ■	**13.** ■

Solve.

14. Joan deposited $5,000 in a savings account at a rate of $7\frac{1}{2}$% interest compounded twice a year. How much was in her account after a year?

OPEN A SAVINGS ACCOUNT
NOW!
6% INTEREST COMPOUNDED SEMIANNUALLY

EXERCISES

Find the interest compounded for each quarter and the new principal at the end of each quarter.

Beginning Principal	Annual Rate	First-Quarter Interest	Principal End of 1st Qtr.	Second-Quarter Interest	Principal End of 2nd Qtr.
$ 500	8%	1. ■	2. ■	3. ■	4. ■
$1,200	6%	5. ■	6. ■	7. ■	8. ■
$2,000	10%	9. ■	10. ■	11. ■	12. ■
$2,295.16	$11\frac{3}{4}$%	13. ■	14. ■	15. ■	16. ■

Solve.

17. Sara Randall
Principal: $495
Rate: 11% compound
Length of period: Month
Second month's
interest: ■
Total in account: ■

18. Rubin Heffer
Principal: $1,436
Rate: 10% compound
Length of period: Quarter
Third quarter's
interest: ■
Total in account: ■

19. Heidi Allen
Principal: $901.30
Rate: $9\frac{1}{4}$% compound
Length of period: Month
Third month's
interest: ■
Total in account: ■

20. Dwight had $1,100 in his savings account at 12% interest, which is compounded daily. Use 360 days per year and determine the principal at the end of 3 days.

Critical Thinking: *Making Judgments*

Assume you have received paychecks totaling $420.48. Your bank offers a special kind of checking account with the following features.

Investor Checking Account

• Initial deposit required: $300

• Interest is compounded monthly and added to the balance.

• The interest rate changes weekly, based on current economic factors.

• The present interest rate is 6% per year.

• You may write only three checks per month on this account.

1. Judge whether this kind of checking account would be useful for you.

2. Describe the steps you used in your thinking as you made your judgment.

3. What mathematics did you use in order to judge the usefulness of this kind of account to you?

4. What changes could occur in your life to change the usefulness to you of the Investor Checking Account?

5. Identify another situation where you had to judge the usefulness of something to you. What steps did you think through to make the judgment in that situation?

3-6 Borrowing Money

Interest is paid when money is borrowed just as it is paid when it is invested. When you borrow money, you pay interest to the lender for the use of the money. The amount of interest depends upon the principal borrowed, the interest rate, and the length of time for which the principal is borrowed.

EXAMPLE 1

Georgia wanted to buy some furniture for her living room. She borrowed $625 to be paid back in 12 monthly payments of $55.40 each. How much interest did she pay for the loan?

Find the interest Georgia must pay for the loan.

Step 1. Find the total amount paid back.
Estimate: $55.40 × 12 = ■ → $60 × 10 = $600

$$\begin{array}{r} \$55.40 \\ \times \quad 12 \\ \hline 110\ 80 \\ 554\ 0 \\ \hline \$664.80 \end{array}$$

  payment
  number of payments

  total amount paid back

The answer $664.80 is reasonably close to the estimate $600 and is a sensible answer.

Step 2. Find the interest.

$$\begin{array}{r} \$664.80 \\ -\ \ 625.00 \\ \hline \$39.80 \end{array}$$

  total amount paid back
  original amount borrowed
  interest paid

Georgia paid $39.80 in interest.

With a calculator and memory, the computation in Example 1 can be simplified.

Key: $\boxed{C_E^C}$ 55.40 $\boxed{\times}$ 12 $\boxed{-}$ 625 $\boxed{=}$ 〱39.80〲
$39.80

Skill Review

To find the interest paid you must be able to multiply by an amount of money and a whole number.

Multiply.
  1. $48.62 × 60
  2. $116.95 × 36
  3. $210.40 × 5
  4. $198.56 × 360
(For additional help, see page 545.)

EXAMPLE 2

Samantha purchased a new car for $8,796. She made a down payment of $900 and borrowed the remainder. The loan is to be repaid in 36 payments of $251.38. How much interest will she pay on the loan?

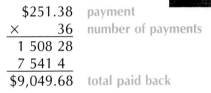

Step 1. Find the amount borrowed.

$$\$8,796 - \$900 = \$7,896$$

Step 2. Find the total paid back.

$$
\begin{array}{rl}
\$251.38 & \text{payment} \\
\times \quad\;\; 36 & \text{number of payments} \\
\hline
1\;508\;28 & \\
7\;541\;4 & \\
\hline
\$9,049.68 & \text{total paid back}
\end{array}
$$

Step 3. Find the interest.

$$\$9,049.68 - \$7,896 = \$1,153.68$$

She will pay $1,153.68 interest.

With a calculator, you can simplify the computation for Example 2.

Key: $\boxed{C^C_E}$ 8796 $\boxed{-}$ 900 $\boxed{M-}$ amount borrowed
     251.38 $\boxed{\times}$ 36 $\boxed{M+}$ $\boxed{M^R_C}$ 1153.68
                       $1,153.68   interest

Class Exercises

Find the amount of interest paid for the following loans.

Amount of Loan	Number of Payments	Amount of Payment	Interest
$ 800	12	$ 71.35	**1.** ■
$ 950	8	$122.49	**2.** ■
$2,200	24	$100	**3.** ■
$1,655	24	$ 72.50	**4.** ■
$4,592	36	$137.95	**5.** ■

Solve.

6. Jeff bought a motorcycle for $3,589. He made a down payment of $1,200 and borrowed the remainder. If he repays the loan in 36 payments of $73.66, how much interest will he pay?

EXERCISES

Find the amount of interest paid for the following loans.

Amount of Loan	Number of Payments	Amount of Payment	Interest
$ 600	6	$107.20	1. ■
$ 825	9	$100.25	2. ■
$9,672	36	$281.35	3. ■

Find the amount of interest paid for the loans.

Cost of Item	Down Payment	Number of Payments	Each Payment	Interest
$ 856	$ 100	8	$ 97.35	4. ■
$6,245	$ 750	24	$241.45	5. ■
$9,825.98	$1,050	36	$255.18	6. ■
$1,275	$ 400	12	$ 81.62	7. ■

Solve.

8. Van Finney
Amount of loan: ■
No. of payments: 6
Each payment: $72.50
Interest: $48.50

9. Scott Clipper
Amount of loan: $1,000
No. of payments: ■
Each payment: $107.50
Interest: $75

10. Sam North
Amount of loan: $956.50
No. of payments: 12
Each payment: ■
Interest: $45.50

11. Explain how you can use mental arithmetic to solve Problem 9.

12. Rita bought a new video camera that cost $1,138. She made a down payment of 25% and borrowed the rest. She repaid the loan in 18 payments of $51.60 each. How much were her interest charges on the amount she borrowed?

13. Amanda purchased a new car for $8,725. She paid $1,725 down and borrowed the remainder. She had to make 24 payments of $308.44. How much interest did she pay?

Challenge: *Computing Rate of Interest*

Katerina purchased a living room sofa for $1,295.95. She bought a recliner for $349.75. She purchased two end tables for $59.50 each. She chose a repayment plan of 12 monthly payments. At the end of that time she had paid a total of $2,174 to the furniture store. What rate of interest did Katerina pay on her purchases?

3-7 Loan Repayment Plans

When you borrow money, there are many different repayment plans available. In the **single-payment plan,** you repay the loan in one payment at a specified date. This type of loan is usually made for short periods of time.

In the **add-on plan,** simple interest is charged on the entire loan. This interest is added to the principal and the entire amount (principal plus interest) is repaid in a specified number of equal payments.

EXAMPLE 1

Farley borrowed $600 from his father at 7% interest to buy a new stereo system. He was to repay it in 18 monthly payments under the add-on plan. How much was each monthly payment?

Think: 7% = 0.07

Skill Review

Knowing how to express a fraction as a decimal will help you compute interest.

Express as decimals.

1. $\frac{2}{5}$

2. $\frac{48}{25}$

3. $\frac{15}{6}$

4. $\frac{45}{18}$

(For additional help, see page 548.)

Hidden Question: How do you represent 18 months in terms of years?

$$\frac{18}{12} = 1\frac{1}{2} = 1.5 \text{ y}$$

Step 1. Compute the total principal and interest.

$$i = p \quad \times \quad r \quad \times t$$
$$i = \$600 \times 0.07 \times 1.5$$
$$i = \$63$$
$$\$600 + \$63 = \$663$$

Step 2. Divide by the number of payments.

$$\$663 \div 18 = \$36.83$$

Farley will pay $36.83 a month for 18 months.

With a calculator, you can streamline the computation for Example 1.

Key: $\boxed{C_E^C}$ 600 $\boxed{\times}$ 7 $\boxed{\%}$ $\boxed{\times}$ 1.5 $\boxed{+}$ 600 $\boxed{=}$ $\boxed{\div}$ 18 $\boxed{=}$ _36.833333_
$36.83   **Round to nearest cent.**

In the **monthly installment plan** interest is charged at an annual percentage rate (APR) only on the unpaid part of the loan. Even though the monthly payments are all equal, the part of the payment that goes toward interest decreases as the loan is repaid. Information for computing payments for this type of loan is available in tables such as the one on the next page.

Monthly Payment Schedule for $100 Installment Loan					
	Number of Payments				
Rate	12	18	24	30	36
8.5%	$8.7221	$5.9369	$4.5456	$3.7118	$3.1568
9.0%	$8.7453	$5.9598	$4.5685	$3.7348	$3.1800
9.5%	$8.7683	$5.9827	$4.5914	$3.7579	$3.2033

To calculate the monthly payment, multiply the amount for $100 in the table by the amount borrowed and divide by 100.

EXAMPLE 2

Tania borrowed $650 from the bank for a typewriter. She made 24 payments and paid $9\frac{1}{2}\%$ interest under a monthly installment plan. How much was her payment?

Step 1: Find the monthly payment per $100.

> **Problem Solving Strategy:** Finding information.
> Find the monthly payment for $100 in the table. Look across the row labeled 9.5% and under the column labeled 24. The payment is $4.5914 for $100.

Step 2. Multiply $4.5914 by 650 (the amount borrowed) and divide by 100.

$4.5914 \times 650 \div 100 = \$29.8441 \rightarrow \$29.84$ Round to nearest cent.

Tania's payments were $29.84 per month.

Class Exercises

Determine the monthly payment under an add-on plan.

Amount Borrowed	Rate of Interest	Amount of Time	Monthly Payment
$ 900	6%	12 mo	1. ■
$1,075	9%	6 mo	2. ■
$1,500	10%	24 mo	3. ■

Determine the monthly payment under a monthly installment plan. Use the monthly payment schedule on this page.

4. $1,200 borrowed for 30 mo at 9.5% interest.

5. $4,000 borrowed for 36 mo at 8.5% interest.

EXERCISES

Determine the monthly payment under an add-on plan.

Amount Borrowed	Rate of Interest	Amount of Time	Monthly Payment
$350	11%	1 y	1. ■
$925	$12\frac{1}{2}$%	24 mo	2. ■
$810	$9\frac{1}{2}$%	24 mo	3. ■

Determine the monthly payment under a monthly installment plan. Use the monthly payment schedule on page 121.

Amount Borrowed	Rate of Interest	Amount of Time	Monthly Payment
$ 865	9%	18 mo	4. ■
$1,150	9.5%	24 mo	5. ■
$3,150	8.5%	30 mo	6. ■

Solve.

7. Nolan Wright
Borrowed: $625
Loan type: single payment
Interest rate: 16%
Time of loan: 3 mo
Amount to repay: ■

8. Darlene Testor
Borrowed: $200
Loan type: add-on
Interest rate: 8%
Number of payments: 18
Monthly payment: ■

9. Billie Geste
Borrowed: $1,438
Loan type: installment
Interest rate: 9%
Number of payments: 36
Monthly installment: ■

10. Investigate the kinds of loans available in your community. What factors might affect your choice of a lending institution or the type of repayment plan you would choose?

Consumer Note: *Consumer Credit—Deciding on a Bank Loan*

You have your eye on a used car, but it costs more money than you have saved. You should consider the possibility of borrowing money from the bank where you have a savings or checking account.

When you know how much you need to borrow, speak with a loan officer at your bank. Find out how much money you need to have in order to make a down payment on the car.

Interest rates may vary from bank to bank, and these rates, along with the pay-back period, determine your monthly payments. Most pay-back periods range from 36 to 48 months, but 60-month periods are becoming common. Do not hesitate to shop around for credit—a lower interest rate can save you a lot of money.

Calculator:
Using the Automatic Constant Feature

On most calculators you can repeat an operation by using the $\boxed{=}$ key. This is called the *automatic constant* or *auto-repeat* function. For example, if you wished to find the sum $19.50 + \$1.25 + 1.25 + \$1.25 + \$1.25$, you could use the following keystrokes:

Key: $\boxed{C_E^C}$ 19.5 $\boxed{+}$ 1.25 $\boxed{=}$ $\boxed{=}$ $\boxed{=}$ $\boxed{=}$ ⟋⟋⟋24.5⟋⟋⟋
$24.50

> The + 1.25 operation is repeated four times and the final answer, 24.5 ($24.50), is displayed.

You can raise a number to a power by using repeated multiplication; to raise 5.3 to the fourth power (5.3^4), use these keystrokes:

Key: $\boxed{C_E^C}$ 5.3 $\boxed{\times}$ $\boxed{=}$ $\boxed{=}$ $\boxed{=}$ ⟋⟋⟋789.0481⟋⟋⟋

Note that the first press of the key gives 5.3^2, the second, 5.3^3, and the third, 5.3^4. So you press the $\boxed{=}$ key one less time than the number of times you are multiplying a number by itself. Example: $165 is invested at 9% interest compounded annually. How much is in the account after 5 years?

The principal is multiplied each year by 1.09 (100% + 9%), so for 5 years, the principal is multiplied by 1.09^5:

Key: $\boxed{C_E^C}$ 1.09 $\boxed{\times}$ $\boxed{=}$ $\boxed{=}$ $\boxed{=}$ $\boxed{=}$ $\boxed{\times}$ 165 $\boxed{=}$ ⟋⟋⟋253.87294⟋⟋⟋
$253.87

EXERCISES
Use the auto-repeat feature of your calculator.

1. $18.75 + \$2.50 + \$2.50 + \$2.50 + \$2.50$

2. $375.40 - \$5.56 - \$5.56 - \$5.56 - \$5.56 - \$5.56 - \$5.56$

3. $3 \times 3 \times 3 \times 3 \times 3$

4. $9.2 \times 9.2 \times 9.2 \times 9.2$

5. $16 \div 2 \div 2 \div 2 \div 2 \div 2$

6. $1.07 \times 1.07 \times 1.07 \times 1.07 \times 1.07 \times 10.75$

7. $105 is invested at 6% interest. How much is it worth after 8 years?

8. How much is $917.66 worth after being invested at 6.5% interest for 12 years?

9. How long will it take an amount of money to double in value if it is invested at 10% interest?

Decision Making:
Selecting a Bank

After graduation Delores Jenkins accepted a job in Baltimore, Maryland. She arranged to move from her home town to the city and to rent a room from her aunt and uncle until she saved enough money to buy furniture and rent an apartment of her own.

Delores realized she would need to find a bank. She asked her Aunt Grace what bank she used.

"I think you need to choose a bank for yourself," Aunt Grace replied. "The bank I use may not meet your needs."

"What features DO I need in a bank?" Delores wondered to herself.

GETTING STARTED

Delores began by listing the overall financial goals she hoped to meet in selecting a bank.

> The Best Bank for me:
> – is located near work or home
> – is open after 5 P.M. or on Saturday
> – offers high interest rates on savings
> – offers low-cost checking accounts
> – offers Automatic Teller Machines (ATM's)

Next Delores thought about what features a bank would need to have to help her meet her personal financial goals. She compiled the following list:

> Goals:
> 1. To have a place to put the part of my net pay that I don't need in cash
> 2. To be able to write checks to pay my living expenses
> 3. To save as much money as I can

Then she thought of the most important feature of all and added—

> – will keep my money safe

Delores decided to use the Yellow Pages of her telephone book to find out addresses of banks.

Answer the following questions.

1. What features might Aunt Grace want in a bank?

2. What information might Delores be able to find out about banks in her Yellow Pages? Under what category other than banks should she look for information?

3. How might Delores get more information about the services available from the banks? What are some questions she might ask when visiting a bank?

COMPARING BANKS

Delores looked in the Yellow Pages under Banks and under Savings and Loans. She found that most of the financial institutions listed were insured either by the FDIC (Federal Deposit Insurance Corporation) or the FSLIC (Federal Savings and Loan Insurance Corporation). She asked her aunt what the difference is between a commercial bank and a savings bank, or savings and loan.

"They are regulated by different laws," Aunt Grace replied. "For instance, a commercial bank must keep more of its funds in reserve than a savings bank. Therefore, savings banks can usually offer a higher interest rate than can commercial banks. However, a commercial bank will usually offer more services, such as a safe deposit box, than a savings bank."

"I'm not sure I need one of those at this point," Delores said.

"Think a bit more about the features you need in a bank," her aunt said. "You might identify some banks that are in good locations for you and visit them to obtain the information you need. Then you can judge whether each bank meets your requirements."

Delores noticed that some banks had many branch offices. She telephoned five banks that were conveniently located and found that three were open after 5 P.M. or on Saturday. Delores visited the two closest banks, Beneficial Commercial Bank and Loyalty Savings Bank, and asked questions about the services each bank provided. She was given pamphlets and lists of current interest rates in the banks she visited.

After reading the pamphlets carefully, Delores decided to make a chart of the important information. This, she thought, would help her compare what one bank offered with the offerings of the other.

Delores' chart:

	BENEFICIAL BANK	LOYALTY SAVINGS BANK
Kind of bank	commercial	savings
Insured by	FDIC	FSLIC
Automatic Teller Machine	– can withdraw up to $200 daily from checking or savings account – no charge for withdrawals	– bank does not have ATMs
Types of Accounts	CHECKING—PLAN A – no minimum balance required – $5 monthly charge CHECKING—PLAN B – must keep a minimum balance of $300 in account at all times – no monthly charge unless balance goes below $300; if it does, charges are $3 per month plus $.35 for each check SAVINGS—PLAN C – must keep a minimum balance of $500 in account – interest rate changes weekly – present rate 5.35% compounded daily to give a yield of 5.47% annually	CHECKING-SAVINGS-PLAN D – must keep a minimum balance of $100 in account at all times – monthly fee of $10 if balance falls below $100 – 5.8% interest rate, compounded monthly – only three checks may be written each month

Since access to an ATM was one of Delores' requirements in a bank, she decided she would definitely open an account at Beneficial Bank.

She looked again at the description of the checking and savings plans. Delores estimated that she would be able to keep an approximate balance of $150 in her checking account, that she would write four checks per month, that she would use the ATM twice per month, and that she could save $50 per month.

Answer the following questions.

4. Which checking account(s) could Delores use?

5. What did you think about when you were judging whether each plan was useful for Delores?

6. What information given about the accounts might change during the time Delores used the bank?

DELORES' DECISION

Clearly, the only checking account plan that Delores could use was Plan A at Beneficial. However, in considering the savings account plans, Delores realized that, while she could use both Plan C and Plan D, Plan D at Loyalty Savings Bank paid a higher rate of interest. Also, Plan D would allow her to open a savings account as soon as she had $100, whereas she would need to wait until she had $500 if she were to use Plan C.

"The savings plan at Loyalty Bank is better," Delores said to herself, "but the checking plan and having the ATM make Beneficial Bank a better choice." She pondered the problem of which bank to choose. Then a new idea occurred to her.

"Who said I had to choose *one* bank?" she exclaimed aloud. "Why can't I use the best of both?"

"What did you decide?" Aunt Grace asked later.

"You'll be surprised," answered Delores. "I'm going to use two banks, one for checking and ATM withdrawals and another for savings. What do you think of that?"

Answer the following questions.

7. What facts favored choosing two banks to meet her needs?

8. How might Delores' bank service needs change after she works for 2 years?

9. When in the process of making her decision did Delores judge the usefulness of something?

10. What action can Delores take if she discovers at any point that she has made a poor decision?

11. Name three decisions Delores might need to make that are more important than her decision about which bank to choose.

DECIDE FOR YOURSELF

How would you choose a bank (or banks) for yourself? Use the decision making steps that Delores used to select a bank in your town or city. Then summarize how you, and Delores, went about choosing a bank.

Chapter 3 Review

VOCABULARY

add-on plan   monthly installment plan   simple interest
compound interest   principal   single-payment plan
interest

For Exercises 1–7, select from the above list the word or words
that complete each statement.

1. Money charged or paid for the use of money is called _____ .

2. When simple interest is added to the amount borrowed and
the total is repaid in an equal number of installments, it is
called the _____ .

3. The amount of money deposited in a checking or a savings
account or borrowed, upon which interest is based, is called
the _____ .

4. A loan-repayment plan in which all the principal plus interest
is repaid at once is called the _____ .

5. _____ is interest paid only on the principal and not on
accumulated interest.

6. When interest is charged on the unpaid part of the loan and
the loan is repaid in equal monthly installments, it is called
the _____ .

7. Interest paid on both the principal and the interest
accumulated on the principal is called _____ .

SKILLS

Add or subtract.

8. $250 − $198   **9.** $408.50 + $299.67   **10.** $700 − $369.50

Multiply.

11. $324 × 5 × 6   **12.** $25.75 × 3 × 4   **13.** $596.95 × 2 × 3

Express as decimals. Round to the nearest thousandth, if necessary.

14. 17%   **15.** 3%   **16.** $19\frac{3}{4}\%$

17. $\frac{7}{25}$ **18.** $\frac{5}{6}$ **19.** $\frac{6}{7}$

CONSUMER TOPICS
Solve.

20. Complete a blank check to show the following: number, 421; date, May 17, 1991; paid to Sally Green; amount, $143.40.

21. Using a deposit slip form, write a deposit slip for the following: checks, $25, $15.75, $163.84; cash, $36; coins, $2.45. Find the total deposit.

22. Find the current balance for Jason's account if he had a balance of $356.49, wrote checks for $24.95, $8.40, and $45.50, and made a deposit of $194.38.

23. Rachel received a bank statement for her account showing a monthly bank charge of $4.75. It also showed that a check for $27.88 had not been cashed. The bank statement showed a balance of $315.98 in the account. Reconcile the statement if Rachel's account showed a balance of $292.85.

24. Find the current balance for Rob's savings account if he had a balance of $608.50, made a $70 deposit, withdrew $28, and earned $4.10 interest.

25. Fill in a savings account deposit slip for $100 in cash and a check for $388.26. Use 172935 for the account number.

26. Fill in a savings withdrawal form for $721.85. Use 3-42298 for the account number.

27. Find the balance in Roberto's account after 2 years for a principal of $2,500 if the bank paid simple interest at 5.25%.

28. Find the principal in Suzanne's account at the end of the second quarter if she invested $500 at 6% and the interest is compounded quarterly.

29. Kurt borrowed $1,295.50. He made 12 payments of $124.20. How much interest did he pay for the loan?

30. Gretchen borrowed $550 at 13% for 60 days. How much does she have to repay under a single-payment plan?

31. Rosa borrowed $750 at 17% interest for 18 months under an add-on-plan. How much does she have to repay?

32. Sandy borrowed $2,300 at 8.5%. She repaid the loan in 36 payments under a monthly installment plan. Find her monthly payment. (Use the table on page 121.)

Chapter 3 Test

1. Complete a blank check to show this information: number, 286; date, November 18, 1990; paid to John Smith; amount, $102.54.

2. Using a deposit slip form, write a deposit slip for the following: checks, $312.69, $186.54; cash, $100; coins, $5.88. Find the total deposit.

3. Find the current balance for Tammy's account if she had a balance of $250.95; wrote checks for $12.95, $39.50, and $23.14; and made a deposit of $198.42.

4. Tammy (Problem 3) received a bank statement for her account showing a monthly charge of $2.50, a check for $39.50 that had not yet been cashed, and a balance of $410.78. Explain how she reconciled the two balances.

5. Find the current balance for Jon's savings account if he had a balance of $325.50, made two $20 deposits, withdrew $75, and earned $3.45 interest.

6. Fill in a savings account deposit slip for $78 in cash and checks for $116.95 and $299.76. Use 1823491 for the account number.

7. Fill in a savings withdrawal form for $265. Use 18970-2 for the account number.

8. Find the balance in Kevin's account after 2 years if he originally deposited $2,250 at 7.5% simple interest.

9. Janet deposited $2,000 at 10% interest compounded quarterly. Find the amount in her account at the end of 2 quarters.

10. Max borrowed $1,500. He made 18 payments of $92.40. How much interest did he pay for the loan?

11. Katie borrowed $750 at 14% interest for 3 months. How much does she have to repay under a single-payment plan?

12. Joe borrowed $895 at 11.5% interest for 24 months under an add-on plan. How much is his monthly payment?

13. Karla borrowed $1,500 at 9.5%. She repaid the loan in 24 payments under a monthly installment plan. She repaid $4.5914 per $100. How much was her monthly installment?

Cumulative Mixed Review

Select the letter corresponding to the correct answer.

1. Craig gets paid $3.70 an hour with time-and-a-half for overtime (over 40 hours). How much did he earn one week when he worked 47 hours?
- **a.** $260.85
- **b.** $186.85
- **c.** $164.50
- **d.** $5.55

2. Chantelle gets paid $.20 per unit for all units produced up to 100. For all units over 100, she gets paid $.25 each. How much did she earn the day she produced 175 units?
- **a.** $38.75
- **b.** $193.75
- **c.** $35
- **d.** $43.75

3. Perry earns $2.90 per hour plus tips. How much did he earn the week he worked 40 hours and made these tips: $25, $22, $28, $30, $20?
- **a.** $125
- **b.** $116
- **c.** $48.20
- **d.** $241

4. Sharon has an annual income of $19,750. She has her employer withhold $6,050 as deductions. What is the amount of each paycheck if she gets paid biweekly?
- **a.** $263.46
- **b.** $759.62
- **c.** $526.92
- **d.** $13,700

5. Aaron gets paid semimonthly. His gross pay for each pay period is $750. He has 20% withheld for taxes and 5% withheld for personal deductions. What is his annual net pay?
- **a.** $9,000
- **b.** $13,500
- **c.** $18,000
- **d.** $562.50

6. Carolyn's beginning balance in her checkbook was $350.50. She made deposits of $275, wrote checks for $189.72, and had to pay a bank charge of $2.75. What was her ending balance for the month?
- **a.** $812.47
- **b.** $438.53
- **c.** $262.47
- **d.** $433.03

7. Serge borrowed $1,575 and made 18 payments of $105.25. How much did he pay in interest?
- **a.** $319.50
- **b.** $3,469.50
- **c.** $1,575
- **d.** $1,894.50

8. Maria borrowed $1,250 for 2 months at an annual rate of 7.5% under a single-payment plan. How much interest must she pay?
- **a.** $93.75
- **b.** $15.63
- **c.** $1,265.63
- **d.** $187.50

9. Trevor deposited $1,150 in a savings account that pays 6.5% interest, compounded quarterly. What was his balance at the end of the second quarter after the interest had been added?
- **a.** $74.75
- **b.** $1,224.75
- **c.** $1,168.69
- **d.** $1,187.68

10. Trina borrowed $600 at 9% for 12 months under a monthly installment plan. She must pay $8.7453 per $100 each month for 12 months. How much is her monthly installment payment?
- **a.** $654
- **b.** $629.64
- **c.** $52.47
- **d.** $54.50

CHAPTER 4
Budgeting

Jason works at a local department store. His take-home pay is $176.60 per week. He is very concerned because he does not seem to have enough money for savings.

- Do you think a budget would help Jason? How?

- How would you advise Jason to go about making a budget?

- What are some typical expenses Jason might have? What kinds of expenses might he be able to cut in order to have more for savings?

How do you think making a budget could help you manage your money more effectively?

4-1 Average Monthly Expenses

A personal **budget,** or plan to balance income and expenses, can help you to plan and meet expenses. To prepare a budget you must keep a record of **expenditures,** or amounts of money actually paid out, over a period of time. Then you can average these expenditures to estimate future **expenses,** or amounts you can expect to spend.

Ellen kept a record of her expenditures during the months of February, March, and April (see page 135). She wanted to see how she was spending her money. To do this she organized her expenses into categories and found a total for each category.

In order to decide how much she was spending for housing, Ellen found her **average monthly expense** for housing, or the average amount spent each month.

Skill Review

Knowing how to find the mean of a set of numbers will help in preparing a budget.

Find the mean.

1. 7; 8; 9; 2; 4
2. $5; $8; $12; $15
3. $175; $96; $74.80; $36.50
4. $376.95; $250.25; $45.50; $87.50

(For additional help, see page 552.)

EXAMPLE 1
Find Ellen's average monthly expense for housing.

Step 1. Find the cost for housing for each month. (Add the electric bill, rent, and phone bill.)

Housing: February March   April
            $324.55 $331.26 $316.29

Step 2. Find the average of the monthly costs.

```
  $324.55
   331.26
+  316.29
  $972.10
```

 Key: $\boxed{C_E^C}$ 324.55 $\boxed{+}$ 331.26 $\boxed{+}$ 316.29 $\boxed{=}$ $\boxed{÷}$ 3 $\boxed{=}$ _324.03333_
$324.03 Round to nearest cent.

```
      $324.033 → $324.03   Round to
3)$972.100                  nearest cent.
```

Ellen's average monthly expense for housing is $324.03.

To help plan what her needs would be, Ellen wanted to find her total average monthly expense.

EXAMPLE 2
Find Ellen's average monthly expense.

$$\text{average monthly expense} = \frac{\text{total expenditures}}{\text{number of months}}$$

Estimate:
$$\frac{\$694.54 + \$664.67 + \$622.44}{3} = \blacksquare \rightarrow$$

$$\frac{\$700 + \$700 + \$700}{3} = \frac{\$2,100}{3} = \$700$$

$$
\begin{array}{r}
\$694.54 \\
664.67 \\
+\ 622.44 \\
\hline
\$1,981.65
\end{array}
$$

Find the sum.

Key: $\boxed{C_E^C}$ 694.54 $\boxed{+}$ 664.67 $\boxed{+}$ 622.44 $\boxed{=}$ $\boxed{\div}$ 3 $\boxed{=}$ 660.55

$660.55

$$
\begin{array}{r}
\$\ 660.55 \\
3\overline{)\$1,981.65}
\end{array}
$$

Divide by number of months.

The answer $660.55 is reasonably close to the estimate $700 and it is a sensible answer.

Ellen's average monthly expense was $660.55.

Date	Amount	For
2/1	$24.76	Groceries
2/4	$10.59	Restaurant
2/5	$172.44	Car payment
2/8	$26.18	Electric bill
2/12	$272.50	Rent
2/19	$4.00	Movies
2/20	$25.87	Phone bill
2/24	$2.50	Donation
2/24	$42.50	Shoes
2/25	$17.50	Stamps
2/26	$19.23	Mag. subscr.
2/28	$23.63	Clothing
2/28	$12.49	Gasoline
2/28	$40.35	Health Ins.
February		
Total	$694.54	

Date	Amount	For
3/2	$4.00	Movies
3/3	$22.00	Dress
3/4	$31.26	Groceries
3/5	$172.44	Car payment
3/9	$25.91	Electric bill
3/11	$13.81	Gasoline
3/12	$272.50	Rent
3/13	$5.85	Restaurant
3/20	$32.85	Phone bill
3/20	$5.50	Cleaners
3/22	$4.35	Carry-out fd.
3/23	$8.50	Gift
3/26	$51.20	Car Repair
3/29	$14.50	Art supplies
March		
Total	$664.67	

Date	Amount	For
4/1	$11.35	Gasoline
4/3	$5.67	Restaurant
4/5	$14.00	Skirt
4/5	$172.44	Car payment
4/9	$28.19	Electric bill
4/11	$28.78	Groceries
4/12	$272.50	Rent
4/19	$25.00	Doctor bill
4/20	$15.60	Phone bill
4/22	$6.78	Restaurant
4/23	$3.50	Bsktball game
4/25	$15.80	Gasoline
4/28	$18.83	Restaurant
4/28	$4.00	Movies
April		
Total	$622.44	

Class Exercises

William kept the following record. Find his average monthly expense for each category. Then find the total for each month.

	September	October	November	Average Monthly Expense
Housing	$251.98	$199.92	$301.05	1. ■
Food	$200.00	$250.00	$300.00	2. ■
Clothing	$ 90.00	$ 86.00	$ 64.00	3. ■
Transportation	$140.00	$150.62	$139.18	4. ■
Recreation	$ 32.72	$ 51.18	$ 73.45	5. ■
Savings	$ 30.00	$ 40.00	$ 50.00	6. ■
Insurance	$325.78	$ 0.00	$ 62.98	7. ■
Other	$ 47.95	$ 81.49	$105.16	8. ■
Total	9. ■	10. ■	11. ■	

Work independently or in small groups to determine the following. Compare your results with those obtained by classmates.

12. Find William's total expenditures for September, October, and November.

13. Find William's average monthly expense based on the 3-month period.

EXERCISES

Find the average monthly expenses for each category in Tashiki's budget. Then find the total for each month.

	January	February	March	Average Monthly Expense
Housing	$421.64	$288.85	$406.74	1. ■
Food	$430.00	$380.00	$390.00	2. ■
Clothing	$120.00	$150.00	$180.00	3. ■
Transportation	$235.64	$207.19	$315.72	4. ■
Recreation	$150.62	$625.18	$ 97.19	5. ■
Savings	$200.00	$125.00	$316.67	6. ■
Insurance	$154.40	$325.10	$ 97.19	7. ■
Other	$201.14	$176.27	$209.52	8. ■
Total	9. ■	10. ■	11. ■	

12. Find Tashiki's total expenses for the 3-month period.

13. Find Tashiki's average monthly expenses for the 3-month period.

14. Merv Grigg's expenditures
June: $590
July: $650
August: $490
September: $700
Average monthly expenses:

15. Ephram Liston's estimated expenditures
May: $700
June: $800
July: $600
August: $700
Average estimated monthly expenses: ■

16. Sue Vladig's expenditures
January: $525.50
February: $450.25
March: $425.25
Average monthly expenses: ■

17. Louella Halpern's expenditures
April: ■
May: $624.98
June: $874.37
Average monthly expenses: $698.37

18. Gil figured that his average monthly expenses, including savings, of $942.88 just fit his take-home income. As part of his expenses he managed to save $1,842 a year. He was anxious to increase the amount of savings. In order to do this, he would have to decrease his other expenses. If he wanted to save $2,200 per year, how much would he have available each month for nonsavings expenses?

Consumer Note: Budgeting Tips

Perhaps you have a part-time job after school or on weekends, and sometimes you wonder what happens to all your earnings. You know that a portion of the money has gone into your savings or checking account, but what about the rest?

To find out, make a list of categories such as clothing, entertainment, and transportation. As you spend your money, write the amount spent—whether small or large—under the appropriate category. Or, make an envelope for each category. Then, put a receipt or note of the amount spent in the appropriate envelope. You now have the beginnings of a budget. At the end of the month, add the amounts in each category. This will give you a clear and accurate picture of where your money went during the month.

Find the average expense over several months for each category and you'll get some idea of just how much you spend for various categories. Now you can anticipate how much you need for each category and can better plan the spending of your money.

4-2 Fixed and Variable Expenses

Expenses such as car and mortgage payments are **fixed expenses,** or expenses that remain the same from month to month. These expenses cannot be changed without selling your car or moving, for example. Expenses that change from month to month, such as recreation and clothing, are **variable expenses.**

Monroe kept track of his expenditures for May. In order to summarize his expenditures, he recorded them on a budget sheet:

Budget Sheet for _Monroe Ellis_	Total Monthly Expense _____
Monthly Variable Expenses	**Monthly Fixed Expenses**
Household expenses $ 54.76	Mortgage $327.49
Paint/hardware 38.47	Car payment 175.49
Groceries 62.80	Fixed saving _____
Shirt/socks 19.98	Total _____
Medicine 7.72	(Monthly fixed savings to cover
Ball game 16.00	annual fixed expenses.)
Gasoline 37.49	Total ÷ 12 = monthly fixed savings
Dinner 12.50	Home insurance _covered by mortgage_
Video rental 9.00	Life insurance _____
New jacket 80.35	Auto insurance _$156.98 X 4 ÷ 12_
Golf supplies 9.61	
Savings 20.00	Property taxes _covered by mortgage_
Total _____	Other _____

Monroe's automobile insurance was a fixed expense that was due four times a year. Monroe wanted to know how much he should put aside each month to have enough to make the quarterly payments.

EXAMPLE 1

How much should Monroe put aside each month so he can make his quarterly auto insurance payments?

Step 1. Compute the annual fixed expense.

Hidden Question: How many payments per year if the payments are quarterly? Quarterly means 4 payments per year.

$$\begin{array}{ccccc} \text{amount of} & & \text{number of} & & \text{annual fixed} \\ \text{payment} & \times & \text{payments yearly} & = & \text{expense} \\ \$156.98 & \times & 4 & = & \$627.92 \end{array}$$

Step 2. Compute the monthly amount needed to cover Monroe's annual fixed expense for auto insurance.

$$\text{annual fixed expense} \div 12 = \text{monthly savings needed}$$
$$\$627.92 \qquad \div 12 = \qquad \blacksquare$$

Estimate: $\$627.92 \div 12 = \blacksquare \rightarrow \$600 \div 12 = \$50$

$$\begin{array}{r} \$\ 52.326 \rightarrow \$52.33 \quad \text{Round to nearest cent.} \\ 12\overline{)\$627.920} \end{array}$$

The answer $52.33 is reasonably close to the estimate $50, and it is a sensible answer.

Monroe would have to save $52.33 each month to cover his annual fixed expense for auto insurance.

With a calculator, you can simplify the computation for Example 1.

Key: $\boxed{\text{C}_\text{E}^\text{C}}$ 156.98 $\boxed{\times}$ 4 $\boxed{\div}$ 12 $\boxed{=}$ ⟍ 52.326666 ⟍

$52.33   Round to nearest cent.

Monroe's mortgage payment covered his home insurance and property taxes, and he had not bought life insurance. So, the only payment for which he had to budget in his fixed savings was the auto insurance payment. Listing his expenditures on the budget sheet allowed Monroe to find his total variable and fixed expenses.

EXAMPLE 2

Find Monroe's total fixed expenses, total variable expenses, and total monthly expenses.

Step 1. Find Monroe's total fixed expenses.

$$\$327.49 + \$175.49 + \$52.33 = \$555.31$$

Step 2. Find Monroe's total variable expenses.

$$\$54.76 + \$38.47 + \$62.80 + \$19.98 + \$7.72 + \$16$$
$$+ \$37.49 + \$12.50 + \$9 + \$80.35 + \$9.61 + \$20 = \$368.68$$

Step 3. Find Monroe's total monthly expenses.

$$\text{fixed expenses} + \text{variable expenses} = \text{total monthly expenses}$$
$$\$555.31 \qquad + \qquad \$368.68 \qquad = \qquad \$923.99$$

Monroe's total monthly expenses are $923.99.

With a calculator, the computation for Example 2 can be streamlined using the memory.

Key: $\boxed{C_E^C}$ 327.49 $\boxed{+}$ 175.49 $\boxed{+}$ 52.33 $\boxed{M+}$ fixed expenses
54.76 $\boxed{+}$ 38.47 $\boxed{+}$ 62.8 $\boxed{+}$ 19.98 $\boxed{+}$ 7.72 $\boxed{+}$ 16 $\boxed{+}$
37.49 $\boxed{+}$ 12.5 $\boxed{+}$ 9 $\boxed{+}$ 80.35 $\boxed{+}$ 9.61 $\boxed{+}$ 20 $\boxed{M+}$ variable expenses
$\boxed{M_C^R}$ 923.99   total monthly expenses
$923.99

Class Exercises

Complete the table.

Monthly Expenses							
Rent	Food Expenses	Car Payment	Other Expenses	Fixed Savings	Variable Expenses	Fixed Expenses	Total Expenses
$205.19	$198.75	$185.37	$108.92	$268.20	*1.* ■	*2.* ■	*3.* ■
$400	$350	$200	$150	$150	*4.* ■	*5.* ■	*6.* ■
$602.60	$428.95	$349.70	$216.98	$342.89	*7.* ■	*8.* ■	*9.* ■

10. Explain why it is more appropriate to compute Exercises 4–6 by using mental math rather than a calculator.

11. Jackie had these annual expenses: insurances, $640; taxes, $342; car registration, $12. How much should she have put in her fixed savings each month to cover these expenses?

EXERCISES

Complete the table.

Monthly Expenses							
Mortgage	Food Expenses	Car Payment	Other Expenses	Fixed Savings	Variable Expenses	Fixed Expenses	Total Expenses
$400	$300	$250	$250	$100	*1.* ■	*2.* ■	*3.* ■
$275	$225	$220	$ 80	$ 50	*4.* ■	*5.* ■	*6.* ■
$205	$185	$110	$100	$210	*7.* ■	*8.* ■	*9.* ■
10. ■	$201.75	$198.72	$126.43	$ 85.67	*11.* ■	$735.68	*12.* ■

13. Agnes Dienes
Variable expenses: $850
Fixed expenses: ■
Total expenses: $1,550

14. Viola Lomax
Variable expenses: $922.18
Fixed expenses: $428.91
Total expenses: ■

15. Show how you would use a calculator to streamline the computation for Exercise 10.

16. Explain how mental arithmetic can be used to find the answer to Exercise 2.

17. Alonzo had the following monthly expenses: mortgage, $281.37; food $212.14; clothing, $145.62; household expenses, $162.18; car payment, $210.14; gas, $104.15; recreation, $108.37; fixed savings, $102.41; regular savings, $120. What were his fixed expenses, variable expenses, and total expenses?

18. Diane's monthly variable expenses were four times as great as her fixed expenses. If she spent $832.17 more in variable than in fixed expenses each month, how much was her annual salary?

19. Make a budget sheet for your expenditures. Evaluate your spending habits. Compare your expenses with those of others in your class.

Mental Math: Using Equivalent Forms

When a budget item is in the amount of $15.99, $24.98, or $54.02—that is, within a few cents of a dollar—you can use equivalent forms to multiply it times a whole number such as 6 or 12 in your head.

Example: Marlene has budget billing for water. Her monthly bill is $19.97. How much should she budget for water in 6 months?

$$\$19.97 \times 6 = (\$20 - \$.03) \times 6 = \$20 \times 6 - \$.18$$
$$= \$120 - \$.18 = \$119.82$$

Find the total amount without pencil and paper.

1. $6.03 each day for 5 days

2. $300.04 each month for 12 months

3. $29.99 each month for 6 months

4. $1.98 each day for 20 days

Fixed and Variable Expenses   **141**

4-3 Making a Budget

Once you have listed your expenditures on a budget sheet, you are ready to make a budget. A budget will help you to decide if you can afford optional purchases. It will help you to plan for vacations and major expenses such as automobile insurance or a new appliance. And, it can help you decide how to adjust your spending if you never seem to have enough money.

Elise had a net monthly income of $1,053.60. She kept track of expenditures for several months and then calculated her average monthly expenses. Based on her expenditures, she decided to budget the amounts shown at the right.

Housing: $238.95
Food: $272.68
Clothing: $84.75
Transportation: $183.48
Recreation: $74.96

Insurance and taxes (fixed expenses): $54.49
Regular savings: $105.67
Other: $38.62

In order to be easily able to compare her budget with other budgets, Elise used percents to show her expenses.

EXAMPLE 1

Develop a budget for Elise by finding the percent of net monthly income for each budget item. First, find what percent Elise's housing was of her net monthly income.

budget item expense ÷ net monthly income = percent for budget item
       $238.95   ÷ $1,053.60   =   ■

$$\frac{0.226 \rightarrow 0.23}{1,053.60\,)\,238.95.000}$$

 Key: 238.95 ÷ 1053.60
= 0.2267938
0.23   **Round to nearest hundredth.**

Then, find what percent each average monthly expense was of her net income.

Item	Average Monthly Expenses	Percent of Net Income
Housing	$ 238.95	238.95 ÷ 1,053.60 = 0.22679 → 23%
Food	272.68	272.68 ÷ 1,053.60 = 0.25880 → 26%
Clothing	84.75	84.75 ÷ 1,053.60 = 0.080438 → 8%
Transportation	183.48	183.48 ÷ 1,053.60 = 0.17414 → 17%
Recreation	74.96	74.96 ÷ 1,053.60 = 0.07114 → 7%
Insurance	54.49	54.49 ÷ 1,053.60 = 0.05171 → 5%
Regular savings	105.67	105.67 ÷ 1,053.60 = 0.10029 → 10%
Other	38.62	38.62 ÷ 1,053.60 = 0.03665 → 4%
	$1,053.60	100%

Elise wanted to picture her budget on a circle graph so she could more easily compare the amounts she was spending on different items. Each section of the circle graph represents an expense. The size of the section represents the percent of the total budget allowed for that budget item.

EXAMPLE 2

Draw a circle graph picturing Elise's budget.

Step 1. Calculate the number of degrees (to the nearest degree) needed to construct a central angle for each section of the circle graph.

Skill Review

Knowing how to represent central angles on a circle will be helpful in making a budget.

Draw a circle and picture each central angle.

1. 90°   **2.** 120°

3. 55°   **4.** 25°

(For additional help, see page 553.)

Items	Percent of Budget Item	×	Degrees in Circle	=	Budget Item Degrees
Housing	0.23		360°		83°
Food	0.26		360°		94°
Clothing	0.08		360°		29°
Transportation	0.17		360°		61°
Recreation	0.07		360°		25°
Insurance	0.05		360°		18°
Regular savings	0.10		360°		36°
Other	0.04		360°		14°

Step 2. Draw a circle. Make sections with the central angles computed in Step 1. Label each section.

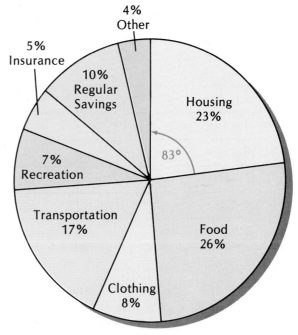

4% Other

5% Insurance

10% Regular Savings

Housing 23%

7% Recreation

83°

Transportation 17%

Food 26%

Clothing 8%

Making a Budget   **143**

Class Exercises

Find the percent represented by each budget item. Where necessary, round to the nearest whole percent.

Net Monthly Income	Item	Expense	Percent
$ 848.72	Food	$185.72	1. ■
$1,000	Savings	$100	2. ■
$1,200	Housing	$330	3. ■
$ 600	Clothing	$ 30	4. ■
$ 973.44	Transportation	$ 63.41	5. ■

Find the percent of the net monthly income represented by each of the following budget items in Blake's budget if his net monthly income is $800. Round to the nearest whole percent.

6. Housing: $200

7. Food: $175

8. Clothing: $50

9. Transportation: $75

10. Recreation: $50

11. Insurance: $25

12. Savings: $50

13. Books: $25

14. Other: $150

EXERCISES

Rob has a monthly income of $1,500. Complete the following chart of monthly expenses. Round to the nearest whole percent.

Item	Monthly Expense	Percent of Monthly Income	Degree in Central Angle
Clothing	$200	1. ■	2. ■
Housing	$350	3. ■	4. ■
Savings	$125	5. ■	6. ■
Transportation	$250	7. ■	8. ■
Recreation	$175	9. ■	10. ■
Food	$225	11. ■	12. ■
Other	$175	13. ■	14. ■

15. Construct a circle graph picturing the budget items listed in Exercises 1–14.

16. Develop a budget showing your average monthly expenses. Picture your budget in a circle graph. Compare your circle graph with the graphs of other students in your class.

17. Ramona had a net monthly income of $1,054.23 and the average monthly expenses listed below. Construct a circle graph picturing Ramona's budget.

> Housing: $303.81
> Food: $276.32
> Clothing: $98.70
> Transportation: $104.32
> Recreation: $40.77
> Insurance: $84.27
> Savings: $33.85
> Other: $112.19

Using a Calculator: Using Memory to Work with a Constant

Sylvia's net monthly income was $1,335.75. Find the percent of net monthly income for each of her budget items.

Key: $\boxed{C_E^C}$ 1335.75 $\boxed{M+}$

Item	Average Monthly Expense	Key: (Do *not* clear memory)	Round to Nearest Percent
Housing	$358.24	358.24 $\boxed{\div}$ $\boxed{M_C^R}$ $\boxed{=}$ 0.2681938	27%
Food	$315.95	315.95 $\boxed{\div}$ $\boxed{M_C^R}$ $\boxed{=}$ 0.2365337	24%
Clothing	$175.50	175.5 $\boxed{\div}$ $\boxed{M_C^R}$ $\boxed{=}$ 0.1313868	13%
Transportation	$ 87.32	87.32 $\boxed{\div}$ $\boxed{M_C^R}$ $\boxed{=}$ 0.0653715	7%
Recreation	$125.79	125.79 $\boxed{\div}$ $\boxed{M_C^R}$ $\boxed{=}$ 0.0941718	9%
Insurance	$ 97.23	97.23 $\boxed{\div}$ $\boxed{M_C^R}$ $\boxed{=}$ 0.0727905	7%
Regular savings	$100.00	100 $\boxed{\div}$ $\boxed{M_C^R}$ $\boxed{=}$ 0.0748643	7%
Other	$ 75.72	75.72 $\boxed{\div}$ $\boxed{M_C^R}$ $\boxed{=}$ 0.0566872	6%

1. Solve Example 1 on page 142 using the memory. Make a table to show your keystrokes.

2. Solve Example 2 on page 143 using the memory. Make a table to show your keystrokes.

Career

Truck Farmer

Today, less than 7% of Americans are involved in farming. But **truck farms** still exist near metropolitan areas. The financial rewards of small farming are not high and there are many risks attached to the work. Farmers need math skills for financial planning, or budgeting.

Profile of a truck farmer. The farmer (or the farm family) may own the land, be employed by a farm manager, or rent the land. There are no educational requirements for farming, although many large farms are managed by college graduates who majored in agriculture. Farm labor is physically demanding.

The truck farm environment. The farmer must work outdoors during the day and is at the mercy of the weather. All farmers depend on farm equipment, so the farmer must also be a mechanic. Spring, summer, and fall are devoted to planting, growing, and harvesting the crops. Winter is the time for repairing equipment and repairing buildings.

All in a day's work. Tom Sardano joined his older sister as a full-time worker on the 75-acre family truck farm. Here are some of the highlights of their business plan for last year.

FINANCIAL PLAN	
	Budgeted Amounts
Revenues	
From farming	$70,000
From sales	8,200
Total	$78,200
Expenses	
Fertilizer	$ 3,000
Pesticides	400
Feed	1,500
Equipment	1,700
Salaries	21,200
Supplies	300
Utilities	2,800
Insurance, interest	14,900
Repairs	2,100
Total	$47,900
Profit	
Gross profit	$_____
Tax (at 18%)	$_____
Net profit	$_____

1. Complete the truck farm's financial plan.

2. Because of unexpected heavy rains, the Sardanos actually spent $700 for pesticides instead of $400. They spent $180 less on summer help than they had budgeted. Repairs were only $900, instead of $2,100, but utilities were $600 more than budgeted. All other expenses were the same as budgeted. By how much did their total expenses change?

4-4 Using a Budget

Preparing and using a budget will help you balance your income and expenses. You must prepare your budget depending upon personal income and personal expenditures. The budget that works for you may not work for someone else. People who earn the same amounts may spend different percentages of their incomes for items such as rent and food.

Suggested Budget for a Single Person

EXAMPLE 1
Paula has a net monthly income of $1,206.87. She uses the budget shown in the circle graph to guide her in her spending. Find how much Paula has budgeted for each budget item.

Problem Solving Strategy: Finding information.
Use the circle graph to find information to solve the problem. For example, 25% of her money is budgeted for housing.

Item	Net Monthly Income	×	Percentage for Item	=	Amount Budgeted
Housing	$1,206.87		25%		$301.72
Food	$1,206.87		21%		$253.44
Clothing	$1,206.87		11%		$132.76
Transportation	$1,206.87		16%		$193.10
Recreation	$1,206.87		8%		$ 96.55
Insurance	$1,206.87		8%		$ 96.55
Savings	$1,206.87		6%		$ 72.41
Other	$1,206.87		5%		$ 60.34

Some of Paula's expenses may be more or less than the amounts she budgeted. When she does not spend her entire budget amount, she leaves the extra money in her checking account. The money is then available for another month when her spending may exceed the budgeted amounts. If money accumulates in her checking account for several months, she places it in a savings account. In a savings account, it earns interest and is available if an emergency arises.

Skill Review

Knowing how to find a percent of a number is helpful in making and using a budget.

Find each percentage.
1. 6% of $426.75
2. 12% of $360.90
3. 49% of $705.75
4. 15.4% of $297.65
(For additional help, see page 551.)

EXAMPLE 2

Last month Paula spent $282.45 on housing. This included her rent, utility bills, and several other items. Is this more or less than she budgeted for this item? How much more or less?

Step 1. Find the amount budgeted for housing.

net monthly income	×	percentage for item	=	amount budgeted
$1,206.87	×	25%	=	■

Think: 25% = 0.25

$1,206.87 × 0.25 = 301.7175

$301.72   Round to nearest cent.

Step 2. Compare the budgeted amount with the amount spent and find the difference.

$301.72 (amount budgeted) > $282.45 (amount spent)

$301.72   budgeted
− 282.45   spent
$ 19.27   under budget

Paula spent $19.27 less than she had budgeted for housing.

With a calculator, the computation for Example 2 can be streamlined.

Key: $\boxed{C_E^C}$ 1206.87 $\boxed{×}$ 25 $\boxed{\%}$ $\boxed{=}$ $\boxed{-}$ 282.45 $\boxed{=}$ ⟋ 19.2675 ⟋

$19.27   Round to nearest cent.

Class Exercises

Complete the table below.

Net Income	Budget Item	Percent of Net Income	Amount Spent on Item
$ 840	Insurance	5%	**1.** ■
$1,200	Housing	25%	**2.** ■
$ 950	Food	21.6%	**3.** ■
$1,492.88	Clothing	9.3%	**4.** ■
$2,055	Transportation	17.3%	**5.** ■
$1,514.13	Savings	8.4%	**6.** ■

Solve.

7. This month Ali spent $201.43 on food. Is this more or less than the amount budgeted in Exercise 3? By how much does it differ?

8. Which of Exercises 1–7 could be done mentally? In which would pencil and paper be more appropriate? Which could best be done using a calculator?

EXERCISES

Complete the table below.

Net Income	Budget Item	Percent of Net Income	Amount Spent on Item
$ 750	Insurance	4%	**1.** ■
$ 910	Food	20%	**2.** ■
$ 880.12	Housing	25%	**3.** ■
$1,010.71	Transportation	12.3%	**4.** ■
$1,196.85	Other	5.1%	**5.** ■
$1,927.35	Clothing	7.4%	**6.** ■
$1,453.76	Savings	11.5%	**7.** ■
$2,002.15	Recreation	9.5%	**8.** ■

9. Clarissa had an annual net income of $12,374.82. She spent 14.3% on transportation. Estimate how much she spent each month on transportation.

10. Tony had a net monthly income of $1,200, of which he spent 25% on housing. How much does he spend in a year on housing?

11. Make a personal budget and compare one month's actual expenditures with your budgeted amounts.

Mixed Review

1. Michael earned $10.78 per hour as an electrician. He was paid time-and-a-half for all hours over 40 hours. He averaged 42 hours per week. What was his annual gross salary?

2. Michael had $7,594.19 a year withheld for deductions. What was his annual net income?

4-5 *Adjusting a Budget*

Sometimes it is necessary to *adjust,* or to make changes in, your budget. For example, you may get a pay raise and want to add money to various categories. Or, you may discover there is not enough money available to cover an unexpected expense.

Rubi's net income was $976.85 per month. He used the budget shown at the right. One month his car needed some repairs, which cost $198.45. In order to meet this unexpected expense, he had to take money from budget items that did not represent fixed expenses. He decided he could take some money that was budgeted for recreation, clothing, and other items to pay for the car repair. He had to determine if there was enough money budgeted for the three items to cover the expense, and how the expense could be evenly distributed among the three items.

Rubi's Budget

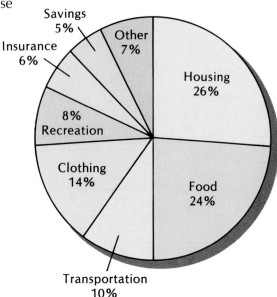

EXAMPLE 1

Determine if Rubi has enough money budgeted for the three items to cover the car repair bill.

Step 1. Find the total percent for the three budget items.

$$\begin{array}{ccccccc} \text{recreation} & + & \text{clothing} & + & \text{other} & = & \text{total} \\ \text{percent} & & \text{percent} & & \text{percent} & & \text{percent} \\ 8\% & + & 14\% & + & 7\% & = & 29\% \end{array}$$

Step 2. Find the amount of money budgeted for the 3 items.

$$\begin{array}{ccccc} \textbf{net income} & \times & \textbf{percentage for items} & = & \textbf{amount budgeted} \\ \$976.85 & \times & 29\% & = & \blacksquare \end{array}$$

Think: 29% = 0.29

$976.85	net income
× 0.29	percent
87 9165	
195 370	
$283.2865	4 decimal places
$283.29	Round to nearest cent.

There is enough money budgeted for the three items to cover the expense of the car repair.

Skill Review

Knowing how to find the sum of percents helps in adjusting a budget.

Find each sum.

1. 4% + 12% + 7%

2. 23% + 30% + 9.5%

3. 41% + 26% + 13%

4. 3.5% + 2% + 5.7%

(For additional help, see page 550.)

EXAMPLE 2
Compute how much Rubi must take from each of the three items
to pay the repair bill.

$$\frac{\text{item}}{\text{percent}} \div \frac{\text{total}}{\text{percent}} \times \frac{\text{amount of}}{\text{unexpected expense}} = \frac{\text{amount}}{\text{taken}}$$

From recreation:

$8 \div 29 \times \$198.45 = \$54.74$

Key: $\boxed{C_E^C}$ 8 $\boxed{\div}$ 29 $\boxed{\times}$ 198.45 $\boxed{=}$　54.744813

$\$54.74$ Round to nearest cent.

From clothing:

$14 \div 29 \times \$198.45 = \$95.80$

Key: $\boxed{C_E^C}$ 14 $\boxed{\div}$ 29 $\boxed{\times}$ 198.45 $\boxed{=}$　95.803444

$\$95.80$ Round to nearest cent.

From other:

$7 \div 29 \times \$198.45 = \$47.90$

Key: $\boxed{C_E^C}$ 7 $\boxed{\div}$ 29 $\boxed{\times}$ 198.45 $\boxed{=}$　47.901722

$\$47.90$ Round to nearest cent.

Rubi must take $54.74 from recreation, $95.80 from clothing, and
$47.90 from other.

Class Exercises

Find the amount that must be taken from recreation and clothing
to cover the amount of unexpected expense.

Recreation Percent	Clothing Percent	Amount of Unexpected Expense	Recreation Amount Taken	Clothing Amount Taken
8%	12%	$200	**1.** ■	**2.** ■
11%	14%	$150	**3.** ■	**4.** ■
7.2%	14.1%	$208.98	**5.** ■	**6.** ■

EXERCISES

Find the amount that must be taken from recreation and clothing
to cover the amount of unexpected expense.

Recreation Percent	Clothing Percent	Amount of Unexpected Expense	Recreation Amount Taken	Clothing Amount Taken
4%	6%	$ 30	**1.** ■	**2.** ■
7%	13%	$122.50	**3.** ■	**4.** ■
9%	10%	$200	**5.** ■	**6.** ■

Solve.

7. Irving Scholl
Net income: $1,000
Percent item 1: 2%
Percent item 2: 8%
Bill due: $94.53
Enough in these items? ■

8. Delores Cota-Robles
Net income: $1,420
Percent item 1: 15%
Percent item 2: 12%
Bill due: $250
Amount taken from item 2: ■

9. Sian needed $128.50 to repair a dishwasher. She plans to take money from the amount budgeted for clothing, savings, and other. From the information below, determine how much will be left in each item after the bill is paid.

Net Income	Clothing	Savings	Other
$1,466.32	13.1%	7.5%	9.4%

10. Most of the time, people take emergency money from their recreation, clothing, or savings budgets to meet unexpected bills. Why do you think they do this? From what other budget items could they take some money for this purpose? Explain.

Critical Thinking: *Identifying Reasons*

You have worked in a fast-food restaurant for three years. The chart below reflects your average rate of pay over the past 3 years and your anticipated rate for the coming year.

Year	Wages	Hours Worked/Week	
		After School	Summer (July)
1	$3.75/h	12	20
2	$4.05/h	12	20
3	$4.35/h	15	25
4	$4.65/h	15	25

Your parents have decided that you should contribute something each month toward your room and board, and so you have to decide how this will affect your budget.

1. Prepare a response to your parents' proposal. Include in your response the percentage of your earnings, if any, that you consider a "fair" payment for room and board. How would percentages you allocate to other categories of your budget have to change if you pay room and board?

2. What was your thought process in selecting information to use in your response to Exercise 1?

Computer:
PRINT Statements

Kaylynn has a monthly income of $1,225. She has budgeted 25.2% for housing and 22.4% for food. She has written a BASIC program to calculate the monthly amount she will spend for each of these.

Kaylynn uses the PRINT command to print alphabetic characters and numbers. The PRINT command can also be used to do arithmetic and print the results.

10 HOME	Clears the screen.
20 PRINT "BUDGET", "PCT OF", "AMOUNT"	Prints the first line of the heading. The quotation marks are not printed.
30 PRINT "ITEM", "TOTAL", "BUDGETED"	Prints the second line of the heading.
40 PRINT	Prints a blank line between heading and output.
50 PRINT "HOUSING", 25.2, .252 * 1225	Prints the first item, the label HOUSING, and its percent. Computes and prints the amount budgeted.
60 PRINT "FOOD", 22.4, .224 * 1225	Prints the second item, the label FOOD, and its percent. Computes and prints the amount budgeted.
70 PRINT "MONTHLY INCOME = $"; 1225	Prints the label MONTHLY TOTAL, and the amount. The $ symbol is part of the label.
80 END	Tells the computer to end the program.

Once all the lines have been entered, the computer must be told what to do. There are three commands to use.

RUN causes the computer to execute the program beginning with the line having the lowest line number, taking the lines in order and ending with the command END.

LIST causes the computer to display a listing of the program's lines.

NEW causes the computer to erase the program and allows you to begin writing a new one. The old program is totally lost.

Type in and RUN the program. Study the output. Because of the commas in each PRINT statement, the output is in neat columns.

EXERCISES

1. If the percent budgeted for housing had been 26.8% instead of 25.2%, what line of the program would have to be changed?

2. Make the change suggested in Exercise 1 by retyping only the line involved. Run the program and observe the difference.

3. Using the program above as a guide, write a program to find the amount budgeted for a monthly income of $982, if clothing is 12.4% of the budget, and transportation is 16.5%.

Decision Making:
Living on Less

Evie Sinclair graduated from high school 2 years ago. Since that time she has worked for Benton's Department Store. She likes her work and has received several promotions. She is interested in moving into a management position, but she would need to be a college graduate to qualify. She is concerned about how she would pay for a college education.

Evie currently earns $6.50 an hour as a head cashier. She normally works a 40-hour workweek. Evie has learned that department managers at Benton's earn an average of $22,000 per year in salary and commissions. If she could obtain a college degree, Evie feels certain she could become a department manager and perhaps go even higher.

Answer the following questions.

1. If you assume Evie is paid for an average of 40 hours per week for 48 weeks per year, how much does she earn for 1 year's work?

2. How much more per year could Evie earn as a department manager? How much more would this be over a 30-year career?

GETTING THE FACTS

Evie brings home about $195 per week. Her current budget is based on this amount.

- Evie shares an apartment with her friend Margaret. They split the rent, utilities, and furniture bill. Evie's half comes to 25% of her take-home pay.

- Evie bought a used car a year ago. Gasoline, insurance, and car payment take 19.5% of her take-home pay.

- Evie budgets 20% of her salary for monthly food costs and another 10% for recreation.

- She gets a 25% discount on her purchases at Benton's. Her discount lets her live within the 7.5% of her take-home pay that she budgets for clothing.

- Evie spends 2.9% of her take-home pay for insurance (life and health).

- She budgets 5% for miscellaneous expenses, and she puts 10% into savings.

Answer the following questions.

3. Using the budget given, how much does Evie spend each month on the following categories: (a) housing; (b) transportation; (c) recreation; (d) savings; (e) food; (f) clothing; (g) insurance; (h) other?

4. Which categories in Question 3 contain primarily fixed expenses and which contain variable expenses?

PLANNING A NEW BUDGET

Evie discovers that Benton's will pay 75% of the cost of her college tuition. The only requirement is that she continue to work for a minimum of 15 hours per week and for 1 year after graduation as well. Tuition at State College, where Evie hopes to go, is $1,000 per year. Evie feels confident she can handle college course work while continuing to work 20 to 25 hours per week.

Answer the following questions.

5. Evie realizes that she must completely rethink her budget. Assuming her rate of pay does not change, how much would Evie earn per week if she worked 20 hours? 25 hours?

6. Evie decides to do all further calculations by assuming that she would be able to work 25 hours per week and that her take-home pay would equal $\frac{3}{4}$ of her gross pay. What does Evie estimate her monthly take-home pay to be using these assumptions?

7. Evie begins work on her new budget by figuring what percent of her reduced salary will have to go for college tuition. Assuming that Evie has to pay only 25% of the tuition charged by State College, what percent of her new budget will need to be reserved for this expenditure?

Evie's parents said that she can move back in with them if she decides to go to college. They would expect her to contribute $100 per month towards the cost of her room and board.

Evie doesn't want to give up the freedom of having her own apartment. If she keeps the apartment, she realizes there is nothing she can do to reduce the $150 per month she pays as her share of the rent.

She considers her other expenses:

- Currently Evie and Margaret each pay $20 per month for a new sofa they bought for the apartment. The sofa will be paid for shortly. They do not intend to buy any other furniture.

- Evie pays half of each month's utility bill. By watching their energy usage, she and Margaret might be able to reduce their utility bill from an average of $50 per month to an average of $40 per month.

- Evie is also certain that she could reduce her food costs to about $80 per month. Much of her food budget currently goes for meals out with friends or for convenience foods.

Evie realizes, however, that if she moves back in with her parents, her only costs for housing and food would be $100.

Answer these questions.

8. Assume Evie can implement all these cost-cutting measures. How much of her salary each month would still need to go for housing and food costs if she keeps her apartment? Compare this to the percent of her budget she would need for housing and food if she moves in with her parents.

9. Obviously this is a major decision. Give some reasons Evie might have for wanting to keep her own apartment.

10. What strategy did you use to answer Question 9?

11. Compare your answers to Questions 9 and 10 with those of a classmate. Share thinking strategies. What thinking steps did your classmate use that you didn't?

Evie does not want to have to give up her car. However, she realizes that a large chunk of her current budget goes to transportation costs. Upon investigation, she also finds:

- A friend would pay $1,000 for her car and take over the payments.

- Subway and bus fares would average $20 per month.

- She would be able to use the health center at the college, but she would still need some type of hospitalization insurance.

- If she drops her life insurance, it will cost more to buy later. Evie does not see any way to reduce her monthly costs for insurance.

Answer the following questions.

12. In addition to reducing her monthly expenditure for transportation, what other advantages are there to selling her car? What disadvantages do you see?

13. Explain your thinking process in answering Question 12. Listen to the explanations of others' thinking and write down one step you might want to try the next time you answer a similar question.

EVIE'S DECISION

Evie would be willing to give up her monthly savings plan while she is in college. She would also work to reduce her clothing and recreation expenditures to a total of no more than 10% of her reduced income. But she is unsure how to handle her expenditures for purchases at the drug store, haircuts, and so on. She knows she must allow something for these expenses, but she doesn't know how much.

Answer this question.

14. Assume Evie does decide to go back to school. Prepare a budget that takes into account her reduced income and some of her preferences for reducing her level of spending. The total expenditures cannot exceed what she would earn working 25 hours per week at Benton's for 48 weeks per year. The fixed costs given must be used as stated. For instance, if she is to keep her apartment, the rent must remain at $150. If you have money left over, you may add new categories of expenditures and/or increase the amount allotted to existing categories. All existing categories except savings must have money allotted to them. Be prepared to present your budget to the class, to explain your thinking, and to justify your decisions.

DECIDE FOR YOURSELF

How would you go about deciding whether to work full time or to get additional training or go to school? What factors would affect your decision? How would having a budget help in your decision? Summarize how you, and Evie, went about making this decision.

Chapter 4 Review

VOCABULARY

average monthly expense   expenditure   fixed expense
budget   expense   variable expense

For Exercises 1–6, select from the list above the word(s) that completes each statement.

1. The amount of money actually spent on an item is called an _____ .

2. The amount of money you can expect to spend on an item is called an _____ .

3. A _____ is a plan to balance net income and expenses.

4. An expense that cannot change monthly is called a _____ .

5. A _____ is an expense that can change monthly, if necessary.

6. The average amount spent each month on expenses is called the _____ .

SKILLS

Find the average.

7. 10; 15; 18; 23; 26   **8.** $12; $18; $30; $8   **9.** $25.50; $12.75; $14; $7.30

Multiply.

10. 201.50 × 4   **11.** $362.43 × 14   **12.** $794.32 × 36

Draw circles. On each, picture one central angle.

13. 90°   **14.** 35°   **15.** 150°

Find the percent of each.

16. 17.2% of $756.20   **17.** 20.25% of $950   **18.** 3.025% of $1,200

Find the sum.

19. 3% + 2.5% + 14%   **20.** 11.6% + 3.2% + 0.8%   **21.** 12% + 19% + 52%

CONSUMER TOPICS

Solve.

22. Aaron had these expenditures for utilities: December, $176.50; January, $195.25; February, $210.50. What is his average monthly expense for utilities?

23. Find the annual fixed expense: Auto insurance, 6 payments, $194.35 each.

24. Karin makes four payments a year of $230.50 each for her life insurance; two payments a year of $450.75 each for real estate taxes; and six payments a year of $55.50 for her auto insurance. How much must Karin put into fixed savings each month to cover her annual fixed expenses of life insurance, auto insurance, and real estate taxes?

25. Kevin's total monthly expenses are $1,595. His fixed expenses amount to $750. How much are his variable expenses?

26. Curt's net monthly income is $1,050. His average monthly expense for rent is $350. What percent of his net monthly income is his rent?

Compute the number of degrees needed to construct a central angle in a circle graph for each of the budget items given for Jason's budget.

27. Housing: 25%

28. Food: 20%

29. Recreation: 10%

30. Transportation: 15%

31. Clothing: 12%

32. Other: 18%

33. Construct a circle graph picturing the information in Problems 27–32.

Solve.

Jason has a net monthly income of $1,200. Use the circle graph you drew in Problem 33 to find the amount he has budgeted for each item.

34. Housing

35. Food

36. Recreation

37. Transportation

38. Clothing

39. Other

Jason received a bill for $125 for car repairs. He had to take the money for the unexpected bill out of the amounts for recreation, clothing, and other. To adjust his budget to cover the car repairs, how much did he have to take from each?

40. Recreation

41. Clothing

42. Other

Chapter 4 Test

Solve.

1. Find the average monthly expense: April, $750; May, $815; June, $795

2. Allen had these expenditures for clothing: November, $75.50; December, $47.25; January, $110.25. What is his average monthly expense for clothing?

3. Craig's net monthly income is $1,200. His average monthly expense for rent is $312.50. What percent of his net monthly income is his rent?

4. Annette makes four payments a year of $175.50 each for her life insurance; two payments a year of $525 each for real estate taxes; and six payments a year of $45.50 for her auto insurance. What is the total of her annual fixed expenses for these three items?

5. How much must Annette (Problem 4) put into fixed savings each month to cover her annual fixed expenses for life insurance, auto insurance, and real estate taxes?

6. Wendy's net monthly income is $1,050. Her average monthly expense for rent is $210. Her average monthly expense for food is $262.50. What percent of her net monthly income are rent and food together?

Compute the number of degrees needed to construct a central angle in a circle graph for each of the budget items given for Enrico's budget.

7. Housing: 25%

8. Food: 35%

9. Savings: 10%

10. Transportation: 5%

11. Clothing: 15%

12. Other: 10%

13. Construct a circle graph picturing the information in Problems 7–12.

Enrico has a net monthly income of $1,500. Use the circle graph you drew in Problem 13 to find the amount he has budgeted for each item.

14. Housing

15. Food

16. Savings

17. Transportation

18. Clothing

19. Other

20. Enrico received a bill for $75 for car repairs. He had to take the money for the unexpected bill out of the amounts for clothing and other. How much did he take from each of the two budget items to adjust his budget?

Cumulative Mixed Review

Select the letter corresponding to the correct answer.

1. Jennifer earns $3.50 an hour plus $.10 for each unit produced. One week she worked 40 h and produced 250 units. What was her weekly wage?
   a. $29
   b. $165
   c. $140
   d. $25

2. Alex earns $6.40 an hour and time-and-a-half for all hours over 40 hours. How much did he earn the week he worked 48.5 h?
   a. $337.60
   b. $9.60
   c. $465.60
   d. $310.40

3. Chrissie receives a net pay of $425.50 biweekly. She has $150 withheld from her pay each pay period. What is her annual gross salary?
   a. $11,063
   b. $575.50
   c. $275
   d. $14,963

4. Scott is self-employed. He earned $18,750 one year and was taxed at the FICA rate of 15.02%. What was the total amount he had to pay in FICA taxes?
   a. $2,816.25
   b. 15.02%
   c. $281.63
   d. $15,933.25

5. Pam earns an annual gross salary of $14,250. She has 20% of her gross salary withheld for taxes and other deductions. If she is paid weekly, what will be her net pay in each paycheck?
   a. $219.23
   b. $2,850
   c. $274.04
   d. $11,400

6. Antonia deposited $2,500 in a savings account that earns simple interest at 7.5% annually. What is the total amount in her savings account at the end of 1 year?
   a. $187.50
   b. $192.84
   c. $2,687.50
   d. $2,692.84

7. Rachael deposited $1,000 in a savings account that pays 8% interest, compounded quarterly. What is the balance in her account at the beginning of the third quarter?
   a. $1,080
   b. $1,020
   c. $1,040.40
   d. $1,040

8. Roberto borrowed $1,795.50 for 2 years. The total amount he repaid was $2,350.95. How much interest did he pay for the loan?
   a. $97.96
   b. $555.45
   c. $2,350.95
   d. $195.91

9. Helen borrowed $2,500 at 10% interest for 3 months. How much interest did she pay on the loan?
   a. $250
   b. $2,562.50
   c. $62.50
   d. $2,750

10. Choun borrowed $1,500 for 2 years at 15% a year under an add-on plan. He repaid the loan, including interest, in 24 equal payments. How much was each payment?
    a. $81.25
    b. $450
    c. $71.88
    d. $1,950

Beth started work and decided to apply for a credit card. She talked to representatives of several banks about the credit cards they offered. She found one with a low interest rate; this card charged interest on purchases from the date of recording. Another had a higher interest rate but gave a grace period to pay all charges before charging interest. A third had a rate of interest between those of the first two but had a yearly fee.

- What kinds of factors should Beth consider in making a decision?

- How might it affect Beth's decision if her income varies each month and some months she has extra money, whereas others she does not?

- If Beth plans to pay her account in full each month, which card would be best?

What factors would you consider in deciding if you want to have a credit card? What factors would you consider in choosing one?

5-1 Sales Tax

When you make a purchase, a sales tax may be added to the total amount of the purchase. A **sales tax** is a percentage of the total sales receipt that is collected on behalf of the state, county, or local government.

EXAMPLE 1

Sam purchased a television set for $296.50. How much sales tax did he have to pay if the tax rate was 4%?

Think: 4% = 0.04

$$\text{cost of purchases} \times \text{rate} = \text{sales tax}$$
$$\$296.50 \qquad \times \ 0.04 = \ \blacksquare$$

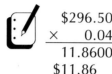

$$
\begin{array}{r}
\$296.50 \\
\times \quad 0.04 \\
\hline
11.8600 \\
\$11.86
\end{array}
$$

 Key: $\boxed{C_E^C}$ 296.50 $\boxed{\times}$ 4 $\boxed{\%}$ ⟋ 11.86 ⟋
$\$11.86$

Sam paid $11.86 for sales tax.

EXAMPLE 2

Melissa purchased equipment from the sporting goods store totaling $127.38. In her state, the sales tax rate is 5%. Determine her after-tax total.

Step 1. Find the sales tax.

$$\text{subtotal} \times \text{tax rate} = \text{sales tax}$$
$$\$127.38 \times \quad 5\% \quad = \quad \blacksquare$$

Think: 5% = 0.05

$$\$127.38 \times 0.05 = \$6.3690 \rightarrow \$6.37$$
Round to nearest cent.

Step 2. Find the total.

$$
\begin{array}{rl}
\$127.38 & \text{subtotal} \\
+ \quad \$6.37 & \text{sales tax} \\
\hline
\$133.75 & \text{total}
\end{array}
$$

Melissa's after-tax total was $133.75.

With a calculator, you can simplify the computation for Example 2.

Key: $\boxed{C_E^C}$ 127.38 $\boxed{\times}$ 5 $\boxed{\%}$ $\boxed{+}$ 127.38 $\boxed{=}$ ⟋ 133.749 ⟋
$\$133.75$ Round to nearest cent.

Skill Review

Knowing how to express a percent as a decimal will help in computing sales tax.

Express as a decimal.

1. 6%

2. 4.5%

3. 12.8%

4. $10\frac{1}{4}\%$

(For additional help, see page 550.)

Problem Solving Strategy: Solving another way.

You can use mental math and properties of percents to solve Example 2 another way.

To find the final cost, add the sales tax to the subtotal:

subtotal   +   sales tax   =   final cost

$$\begin{array}{ccc} 100\% \\ \text{of subtotal} \end{array} + \begin{array}{c} 5\% \\ \text{of subtotal} \end{array} = \text{final cost}$$

105% of subtotal   =   final cost

$127.38 × 1.05 = $133.7490 → $133.75   Round to nearest cent.

Class Exercises

Determine the amount of sales tax for each purchase.

Amount of Purchase	Sales Tax Rate	Sales Tax
$200	5%	1. ■
$158.62	6%	2. ■
$248.97	5.5%	3. ■

Determine the sales tax and total purchase price for each purchase.

Amount of Purchase	Sales Tax Rate	Sales Tax Amount	Total of Purchase
$300	4%	4. ■	5. ■
$ 63.81	5.5%	6. ■	7. ■
$ 12.49	6%	8. ■	9. ■

10. Which of Exercises 1–9 could be done using mental arithmetic? In which would pencil and paper be appropriate? In which would a calculator help streamline the computation?

EXERCISES

Determine the amount of sales tax for each of the following purchases.

Amount of Purchase	Sales Tax Rate	Sales Tax
$200	5.5%	1. ■
$ 16.52	3%	2. ■
$ 25.13	4.5%	3. ■
$122.50	6%	4. ■

Determine the sales tax and total purchase price for each of the following.

Amount of Purchase	Sales Tax Rate	Sales Tax Amount	Total of Purchase
$ 10	5%	5. ■	6. ■
$ 50	4%	7. ■	8. ■
$ 14.91	3%	9. ■	10. ■
$ 72.95	5.5%	11. ■	12. ■
$139.08	5.5%	13. ■	14. ■

Solve.

15. Lawn chair
Unit Price: $12.14
Quantity purchased: 3
Tax rate: 3%
Sales tax: ■

16. Calendar
Unit price: $6.25
Quantity purchased: 2
Tax rate: 5%
Total price ■

17. Notebook
Unit price: $2.62
Quantity purchased: 4
Tax rate: 6.25%
Total price: ■

18. Crandall used his calculator to compute the sales total on his purchase of 4 bags of peat moss at $2.89 each. The sales tax rate is 7.5%. Describe how he would key his calculator to find the amount he will have to pay.

19. Melissa bought two books at $14.95 each and a magazine for $1.50. The amount she paid the clerk, including sales tax, was $33.36. What was the sales tax rate?

Critical Thinking: Reasoning by Analogy

One Saturday you decide to visit your cousin in another state. You have a total of $98.20 in cash. On the way, you pay a cost of $9.95 plus $.60 sales tax in cash for a new fan belt.

After you arrive, you go shopping with your cousin and notice a lamp you like very much. The price is $85.

1. Do you have enough cash with you to pay for the lamp?

2. Explain your thought processes in answering Question 1.

3. How did you use math to help you answer Question 1?

In responding to Question 1, you reason by analogy—that is, you apply your understanding of one situation to another situation you believe to be similar. Whether analogical reasoning results in wise decisions depends on whether two situations being considered are alike.

4. What question(s) can you ask to decide the extent to which the relationship of a sales tax to a purchase in your state is like the relationship of a sales tax to a purchase in your cousin's state?

5. Describe in general terms how people think when they reason by analogy.

5-2 Cash Purchases and Sales Receipts

There are many different ways to pay for purchases. One way is to pay cash, either with coins or bills or by writing a check. When you make a cash purchase, the seller gives you a **sales receipt** as a record of your purchase. The sales receipt shows the items you bought, the price you paid for each, the subtotal, the sales tax, and the total of the purchase. Sometimes the sales receipt is handwritten and sometimes it is generated by a computer or cash register.

EXAMPLE

Luwanda works at Martha's Boutique. A customer purchased the items shown on the sales receipt. Complete the receipt for the purchases. How much did the customer spend?

Step 1. Compute the *extension*, or price, for each kind of item purchased.

quantity	×	unit price	=	extension	
1	×	$18.75	=	$18.75	blouse
2	×	$36.50	=	$73	shoes
1	×	$ 9.95	=	$ 9.95	slippers

Step 2. Find the subtotal.

$18.75 + $73 + $9.95 = $101.70

Step 3. Compute the tax.

tax rate × subtotal = sales tax
5%   × $101.70 =   ■

Think: 5% = 0.05

$101.70 × 0.05 = $5.0850   Round to
                $5.09   nearest cent.

Step 4. Find the total.

$101.70 + $5.09 = $106.79

The customer spent $106.79.

Many people prefer to pay cash for purchases when possible. This helps them to be more careful with spending. Also, they can take advantage of special savings that are often offered for cash purchases. It is wise to count the change when a cash purchase is made.

Skill Review

Knowing how to multiply decimals by whole numbers will help you to complete or check sales receipts.

Multiply.

1. $17.95 × 2

2. $20.60 × 4

3. $197.48 × 5

4. $205.50 × 7

(For additional help, see page 545.)

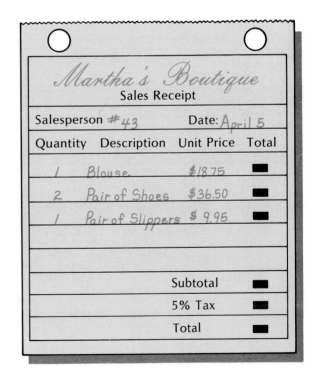

Class Exercises

Complete the sales receipt below.

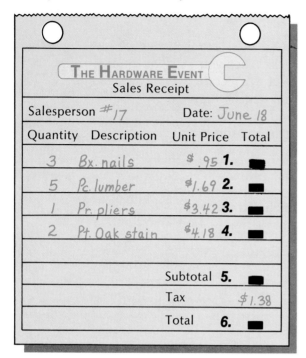

THE HARDWARE EVENT Sales Receipt			
Salesperson #17		Date: June 18	
Quantity	Description	Unit Price	Total
3	Bx. nails	$ .95	**1.** ■
5	Pc. lumber	$1.69	**2.** ■
1	Pr. pliers	$3.42	**3.** ■
2	Pt. Oak stain	$4.18	**4.** ■
		Subtotal	**5.** ■
		Tax	$1.38
		Total	**6.** ■

EXERCISES

Complete the sales receipts below.

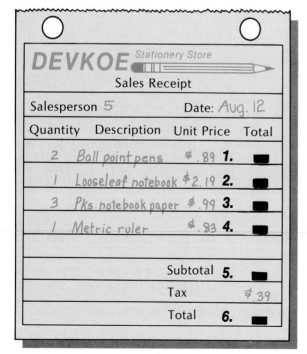

DEVKOE Stationery Store Sales Receipt			
Salesperson 5		Date: Aug. 12	
Quantity	Description	Unit Price	Total
2	Ball point pens	$ .89	**1.** ■
1	Looseleaf notebook	$2.19	**2.** ■
3	Pks. notebook paper	$ .99	**3.** ■
1	Metric ruler	$ .83	**4.** ■
		Subtotal	**5.** ■
		Tax	$ .39
		Total	**6.** ■

Burger Palace Sales Receipt			
Salesperson #13		Date: January 4	
Quantity	Description	Unit Price	Total
3	Hamburgers	$1.19	**7.** ■
2	Fried chicken boxes	$2.29	**8.** ■
4	French fries	$ .79	**9.** ■
2	Salad fixings	$1.39	**10.** ■
5	Milk	$ .85	**11.** ■
		Subtotal	**12.** ■
		Tax	$ .92
		Total	**13.** ■

14. How much change will the buyer receive in Exercise 6 if he gives the cashier a $50 traveler's check?

15. How much change will the buyer receive in Exercise 13 if she gives the cashier a $20 bill?

Solve.

16. 2 newspapers at $.35 each
3 magazines at $1.25 each
2 book marks at $.45 each
Subtotal: ■
Tax: $.45
Total: ■
Gives: $10
Change: ■

17. 3 loaves bread at $.89 each
4 cans tomatoes at $.63 each
3 cans coffee at $2.79 each
Subtotal: ■
Tax: $.54
Total: ■
Gives: $20
Change: ■

18. 5 tubes paint at $2.49 each
3 brushes at $3.17 each
2 cans solvent at $1.99 each
Subtotal: ■
Tax: 5%
Total: ■
Gives: $50
Change: ■

19. Amos made the purchases listed below. Fill out a sales receipt form and compute the totals.
2 pairs gloves at $5.31 per pair
6 pairs socks at $1.38 per pair
3 shirts at $7.98 each
1 tie at $11.98
Tax: 4%

20. Becky made the purchases listed below. Write them on a sales receipt form and compute the totals.
1 can paint remover at $8.29
2 gal paint at $12.48 per gallon
2 sash brushes at $4.75 each
1 box patching plaster at $2.19
Tax: 6%

21. Don purchased some scarves at $2.24 each, and some socks at $1.54 for each pair. The subtotal on his sales receipt for these items was $14.42. How many of each item did he buy?

Mental Math: *Compensating*

Sometimes when you are making cash purchases, you want to find a sum or difference quickly without using a calculator or paper and pencil. Sometimes you can do this by *compensating*. Example: Find the cost of two items you want to buy if they cost $32.78 and $5.39.

Think: $32.78 + $.02 = $32.80   Add $.02 to make $32.78 easier to work with.
$5.39 − $.02 = $5.37   Compensate by subtracting $.02 from $5.39
$32.80 + $5.37 = $38.17

Can you see another way to compensate that would also make the problem easy to do?

Find each sum mentally.

1. 128 + 56

2. 52 + 37

3. $1.98 + $.76

4. $10.02 + $8.61

5. $20.41 + $16.88

6. $110.78 + $80.29

5-3 Installment Buying

Many stores offer **installment plans,** which are the store's way of extending credit to a buyer. The plans allow the buyer to purchase an item and pay for it over an extended period of time. The interest charged for buying on the installment plan is called the **finance charge.**

EXAMPLE 1

Bret wanted a microwave oven for his apartment. He decided on a microwave at the Town Appliance Center that fit his needs. The purchase price was $394.98. He purchased it on an installment plan. Using this plan, he paid $45 down and made 12 monthly payments of $32.10. Find the finance charge Bret paid on the microwave.

Step 1. Find the amount borrowed.

purchase price − down payment = amount borrowed
$394.98 − $45 = $349.98

Step 2. Find the finance charge.

$32.10	amount of each payment
× 12	number of payments
$385.20	total paid
− 349.98	amount borrowed
$35.22	finance charge

Bret paid a finance charge of $35.22.

EXAMPLE 2

Georges purchased a computer for his home. The purchase price of the computer system was $2,150. He paid $250 down. He paid the remaining amount in equal monthly installments over a period of $1\frac{1}{2}$ years. The finance charge was $295. How much did Georges pay each month?

Step 1. Find the amount borrowed.

$$\$2,150 - \$250 = \$1,900$$

Step 2. Find the monthly payments.

Hidden Question: How many months in $1\frac{1}{2}$ years?
$$1\frac{1}{2} \, y = 1\frac{1}{2} \times 12 = 18 \text{ mo}$$

$$\left(\begin{array}{c}\textbf{amount} \\ \textbf{borrowed}\end{array} + \begin{array}{c}\textbf{finance} \\ \textbf{charge}\end{array}\right) \div \begin{array}{c}\textbf{number of} \\ \textbf{payments}\end{array} = \begin{array}{c}\textbf{monthly} \\ \textbf{payment}\end{array}$$
$$(\$1,900 + \$295) \div 18 = \blacksquare$$

Think: $1,900 + $295 = $2,195
Estimate: $2,195 \div 18 = \blacksquare \rightarrow $2,000 \div 20 = $100

$$\underset{18\overline{)\$2195.000}}{\$121.944} \rightarrow \$121.94 \quad \text{Round to nearest cent.}$$

The answer $121.94 is sensible and is reasonably close to the estimate $100.
Georges made monthly payments of $121.94 each.

Class Exercises

Compute the finance charge.

Amount Borrowed	Monthly Payment	Number of Payments	Finance Charge
$400	$40	12	1. ■
$ 74.35	$ 7.95	12	2. ■

Compute the monthly payment on the following purchases.

Amount Borrowed	Finance Charge	Number of Payments	Monthly Payment
$147.80	$24.46	18	3. ■
$200	$40	12	4. ■

EXERCISES

Compute the finance charge.

Amount Borrowed	Monthly Payment	Number of Payments	Finance Charge
$100	$10	12	1. ■
$ 86.33	$15.19	6	2. ■
$619.54	$26.65	30	3. ■

Compute the monthly payment from the information given.

Amount Borrowed	Finance Charge	Number of Payments	Monthly Payment
$210	$ 54	24	4. ■
$300	$ 60	12	5. ■
$477.39	$119.33	24	6. ■

Complete the table by computing the missing values.

Purchase Price	Down Payment	Finance Charge	Number of Installments	Amount of Each Installment
$260	$60	$ 40	12	**7.** ■
$372.50	$45	**8.** ■	18	$20.90
$491.83	$55	$103.17	**9.** ■	$22.50
$327.49	**10.** ■	$ 38.47	12	$27.58

Solve.

11. Chair—purchase price: $91.70
Finance charge: ■
Down payment: $10
Number of payments: 12
Monthly payment: $9.17

12. Miniblinds—purchase price: $477.19
Finance charge: $62.50
Down payment: $50
Number of payments: 18
Monthly payment: ■

13. Leonard purchased a boat and outboard motor priced at $962.50. He chose to make 24 payments of $44.03. A finance charge of $194.22 was added. How much did he pay as a down payment?

14. Assif bought a $136.75 television set on the installment plan. He was required to pay 10% down. A finance charge of 14% was put on the remainder, which he was to pay off in 12 payments. How much was each payment?

15. Iris purchased a power lawn mower but forgot how much she paid for it. She knows that she had to pay 10% down and made 12 payments of $24.59 each. After her final payment, she received a notice that she had paid $26.88 in finance charges. What was the original purchase price of the lawn mower?

Challenge: *Figuring Finance Charges*

Mary purchased a video camera for $1,695, a VCR for $475.50, a tripod for $39.95, 12 video tapes for $3.95 each, connector cords for $27.95, and a camera case for $24.50. Where Mary lives, there is a 6.25% sales tax. Mary will pay for the purchases on an installment repayment plan that requires a payment of $114.75 each month for 24 months. How much will Mary pay as a finance charge when all the payments are made?

5-4 Bank Credit Cards

Bank credit cards allow you to charge purchases at many different locations. Some banks charge interest from the date your purchase is recorded. Others give you a 25-day period from the time of billing to pay the amount due. With any charge account, you may pay your account in full each month. Or, you may make payments in installments. A finance charge is added to any unpaid balance in the account. Most banks have a minimum finance charge of $.50 or $1.

When Leona makes a purchase with her credit card, she receives a sales receipt. Once a month, Leona's bank sends her a statement, which lists all the transactions processed for that month. A finance charge is added when a previous bill is not paid in full. Leona's statement also shows the finance charge and new balance.

Finance charges are usually computed using one of two methods: the unpaid balance method or the average daily balance method. The average daily balance method is considered in Lesson 5-5. Leona's bank uses the **unpaid balance method,** in which interest is charged only on the balance remaining in the account.

Skill Review

Knowing how to find a percent of a number will help in computing finance charges.

Find the percent of the number.

1. 9% of $57.34

2. $7\frac{1}{2}$% of $248.75

3. 11.3% of $961.42

4. $15\frac{3}{4}$% of $1,845.16

(For additional help, see page 551.)

EXAMPLE

Paul received the following statement, or monthly account record, for his bank credit card. Find Paul's finance charge and his new balance. There is a minimum finance charge of $.50.

Previous Balance	Finance Rate	Finance Charges	New Purchases	Credits	Payments	Annual Card Fee	New Balance
$22.33	$1\frac{3}{4}$%	_____	$196.08	$11.82	$10	$15	_____

Step 1. Find the finance charge.

$$\textbf{previous balance} \times \textbf{rate} = \textbf{finance charge}$$
$$\$22.33 \qquad \times 1\tfrac{3}{4}\% = \quad \blacksquare$$

Think: $1\frac{3}{4}\% = 1.75\% = 0.0175$

$$
\begin{array}{r}
22.33 \\
\times 0.0175 \\
\hline
11165 \\
15631 \\
2233 \\
\hline
\$.390775
\end{array}
$$
$\$.390775 \rightarrow \$.39$ Round to nearest cent.

Key: $\boxed{\text{C}^{\text{C}}_{\text{E}}}$ 22.33 $\boxed{\times}$ 1.75 $\boxed{\%}$
0.390775
$.39   Round to nearest cent.

Even though the actual finance charge is $.39, Paul's bank charges a minimum finance charge of $.50.

Step 2. Find the new balance.

Start with the previous balance. Add to it the finance charge, new purchases, and any additional charges, such as the annual card fee of $15. From this subtotal subtract all credits and payments.

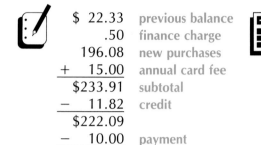

$ 22.33	previous balance
.50	finance charge
196.08	new purchases
+ 15.00	annual card fee
$233.91	subtotal
− 11.82	credit
$222.09	
− 10.00	payment
$212.09	new balance

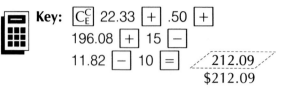

Key: $\boxed{C_E^C}$ 22.33 $\boxed{+}$ .50 $\boxed{+}$ 196.08 $\boxed{+}$ 15 $\boxed{-}$ 11.82 $\boxed{-}$ 10 $\boxed{=}$ ⟋212.09⟋ $212.09

Paul's new balance is $212.09.

Class Exercises

Compute the missing information. Assume there is a minimum finance charge of $.50.

Previous Balance	Finance Rate	Finance Charges	New Purchases	Credits	Payments	New Balance
$100	1.50%	**1.** ■	$120	$20	$80	**2.** ■
$167.92	1.25%	**3.** ■	$239.45	$16.42	$30	**4.** ■
$205.29	1.50%	**5.** ■	**6.** ■	$ 3.15	$30	$273.03
$307.80	1.50%	**7.** ■	$ 40.38	$18.75	**8.** ■	$289.05

9. Which of Exercises 1–8 could be done using mental arithmetic? In which would pencil and paper be appropriate? In which would a calculator help streamline the computation?

EXERCISES

Compute the missing information. Assume that there is a minimum finance charge of $.50.

Previous Balance	Finance Rate	Finance Charges	New Purchases	Credits	Payments	New Balance
$100	1.50%	**1.** ■	$ 30	$10	$20	**2.** ■
$118.30	1.25%	**3.** ■	$ 25.90	$12.45	$15	**4.** ■
$827.94	1.50%	**5.** ■	$282.49	$78.51	**6.** ■	$919.34
$124.75	1.50%	**7.** ■	**8.** ■	$ 5.98	$20	$100.64

Solve.

9. Melba Haynes
Previous balance: $250
Monthly rate: 1.50%
Finance charge for month: ■

10. Merle Lowles
Previous balance: $163.75
Monthly rate: 1.075%
Finance charge for month: ■

11. Verna's bank requires a minimum monthly payment of 10% (rounded to the nearest dollar) of the new balance. Her account is shown below. First complete the statement, and then determine the amount of her minimum payment.

Previous Balance	Finance Rate	Finance Charges	New Purchases	Credits	Payments	New Balance
$62.50	1.25%		$107.35	$50.39	$10	

12. Hogan's account statement was partially destroyed. The piece below is all he has left. He knows that his bank charges a 2% monthly interest rate. Using the information that remains, determine his previous balance and his finance charges.

New Purchases	Credits	Payments	New Balance
$157.28	$39.85	$65	$312.02

13. Explain how mental arithmetic can be used to find the answer to Exercise 9.

Consumer Note: *Credit Cards*

Credit cards provide an easy way to "buy now and pay later." You can find brochures explaining credit card requirements and terms at banks, retail stores, and restaurants. In addition, you can write to credit card companies for information, or they may send information to you because you have a good credit rating.

You should compare credit card terms and understand them before you sign any agreement. In general, creditors must tell you:

• their annual percentage rate (APR)

• their method of calculating finances charges

• when the finance charges begin to be charged to your account

Shopping with credit cards is easy, but it is also easy to overspend. Keep track of your credit card charges and stay within your monthly budget. Remember to pay your bills promptly to keep up your good credit rating and to avoid high finance charges.

One final tip: keep a list of all your credit card numbers in case of loss or theft and keep a good record of your purchases, returns, and payments.

5-5 Charge Accounts

Many stores offer charge cards similar to bank credit cards, except that you may use a store's charge card only in that particular store. Stores usually require a finance charge to be paid on the unpaid balance in the account. When you have an unpaid balance, a store may compute interest on that unpaid balance. Or, they may use the **average daily balance method,** in which interest is charged on your average daily balance.

Eric opened a charge account with the Ace Department Store. Eric does not have to pay an annual fee or minimum finance charge. Ace computes monthly finance charges by the average daily balance method.

EXAMPLE

The store used the following balances to find the finance charge and new balance for Eric's account. Use the balances and the account summary to find the finance charge and new balance.

Daily Balance	Number of Days	Balance × Number of Days
$330	6/1–6/12 = 12 da	$3,960
$358.64	6/13–6/18 = 6 da	$2,151.84
$293.64	6/19–6/24 = 6 da	$1,761.84
$339.62	6/25–6/30 = 6 da	$2,037.72
Totals:	30 da	$9,911.40

Summary of Account						
Previous Balance	Finance Rate	Finance Charges	New Purchases	Credits	Payments	New Balance
$330	2.0%	____	$74.62	$.00	$65	____

Step 1. Find the average daily balance.

$$\begin{array}{ccccc} \text{sum of} & & \text{number} & & \text{average} \\ \text{daily balances} & \div & \text{of days} & = & \text{daily balance} \\ \$9,911.40 & \div & 30 & = & \$330.38 \end{array}$$

Step 2. Compute the finance charge. The rate is 2%.

Think: 2% = 0.02

$$\begin{array}{ccccc} \textbf{average daily balance} & \times & \textbf{monthly rate} & = & \textbf{finance charge} \\ \$330.38 & \times & 0.02 & = & \$6.6076 \rightarrow \$6.61 \end{array}$$ Round to nearest cent.

Skill Review

To compute finance charges based on the average daily balance, it is helpful to know how to divide decimals by whole numbers.

Divide. Round your answers to the nearest cent.

1. $256.48 ÷ 30

2. $189.54 ÷ 28

3. $396.89 ÷ 31

4. $1,075.95 ÷ 30

(For additional help, see page 546.)

Step 3. Find the new balance.

previous balance	+	new charges	−	credits and payments	=	new balance
$330	+	(6.61 + 74.62)	−	$65	=	$346.23

Eric's new balance is $346.23.

Class Exercises

Find the average daily balance.

Sum of Daily Balances	Number of Days	Average Daily Balance
$4,500	30	**1.** ■
$3,825.30	30	**2.** ■
$8,525.25	27	**3.** ■

Complete the following table.

Daily Balance	Number of Days	Daily Balance × Number of Days
$145.19	7	**4.** ■
$216.68	7	**5.** ■
$197.96	6	**6.** ■
$162.46	10	**7.** ■
Totals	**8.** ■	**9.** ■
Average daily balance	**10.** ■	

Use the average daily balance above and the following chart to compute the interest due and the new balance.

Previous Balance	Finance Rate	Finance Charge	New Purchases	Credits	Payments	New Balance
$145.19	1.75%	**11.** ■	$71.49	$18.72	$35.50	**12.** ■

EXERCISES

Find the average daily balance.

Sum of Daily Balances	Number of Days	Average Daily Balance
$ 3,900	30	**1.** ■
$ 2,699.10	30	**2.** ■
$18,751.59	33	**3.** ■

Complete the following chart.

Daily Balance	Number of Days	Daily Balance × Number of Days
$ 88.54	12	**4.** ■
$143.02	8	**5.** ■
$355.10	6	**6.** ■
$278.54	4	**7.** ■
Totals	**8.** ■	**9.** ■
Average daily balance	**10.** ■	

Use the average daily balance above and the following chart to compute the interest due and the new balance.

Previous Balance	Finance Rate	Finance Charge	New Purchases	Credits	Payments	New Balance
$288.10	1.5%	**11.** ■	$138.09	$.00	$200	**12.** ■

Solve.

13. Nolan Brown
Average daily balance: $200.50
Monthly rate: 1.5%
Finance charge for month: ■

14. Marguerita Aspen
Average daily balance: $321.60
Monthly rate: 1.25%
Finance charge for month: ■

15. On August 10, Gina charged a pair of slacks for $29.38. She made a payment of $75 on August 19. Her average daily balance for August was $220.54. How much did her account show at the beginning of August?

Reading in Mathematics: *Vocabulary*

Use the words listed below to complete the given sentences.

average daily
balance method

daily balance
finance charge

finance rate
new purchases

1. When your charge statement comes, it will show the _____ , or the charge on unpaid amounts of your bill.

2. The rate at which a store charges interest on unpaid balances is called the _____ .

3. Each day, the store computes the _____ , or the amount you owe the store that day.

4. The _____ is a method in which interest is charged on your average daily balance.

Career
Retail Salesperson

Manufactured goods reach the consumer through a "chain of sales," from manufacturer to wholesaler or distributor to retailer. Personal services, such as income tax preparation and hair styling, are sold as well.

Mathematical knowledge and skills are essential, especially in **retail selling.** Math is used in computing sales taxes, handling and shipping charges, finance charges, and discounts.

Profile of a retailing person. Many of the jobs in retailing do not require special training, but a high school education is certainly helpful. An interest in people and an outgoing personality are essential.

The retailing environment. Most work of this kind is performed indoors, but some retail establishments are outdoors. Retailing is a people-oriented environment. In addition to customers, salespeople must work with other salespersons, stock clerks, delivery persons, accounting personnel, and supervisors.

All in a day's work. Chris worked in Cohen's Department Store, which was having a storewide sale. Everything was reduced 20%, with items in the electronics, sporting goods, and appliance departments reduced an extra 10% if they originally cost over $50. All sales were cash and carry, except for large items, which had a surcharge of $2 each for delivery. Sales tax for all items except food was 6%.

1. What is the sale price of a clock originally selling for $15?

2. Find the sale price of a sofa originally selling for $680.

3. Chris sold 3 clock radios originally priced at $28.50. What was the total amount of the bill, including tax?

4. Chris sold a television set originally priced at $210. Find the total amount of the bill, including tax and delivery.

5. A customer bought two microwave ovens originally priced at $295 each. Find the total amount of the bill, including tax and delivery.

6. A customer had $84 to spend on a sleeping bag. What was the original price of the best sleeping bag the customer could afford if she allowed $5 for sales tax?

7. Mario had $100. Could he afford to purchase a small stereo originally priced at $119.99 if he did not have it delivered?

5-6 Comparing Credit Plans

If you plan to finance a purchase from a store, you should compare credit plans to find the best one. For instance, the store might offer an installment plan, or you might be able to borrow the money or use your charge card. One way to compare plans is to compare the **annual percentage rate (APR),** or yearly rate of interest of the plans. You can use a table like the one below to find APR.

Number of Payments	APR for Various Amounts of Interest per $100								
	14.25%	14.50%	15.00%	15.50%	16.00%	16.50%	17.00%	17.25%	17.50%
6	4.20	4.27	4.42	4.57	4.72	4.87	5.02	5.09	5.17
12	7.89	8.03	8.31	8.59	8.88	9.16	9.45	9.59	9.73
18	11.66	11.87	12.29	12.72	13.14	13.57	13.99	14.21	14.42
24	15.51	15.80	16.37	16.94	17.51	18.09	18.66	18.95	19.24
30	19.45	19.81	20.54	21.26	21.99	22.72	23.45	23.81	24.18

Denise wants to purchase a couch priced at $479. She could charge it on her charge card or buy it from the store on the installment plan. If Denise bought the couch through the store's credit plan, she would have to pay 10% down and then make 12 monthly payments of $39.22.

EXAMPLE 1

What is the APR on the installment plan through the store?

Step 1. Find the amount borrowed.

Hidden Question: What is 10% of $479?
$479 × 0.1 = $47.90

purchase price − down payment = amount borrowed
$479 − $47.90 = $431.10

Step 2. Find the finance charge.

Hidden Question: What are the total payments?
$39.22 × 12 = $470.64

total payments − amount borrowed = finance charge
$470.64 − $431.10 = $39.54

Step 3. Find the apparent rate of interest. Round to the nearest ten-thousandth.

finance charge ÷ amount borrowed = apparent rate
$39.54 ÷ $431.10 = 0.0917

Step 4. Find the interest paid per $100.

apparent rate × $100 = interest paid per $100
$$0.0917 \times \$100 = \$9.17$$

Step 5. Use the table on page 180 to find the APR. Look across the row for 12 payments to find the number closest to $9.17. It is $9.16. Move up the column to find the APR, 16.50%.

The APR is 16.5%.

EXAMPLE 2

Denise's credit card charges 1.3% interest per month on the unpaid balance. Which credit plan has the better APR?

Step 1. Find the APR of the credit card.

monthly rate × 12 = APR
$$1.3\% \times 12 = 15.6\%$$

Step 2. Compare credit plans.
The APR on the installment plan, 16.5%, is higher than the APR on the credit card, 15.6%.

The credit card has the better APR.

Class Exercises

Complete the table.

Monthly Interest Rate	APR	Monthly Interest Rate	APR
2%	1. ■	1.5%	2. ■
2.4%	3. ■	1.25%	4. ■

Find the APR. Use the table on page 180.

Cost	Down Payment	Number of Installments	Monthly Installment	APR
$375	0	12	$34.24	5. ■
$236.78	15%	6	$34.95	6. ■

EXERCISES

Complete the table.

Monthly Interest Rate	APR	Monthly Interest Rate	APR
1%	1. ■	1.45%	2. ■
0.9%	3. ■	1.75%	4. ■

Find the APR. Use the table on page 180.

Cost	Down Payment	Number of Installments	Monthly Installment	APR
$650	$25	24	$31	5. ■
$400	10%	12	$32.92	6. ■

Solve.

7. Maryanne bought a stereo for $1,645. She could use her credit card, which charges 1.3% per month on the unpaid balance; or she could borrow the money from her credit union, where the APR is $12\frac{1}{2}$%. Which credit plan has the lower APR?

8. Roberto wants a refrigerator costing $879. He could use his credit card, which charges 1.45% per month on the unpaid balance; or he could pay 15% down and $46.96 per month for 18 months. Which plan has the lower APR?

9. Liam bought a set of golf clubs for $228.50. He paid 10% down and paid the rest in 18 monthly installments. The store added a finance charge of $28.50. Find his monthly payments and the APR on the amount borrowed. Is this rate better than what he would have paid using a bank credit card with an APR of 21%?

10. In the example in this lesson, what are some of the factors Denise might consider in choosing a borrowing plan other than the APR? Discuss your answers with your classmates.

Using a Calculator: Finding APR

You can use your calculator to do the computations for finding the interest paid per $100. Then you can use the table on page 180 to find the APR. In Example 1, find the interest paid as follows:

Key: $\boxed{C_E^C}$ 479 $\boxed{M+}$ $\boxed{\times}$ 10 $\boxed{\%}$ $\boxed{M-}$ $\boxed{M_C^R}$ $\boxed{M_C^R}$ $\boxed{M-}$ Amount borrowed
39.22 $\boxed{\times}$ 12 $\boxed{M+}$ $\boxed{M_C^R}$ finance charge
$\boxed{\div}$ 431.1 $\boxed{\times}$ 100 $\boxed{=}$ 9.17188
$9.17   Round to nearest cent.

From the table, the APR is 16.5%

Use your calculator to help find the APR for each case.

Cost	Down Payment	No. of Inst.	Monthly Inst.
$193.50	10%	18	$10.82
$525	$25	12	$45.12

Computer:
Variables and Arithmetic

Brandon wrote a BASIC program to compute sales tax. The tax rate in his state is 6% (0.06). He gave the computer this number (0.06) and named it R. He can recall the tax rate by using its name. A number or any set of characters stored in the computer is called a *variable*. Variables that are numbers are given names consisting of a letter, two letters, or a letter followed by a digit. Variables that consist of letters or a string of letters and other characters are called *string variables*. A $ is annexed to the name of a string variable. String variables are used to store words rather than numbers. The *value* of a variable can be set using a statement with an = symbol in it:

    70 T = 25 + 15   or   80 A$ = "STRAWBERRIES"

The value of a variable can be changed as needed during a program. Here is Brandon's program.

10 HOME	Clears the screen.
20 R = .06	Assigns tax rate, 0.06, to the variable, R.
30 PRINT "ITEM", "COST", "SALES TX"	Prints the heading.
40 A$ = "SHIRTS"	Assigns the value "SHIRTS" to the variable, A$. The quotation marks are required.
50 C = 17.95	Assigns the cost, 17.95, to the variable C.
60 PRINT A$, C, C*R	Prints the value of A$ (SHIRTS) and C (17.95). Computes and prints the tax, C * R.
70 A$ = "GLOVES"	Assigns the value "GLOVES" to the variable, A$. This replaces the old value "SHIRTS".
80 C = 9.45	Assigns the cost, 9.45, to the variable C.
90 PRINT A$, C, C*R	Prints the value of A$ (GLOVES) and C (9.45). Computes and prints the tax, C * R.
200 END	Tells the computer to end the program.

Enter the program into your computer and RUN it.

EXERCISES

1. What program line would have to be changed if the sales tax were 5% instead of 6%?

2. Make the change suggested in Exercise 1 by retyping one line. RUN the program and observe the change in output.

3. Using the program lines as guides, add three lines numbered 100, 110, and 120 to find the sales tax on a pair of shoes that cost $38.95.

4. Using the program lines as guides, add three lines numbered 130, 140, and 150 to find the sales tax on a jacket that cost $19.46.

Decision Making:
Comparison Shopping

"The music was great!" Joe remarked, as he was leaving.

"My new stereo system," said Jennifer. "This is the first party I've had since I bought it. I'm really pleased with it."

Later, Joe thought about Jennifer's stereo system. He had always liked music. His stereo was a small one that didn't really do justice to his tapes. Joe wanted to give good parties and he reasoned that, since the music Jennifer played on her stereo had helped make her party fun, it would do the same for his parties.

Joe decided he could afford a good system like Jennifer's, since Jennifer's job paid about the same as his, and, if she could afford such a system, so could he.

USING ANALOGIES

In deciding to buy a stereo system Joe reasoned the way many people do. He reasoned by analogy. He thought, "Jennifer's new stereo system is related to her party in the same way that my new stereo system will be related to the party I want to give." He reasoned that in both cases it would be the stereo system that made a good party.

Answer the following question.

1. Do you think that Joe reasoned correctly? Will a particular stereo system guarantee a good party? Why or why not?

PITFALLS IN USING ANALOGIES

In the analogy Joe used, he compared relationships that he saw as similar. If the relationships expressed are really not similar or if the differences in the situations are greater than the similarities, then the analogy would lead him to draw an incorrect conclusion. For example, if Joe's parties are very different from Jennifer's party, then getting a stereo system like Jennifer's may not affect Joe's parties. If Joe is using part of his salary to pay for a new car and Jennifer is not, then Joe will not have as much of his salary available for a stereo system as Jennifer does, even though they receive similar pay.

Answer the following questions.

2. Joe's parties could not be exactly like Jennifer's party. What might be some differences between Jennifer's party and parties Joe might have?

3. What might be some similarities between Joe's and Jennifer's parties that would make his analogy correct?

STATING ANALOGIES FORMALLY

Analogies are usually stated formally. The formal way of stating the analogy upon which Joe's reasoning is based is

stereo system :   party   : : stereo system : party
(Jennifer's)   (Jennifer's)   (Joe's)   (Joe's)

This may be read, "Jennifer's stereo system is related to Jennifer's party as Joe's stereo system is related to Joe's party."

Answer the following questions.

4. Joe reasoned by analogy that he could afford the kind of stereo system Jennifer bought. Write in formal terms the analogy upon which this reasoning is based.

5. What is the relationship being compared in the analogy described in Question 4?

6. Give an example of a time when you reasoned by analogy in deciding to buy something.

7. Write in formal terms the analogy you used in the situation you described in Question 6.

GETTING THE FACTS

Having decided to buy a stereo system, Joe planned how he would proceed. He realized that several decisions were involved.

• Deciding what components of a stereo system he wants and which brand he prefers for each component of the system.

• Deciding where to buy the stereo system.

• Deciding upon a method of payment.

Joe began by gathering all the information he could find about stereo systems:

• what parts are necessary in a system and what parts are optional

• what manufacturers make products of the best quality

• what prices he could expect to pay

To get this information he talked with his friends and listened to their stereo systems. He read advertisements. He also consulted reports by consumer organizations about the performance of components made by various manufacturers. He also shopped in the stores to see what systems were available and to listen to their sound.

Joe planned to include a receiver, an amplifier, four speakers, a tape deck, and a CD player in his stereo system. He tentatively decided to get a Lucidtone receiver and amplifier, Bellsound speakers, and a Sonovox tape deck and CD player.

Reports by consumer organizations had been particularly helpful in deciding about the CD player. *Consumer Concerns* had rated Sonovox as best and Lucidtone second. Based on this report Joe had decided he would buy the Sonovox CD player.

Answer the following question.

8. State in formal terms the analogy upon which Joe's decision about the Sonovox CD player was based.

BUYING THE SYSTEM

Next Joe needed to decide where to buy these items. Gordner's, a discount electronics store, advertised the items Joe wanted at the lowest prices. However, Joe had once bought a portable television set from Gordner's. He remembered that it had broken down soon after it was purchased and that he had had considerable difficulty getting Gordner's to repair it. Recalling this experience, Joe decided against buying his stereo system at Gordner's. When two friends recommended Green's Music Corner, Joe decided to buy his system at Green's.

Answer the following questions.

9. Write the analogy Joe used in deciding not to buy his set at Gordner's.

10. Write the analogy Joe used in deciding to buy his set at Green's.

CHOOSING SPEAKERS

Joe was pleased with the service at Green's. The salesperson was able to answer his questions, and the prices were only slightly higher than those advertised at the discount store. Joe spent a long time listening to the quality of the sound with each kind of speaker. He recalled buying a chair, which appeared different in color at home in the light of his living room than it had in the store. Joe wondered if the high fidelity he heard in the listening room at the store would be duplicated in his own house. When he raised this question with the salesperson, he was assured that he could return any component of the stereo system with which he was not satisfied within certain time limits. Joe decided on medium-priced Bellsound speakers.

Answer the following question.

11. To what extent is buying a chair analogous to buying stereo speakers?

FINANCING THE PURCHASE

When Joe had selected all the components of his stereo system, the salesperson computed the cost, which came to $1,985 plus 5% sales tax. Joe would either have to pay the whole sum within one month or agree to pay $200 down and 12 monthly installments of $183.

Answer the following questions.

12. What is the total price of Joe's stereo system, including the sales tax?

13. How much finance charge will Joe pay if he chooses the installment plan?

Joe had saved $1,950 and knew he could add $135 to that from paychecks he would be getting during the next month. Besides, he remembered that when he had been paying for a camera in installments, he was required to pay a finance charge. So, Joe decided to pay the whole sum within one month after his purchase.

Answer the following questions.

14. When might using credit be a good idea even if Joe disliked paying interest?

15. How did Joe use analogical reasoning to help him decide to pay for the stereo system in one sum?

16. Construct an analogy about credit cards.

17. Explain how you thought in constructing an analogy about credit cards.

DECIDE FOR YOURSELF

Suppose you want to buy a stereo system. What facts will you need in deciding what to buy? What analogies might you use? Summarize how you, and Joe, went about deciding what to buy.

Chapter 5 Review

VOCABULARY

annual percentage rate (APR)
average daily balance method
bank credit cards

finance charge
installment plans
sales receipt

sales tax
unpaid balance method

For Exercises 1–8, select the words that complete each statement.

1. _____ is a percentage of the total sales receipt collected on behalf of the local, state, or county government.

2. A _____ shows the total amount paid for an item, including sales tax.

3. Stores extend credit to a buyer through _____ .

4. A _____ is the interest a store charges for buying on the installment plan.

5. _____ allow you to purchase items at different locations and charge them to your account.

6. The _____ charges interest only on the balance remaining in the account.

7. With the _____ , interest is charged on the average daily balance on your charge card.

8. The yearly rate of interest on a charge card is called the _____ .

SKILLS
Multiply.

9. $13.45 × 2

10. $30.20 × 5

11. $159.21 × 3

Find the percent of the number.

12. 8% of $32.25

13. $6\frac{1}{2}$% of $188.50

14. 12.4% of $752.12

Divide. Round to the nearest cent.

15. $187.15 ÷ 12

16. $275.60 ÷ 30

17. $1,015.88 ÷ 18

CONSUMER TOPICS
Solve.

18. Rob purchased a lawn mower for $325.99. How much sales tax did he have to pay if the tax rate was 6%?

19. Jennifer Williams bought a sweater on sale for $29.57. In her state, the sales tax rate is 5%. Determine her after-tax total.

20. Mia purchased a hammer for $12.85, a paint brush for $3.79, and a paint scraper for $4.59. The sales tax was 5%. What was the total purchase price?

21. In Problem 20, Mia gave the salesperson a $20 bill and a $10 bill. How much change did she receive?

22. Rosa bought a leather sofa on the installment plan. The purchase price was $1,600. She paid $400 down and made 12 monthly payments of $112.30. Find the finance charge she paid.

23. Mark bought a desk for his home office on the installment plan. The purchase price was $850. He paid $200 down. He paid off the remaining amount in equal monthly installments over a period of 8 months. The finance charge was $117. Find out how much he paid each month.

24. Purchase price: $192.50
Finance charge: ■
Down payment: $15
Number of payments: 12
Monthly payment: $17

25. Purchase price: $367.85
Finance charge: $47.68
Down payment: ■
Number of payments: 18
Monthly payment: $20.31

26. Rusty had an outstanding balance on his credit card account of $379.85 for purchases he made. Find the finance charge if it was 1.5% per month.

27. Marsha Stewart
Previous balance: $270
Monthly rate: 1.5%
Finance charge for month: ■

28. Carl Larsen
Previous balance: $115.91
Monthly rate: 1.25%
Finance charge for month: ■

29. Which of the credit plans in Exercises 27 and 28 has the lower APR?

30. Sum of daily balances: $6,835.44
Number of days: 31
Average daily balance: ■

31. Compute the finance charge (at 2%) for one month on an average daily balance of $345.71.

32. Monthly interest rate: 1.35%
APR: ■

33. Monthly interest rate: 1.6%
APR: ■

Chapter 5 Test

Solve.

1. Purchase: $18.95
   Sales tax: 6%
   Total: ■

2. Purchase: $169.59
   Sales tax: 5%
   Total: ■

3. Purchase: $345.50
   Sales tax: 7%
   Total: ■

4. Scott purchased a toothbrush for $1.39, cologne for $9.55, and shampoo for $2.79. The sales tax was $.69. He gave the clerk a $20 bill. How much change did he receive?

5. Rhonda purchased a winter coat priced at $265 on the installment plan. She made 12 payments of $19. A finance charge of $28 was added. How much was her down payment?

6. Justine bought an $800 dining room table on the installment plan. She was required to pay 10% down. A finance charge of 15% was put on the remainder, which she had 12 months to pay off. How much was her monthly payment?

7. Peg received a statement for her bank credit card showing a previous balance of $129.62. She had made one new purchase of $18.25. If there is a finance charge of 1.5% per month, what will the charge be if she does not make a payment this month?

8. Jed Owens
   Previous
   balance: $361.85
   Monthly rate: 1.6%
   Finance charge: ■

9. Sum of daily
   balances: $5,241.48
   Number of days: 30
   Average daily
   balance: ■

10. Find the finance charge (at 1.75%) for one month on the average daily balance in Problem 9.

11. Average daily
    balance: $178.52
    Monthly rate: 1.5%
    Finance charge for
    month: ■

12. Average daily
    balance: $202.12
    Monthly rate: 1.25%
    Finance charge for
    month: ■

13. Average daily
    balance: $300.60
    Monthly rate: 1.75%
    Finance charge for
    month: ■

14. A bank credit card has a monthly finance charge of 1.5%. Find the APR.

15. Joey bought a snowblower costing $549.90. He could charge it on his store credit card, which charges 1.25% per month on the unpaid balance, or he could borrow the money from his bank, where the APR is 14%. Which of the two credit plans has the lower APR?

Cumulative Mixed Review

Select the letter corresponding to the correct answer.

1. Webster earns $7.50 per hour and time-and-a-half for all hours he works over 40 hours. Find his weekly pay if he worked 47 hours.
   - **a.** $352.50
   - **b.** $385.50
   - **c.** $378.75
   - **d.** $375.25

2. Jill bought a cassette player for $29.95. The sales tax rate was 5%. What was her after-tax total?
   - **a.** $31.65
   - **b.** $31.45
   - **c.** $32.45
   - **d.** $31.44

3. Melissa borrowed $1,200 at 13.5% interest for 3 months. How much does she have to repay under a single-payment plan?
   - **a.** $1,200
   - **b.** $162
   - **c.** $1,362
   - **d.** $1,240.50

4. Alana earns $18,350 per year. She pays $8\frac{1}{2}$% of her gross income in state and local taxes. How much is withheld from each paycheck for these taxes if she is paid semimonthly?
   - **a.** $1,559.75
   - **b.** $129.98
   - **c.** $64.99
   - **d.** $764.58

5. Sean makes 4 payments a year of $250.98 for life insurance; 2 payments of $388.94 for real estate taxes; 2 payments of $445.20 a year for auto insurance; and 12 payments a year of $90.32 for health insurance. What is the total of his annual fixed expenses for these items?
   - **a.** $1,175.44
   - **b.** $3,756.04
   - **c.** $2,350.88
   - **d.** $2,756.94

6. Martin purchased software for his computer for $79. The sales tax was $4.74. He gave the salesperson a $100 bill. How much change did he receive?
   - **a.** $16.26
   - **b.** $16.36
   - **c.** $15.26
   - **d.** $17.26

7. Find the balance in Clara's account after $2\frac{1}{2}$ years if her bank paid 6.5% simple interest on her deposit of $8,000.
   - **a.** $9,300
   - **b.** $520
   - **c.** $8,520
   - **d.** $1,300

8. Jack has an outstanding balance of $423.81 on his bank credit card. Find the finance charge for the month if it is calculated at 1.5%.
   - **a.** $63.57
   - **b.** $6.36
   - **c.** $.64
   - **d.** $6.35

9. Sandra estimates her expenditures for clothing as follows: April, $354; May, $33.88; June, $132.98; and July, $202. What is her estimated average monthly expense for clothing?
   - **a.** $722.86
   - **b.** $240.95
   - **c.** $60.24
   - **d.** $180.72

10. Ray has an account with his local department store. His daily balance for the first 12 days of September was $162.58. His daily balance for the next 7 days was $185.13; for the last 11 days, it was $132.44. What was his finance charge if the store used a rate of 2%?
    - **a.** $.32
    - **b.** $156.79
    - **c.** $3.14
    - **d.** $.97

CHAPTER 6
Buying Food

Kirby is buying groceries for a 4-day camping trip he and three friends are taking. He is trying to decide what food items to buy and how much food will be needed without going above the group's budget.

- What kinds of food would you advise him to buy?

- How can he figure out how much food will be needed?

- What are some ways he can save money on the groceries?

If you were going on a similar trip and had allotted a fixed amount of money per person, how would you go about preparing your shopping list?

6-1 Nutrition

Nutrients are substances the body needs. Of these nutrients, *protein* builds tissue; *carbohydrates* and *fat* supply energy; certain *minerals* and *vitamins* help to maintain good health. The energy supplied by food is measured in **calories.** You can use the labels on food packages to help choose nutritious foods and keep track of the calories you are consuming.

EXAMPLE 1

While Duane was eating breakfast, he noticed the nutrition label on the Kriskit's box. Duane had poured $1\frac{1}{2}$ ounces of cereal in his bowl. How many calories were there in his serving of cereal?

Since 1 ounce is 1 serving, $1\frac{1}{2}$ ounces is $1\frac{1}{2}$ servings.

calories per serving × servings consumed = total calories

$$110 \qquad \times \qquad 1\tfrac{1}{2} \qquad = \qquad 165$$

Duane had 165 calories in his serving of cereal.

The cereal label gives Duane the amount of each nutrient as a percentage of the **U.S. Recommended Daily Allowance** (%U.S. RDA). The U.S. RDA is the approximate amount of proteins, vitamins, and minerals a person needs each day. The U.S. RDA figures for some of the nutrients and calories are listed below:

KRISKIT'S CEREAL NUTRITION INFORMATION	
Serving size:	Servings per package:
1 oz	12
Calories per serving	110
Protein per serving	2 g
Carbohydrates per serving ..	25 g
Fat per serving	0 g

PERCENTAGES OF U.S. RECOMMENDED DAILY ALLOWANCES (% U.S. RDA) per serving:

Protein	4
Vitamin A	25
Thiamin	25
Riboflavin	25

U.S. Recommended Daily Allowances				
	Girls (14–18)	**Boys (14–18)**	**Women (23–50)**	**Men (23–50)**
Calories	2,400	2,600	1,800	3,000
Protein (g)	46	56	44	56
Vitamin A (IU)	800	1,000	800	1,000
Thiamin (mg)	1.1	1.4	1.0	1.4
Riboflavin (mg)	1.3	1.7	1.2	1.6
(g) grams (IU) international units	(mg) milligrams	1 g = 1,000,000 IU		

EXAMPLE 2

Margo had $\frac{1}{2}$ cup of peas for dinner. What percentage of her U.S. RDA of thiamin did this represent if there is 0.22 mg of thiamin per half cup of peas and Margo is 15 years old?

Problem Solving Strategy: Finding information.
Use the table above to find the U.S. RDA for thiamin for a girl 14–18. It is 1.1 mg.

$$\begin{array}{c} \text{mg of thiamin} \\ \text{in serving} \end{array} \div \begin{array}{c} \text{recommended mg} \\ \text{of thiamin} \end{array} = \% \text{ U.S. RDA}$$

$$0.22 \quad\div\quad 1.1 \quad=\quad \blacksquare$$

$$1.1\overline{)0.22}^{\,0.2\ \to\ 20\%}$$

The serving represents about 20% of her U.S. RDA of thiamin.

Class Exercises

Complete the table to find the number of calories consumed.

Calories per Serving	Servings Consumed	Calories Consumed
188	$1\frac{1}{2}$	1. ∎
35	3	2. ∎
325	4	3. ∎
145	10	4. ∎
178	1.25	5. ∎

Use the table on page 194 to complete the following table.

Person	Item	Amount Provided by Serving	%U.S. RDA
17-y-old girl	Thiamin	0.2 mg	6. ∎
23-y-old man	Protein	10 g	7. ∎
14-y-old boy	Vitamin A	700 IU	8. ∎
48-y-old woman	Calories	500	9. ∎

EXERCISES

Complete the table to find the number of calories consumed.

Calories per Serving	Servings Consumed	Calories Consumed
140	2	1. ∎
85	3	2. ∎
125	1.5	3. ∎
205	$\frac{1}{2}$	4. ∎

Use the table on page 194 to complete the following table.

Person	Item	Amount Provided by Serving	%U.S. RDA
15-y-old girl	Calories	300	**5.** ▪
25-y-old man	Thiamin	0.24 mg	**6.** ▪
24-y-old woman	Riboflavin	0.18 mg	**7.** ▪
18-y-old boy	Protein	63 g	**8.** ▪

9. Which of Exercises 1–8 could be done mentally? In which would pencil and paper be appropriate? Which could best be done by using a calculator?

Solve.

10. Kevin McLeod
15 years old
1,400 calories
%U.S. RDA: ▪

11. Jennifer Chin
18 years old
600 IU vitamin A
%U.S. RDA: ▪

12. Ellen Curtis
49 years old
0.4 mg riboflavin
%U.S. RDA: ▪

13. Mario, who is 16, ate 3 slices of pizza, each containing 145 calories, a glass of milk containing 160 calories, and a salad containing 163 calories. What percent of his U.S. RDA of calories did he consume?

14. Explain how you would use a calculator to help streamline the computation in Problem 13.

15. Elaine, who is 45, bought a box of cereal. Each 1-ounce serving contained 0.3 milligram of riboflavin. She ate $\frac{3}{4}$ ounce of the cereal. What percent of her U.S. RDA of riboflavin did she consume?

16. Why do you think calorie and nutrient requirements are different for young people and older people? For men and women? What kinds of factors might affect your total calorie requirements?

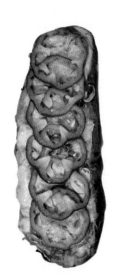

Reading in Math: *Vocabulary*

Unscramble the words in the sentences to make true statements.

1. IOCLSERA measure the energy supplied by foods.

2. You need NPTORIE to help build tissue.

3. You can use food labels to help choose UTTRNISIUO foods.

4. DRABCHYTOSEAR help supply energy.

6-2 Planning Meals

A **balanced diet** gives you the nutrients you need each day. To plan a balanced diet, you need to select foods from each of the four main food groups.

Group 1: Meats, eggs, poultry, fish, dried beans
Group 2: Milk, cheese, milk products
Group 3: Grains, cereals, rice, bread, spaghetti, cake
Group 4: Fruits and vegetables

A well-planned meal contains foods from each food group. In the course of a day, you should have the following:

2 servings from group 1   3-4 servings from group 2
4 servings from group 3   4 servings from group 4

In addition to planning a well-rounded and nutritious diet, you should be concerned about the number of calories you eat each day.

Skill Review

To find the number of calories in your diet, it is helpful if you can add whole numbers.

Find each sum.

1. 330 + 58 + 110

2. 115 + 280 + 350

3. 248 + 110 + 55 + 186

4. 375 + 548 + 720 + 110

5. 76 + 128 + 98 + 326

(For additional help, see page 542.)

EXAMPLE 1

For lunch, Jeanette had 6 ounces of fried chicken, an 8-ounce glass of milk, and an apple. How many calories were in her lunch?

Problem Solving Strategy: Finding information.
Use the table of calories to find the information needed to solve the problem.

Food	Unit	Calories	Protein (g)	Fat (g)	Vitamin A (IU)	Thiamin (mg)	Riboflavin (mg)
Apple, raw	1	70	0.3	0.7	50	0.04	0.02
Beans, green	1 c	30	2	0.3	680	0.09	0.11
Bread, white	slice	70	2	1	0	0.1	0.06
Butter	1 tbsp	100	0	12	430	0	0
Cheese, cheddar	1 oz	115	7	9	300	0.01	0.11
Chicken, fried	3 oz	140	23	5	60	0.04	0.15
Egg, fried	1	85	5	6	290	0.03	0.13
Hamburger	3 oz	245	21	17	30	0.07	0.18
Milk, whole	8 oz	160	9	9	350	0.07	0.41
Orange juice	6 oz	90	1	0	400	0.18	0.02
Pizza, cheese	slice	145	6	4	230	0.16	0.18
Potato, baked	1	145	4	0	0	0.15	0.07

Source: U.S. Department of Agriculture

Estimate: $2 \times 140 + 160 + 70 = \blacksquare \rightarrow 2 \times 150 + 150 + 50 = 500$

$$
\begin{array}{r}
280 \quad \textbf{140} \times \textbf{2} \\
160 \\
+ \ 70 \\
\hline
510
\end{array}
$$

The answer 510 is reasonably close to the estimate 500 and is a sensible answer. Jeanette had 510 calories at lunch.

EXAMPLE 2

In planning dinner for himself, Mark looked over the foods he had on hand and arranged them by food groups:

Group 1: meat loaf   Group 2: milk, cheese
Group 3: bread, crackers   Group 4: salad, peas, potatoes

How many different meals could Mark plan from the food he had on hand if he had one food from each group?

To find how many different meals he could make, multiply the numbers of items in each group.

number of foods in group 1	×	number of foods in group 2	×	number of foods in group 3	×	number of foods in group 4	=	total possible meals
1	×	2	×	2	×	3	=	12

Mark could plan 12 different meals.

Class Exercises

Use the lunch menu shown and the table on page 197 to answer Exercises 1–4. You will also need to use the table on page 194. Use the U.S. RDA for a 17-year-old girl.

1. How many calories are in the meal?

2. How many grams of fat are in the meal?

3. What percent of the U.S. RDA of protein is in the meal?

4. What percent of the U.S. RDA of vitamin A is in the meal?

5. Using the breakfast menu from Harry's Diner, how many different breakfasts are there if each breakfast consists of one food from each group?

EXERCISES

Use the dinner menu shown and the table on page 197 to answer Exercises 1–6. You will also need to use the table on page 194. Use the U.S. RDA for an 18-year-old boy.

1. How many grams of fat are in the meal?

2. How many calories are in the meal?

3. How many grams of protein are in the meal?

4. What percentage of the U.S. RDA of vitamin A is in the meal?

5. What percentage of the U.S. RDA of protein is in the meal?

6. What percentage of the U.S. RDA of calories is in the meal?

7. How many different meals can be made from the available foods at the right if each meal consists of one food from each group?

Group 1: tuna, ham

Group 2: milk, cottage cheese

Group 3: rice, noodles, spaghetti

Group 4: potatoes, green beans

Available foods

8. 45-year-old man
2 fried eggs
Percentage of U.S. RDA calories:

9. 17-year-old girl
4 oz fried chicken
Percentage of U.S. RDA vitamin A:

10. Explain how mental arithmetic can be used to find the answer to Exercise 9.

11. Carla had 2 fried eggs, 2 slices of bread, 2 tablespoons of butter, and 12 ounces of milk. How much fat did she have?

12. Beth had a dinner that contained a quarter-pound of fried chicken, two slices of bread, an 8-ounce glass of milk, and an apple. Her friend offered her three 1-ounce slices of cheddar cheese. How many could she eat and still keep her dinner under 800 calories if she planned on finishing everything else?

13. Plan two different meals from those listed in the table on page 197 that are nutritious and have about 500 calories.

14. Keep track of the foods you eat in one day. Find a calorie chart and decide how many calories you consumed. (If you eat fast foods, see if the restaurant has a nutrition chart available.) Did you eat foods from each food group? How could you improve your diet?

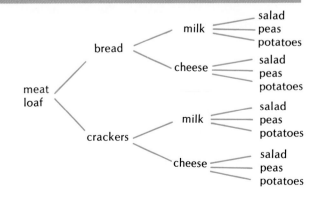

Challenge

One way to show the total possible meals in Example 2 is to use a *tree diagram*. Using the tree diagram, the first possible meal consists of meat loaf, bread, milk, and salad.

1. Use the tree diagram to list the other possible meals in Example 2.

2. Make tree diagrams for Class Exercise 5 and Exercise 7.

meat loaf
bread
milk
salad
peas
potatoes
cheese
salad
peas
potatoes
crackers
milk
salad
peas
potatoes
cheese
salad
peas
potatoes

6-3 Comparison Shopping

When you are shopping, you can use unit prices to determine the better buy. The **unit price** for an item is the cost for one unit of measure. If other things are equal, the food with the lower unit price is the better buy. To find the unit price of any item, divide the price by the number of units it contains.

OLIVES
1 lb 2 oz @ $1.29

OLIVES
15 oz @ $.89

EXAMPLE

Cynthia noticed these two jars of olives on the supermarket shelf. Which is the better buy?

Find the unit price of each jar.

> **Hidden Question:** How many ounces in 1 pound 2 ounces?
> 1 lb 2 oz = 16 oz + 2 oz = 18 oz

	price	÷	number of units	=	unit price
First jar:	$1.29	÷	18	=	■
Second jar:	$ .89	÷	15	=	■

$$\begin{array}{r} \$0.0716 \rightarrow \$.072 \\ 18\overline{)\$1.2900} \\ \underline{1\ 26} \\ 30 \\ \underline{18} \\ 120 \\ \underline{108} \\ 12 \end{array}$$
Round to nearest tenth of a cent.

$$\begin{array}{r} \$0.0593 \rightarrow \$.059 \\ 15\overline{)\$0.8900} \\ \underline{75} \\ 140 \\ \underline{135} \\ 50 \\ \underline{45} \\ 5 \end{array}$$
Round to nearest tenth of a cent.

The second jar has a lower unit price than the first. If the quality of olives is equal, the second jar is the better buy.

Class Exercises

Complete the table.

Size	Price	Unit Price
15 oz	$ .69	1. ■
1 lb 4 oz	$ .85	2. ■
1 pt 9 oz	$1.15	3. ■
4 lb	$2.80	4. ■

Determine the better or best buy.

5. An 8-ounce can of orange juice for $.69 or a 12-ounce can for $.98

6. A 2-ounce granola bar for $.98 or a 6-ounce granola bar for $2.49

7. An 8-ounce bottle of ketchup for $.55, a 12-ounce bottle for $.95, or a 1-pound 3-ounce bottle for $1.65

EXERCISES

Complete the table.

Size	Price	Unit Price
9 oz	$ .45	1. ■
12 oz	$1.45	2. ■
1 pt	$ .88	3. ■
3 lb	$2.75	4. ■
18 oz	$ .75	5. ■

Determine the better or best buy.

6. 4 oz for $.98
12 oz for $1.75

7. 7 oz for $.98
10 oz for $2.50

8. 3 for $1
8 for $2.75

9. 5 pt for $3.59
6 pt for $4.20

10. 1 lb 2 oz for $1.50
2 lb 6 oz for $3.25

11. 1 pt 1 oz for $.75
1 pt 7 oz for $1.25
2 pt for $1.75

Solve.

12. A can of tuna that costs $1.49 will serve 3 people. What is the cost per serving?

13. A large bottle of juice serves 6 and costs $1.75. What is the cost per serving?

14. Which is the better buy, a $.79 bag of corn chips that serves 6 or a $1.39 bag that serves 12?

15. Which is the better buy, a half-dozen eggs for $.59 or a dozen eggs for $.98?

16. A 6-pack of 12-ounce cans of juice costs $2.19 and a 2-quart bottle costs $1.79. Determine the better buy.

17. A spice comes in a 1-ounce jar for $1.25 or in a 1.5-ounce box for $1.98. Determine the unit price of each and determine the better buy.

18. Tuna comes in 3.5-ounce cans for $.76; 6.75-ounce cans for $1.45; or 7-ounce cans for $1.70. Calculate the unit cost of each and determine the best buy.

19. One brand of cereal comes in three sizes. The unit price of size A is $13\frac{1}{3}$¢ per ounce. The unit price of size B is $12\frac{4}{5}$¢ per ounce and the unit price of size C is $11\frac{3}{4}$¢ per ounce. Matt paid $1.88 for a box of cereal. After several weeks he had eaten an equal number of 1-ounce servings and finished the box. Which size did he buy? How many servings did he eat?

Critical Thinking: *Judging Consumer Goods*

Rosalyn and Jamie each want to buy milk. Rosalyn prefers milk low in fat. She does not want a lot of milk because the milk tends to sour before she can use it all.

Jamie is buying milk for his family. His mother doesn't want milk containing too much fat, but the rest of his family doesn't like skim milk.

Use the table to find the sizes and types of milk available.

1. Judge which type and size of milk would suit the needs of Jamie's family. Which type and size fits Rosalyn's needs?

2. Describe what you thought about as you made your decision. Did you see different thought processes for the different people?

3. Compare and discuss your thinking process with another student in your class. How was your thinking similar to your classmate's? How did it differ?

4. How does Rosalyn's desire to buy a small amount of milk conflict with her desire to get the lowest price possible?

Type	Size	Fat Content	Cost
Whole	1 qt	4%	$ .69
Whole	$\frac{1}{2}$ gal	4%	$1.04
Whole	1 gal	4%	$1.89
Low fat	1 qt	2%	$ .67
Low fat	$\frac{1}{2}$ gal	2%	$1.07
Low fat	1 gal	2%	$1.79
Skim	1 qt	0%	$ .63
Skim	$\frac{1}{2}$ gal	0%	$ .95
Skim	1 gal	0%	$1.59

5. Which type and size of milk would be best for your family? Why?

6. How is the concept of unit price helpful in judging consumer goods?

6-4 Saving Money on Groceries

A smart shopper can save money on food in the following ways:

• purchasing food in larger quantities if they are better buys

• comparing unit prices

• considering cost per serving on expensive items

• taking advantage of food specials or lower prices when food items are plentiful and inexpensive

• buying store brands or generic products instead of name brands

• making a shopping list

• using rebates and discount coupons

Skill Review

Calculating savings on groceries will be easier if you can subtract money amounts.

Find each difference.

1. $1.93 − $1.76

2. $25.17 − $20.89

3. $.87 − $.78

4. $2.81 − $1.95

(For additional help, see page 544.)

EXAMPLE 1

Lin used a newspaper ad as a guide to make up a shopping list for a week's groceries. Part of his list, along with brand-name and generic prices, is shown below. Compute his savings if he buys generic products.

Quantity	Item	Brand-Name Cost	Generic Cost
6 oz	Bologna	$1.19	$1.07
1 loaf	Whole-wheat bread	$ .75	$ .68
1 bag	Potatoes	$1.68	$1.68
2 pkg	Frozen broccoli	$1.70	$1.50
1 pkg	American cheese	$1.89	$1.79
	Totals:	$7.21	$6.72

$$\$7.21 - \$6.72 = \$.49$$

Lin can save $.49 by purchasing generic items.

With a calculator, the computation in Example 1 can be simplified by using memory.

Key: $\boxed{C^C_E}$ 1.19 $\boxed{+}$ .75 $\boxed{+}$ 1.68 $\boxed{+}$ 1.70 $\boxed{+}$ 1.89 $\boxed{M+}$
1.07 $\boxed{+}$ .68 $\boxed{+}$ 1.68 $\boxed{+}$ 1.50 $\boxed{+}$ 1.79 $\boxed{M-}$
$\boxed{M^R_C}$ ⟋ 0.49 ⟋
$.49

EXAMPLE 2

Lin has coupons for the following amounts, which save some money but can be used only on brand-name items.

15¢ off the 2 cans of corn
25¢ off on spaghetti

Use the table to decide which coupon(s) would save him money.

Item	Brand-Name Cost	Generic Cost
2 cans of corn	$1.06	$ .85
Spaghetti	$1.89	$1.79

Corn: $1.06 - .15 = $ .91

The generic brand is still cheaper since 2 cans cost $.85.

Spaghetti: $1.89 - .25 = $1.64

The brand-name spaghetti is cheaper than the generic brand.

Class Exercises

Subtract any brand-name coupon amounts from the brand-name cost. Calculate the costs of the generic products and the brand-name products. Decide which is the better deal and find how much you would save by buying the less expensive product.

Quantity	Item	Brand-Name Cost	Coupon	Generic Cost	Savings
2 boxes	Wheat flakes	$1.59 each	15¢ off each box	$1.39 each	*1.* ■
4 cans	Peaches	$ .73 each	none	$ .65 each	*2.* ■
3 pkg	Broccoli spears	$ .85 each	10¢ off each pkg	$ .75 each	*3.* ■
3 loaves	Bread	$ .75 each	none	$ .68 each	*4.* ■

5. Find the total savings on these items.

EXERCISES

Subtract any brand-name coupon amounts from the brand-name cost. Calculate the costs of the generic products and the brand-name products. Decide which is the better deal. Find how much you would save by buying the less expensive product.

Quantity	Item	Brand-Name Cost	Coupon	Generic Cost	Savings
2 pkg	Sandwich steaks	$2.79 each	25¢ off each pkg	$2.39 each	*1.* ■
4 lb	Margarine	$ .79 each	15¢ off 1 lb	$ .71 each	*2.* ■
3 lb	Wieners	$2.49 each	none	$1.99 each	*3.* ■
4 cans	Orange juice	$1.09 each	10¢ off 1 can	$ .99 each	*4.* ■

5. A 2-pound block of cheese costs $6.39. An 8-ounce package of the same cheese costs $1.89. What is the difference in price per 2-ounce serving?

6. Six pounds of chicken cost $7.74. Three pounds cost $4.17. Which is the better buy?

7. It would cost Tashia an average of $3.85 per day to eat lunch in a restaurant. She makes herself a bologna sandwich and adds some oatmeal cookies for lunch each day. She can get 3 sandwiches from a package of bologna (at $1.07 per package), 8 sandwiches from a loaf of whole wheat bread (at $.68 per loaf), and 10 lunches from a box of oatmeal cookies (at $1.19 per box). In addition, she spends $.50 for a carton of milk each day. How much can she save on lunch each day by making her own lunch?

8. Andre uses his calculator to determine the savings on purchasing 3 cans of generic-brand tomato sauce (at 2 for $.85) instead of a national brand (at 2 for $.98). Study the keystrokes he used and answer the questions that follow.

Key: .98 $\boxed{-}$ .85 $\boxed{=}$ $\boxed{\div}$ 2 $\boxed{\times}$ 3 $\boxed{=}$ .195

a. Explain his procedure.
b. Should he round his answer to 19 cents or 20 cents? Why?

9. Make a grocery list of ten items your family would buy at the grocery store. Use store ads to find the best buys. How much can you save by shopping wisely?

Consumer Note: *Comparison Shopping*

You have several choices when you plan your grocery shopping. You can shop at large supermarkets, which have everything under one roof; you can visit several small specialty stores for different items like meat, produce, dairy, or ethnic foods; or you can shop at a 24-hour convenience store.

In the supermarket, you can stock up on many different items and buy in bulk if you want. Many of these stores offer weekly specials and honor money-saving coupons issued by food companies. However, your choice of some items may be greater in a specialty store—for instance, the produce you purchase may be fresher and of greater variety at a produce market than at a supermarket. If you shop in a convenience store, you may pay a premium for the convenience as prices are generally higher than in a supermarket. However, if you need one or two items quickly, you may prefer to shop at such a store.

Supermarkets usually advertise specials each week to draw you into their stores. If a store at which you do not usually shop has a great bargain, it may be worth stopping there just for the featured item or even making other purchases there. However, you should consider the costs of gasoline and time before you plan to drive around to several stores to take advantage of specials. It may be just as economical to take advantage of the specials at your usual store and purchase other items there as well.

Career
Dietitian

Dietitians are people who specialize in knowing what foods contain needed nutrients and vitamins, and what foods are of little value to us. Besides knowing these healthful things, they know how to make food look attractive, taste pleasant, and be generally satisfying.

Profile of a dietitian. The dietitian must be a college graduate and must be able to communicate easily in speech and writing. The dietitian must have an interest in science. Dietitians are salespeople, in that they must know how to encourage people to eat well and perhaps even change their eating habits.

The dietitian's environment. The workplace of the dietitian can vary from the hospital kitchen

to the school kitchen or the experimental kitchens of food companies. Dietitians are also teachers or are engaged in researching foods and health problems. Dietitians interpret prescribed diets in terms of specific foods. School menus are made by dietitians, who may order the food as well as supervise its preparation.

All in a day's work. Kimberly had found her first few weeks working at the Pleasant Valley Nursing Home very interesting because of the variety of her tasks. One day she had the task of ordering the food for 60 senior citizens with different health needs.

1. The recipe for a certain dessert called for 12 quarts of fruit. Kimberly wanted to order enough fruit to serve the dessert 9 times during the month. How many gallons of fruit should she order?

2. Each person in the nursing home ate an average of 150 grams of meat each day. How many kilograms of meat should Kimberly order per week?

3. For one week's meals, Kimberly had the following supplies:
   Group 1: chicken, fish, beef
   Group 2: milk, cottage cheese
   Group 3: bread, rice, noodles
   Group 4: peas, apples, salad,
        grapefruit
Kimberly wanted to determine the number of meals she could make using one food from each group. Make a tree diagram to show the possible meals.

4. How many possible meals could Kimberly make? Count the meals in Question 3 and then use multiplication to check your answer.

6-5 Preparing Meals

Convenience foods are foods that have been prepared (cleaned and cut up), assembled, cooked, and packaged by the manufacturer. All canned and dried foods and nearly all frozen foods are convenience foods. Many of these foods need only to be heated and served. Convenience foods can save time in the kitchen, and they allow year-round use of foods that may not be available fresh all year long. Also, you do not have to keep large supplies of rarely used ingredients on hand. However, convenience foods tend to be more expensive than the same foods prepared at home, and some may also contain preservatives.

Skill Review

To compare food costs, it will help if you can divide money amounts by whole numbers.

Divide. Round to the nearest cent.

1. $1.58 ÷ 12
2. $.75 ÷ 2
3. $4.60 ÷ 6
4. $10.88 ÷ 5
5. $8.70 ÷ 15

(For additional help, see page 546.)

EXAMPLE 1

Sometimes Cindi uses convenience foods, but she prefers to prepare pizza herself whenever she can. Her recipe is shown below. The cost of a 12-inch fully prepared frozen pizza, which serves 3, is $3.79. The baking time for both pizzas is the same. Which costs less, the fully prepared pizza or the pizza Cindi makes herself?

Recipe for Pizza

Serves 3

$1\frac{1}{2}$ cups flour

$\frac{1}{4}$ tsp salt

1 oz shortening

1 pkg yeast

1 can tomato sauce

2 oz cheese

$\frac{1}{4}$ tsp each of basil, oregano, and garlic salt

Grocery Receipt

16 oz shortening	$1.69
5 lb flour	$1.60
2 cans tomato sauce	$ .67
8 oz cheese	$1.98
3 pkg yeast	$ .95

The cost of salt and spices is about $.15

Step 1. Determine the unit cost of each item in the homemade pizza. (A pound of flour contains 4 cups.)

Item	Total Cost ÷	Number of Units =	Unit Cost
Flour	$1.60	20	$.08 per cup
Shortening	$1.69	16	$.11 per ounce
Yeast	$ .95	3	$.32 per package
Tomato sauce	$ .67	2	$.34 per can
Cheese	$1.98	8	$.25 per ounce

Step 2. Find the total cost of the homemade pizza.

Item	Unit Cost × Number of Units = Total Cost		
Flour	$.08	1½	$ .12
Shortening	$.11	1	$ .11
Yeast	$.32	1	$ .32
Tomato sauce	$.34	1	$ .34
Cheese	$.25	2	$ .50
Spices			$ .15
		Total:	$1.54

Step 3. Find the difference in cost.
$3.79 − $1.54 = $2.25

The difference in cost between the frozen pizza and the homemade pizza is $2.25.

EXAMPLE 2
Determine to the nearest cent the cost per serving of the homemade pizza.

cost ÷ number of servings = cost per serving
$1.54 ÷   3   = $.513 → $.51
                              Round to nearest cent.

The homemade pizza costs about $.51 per serving.

Class Exercises

Compute the savings per serving for the more economical form.

Food	Cost per Serving		Savings
	Convenience	Homemade	
Omelet	$ .37	$.43	**1.** ■
Spaghetti	$1.29	$.86	**2.** ■

Determine to the nearest cent the cost per serving of each food.
Compute the savings per serving of the less expensive form.

Food	Convenience Form			Homemade Form			Savings per Serving
	Cost	Number of Servings	Cost per Serving	Cost	Number of Servings	Cost per Serving	
Turkey	$2.49	2	**3.** ■	$6.19	8	**4.** ■	**5.** ■
Breakfast	$1.77	2	**6.** ■	$ .59	1	**7.** ■	**8.** ■

EXERCISES

Compute the savings per serving for the more economical form.

Food	Cost per Serving Convenience	Homemade	Savings
Main dish	$3.19	$2.24	**1.** ■
Canned corn	$ .224	$ .238	**2.** ■

Determine to the nearest cent, the cost per serving of each food. Compute the savings of the less expensive form.

Food	Convenience Form Cost	Number of Servings	Cost per Serving	Homemade Form Cost	Number of Servings	Cost per Serving	Savings per Serving
Soup	$ .73	2	**3.** ■	$1.19	5	**4.** ■	**5.** ■
Ham	$3.99	4	**6.** ■	$6.43	8	**7.** ■	**8.** ■

Solve.

9. Pancakes: $.98 per 9-oz package
Serves 3
Cost per serving: ■

10. Orange juice: $1.08 per 64 oz
6-oz serving
Cost per serving: ■

11. Homemade pancakes use 1 cup of flour, 8 ounces of milk, 1 egg, and $\frac{1}{2}$ ounce of oil to make two servings. What is the cost per serving of homemade pancakes if milk costs $.89 for 32 ounces, eggs cost $.96 per dozen, 5 pounds (20 cups) of flour cost $1.60, and 32 ounces of oil cost $1.28?

12. How much, to the nearest cent, can you save by using the less expensive pancakes (Problems 9 and 11)?

Using a Calculator: *Whole-Number Remainders*

You can use your calculator to find the whole-number remainder in a division problem such as 364 ÷ 32.

Key: C̲E̲C̲ 364 ÷ 32 = ╱ 11.375 ╱   Divide 364 by 32.

Key: 11 × 32 M−   Multiply the whole number part of the answer by the divisor. Store the answer in M− .

Key: 364 M+ M̲C̲R̲ ╱ 12 ╱   Subtract the answer from the original dividend.

Divide. Find the whole-number remainders. Check.

1. 260,177 ÷ 792   **2.** 84,889 ÷ 146   **3.** 1,095,760 ÷ 2,513

6-6 *Eating in a Restaurant*

More and more people are eating in restaurants or buying fast food to take home. If you are on a budget, you may want to consider carefully the cost of eating out. It may be helpful to allot some specific amount for restaurant meals so you do not spend too much.

EXAMPLE 1

Lorraine enjoys eating out. She selected the items shown from a restaurant's menu. Estimate the cost of her meal if she must pay sales tax of 5% and she plans to leave a 15% tip.

Step 1. Estimate the cost of the food.

$2.50 + $.60 + $8.95 + $2.25 → $3 + $1 + $9 + $2 = $15

Step 2. Estimate the amount of the tip.

Think: 15% of $15 = 10% of $15 + 5% of $15
                     = $1.50   + $.75
                     = $2.25

Clam chowder	$2.50
Iced tea	$ .60
Broiled haddock with baked potato and salad	$8.95
Carrot cake	$2.25

Step 3. Estimate the amount of the sales tax.

Think: 5% of $15 is half of 10%, or $.75

Step 4. Find the total estimate.

cost of food +   tip   + sales tax = estimated cost
    $15   + $2.25 + $.75   = $18

The estimated cost of Lorraine's meal is $18.

EXAMPLE 2

Caleb budgeted $45 per month for eating out. If each meal cost an average of $6, how often could he eat out each month?

Estimate: $45 ÷ $6 = ■ → $40 ÷ $5 = 8

Key: $\boxed{C_E^C}$ 45 $\boxed{\div}$ 6 $\boxed{=}$ 7.5

The answer 7.5 is close to the estimate 8 and is a sensible answer. Since the question asks how many times Caleb can eat out, the remainder is ignored.
Caleb can eat out 7 times.

Skill Review

In order to estimate the cost of eating in a restaurant, you need to know how to estimate sums.

Estimate each sum.

1. $2.72 + $1.15 + $3.46
2. $4.29 + $6.82 + $3.72 + $.77
3. $2.08 + $.65 + $1.02 + $3.97
4. $8.50 + $3.75 + $2.10 + $4.63

(For additional help, see page 541.)

Class Exercises

Use the menu from Genrie's Restaurant and Carry-Out. Estimate the total cost of each meal.

Soup	Main Dish	Dessert	Beverage	Cost
Onion	Chicken	Ice cream	Milk	1. ■
Chowder	Ham	Apple pie	Milk	2. ■
Chowder	Beef	Apple pie	Tea	3. ■
Onion	Halibut	Ice cream	Milk	4. ■

5. Karen budgets $376 per year for eating out. How many times can she eat out if the average cost of each meal is $7.50?

EXERCISES

Use the menu from Genrie's Restaurant. Find the total cost of each meal including 5% sales tax and 15% tip.

Soup	Main Dish	Dessert	Beverage	Cost
Chowder	Chicken	Apple pie	Milk	1. ■
Chowder	Chicken	Banana bread	Milk	2. ■
Onion	Beef	Banana bread	Milk	3. ■
Onion	Halibut	Apple pie	Juice	4. ■

5. $248 budgeted per year
$4.50 per meal
Number of meals: ■

6. $38 budgeted per week
$9 per meal
Number of meals: ■

GENRIE'S

Soups
French Onion Soup	$1.05
Clam Chowder	$1.10

Main Meals
Roast Beef	$4.95
Fried Chicken	$3.75
Halibut Steak	$4.15
Ham Steak	$3.95

Desserts
Ice Cream	$.85
Apple Pie	$1.25
Banana Bread	$1.45

Beverages
Milk	$.65
Juice	$.65
Iced Tea	$.60

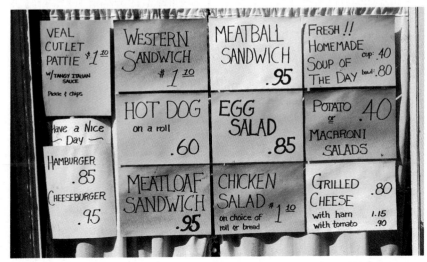

7. How many possible dinners can be made by selecting one soup, main dish, desert, and beverage from Genrie's menu?

8. Norris ate at The Health Food Restaurant and had one item from each group. He paid $5.45 for his meal (without the tip). What did he have for dinner?

9. What are some of the advantages of eating at a fast-food restaurant rather than one where food is served by waiters and waitresses? What are some of the disadvantages?

10. Why do many families use carry-out services for some of their meals? What advantages has this type of food service over home-cooked meals or over restaurant meals?

THE HEALTH FOOD RESTAURANT

Meats:	Chicken	$2.50
	Roast Beef	$3.25
Dairy:	Milk	$ .65
	Cheese	$1.25
Vegetable:	Potato	$ .65
	Salad	$ .95
	Peas	$ .55

Bread included with dinner.

One way to estimate sums is to use front-end estimation.

Estimate: $3.88 + $8.16 + $6.45 + $3.62 + $5.38

First, estimate the front.

$$\$25 \begin{cases} \$10 \begin{cases} \$3.88 \\ \$8.16 \end{cases} \$1 \\ \$10 \begin{cases} \$6.45 \\ \$3.62 \end{cases} \$1 \\ \$5 \quad +\$5.38 \quad \$.50 \end{cases} \$2.50$$

Then, estimate the back.

The total estimate is $25 + $2.50, or $27.50.

1. Estimate the above sum by rounding. Which estimate is easier to do? Which is more accurate?

2. Estimate each of the sums in the Skill Review using front-end estimation.

Computer:
READ and DATA Statements

Kyra used her computer to find the unit prices of these items: peas, 11 ounces for $.56; corn, 12 ounces for $.63; and juice, 72 ounces for $1.49. She placed each item, its cost, and size in a BASIC statement called a DATA statement. DATA statements may go anywhere in a program but are usually at the end. The first statement is

    200 DATA PEAS, .56, 11

The command READ captures data from the DATA statement. It is followed by a set of variable names, one for each value to be captured. The first READ statement is

    30 READ I$, C, S

where I$ captures the item name, C captures its cost, and S captures its size. The calculation of the unit price is done in a PRINT statement, which follows each READ statement.

10 HOME	Clears the screen.
20 PRINT "ITEM NAME", "UNIT PRICE"	Prints the heading.
30 READ I$, C, S	Reads the first 3 values. I$ = "PEAS", C = .56, and S = 11.
40 PRINT I$, C/S	Prints the item name (PEAS). Computes and prints the unit cost (.56 ÷ 11).
50 READ I$, C, S	Reads the next 3 values. I$ = "CORN", C = .63, and S = 12.
60 PRINT I$, C/S	Prints the item name (CORN). Computes and prints the unit cost (.63 ÷ 12).
70 READ I$, C, S	Reads the next 3 values. I$ = "JUICE", C = 1.49, and S = 72.
80 PRINT I$, C/S	Prints the item name (JUICE). Computes and prints the unit cost (1.49 ÷ 72).
200 DATA PEAS, .56, 11	First DATA statement.
210 DATA CORN, .63, 12	Second DATA statement.
220 DATA JUICE, 1.49, 72	Third DATA statement.
240 END	Tells the computer to end the program.

Enter and RUN the program.

EXERCISES

1. What statement would change if the cost of a 12-oz can of corn were $.72?

2. Make the change suggested in Exercise 1. RUN the program and observe the change.

3. What 3 program lines would have to be added to add tuna at $1.62 per 7-oz can?

4. Make the additions suggested in Exercise 3. RUN the program and observe the changes.

Decision Making:
Planning a Party

Peter and Julio are members of the Health Careers Club at Central High School. The club members selected them to plan the food for their semester party.

GETTING THE FACTS

The two boys met briefly with the club sponsor, Ms. Thomas, and were given the following information:

1. The foods served at the party must represent healthy food choices from the four food groups. (This is a club interested in promoting good health.)

2. The foods should be items that most club members like to eat.

3. They must stay within the club's budget of $50 and have enough food for all 20 club members.

"Peter, how do you think we should begin?" Julio asked.

"Well, Julio, I think the information Ms. Thomas gave us helps a lot. We know that our goal is to select foods that meet the three criteria she gave us. The hardest one to me is to select foods that most club members like to eat," Peter replied.

"You're right. We already know a lot about healthy food choices from the course we took last year in foods and nutrition. We really can't do a whole lot with the budgeting idea until we have some idea of what people like to eat. Suppose we ask people what they would like us to serve," Julio suggested.

Julio and Peter prepared a questionnaire and distributed it to members of the club.

Answer the following questions.

1. From what other sources could Julio and Peter get information about healthy foods?

2. Other than distributing a questionnaire, how else could they collect information to assist them in their decision making?

FAVORITE FOODS

The club members returned the questionnaires and Julio and Peter tallied the results. They got the following information:

Type of Food	Club members	
	1st Choice	2nd Choice
Group 1: Protein-Rich Foods		
Fried chicken	7	6
Tuna	3	4
Pizza (also Group 3)	10	10
Group 2: Dairy Products		
Cheese	5	15
Ice cream	15	5
Group 3: Breads and Cereals		
Rolls	7	12
Crackers	13	5
Noodles	0	3
Group 4: Fruits and Vegetables		
French fries	12	3
Tossed salad	5	10
Fruit cocktail	3	7

Peter and Julio studied the responses of the club members and began to discuss what they should serve.

"Suppose we just pick the food in each category that has the most first-choice votes," Julio suggested.

"I'm not sure that would give us a good meal, Julio," Peter replied.

"I see what you mean. If we do that we would have pizza, ice cream, crackers, and french fries," Julio laughed. "We need to make some decisions about what is most logical given what people like," he continued.

Answer the following questions.

3. Given the food preferences of the club members, the other criteria the boys have to satisfy, and what you know about planning well-balanced meals, what foods would you serve at the party?

4. How did you arrive at your decision?

CHOOSING A MENU

After much discussion and thinking about the other criteria they had to satisfy, Julio and Peter decided that the menu for the party would consist of pizza, tossed salad, and ice cream. Since they had not asked the club members about beverages, they decided to get either fruit punch or an assortment of juices, depending upon the cost.

Answer the following questions.

5. How well does Julio's and Peter's menu match the criteria they were given? Explain your answer.

6. In answering Question 5, you were judging the usefulness of the boys' menu. Describe your thought processes in doing this.

7. How is judging the usefulness of something important in the decision making process?

PURCHASING THE FOOD

After the club members approved the menu, Peter and Julio began collecting information on where they could get the food and how much it would cost. Although they wanted to get good buys for their money, the boys also had to consider convenience, taste, and avoiding waste. The boys decided to have the pizza delivered to school already cooked. They collected the following information from pizza stores in their neighborhood for prepared cheese pizzas:

Store	Cost	Servings
Jet Pizza	$6.95	12 slices
Friendly Pizza	$9.25	16 slices
Gourmet Pizza	$5.00	8 slices

There are 20 people planning to attend the party. Julio and Peter estimated that each person would want at least two pieces of pizza.

Answer the following questions.

8. In order to have enough pizza for everyone to get at least two slices, how many pizzas would the boys have to buy from each of the stores listed? How much would they have to spend at each store? How much pizza would be left over assuming each person eats exactly two slices?

9. In your opinion, where should the boys buy the pizza? Explain the reasons for your choice.

The boys collected the information shown below about the cost of the ingredients they will put in their tossed salad.

Answer the following questions.

10. How much will the amount of salad the boys need cost to prepare from the ingredients listed?

11. P & L Grocery Store has a salad bar that sells salad for $1.85 a pound. Peter and Julio estimated that they would need 6 pounds of salad. How much would it cost if they buy it this way?

Item	Cost per Unit	Amount Needed
lettuce	$ .45 a head	3 heads
cucumbers	$1.00 for 3	6 cucumbers
carrots	$ .45 a bag	1 bag
onions	$ .59 a pound	$\frac{1}{3}$ lb
broccoli spears	$ .79 a pound	2 lb
tomatoes	$1.00 for 3 lb	6 lb
3-bean salad	$ .65 a can	4 cans

12. The boys decided to buy the salad from the salad bar. Give several reasons why they may have made this decision.

13. Describe your thought processes in coming up with the reasons you gave above.

The boys can buy 24 party blocks of Neopolitan ice cream for $5.98. Because they would not have to scoop out ice cream, they decided to buy the ice cream this way, even though it is more expensive than buying two half-gallons at $2.39 per half-gallon.

Answer the following questions.

14. How much extra did the boys pay for the convenience of purchasing the party blocks?

15. Give two other examples of times when people may pay extra money for the sake of convenience.

16. List several factors a person needs to consider when paying extra money for a convenience item.

DECIDE FOR YOURSELF

Suppose that you have to plan a party for a group of friends. Collect information and use the information to plan the party. Try to go through the steps Peter and Julio used. Then summarize how you, and the boys, went about planning a party.

Chapter 6 Review

VOCABULARY

balanced diet   nutrients   U.S. Recommended Daily Allowance
calories   unit price   (U.S. RDA)
convenience foods

For Exercises 1–5, select the word or words that complete each statement.

1. The approximate amount of vitamins, minerals, protein, and calories each person needs per day is called the _____ .

2. The cost of an item per unit of measure is called the _____ .

3. You get the nutrients you need each day from a _____ .

4. Foods that have been prepared, cooked, and packaged by the manufacturer are called _____ .

5. _____ measure the energy that food supplies.

SKILLS

Find each product.

6. 134 × 6

7. 27 × 265

8. 412 × 678

Convert each amount.

9. 1 lb 6 oz to ounces

10. 3 qt 1 pt to pints

11. 4 gal 3 qt to quarts

Divide.

12. $2.08 ÷ 13

13. $5.12 ÷ 8

14. $8.82 ÷ 7

Estimate each sum.

15. $2.19 + $1.05 + $3.52

16. $1.89 + $4.25 + $3.72 + $6.45

17. $13.50 + $11.29 + $1.85 + $3.17

CONSUMER TOPICS

Solve. Use the table on page 197 if needed.

18. Mark fixed a packaged macaroni and cheese dinner and ate half of it. The nutrition label on the box indicated that the box contained 4 servings and that each serving had 290 calories. How many calories did Mark consume?

19. If each serving in Problem 18 had 9 grams of protein and the U.S. RDA for a boy Mark's age is 56 grams, what percentage of his daily requirement did the macaroni and cheese provide?

20. For dinner, Chuck had 6 ounces of fried chicken, 1 slice of white bread with $\frac{1}{2}$ tablespoon of butter, $\frac{2}{3}$ cup of green beans, and a glass of whole milk. How many calories did he eat?

21. In Problem 20, how many grams of fat are in the meal?

Use the tables on page 194 and 197 to solve.

22. What percentage of the calories Chuck needed for the day were provided by his dinner in Problem 20? (He is 17).

23. What percentage of Chuck's daily requirement of vitamin A was provided?

Solve.

24. Which can of cat food is the better buy, a 3-ounce can that sells for 37¢ or a 5-ounce can that is priced 2 for 89¢?

25. One brand of hand lotion sells for $2.69 for 6 ounces. Another costs $2.93 for 8 ounces. Which is the better buy?

26. Find the savings for the better buy on 3 cans: 3 cans for $1.58 with coupons for $.10 off each can, or 1 can for $.49.

27. Sarah calculates that it would cost her $3.50 to eat lunch in a restaurant. She makes a lunch consisting of a ham sandwich and an apple. She can get 4 sandwiches from a package of ham (at $1.29 per package) and 8 sandwiches from a loaf of bread (at $1.09 per loaf). There are 16 apples in a bag that sells for $2.39. How much can she save each week by taking her lunch for the five days a week she works?

Determine the cost per serving to the nearest cent.

28. Chicken dinner
$2.59, 2 servings

29. Canned spaghetti sauce
$2.61, 8 servings

30. Canned soup
$1.45, 2 servings

31. Find the number of meals consisting of one food from each food group that can be made from 2 kinds of protein, 3 milk products, 3 kinds of bread, and 5 kinds of fruit.

32. Meghan ordered cream of broccoli soup ($2.50), baked chicken ($8.75), salad ($2.40), and mineral water ($1.30). Estimate the cost of her meal if she leaves a 15% tip.

33. Luis budgeted $750 per year for eating out. If he estimated that each meal would cost $6, how often can he eat out?

Chapter 6 Test

Solve. Use the table on page 197 for Problems 3 and 4.

1. A serving of cereal contains 145 calories. If Tom ate 2 servings, how many calories did he have?

2. Find the number of meals consisting of one food from each food group that can be made from 2 kinds of protein, 3 milk products, 5 kinds of bread and grain, and 7 kinds of fruits and vegetables.

3. Find the total calories in a meal consisting of 2 fried eggs, 2 pieces of toast with 1 tablespoon butter, and a glass of orange juice.

4. If the U.S. RDA of riboflavin for a 17-year-old girl is 1.3 milligrams, what percentage of her requirement would be met by the meal of Problem 3?

5. A 64-ounce bottle of laundry detergent sells for $3.79. A 38-ounce bottle costs $1.90. Which is the better buy?

6. Milk is available in 1-quart, $\frac{1}{2}$-gallon, or 1-gallon containers. If 1 quart costs $.39, $\frac{1}{2}$ gallon costs $.77, and 1 gallon costs $1.52, which is the best buy?

7. Jonathan has a coupon for 15¢ off a roll of paper towels. The roll has 84 sheets and sells for $1.09. Another brand offers 98 sheets and sells for $1.07. If he uses the coupon on the first brand, which will be a better buy?

8. Judy has a coupon for 25¢ off brand A frozen waffles that sell for $.99 for 10 oz. She sees a brand B that is $.89 for 10 oz. Assuming that she uses the coupon for brand A, how much would she save by purchasing the better buy?

Find the cost per serving to the nearest cent.

9. Ice cream
   $2.19, 4 servings

10. Powdered milk
    $1.79, 12 servings

11. Macaroni and cheese
    $.59, 4 servings

Solve.

12. Theresa made 2 quarts of homemade soup. Her cost was $1.79. Canned soup costs $.75 for a can with $2\frac{3}{4}$ eight-ounce servings. Determine Theresa's savings by making soup.

13. Ben ordered a pizza ($10.95) with two extra toppings ($1.60 each) and two cartons of milk ($1.25 each). Estimate the cost of his meal.

14. Find the number of meals. $375 budgeted per year, $5.50 per meal.

Cumulative Mixed Review

Select the letter corresponding to the correct answer.

1. Rhonda worked for a travel agency, where she earned a 6% commission on all plane tickets she sold. One week she sold tickets worth $466, $98, $265, and $108. How much commission did she earn?
   - **a.** $937
   - **b.** $56.22
   - **c.** $562.20
   - **d.** $27.96

2. The U.S. RDA for vitamin A for a man is 1,000 IU. If 1 ounce of cheese contains 300 IU of vitamin A, how many ounces would the man have to eat to satisfy his requirement?
   - **a.** 4 oz
   - **b.** 3 oz
   - **c.** $3\frac{1}{3}$ oz
   - **d.** $4\frac{1}{3}$ oz

3. Marti purchased some new furniture at a local department store. The cost of the furniture was $984.50. She paid for the furniture in 12 equal installments of $96.81. How much interest did she pay?
   - **a.** $177.22
   - **b.** $1,161.72
   - **c.** $14.77
   - **d.** $984.50

4. A 64-ounce bottle of juice sells for $1.59. What is the unit price?
   - **a.** $.25
   - **b.** $.40
   - **c.** $.035
   - **d.** $.025

5. Heather had an opening balance in her checking account of $487.22. She made deposits of $100.45 and had bank charges of $3.88. If her ending balance was $286.39, how much did she write in checks?
   - **a.** $382.89
   - **b.** $100.38
   - **c.** $297.40
   - **d.** $305.16

6. Homemade French toast uses 6 slices of bread, 2 eggs, and 4 ounces of milk to make 3 servings. What is the cost per serving (2 slices) if milk costs $.64 for 32 ounces, eggs cost $.84 a dozen, and bread (25 slices) costs $1.01?
   - **a.** $.14
   - **b.** $1.25
   - **c.** $2.49
   - **d.** $.15

7. Jill had lunch at a Chinese restaurant. She ordered sweet and sour soup ($.95), egg rolls ($2.25), and kung pao chicken ($4.95). Estimate the cost of her meal if she leaves a 15% tip.
   - **a.** $9
   - **b.** $10
   - **c.** $8
   - **d.** $11

8. Larry pays $1,398 in state taxes each year. If he is paid semimonthly, how much is withheld from his paycheck for state taxes each pay period?
   - **a.** $58.25
   - **b.** $116.50
   - **c.** $26.88
   - **d.** $233

9. Ron deposited $2,500 in a savings account. How much would he earn in 2 years if the bank paid $6.37% simple interest?
   - **a.** $159.25
   - **b.** $2,818.50
   - **c.** $2,659.25
   - **d.** $318.50

10. Sean budgeted $75 per month for eating out. At an estimated $5 per meal, that allows him 15 meals per month. He would like to eat 22 meals out per month. How much more does he have to budget?
    - **a.** $110
    - **b.** $75
    - **c.** $35
    - **d.** $185

CHAPTER 7
Buying Clothing

Andrea is shopping for holiday gifts for her out-of-town cousins. She has seen several things she likes in the catalogs that she has at home, but she is thinking of going to a nearby shopping center to look around for gifts.

• Which way would probably save her the most time and money? Why?

• What would be some of the advantages of shopping at the shopping mall for her gifts? What would be some of the disadvantages?

• What factors add to her expense if she goes to a shopping center and mails the packages herself?

• Can you see any disadvantages of using a catalog?

Which method of shopping would you prefer, using a catalog or going to a store? Why?

7-1 Discount and Markdown

The store signs shown below give information about sale items for which you can find the discount, or markdown. The **discount,** or **markdown,** is the amount of money you save by buying an item at a discounted price, or **sale price.** To compute the markdown when the percent of reduction is given, express the percent as a decimal and multiply it by the regular price.

EXAMPLE 1

Ariel purchased a pair of slacks on sale for $19.99. The regular price was $29.98. What was the markdown of the slacks?

$$\text{regular price} - \text{sale price} = \text{markdown}$$
$$\$29.98 \quad - \quad \$19.99 \quad = \quad \$9.99$$

The markdown on the slacks was $9.99.

EXAMPLE 2

Ramon purchased a sweater at Reese's. The regular price was $29.50. The markdown rate was 25%. What was the sale price?

Think: $25\% = 0.25$, or $\frac{1}{4}$

Step 1. Find the markdown.

$$\text{rate of markdown} \times \text{regular price} = \text{markdown}$$
$$25\% \qquad \times \qquad \$29.50 \qquad = \qquad \blacksquare$$

Estimate: $25\% \times 29.50 = \blacksquare \rightarrow \frac{1}{4} \times \$28 = \$7$

$$\begin{array}{ll} \$29.50 & \text{regular price} \\ \underline{\times \quad 0.25} & \text{rate of markdown} \\ \$7.3750 \rightarrow \$7.38 & \text{Round to nearest cent.} \end{array}$$

The answer $7.38 compares reasonably with the estimate $7 and is a sensible answer.

Step 2. Find the sale price.

$$\text{regular price} - \text{markdown} = \text{sale price}$$
$$\$29.50 \quad - \quad \$7.38 \quad = \quad \$22.12$$

The sale price was $22.12.

Sale on all Winter Garments!
Discounts of 15% to 50%
Now through Saturday
Reese's Clothing Outlet

Special This Week Only at Numan's!
✦✦✦✦✦✦✦✦✦✦✦✦✦✦
Women's Slacks
Reg. $29.99
Now $19.99

Spring Clearance Sale
$\frac{1}{4}$ off the Regular Price of All Shoes
The Shoe Factory

Problem Solving Strategy: Solving another way.
Since the sale price in Example 2 is the original price (100%) minus the discount (25%), the sale price is 100% − 25%, or 75%, of the original price.

$$\$29.50 \times 0.75 = \$22.1250$$
$$\$22.13 \quad \text{Round to nearest cent.}$$

Class Exercises

Complete the following table by calculating the markdown.

Sale Item	Regular Price	Sale Price	Markdown
Dress	$40	$30	**1.** ■
Socks	3 for $8	3 for $6.50	**2.** ■
Sweatsuits	$19.45	$14.98	**3.** ■

Complete the following table.

Sale Item	Regular Price	Markdown Rate	Markdown	Sale Price
Jacket	$48	20%	**4.** ■	**5.** ■
Men's shoes	$48.90	15%	**6.** ■	**7.** ■
Scarf	$12	$\frac{1}{3}$	**8.** ■	**9.** ■

10. Which of Exercises 1–9 could be done mentally? In which of the exercises would pencil and paper be appropriate? Which exercises could best be done using a calculator?

EXERCISES

Complete the following table by calculating the markdown.

Sale Item	Regular Price	Sale Price	Markdown
Suit	$50	$40	**1.** ■
Snowpants	$13.99	$10.99	**2.** ■
Shoes	$22.50	$18.75	**3.** ■
Jacket	$39.45	$25.67	**4.** ■

Complete the table below by filling in the missing values.

Sale Item	Regular Price	Markdown Rate	Markdown	Sale Price
Leather belt	$15	20%	**5.** ■	**6.** ■
Slacks	$19.75	15%	**7.** ■	**8.** ■
Handkerchief	$ 3	$\frac{1}{3}$	**9.** ■	**10.** ■
Necktie	$16	$\frac{1}{2}$	**11.** ■	**12.** ■

Solve.

13. Wool ski cap
Regular price: $7.95
Markdown: $\frac{1}{2}$ off
Sale price: ■

14. Cotton vest
Regular price: $12.49
Markdown: ■
Sale price: $7.39

15. Sport shirt
Regular price: $13.75
Markdown rate: 15%
Sale price: ■

Use the prices shown at the right to solve.

> Blouses: regularly $17.65, now $\frac{1}{4}$ off
> Shoes: regularly $38.75, now 28% off
> Socks: regularly $4, now 10% off
> Slacks: regularly $30, now $\frac{1}{3}$ off

16. Sandra purchased a blouse and a pair of shoes. Did she spend over $50?

17. Evan bought a pair of slacks and 2 pairs of socks. How much did he spend?

18. Explain how mental arithmetic can be used to find the answer to Exercise 17.

19. Norma bought a pair of shoes, a pair of socks, and 2 blouses. How much did she save because of the sale prices?

20. Show how you would use a calculator to simplify the computation for Problem 19.

21. The Namebrand Department Store advertised a markdown of $2.43 on each shirt and a markdown of $6.72 on each pair of pants. Jerry purchased a total of 7 of these items and saved $25.59. How many of each item did he purchase?

Challenge

Markdown Mart regularly sells its appliances at 17.5% less than the suggested list prices. Top-Notch Appliance Store sells its appliances at list price but holds sales regularly. In the following problems, determine whether it would be better for you to purchase each item from Markdown Mart or Top-Notch Appliance Store. Tell how much you would save by making your purchase in the store of your choice.

1. A dishwasher that lists for $539.50 is on sale at Top-Notch for $450.

2. A clothes dryer that lists for $695.50 is on sale at Top-Notch for $100 off.

3. A washer that lists for $450 is on sale at Top-Notch for a 20% discount.

4. Are there reasons other than price that you might choose one store over another?

7-2 Catalog Orders

Ordering by mail is a very convenient way to shop. Be sure you shop with a reputable company. When you place your order, you should keep a record of what you ordered, when you ordered it, and a phone number or address to use as a contact in case your order has not come within a reasonable period of time.

To order, you need to fill out an order form. Usually you will have to calculate the total cost of your order, including tax and shipping costs, and the total weight of the items you are ordering. Then, you enclose payment and send your order. Most mail-order companies accept checks or credit cards. If you use a credit card to pay for your purchases, you may be able to order by phone, which will speed up the process.

EXAMPLE 1

Thelma placed an order with A. A. Rice Co. The cost of her order was $24.43 and the weight was 2 pounds 3 ounces. She lives in Indiana and must pay 5% sales tax. She is in shipping zone I. Find the total cost of her order.

Step 1. Find the amount of tax.

$$\text{cost of order} \times \text{tax rate} = \text{tax}$$
$$\$24.43 \quad \times \quad 5\% \quad = \blacksquare$$

Think: 5% = 0.05

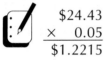

$$\begin{array}{r} \$24.43 \\ \times \quad 0.05 \\ \hline \$1.2215 \\ \$1.22 \end{array}$$ Round to nearest cent.

Key: $\boxed{\text{C}^{\text{C}}_{\text{E}}}$ 24.43 $\boxed{\times}$ 5 $\boxed{\%}$ $\underline{1.2215}$
$1.22 **Round to nearest cent.**

Step 2. Find the cost of shipping.

> **Problem Solving Strategy:** Finding information.
> The shipping charge depends upon the distance the package must be shipped as well as the weight of the order. Use the table at the right to find the shipping cost.

The table shows that the cost of shipping 2 pounds 3 ounces to Zone I is $1.62.

Step 3. Find the total cost.

$$\text{cost of goods} + \text{tax} + \text{shipping cost} = \text{total cost}$$
$$\$24.43 \quad + \$1.22 + \quad \$1.62 \quad = \quad \$27.27$$

The total cost of Thelma's order was $27.27.

(For additional help, see page 552.)

Skill Review

To find the total shipping weight, you need to be able to add customary measures.

Find each sum.

1. 2 lb 8 oz + 3 lb 7 oz + 1 lb 9 oz

2. 7 lb 14 oz + 3 lb 9 oz

3. 4 lb 1 oz + 2 lb + 7 lb 15 oz

4. 6 lb 2 oz + 23 oz + 17 oz

A. A. Rice Co. Shipping Charges

Weight	Zone I	Zone II
0 to 1 lb	$1.25	$1.67
1 lb 1 oz to 3 lb	$1.62	$2.03
3 lb 1 oz to 5 lb	$1.76	$2.82
5 lb 1 oz to 8 lb	$2.01	$3.59
8 lb 1 oz to 11 lb	$2.29	$4.01
11 lb 1 oz to 15 lb	$2.45	$4.39
15 lb 1 oz to 18 lb	$2.58	$4.95
18 lb 1 oz to 21 lb	$2.83	$5.25
Over 21 lb please call for rates.		

EXAMPLE 2

Frank decided to order several items from the A. A. Rice catalog and began filling out an order form like the one shown. Find the total cost if Frank lives in the Zone II shipping area.

Step 1. Find the shipping charge.

> **Hidden Question:** What is the total weight of the items Frank ordered?
> 1 lb 2 oz + 3 lb 5 oz + 2 lb 11 oz =
> 6 lb 18 oz = 7 lb 2 oz

Find the rate for shipping 7 pounds 2 ounces to Zone II in the shipping table.
The shipping charge is $3.59.

Step 2. Find the total cost.

total cost of goods + tax + shipping cost = total cost
$108.26   +   0   + $3.59   = $111.85

The total cost of Frank's order is $111.85.

A. A. Rice Co. Catalog Order Form

Name: **Frank Satterfeld**

Address: **18 Western Pike**

City: Loistown   State **CA**   Zip: **91345**

Area code: **818**   Tel No: **211-2121**

Catalog Number	Qty	Item Name	Unit Price	Cost	Weight Lb Oz
17172X	2	Sport Shirts	17.99	35.98	1 2
22693B	1	Shoes 11 C	24.99	24.99	3 5
53214M	1	Blazer	47.29	47.29	2 11

Total for goods: $108.26   Total Weight: 7 lb 2 oz

Tax* $.00

Shipping charge:

Total:

*Indiana residents add 5% sales tax.

Class Exercises

Use the table of shipping charges for A. A. Rice to find the cost of shipping the items.

Item 1 lb oz	Item 2 lb oz	Item 3 lb oz	Total Weight lb oz	Zone	Shipping Cost
1 3	3 9	1 5	6 1	II	1. ■
5 2	2 11	7 9	2. ■ ■	I	3. ■
1 12	0 7	2 3	4. ■ ■	II	5. ■

Determine the missing information. Use the table of shipping charges for A. A. Rice to find the cost of shipping the items.

Total of Goods	Weight lb oz	Zone	Sales Tax	Shipping Cost	Total Price
$ 72.45	3 7	I	5%	6. ■	7. ■
$ 11.37	1 6	II	none	8. ■	9. ■
$147.37	12 13	I	5%	10. ■	11. ■

Exercises

Use the table of shipping charges for A. A. Rice to find the cost of shipping the items.

Item 1 lb oz	Item 2 lb oz	Item 3 lb oz	Total Weight lb oz	Zone	Shipping Cost
2 1	5 7	6 2	1. ■ ■	II	2. ■
0 5	0 9	1 2	3. ■ ■	I	4. ■
9 13	5 12	3 2	5. ■ ■	II	6. ■
11 6	4 7	1 9	7. ■ ■	II	8. ■

Determine the missing information. Use the table of shipping charges for A. A. Rice to find the cost of shipping the items.

Total of Goods	Weight lb oz	Zone	Sales Tax	Shipping Cost	Total Price
$100	6 1	I	5%	9. ■	10. ■
$ 42.50	8 2	II	none	11. ■	12. ■
$ 78.91	11 15	I	none	13. ■	14. ■
$101.19	8 5	I	5%	15. ■	16. ■

Solve. Use the table of shipping charges for A. A. Rice to find the shipping charge.

17. Item: Coat
Cost: $49.62
Weight: 4 lb 12 oz
Zone: II
Sales tax: none
Total cash price: ■

18. Item: 2 pairs of slacks
Cost: $17.55 each
Weight: 2 lb 6 oz each
Zone: II
Sales tax: 6%
Total cash price: ■

19. Item: Beach robe
Cost: ■
Weight: 3 lb 1 oz
Zone: II
Sales tax: none
Total cash price: $30.70

20. Vern ordered 5 pairs of slacks from A. A. Rice. Each one weighed 1 lb 14 oz and cost $21.55. Vern lived in Indiana, in Zone I, and had to pay 5% sales tax. Determine the total cost of Vern's order.

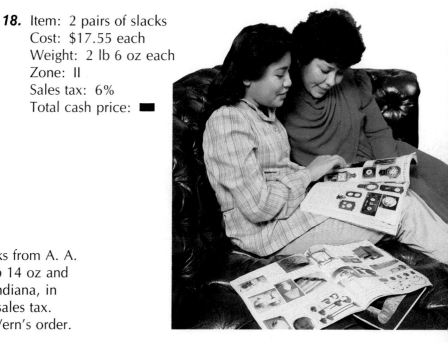

21. Deedee ordered the following from A. A. Rice. She lives in Zone II and pays no sales tax. Fill in an order form using the following information: 2 pairs of gloves, $8.25 each, 9 oz each; 3 pairs of socks, $2.25 per pair, 8 oz per pair; 1 overcoat, $79.56, 6 lb 2 oz

22. Greta sent a mail order to the A. A. Rice Co. Her order form is shown below. She forgot to fill in parts of the form. She had to pay 5 percent sales tax on the order and she lives in Zone I. Complete the order form.

Catalog Number	Quantity	Item Name	Unit Price	Cost	Weight lb	oz
19992X	■	Slacks	$19.50	■	1	7
71141B	■	Socks	$ 2.88	■	0	10
88774M	■	Blouse	$12.59	■	1	9

Total for goods: ■   Total Weight   lb
Tax: ■
Shipping Cost: ■
Total Cash Price: $60.77

Using a Calculator: *Adding Customary Measures*

You can use your calculator to add customary measures. For example, to find the sum of 1 lb 2 oz, 4 lb 5 oz, and 3 lb 7 oz:

Key: $\boxed{C^C_E}$ 1 $\boxed{\times}$ 16 $\boxed{+}$ 2 $\boxed{M+}$ Express each weight in terms of ounces.
     4 $\boxed{\times}$ 16 $\boxed{+}$ 5 $\boxed{M+}$
     3 $\boxed{\times}$ 16 $\boxed{+}$ 7 $\boxed{M+}$ $\boxed{M^R_C}$
     $\boxed{\div}$ 16 $\boxed{=}$ *8.875*   Divide by 16 to convert total ounces to pounds.

The answer, 8.875, is expressed in pounds. To change to ounces:

Key: 8.875 $\boxed{-}$ 8 $\boxed{=}$ $\boxed{\times}$ 16 $\boxed{=}$ *14*   0.875 lb = 14 oz

So, 8.875 lb = 8 lb 14 oz.

Use your calculator to find each sum. Express your answer first in pounds and then in pounds and ounces.

1. 3 lb 4 oz + 2 lb 8 oz + 9 lb 12 oz

2. 45 oz + 3 oz + 5 lb

3. 9 oz + 2 lb 4 oz + 3 lb 8 oz + 1 lb 7 oz

4. 3 lb 6 oz + 2 lb 9 oz + 1 lb 10 oz

7-3 Using the Postal Service

As a consumer, you will have many occasions to use the U.S. Postal Service. You may send letters or packages to friends or relatives, you may send a letter of inquiry or complaint, for which you want proof of arrival, or you may wish to return merchandise that was damaged or otherwise unsatisfactory.

EXAMPLE 1
Rob wanted to mail a first-class letter weighing 3.6 ounces. How much would it cost?

Problem Solving Strategy: Finding information.
Use the table of postal rates to find the cost of the letter. The rate that applies is $.25 for the first ounce and $.20 for each additional ounce or fraction of an ounce over the first.

Hidden Question: How many ounces over 1 ounce are there?
$$3.6 - 1 = 2.6$$
Use 3 ounces, since the charge is for each ounce or fraction of an ounce over 1 ounce.

$.25 + (number of ounces over 1 oz × $.20) = cost of postage
$.25 +   (3 × $.20)   = ■
$.25 + $.60   = $.85

The letter costs $.85 to mail.

Skill Review

To compute postal rates, you need to be able to multiply decimals.

Find each product.
1. 5 × 0.22
2. 12 × 1.34
3. 0.6 × 4.22
4. 3.9 × 6.8

(For additional help, see page 545.)

Table of Postal Rates

First class letter: $.25 Up to 1 oz
$.20 For each oz or fraction thereof over 1 oz

Post cards: $.15

Express mail: Guaranteed next day delivery $8.75 for up to ½ lb, $12.00 for ½ lb to 2 lb

Certified mail: $.80 + first class postage (The post office guarantees that your letter will be delivered.)

Return receipt: $.90 (The post office gives you a receipt that is signed and dated by the person who receives your letter.)

Insured Mail:		Parcel Post: Packages are priced by weight and zone				
			Zones			
Value	Cost	Not exceeding	I & II	III	IV	V
$.01 to $50	$ .70	2 lb	$1.49	1.61	1.77	2.04
$50.01 to $100	$1.50	3 lb	$1.58	1.75	2.00	2.39
$100.01 to $150	$1.90	4 lb	$1.66	1.90	2.22	2.74
$150.01 to $200	$2.20	5 lb	$1.75	2.04	2.45	3.09
$200.01 to $300	$3.15	6 lb	$1.84	2.19	2.67	3.44

EXAMPLE 2

Sun is sending a pair of slacks to her mother using parcel post and insured mail. How much will the package cost if it weighs 3 pounds 2 ounces and is insured for a value of $16.75? Her mother is in Zone III.

postage + cost of insurance = cost of mailing

$1.90 + $.70 = ■

↑   ↑

Look across the   Cost of insuring
row "Not   up to $50
exceeding 4 lb"
and under the
Zone III column.

$1.90   postage
+ .70   cost of insurance
─────
$2.60   total cost

Key: $\boxed{C_E^C}$ 1.90 $\boxed{+}$ .70 $\boxed{=}$ 2.6 $2.60

The cost of sending the package is $2.60.

Class Exercises

Find the cost of first-class postage for each letter.

1. 2.1 oz   **2.** 4 oz   **3.** 6.8 oz   **4.** 1 oz

5. Find the cost of sending a letter that weighs 3.5 ounces by certified mail, return receipt requested.

Find the cost of mailing the packages by parcel post.

Weight	Zone	Postage
3 lb 4 oz	IV	**6.** ■
4 lb 12 oz	II	**7.** ■
1 lb	V	**8.** ■
5 lb 9 oz	IV	**9.** ■

EXERCISES

Find the cost of first-class postage for each letter.

1. 5 oz   **2.** 7 oz   **3.** 1.1 oz   **4.** 5.2 oz

Find the cost of sending each letter by certified mail, return receipt requested.

5. 1.5 oz   **6.** 9.3 oz   **7.** 4.6 oz   **8.** 11.4 oz

Find the cost of mailing the packages by parcel post.

Weight	Zone	Postage
4 lb 1 oz	II	9. ■
1 lb 9 oz	I	10. ■
3 lb 1 oz	III	11. ■
4 lb 9 oz	IV	12. ■

Find the total cost of sending the packages by parcel post and insuring them for the amounts indicated.

Weight	Zone	Postage	Value of Package	Cost of Insurance	Mailing Cost
3 lb 5 oz	II	13. ■	$ 30.04	14. ■	15. ■
1 lb 2 oz	IV	16. ■	$128	17. ■	18. ■
2 lb 13 oz	V	19. ■	$ 75	20. ■	21. ■
4 lb 4 oz	III	22. ■	$225	23. ■	24. ■

Solve.

25. A letter weighing 3.1 ounces is sent by certified mail with return receipt. Will the cost of mailing be more than $1.75?

26. Explain how estimation can be used to solve Problem 25.

27. A package weighing 11 ounces is sent first class. How much is the postage?

28. How much will it cost to send a 1-pound 3-ounce package by parcel post to Zone I and insure it for a value of $55?

29. Murray sent a first class package by certified mail and paid $8.25. How much did the package weigh?

Consumer Note: *Choosing a Transportation Service*

Whether you are sending a letter or package across town or across the country, as a consumer you now have a wide choice of services. The U.S. Postal Service still handles most of the millions of letters that are sent out daily in this country. Increasingly though, many people are using private carriers to deliver important letters, documents, and packages more quickly around the country. These couriers offer overnight service for a flat fee based on weight and size. Many businesses use these rush services to meet deadlines and increase productivity.

Even the U.S. Postal Service now offers its own overnight express service.

Many local companies offer same-day delivery service within a particular region or metropolitan area. Some of these companies serve particular kinds of businesses, such as printing, advertising, and publishing. Even local taxi companies offer package delivery service around town. Look in your local Yellow Pages and you'll get some idea of the number of options available for sending letters and packages.

Career
Graphic Artist

Graphics are everywhere. Cereal boxes, food wrappers, magazine advertisements, and television all require the special services of a **graphic artist.** There are nearly a quarter million graphic artists employed by advertising agencies, publishers, direct-mail houses, large corporations, and studios that serve small companies and individuals.

Profile of a graphic artist. Most graphic artists are high school graduates with one or two years of art training. An artist's most important credential, however, is a portfolio, or collection, of his or her work. Graphic artists usually have been drawing or painting for many years. They have the ability to express a phrase or idea visually. Three out of five graphic artists are self-employed. They work closely with writers, photographers, advertising account executives, and customers.

The graphic arts environment. A graphic artist may work in a publishing company or large

advertising agency with ten or more artists on staff. However, a small studio may have only one or two artists on staff and use free-lance artists extensively. Graphic artists must be able to complete their work in time to meet deadlines. Mathematical precision is also needed. An important concept to the artist is ratio, since many drawings are done larger or smaller than they will actually appear.

All in a day's work. Arturo is a free-lance artist. He is preparing an ad for a major catalog sales company to use in its fall catalog.

1. In the fall catalog, all jackets and coats will be reduced 25%; slacks, shirts, and sweaters will be reduced 20%; and shoes will be reduced 30%. Arturo is given the following regular prices to use in the ads:

   dress shoes, $30; sports shoes, $20; slacks, $18; shirts, $10; jacket, $30; sweater, $15; coat, $60

   He also has to give the sale prices. Calculate the sale price of each item.

2. The picture of the shoes that Arturo draws will be 4 times as large as the final ad. If he wants the shoes in the ad to be $2\frac{1}{2}$ inches long, how long should they be in his drawing?

3. Arturo has drawn a picture of a jacket that will be reduced by 25% when it appears in the catalog. His drawing is 4 inches by 6 inches. How large will it be in the catalog?

4. The picture that Arturo draws of a sweater is to be $1\frac{1}{2}$ inches by 2 inches in the catalog. If he uses the scale 1 inch = $\frac{1}{2}$ foot, how large will the drawing be?

7-4 Making Your Own Clothes

One way to save money on clothing costs is to make some or all of your own clothing. You can then choose the style of clothing you like and have a choice of fabrics with which to work. To compute the cost of fabric, multiply the number of yards needed by the price per yard.

Skill Review

In order to compute the cost of fabric, you must be able to express mixed numbers as fractions.

Express as fractions.

1. $2\frac{3}{4}$
2. $5\frac{7}{8}$
3. $4\frac{1}{6}$
4. $3\frac{2}{3}$

(For additional help, see page 547.)

EXAMPLE 1

Gil needed $2\frac{7}{8}$ yards of 44-inch-wide fabric to sew a pair of slacks. If the fabric costs $2.48 per yard, how much will the fabric cost?

yards needed × price per yard = cost
$$2\frac{7}{8} \quad \times \quad \$2.48 \quad = \quad \blacksquare$$

Think: $2\frac{7}{8} = \frac{23}{8}$

 $\dfrac{23}{8} \times \$2.48 = \dfrac{\$57.04}{8} = \$7.13$

 Key: $\boxed{C_E^C}$ 23 $\boxed{\times}$ 2.48 $\boxed{\div}$ 8 $\boxed{=}$ ⟋ 7.13 ⟋
$\$7.13$

The fabric costs $7.13.

EXAMPLE 2

In addition to the fabric, Gil needed thread, a zipper, and a pattern to complete the slacks. Find the total cost of the slacks.

$$
\begin{array}{r}
\$2.75 \\
2.38 \\
1.20 \\
+\ 7.13 \\
\hline
\$13.46
\end{array}
$$

Key: $\boxed{C_E^C}$ 2.75 $\boxed{+}$ 2.38 $\boxed{+}$ 1.2 $\boxed{+}$ 7.13 $\boxed{=}$ ⟋ 13.46 ⟋
$\$13.46$

The cost of the slacks is $13.46.

Pattern	Zipper
$2.75	$2.38

Thread	Fabric
$1.20	$7.13

EXAMPLE 3

If Gil had purchased the slacks at a clothing store, he would have paid $22.25 for them. About how much money will he save by making his own slacks?

cost of store slacks − cost of homemade slacks = savings
$$\$22.25 \quad - \quad \$13.46 \quad = \quad \blacksquare$$

Estimate: $\$22.25 - \$13.46 = \blacksquare \rightarrow \$22 - \$13 = \$9$

Gil will save about $9 by making the slacks.

Class Exercises

Determine the cost of the fabric.

Price per Yard	Yards Needed	Cost	Price per Yard	Yards Needed	Cost
$1.98	$3\frac{1}{8}$	**1.** ■	$2.31	$2\frac{1}{2}$	**2.** ■
$4.75	$2\frac{1}{2}$	**3.** ■	$5.18	$2\frac{1}{8}$	**4.** ■
$2.65	$4\frac{1}{4}$	**5.** ■	$3.24	$3\frac{1}{8}$	**6.** ■

Determine the total cost of the homemade garment and about how much money is saved (if any).

Garment	Yards Needed	Cost per Yard	Pattern	Thread and Notions	Cost to Make	Store Price	Estimated Savings
Jacket	3	$2.50	$2.50	$2.25	**7.** ■	$19.95	**8.** ■
Blouse	$2\frac{1}{2}$	$2.79	$1.98	$ .90	**9.** ■	$13.25	**10.** ■
Shirt	$2\frac{5}{8}$	$1.95	$1.80	$1.75	**11.** ■	$ 7.50	**12.** ■

EXERCISES

Determine the cost of the fabric.

Price per Yard	Yards Needed	Cost	Price per Yard	Yards Needed	Cost
$2	$2\frac{1}{2}$	**1.** ■	$2.40	$2\frac{1}{8}$	**2.** ■
$3.29	$2\frac{7}{8}$	**3.** ■	$3.88	$2\frac{1}{4}$	**4.** ■
$1.89	$3\frac{3}{8}$	**5.** ■	$2.35	$2\frac{3}{4}$	**6.** ■

Determine the total cost of the homemade garment and about how much money is saved (if any).

Garment	Yards Needed	Cost per Yard	Pattern	Thread and Notions	Cost	Store Price	Estimated Savings
Slacks	2	$3	$2	$1	**7.** ■	$13.50	**8.** ■
Skirt	$2\frac{1}{4}$	$3.45	$2.75	$2.15	**9.** ■	$19.95	**10.** ■
Dress	$2\frac{7}{8}$	$2.98	$2.50	$2.75	**11.** ■	$26.92	**12.** ■
Bathrobe	$3\frac{3}{8}$	$2.71	$1.65	$1.30	**13.** ■	$10.38	**14.** ■

Solve.

15. Belinda wants to knit a wool sweater that would cost about $35 at the store. She will need 3 skeins of wool at $4.25 per skein and buttons for $1.17 to make the sweater. About how much will she save by knitting the sweater herself?

16. Stan used his calculator to compute the cost of $3\frac{7}{8}$ yards of fabric at $3.76 per yard. Study his keystrokes and answer the questions that follow.

Key: $\boxed{\text{C}^\text{C}_\text{E}}$ 7 $\boxed{\div}$ 8 $\boxed{+}$ 3 $\boxed{=}$ $\boxed{\times}$ 3.76 $\boxed{=}$ $\overline{\;14.57\;}$

a. Explain his procedure.

b. What keystrokes would change if he needed only $2\frac{1}{8}$ yards of the same fabric?

17. Nora saw a dress that cost $49.77, including tax. If she made the dress, she would save $1.42 in sales tax alone. In her state the sales tax on all the materials she needs is 5%. How much would it cost her to make the dress, including tax?

18. Choose an item of clothing you would like to make. Estimate how much it would cost to make the item and how much it would cost to purchase it in a store. What else should you consider besides cost?

Critical Thinking: *Identifying Reasons*

When you identify reasons, you point out the ideas that explain your thoughts, actions, or statements. For example, you might buy one brand of juice because you prefer its taste.

Rob wanted to make some clothes for school in order to supplement his wardrobe. He made a table showing comparative costs for buying and making three items.

	Shirt	Jacket	Sweat Pants
Cost to make	$ 8.45	$24.88	$2.37
Cost to purchase	$15.99	$55.75	$6.50

Match the following actions with the reasons Rob might give for taking them.

Action 1: Make a shirt.
Reasons: **a.** I could save a lot of money.
      b. A sports shirt might not be too difficult to make and the quality would be better.

Action 2: Make sweat pants but buy a jacket at the store.
Reasons: **a.** I need the jacket within a few days and I do not have time to make it.
      b. A jacket would be hard to make but sweat pants easy.

1. What reason did you identify for each action?

2. Describe your thought processes as you identified reasons.

7-5 Reading Advertisements

Advertisements in newspapers, in magazines, and on television are a common way for stores and businesses to tell you about the products or services they have for sale. When you read an advertisement, you must decide what features and prices are advertised and if these features and prices are acceptable.

EXAMPLE 1

Anita saw this newspaper ad. She wanted a pink wool sweater and a white wool sweater, both in a size M. What is the cost of the sweaters?

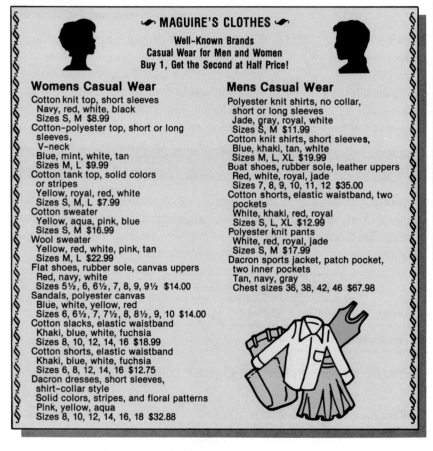

➤ MAGUIRE'S CLOTHES ➤
Well-Known Brands
Casual Wear for Men and Women
Buy 1, Get the Second at Half Price!

Womens Casual Wear
Cotton knit top, short sleeves
  Navy, red, white, black
  Sizes S, M $8.99
Cotton-polyester top, short or long sleeves,
  V-neck
  Blue, mint, white, tan
  Sizes M, L $9.99
Cotton tank top, solid colors
  or stripes
  Yellow, royal, red, white
  Sizes S, M, L $7.99
Cotton sweater
  Yellow, aqua, pink, blue
  Sizes S, M $16.99
Wool sweater
  Yellow, red, white, pink, tan
  Sizes M, L $22.99
Flat shoes, rubber sole, canvas uppers
  Red, navy, white
  Sizes 5½, 6, 6½, 7, 8, 9, 9½ $14.00
Sandals, polyester canvas
  Blue, white, yellow, red
  Sizes 6, 6½, 7, 7½, 8, 8½, 9, 10 $14.00
Cotton slacks, elastic waistband
  Khaki, blue, white, fuchsia
  Sizes 8, 10, 12, 14, 16 $18.99
Cotton shorts, elastic waistband
  Khaki, blue, white, fuchsia
  Sizes 6, 8, 12, 14, 16 $12.75
Dacron dresses, short sleeves,
  shirt-collar style
  Solid colors, stripes, and floral patterns
  Pink, yellow, aqua
  Sizes 8, 10, 12, 14, 16, 18 $32.88

Mens Casual Wear
Polyester knit shirts, no collar,
  short or long sleeves
  Jade, gray, royal, white
  Sizes S, M $11.99
Cotton knit shirts, short sleeves,
  Blue, khaki, tan, white
  Sizes M, L, XL $19.99
Boat shoes, rubber sole, leather uppers
  Red, white, royal, jade
  Sizes 7, 8, 9, 10, 11, 12 $35.00
Cotton shorts, elastic waistband, two pockets
  White, khaki, red, royal
  Sizes S, L, XL $12.99
Polyester knit pants
  White, red, royal, jade
  Sizes S, M $17.99
Dacron sports jacket, patch pocket,
  two inner pockets
  Tan, navy, gray
  Chest sizes 36, 38, 42, 46 $67.98

Step 1. Find the cost of the second sweater at half price.

cost of the first sweater × ½ = **cost of second sweater**

$22.99   × ½ =   ■

$22.99
×   0.5
$11.495
$11.50   Round to nearest cent.

Step 2. Add the cost of the second sweater to that of the first one.

$22.99   first sweater
+ 11.50   sweater at half price
$34.49   total cost

The cost of the two sweaters is $34.49.

With a calculator, the calculations in Example 1 can be simplified.

Key: $\boxed{C^C_E}$ 22.99 $\boxed{M+}$ $\boxed{\times}$ .5 $\boxed{M+}$ $\boxed{M^R_C}$ ⟋ 34.485 ⟋
                                                    $34.49   Round to nearest cent.

EXAMPLE 2

Jerome needed two pairs of pants, two pairs of shoes, and a cotton knit shirt. How much would these items cost? The sales tax is 6%.

Step 1. Find the cost of each kind of clothing.

Pants: $17.99   full price
         + 9.00   half price $\frac{1}{2} \times \$17.99 = \$8.995$
         $26.99 $9.00   Round to nearest cent.

Shoes: $35.00   full price $\frac{1}{2} \times \$35 = \$17.50$
        +$17.50   half price
         $52.50

Shirt: $19.99

Step 2. Find the total cost of the clothing.

$26.99   pants
 52.50   shoes
+ 19.99   shirt
$99.48

Step 3. Find the sales tax.

cost of clothing × **tax rate** = **tax**
     $99.48   ×   6%   = ■

Think: 6% = 0.06

$99.48   cost of clothing
× 0.06   tax rate
$5.9688
$5.97   Round to nearest cent.

Step 4. Find the total cost.

$99.48   cost of clothing
+ 5.97   tax
$105.45

With a calculator, the calculations in Example 2 can be streamlined.

Key: $\boxed{\text{C}^{\text{C}}_{\text{E}}}$ 17.99 $\boxed{\text{M}+}$ $\boxed{\times}$ .5 $\boxed{\text{M}+}$ 35 $\boxed{\text{M}+}$ $\boxed{\times}$ .5 $\boxed{\text{M}+}$
   19.99 $\boxed{\text{M}+}$ $\boxed{\text{M}^{\text{R}}_{\text{C}}}$ $\boxed{\times}$ 6 $\boxed{\%}$ $\boxed{\text{M}+}$ $\boxed{\text{M}^{\text{R}}_{\text{C}}}$ ╱ 105.4435 ╱

   $105.44   **Round to nearest cent.**

The $.01 difference in the answers occurs because the rounding is
done at different points in the computation.

Class Exercises

Use the Maguire's ad to find the total cost of each purchase.
Do not include items if they are not available in the color or size
indicated. Assume there is a sales tax of 6%.

1. 2 pairs of women's sandals

2. 1 cotton sweater and 2 cotton tank tops

3. 1 pair of men's boat shoes and 2 men's
cotton knit shirts

4. 1 women's cotton knit top (yellow,
size S) and 2 cotton sweaters (one white,
one blue)

5. 2 dresses (pink and yellow, size 8) 1 pair
of flat shoes, and two cotton tank tops.

6. 3 pairs of men's cotton shorts

EXERCISES

Use the Maguire's ad to find the total cost of each purchase.
Do not include items if they are not available in the color or size
indicated. Assume there is a sales tax of 6%.

1. 1 pair of men's shorts

2. 1 pair of men's pants and 1 men's jacket

3. 2 pairs of men's shoes and 1 men's
polyester knit shirt

4. 2 pairs of women's slacks, 2 cotton tank
tops, and 2 pairs of sandals

5. 2 pairs of women's slacks

6. 1 pair of women's flat shoes

7. 2 men's cotton knit shirts and 2 pairs of
polyester knit pants

8. 2 women's cotton tank tops (yellow and
red, size M)

9. 2 cotton knit tops (navy and pink, size M)
and 1 cotton-polyester top (white, size L)

10. 3 pairs of cotton slacks (khaki, size 14)

11. 1 pair of navy women's flat shoes and 1
pair of yellow sandals (both pairs, size $8\frac{1}{2}$)

Solve. Use the Maguire's ad. Assume there is a sales tax of 6%.

12. Marjorie wants two cotton sweaters. She could buy them in a
discount store for $13.75 each. Would she save money by
purchasing them at Maguire's? If so, how much?

13. Kristie wants to buy two pairs of cotton slacks (blue and white) and two cotton knit tops (blue and white). They should be from the same store because she wants the colors to match exactly. She can buy the slacks for $12.95 each and the tops for $7.75 each in a discount store. Where should she purchase the items so that the total price is lower?

14. Hank would like to buy two pairs of shoes, a sports jacket, and two pairs of pants. He can buy the shoes for $22.50 a pair and the jacket for $56.25 in a discount store. The pants can be obtained at the same discount store for $13.75. How could he purchase the items at the least possible cost?

15. A pair of men's swim trunks were advertised at 22% off. The sale price was $11.94. What was the regular price?

Mental Math: *Multiplying by $\frac{1}{2}$*

There is an easy way to find the cost of an item selling at half price—instead of multiplying the original cost by $\frac{1}{2}$, you can just divide it by 2. Most of the time, you can do the division mentally.

$$384 \times \tfrac{1}{2} = 384 \div 2 = 192$$

When dividing dollars and cents by 2, it is sometimes easier to do the division in two steps.

$$\$5.36 \times \tfrac{1}{2} = 5.36 \div 2 \qquad$$ **Think:** $\$5 \div 2 = \$2.50$
$$\$.36 \div 2 = \$\ .18$$
$$\$2.50 + \$.18 = \$2.68$$

So, $\$5.36 \div 2 = \$2.68$

Multiply each amount by $\frac{1}{2}$ by dividing by 2.

1. $254   **2.** $18.22   **3.** $25.76   **4.** $134.60   **5.** $25.99

7-6 The Consumer Price Index

The **consumer price index (CPI)** measures inflation, or the changing cost of consumer goods. The CPI is calculated by the U.S. Bureau of Labor Statistics using prices of food, housing, fuel, clothes, travel, and many other goods and services. Each year the average price of many items is found and a single figure is given for that year. Individual figures are also given for food, clothing, housing, and so on. The number 100 (100%) is assigned for the base year, 1967, and all other years are compared to it. For example, if the CPI for food is 254, a quantity of food that cost $100 in 1967 now costs $254.

A line graph is useful for showing the change in the cost of consumer goods over a period of time.

The statistics in the line graph below are for clothing. By reading the graph, you should be able to see that the CPI for clothing in 1975 was 145 and that the CPI for clothing was about 200 in 1983.

To determine the CPI for clothing in a year not shown on the graph or for other goods and services for a given year, divide the average price of an item in that year by its price in 1967 and multiply by 100.

EXAMPLE 1

Determine the CPI for shoes that cost $38.79 now and cost $16 in 1967. Compare it to the CPI for recent years.

$$\text{cost now} \div \text{cost in 1967} \times 100 = \text{CPI}$$
$$\$38.79 \div \$16 \times 100 = \blacksquare$$

$$
\begin{array}{r}
2.424 \rightarrow 2.42 \\
\$16\overline{)\$38.790} \\
\underline{32} \\
6\ 7 \\
\underline{6\ 4} \\
39 \\
\underline{32} \\
70 \\
\underline{64} \\
6
\end{array}
$$

Round to nearest hundredth.

Key: $\boxed{\text{C}^\text{C}_\text{E}}$ 38.79 $\boxed{\div}$ 16 $\boxed{\times}$ 100 $\boxed{=}$ 242.4375

242 Round to nearest whole number.

Think: 2.42 × 100 = 242

The CPI is 242; it is somewhat higher than the recent CPI for clothing of about 200.

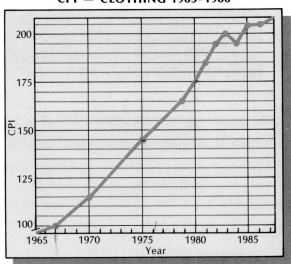

CPI — CLOTHING 1965–1986

EXAMPLE 2

If an article of clothing cost $6 in 1974, what might you expect it to have cost 11 years later?

Step 1. Find the rate of inflation for clothing between 1974 and 1985.

$$\textbf{CPI for 1985} \div \textbf{CPI for 1974} = \textbf{inflation rate}$$
$$205 \quad \div \quad 140 \quad = \quad 1.464 \rightarrow 1.46 \quad \textit{Round to nearest hundredth.}$$

The rate of inflation between 1974 and 1985 was 1.46.

Step 2. Find the expected cost in 1985.

$$\textbf{cost in 1974} \times \textbf{inflation rate from 1974 to 1985} = \textbf{cost in 1985}$$
$$\$6 \quad \times \quad 1.46 \quad = \quad \$8.76$$

The clothing was expected to cost $8.76 in 1985.

With a calculator, the calculations for Example 2 can be streamlined.

Key: 205 $\boxed{\div}$ 140 $\boxed{\times}$ 6 $\boxed{=}$  8.7857142
$8.79   Round to nearest cent.

The $.03 difference in the answers occurs because the rounding is done at different places in the computation.

Class Exercises

1. What was the CPI for clothing in 1970?

2. In what year was the CPI for clothing about 185?

3. If a coat cost $23.75 in 1967, about how much did it cost in 1980?

4. Find the rate of inflation between 1970 and 1975.

5. A certain kind of jacket cost $38.95 in 1975. About how much did a similar jacket cost in 1985?

6. A women's dress sold for $17.56 in 1970. How much will the dress cost when the CPI reaches 245?

EXERCISES

1. What was the CPI for clothing in 1983?

2. What was the CPI for clothing in 1965?

3. In what year was the CPI for clothing about 125?

4. In what year was the CPI for clothing about 175?

5. Determine the rate of inflation of clothing between 1970 and 1985.

6. Determine the rate of inflation of clothing between 1976 and 1982.

7. A pair of socks cost $1.22 in 1982. About how much would they have cost in 1986?

8. A sweater cost $28 in 1967. How much would it have cost in 1985?

9. A pair of pants cost $40 in 1980. About how much would the pair of pants have cost in 1970?

10. If a pair of slacks cost $32.60 in 1975, how much more would they have been 8 years later?

11. A pair of gloves cost $11.98 in 1985. About how much less would they have been in 1965?

12. A family spent $628 on clothing in 1970. About how much would that family have spent in 1985?

13. A piece of clothing cost $4.98 in 1967. How much will that piece of clothing cost when the CPI reaches 265?

14. Felicity spent $436.82 on clothes in 1979. If she purchased similar clothes in the same quantity, about how much would she have spent in 1984?

15. Harvey purchased a suit for $113.88. Five years later, he purchased another similar to the first for $143.39. In what year did he purchase the second suit, if the years in which he purchased both suits are multiples of 5?

16. Estimate the average cost of a pair of jeans this year. Find out the average cost of a pair of jeans several years ago from an outside source. What is the rate of inflation for the jeans between the two years?

17. Investigate the current CPI for food and clothes. What was the rate of inflation last year? What is it at present? Share your findings with the class.

Consumer Note: *Inflation*

Have you ever wondered why the things you buy seem to cost more each year? The increase in prices is called *inflation,* and it affects every part of our lives, from earning power to the cost of goods and services.

The *consumer price index* (CPI) reflects the rate of inflation and is based on cost-of-living patterns around the country, including the cost of energy, food, durable goods, and services. The CPI is commonly used to adjust pension benefits, union scales, and retail prices of consumer goods.

One way your family can cope with inflation is to budget your money and spend less on unnecessary items or services. For example, if the cost of heating your home increased dramatically (as it did during the oil crisis of the 1970s), you might need to adjust how much you spend for luxury items or entertainment.

Ask your parents or grandparents about the cost of food or clothes when they were young, and then ask them how much they earned on a weekly basis. You'll be surprised at their answers!

Computer:
FOR/NEXT Statements

Nigel wants to buy 3 pairs of socks for $1.29 each, 2 pairs of shorts at $4.98 each, and 4 shirts at $7.22 each. He wrote a BASIC program to find the amount spent on each item and the total amount spent. The statements needed to read, compute, print, and tally are repeated 3 times, once for each item of data. He uses a FOR/NEXT loop—FOR and NEXT statements and all statements in between—to cause the statements to be repeated.

10 HOME	Clears the screen.
20 PRINT "ITEM", "AMOUNT SPENT"	Prints the heading.
30 PRINT	Prints a blank line.
40 S = 0	Initializes the sum to zero.
50 FOR K = 1 TO 3	Opens the FOR/NEXT loop.
60 READ I$, N, U	Reads the values of I$, N, and U.
70 A = N * U	Computes the cost, N * U.
80 PRINT I$, A	Prints the item name and amount spent.
90 S = S + A	Adds the value of amount spent to the total spent.
100 NEXT K	Closes the FOR/NEXT loop.
110 PRINT "TOTAL SPENT = $"; S	Prints the label TOTAL SPENT and the total spent.
200 DATA SOCKS, 3, 1.29	Data set for this program
210 DATA SHORTS, 2, 4.98	Data set for this program.
220 DATA SHIRTS, 4, 7.22	Data set for this program.
300 END	Tells the computer to end the program.

Enter the program and RUN it. Observe the output.

EXERCISES

1. What do you think would be the output of the program if line 50 were changed to the following?
    50 FOR K = 1 TO 2

2. Make the change suggested by Exercise 1 by retyping only line 50. Run the program and observe the output.

3. Suppose that 230 DATA TIES, 2, 10.99 was inserted into the program. What small change to line 50 would have to be made in order to capture and process the new data?

4. Make the changes suggested by Exercise 3 by typing line 230 and changing one line of the program. Run the program and observe the change.

Decision Making:
Building a Wardrobe

Jamil and Tanya are planning to use some of the money they earned to buy school clothes. Jamil wants to purchase three pairs of jeans, a pair of tennis shoes, a pair of dress slacks, and three or four tops. He has budgeted $200 for clothes. Tanya has $350 left. She doesn't want to spend it all on clothes, but she has not set a limit on what she is willing to spend. She wants an assortment of pants, skirts, and tops to add to her wardrobe. She has a new pair of tennis shoes and a pair of casual shoes that she can wear to start the school year.

SETTING GOALS
One evening, Jamil and Tanya discussed their shopping plans.

"Applebaum's Department Store has an advertisement in tonight's paper for their back-to-school clothing sale. Perhaps we can find information in there that would help us," Jamil commented.

"That's a good idea, but I'm not as sure of what I want as you are. Let's write out our goals," Tanya replied.

After thinking for awhile, Jamil wrote the following:

> Goal- To spend no more than $200 for the items
> of clothing I need (3 pairs of jeans, a pair
> of tennis shoes, a pair of dress slacks,
> and 3 or 4 tops)

Tanya had a more difficult time. When she was finished her paper read as follows:

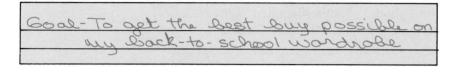

Goal—To get the best buy possible on my back-to-school wardrobe

Answer the following questions.

1. How do these goal statements differ?

2. What advantages and disadvantages do you see in Jamil's statement?

3. What advantages and disadvantages do you see in Tanya's statement?

4. Describe your thought processes as you identified advantages and disadvantages.

GETTING THE INFORMATION

The Applebaum's ad contained the following information:

BACK-TO-SCHOOL SPECIALS
Designer Jeans Regularly $34–$42
ON SALE 30% OFF

Applebaum's Own Top-Quality Men's Jeans Regularly $27, ON SALE $21.99 A PAIR. FOR EACH PAIR OF JEANS YOU BUY, GET ⅓ OFF A COORDINATING COTTON KNIT TOP.	Misses and Junior Casual Dresses This season's must-have brand-name dresses ON SALE FOR $34.99–$42.99 (Regularly $42–$56)
•	•
Men's Cotton Knit Tops A Variety of Styles and Colors ON SALE FOR $15.95–$23.95 (Regularly $19–$28)	Misses and Junior "Top-line" Separates Coordinating Colors, Fantastic Fit, Great Looks for Fall Tops regularly $17–$26 Pants regularly $19–$35 Skirts regularly from $22
•	Jackets regularly starting at $50
Men's Dress Slacks and Sportcoats ON SALE FOR 20% OFF (Slacks regularly $25–$40) (Sportcoats regularly starting from $52)	ALL ON SALE FOR 25% OFF

Tanya decided she wanted to get at least two dresses, a jacket, four or five tops, and an assortment of pants, jeans, and skirts.

Answer the following questions.

5. What additional information does Jamil need before deciding what to purchase?

6. In order to shop more wisely, what additional decisions might Tanya want to make before going to the store?

7. To answer Question 5, you had to decide what information was missing. Describe your thought processes as you did this.

MAKING A DECISION

"Jamil, why don't we also look at Blackmon's Catalog to see if they have a better price on any of the items we want? I bet they also have information on the price of tennis shoes," Tanya suggested. Tanya and Jamil got the following information from Blackmon's Catalog.

Item Number	Item Name	Unit Price	Lb	Oz.	Color
226-9082	Men's designer jeans	$31.50	2	0	
226-7946	Blackmon's men's jeans	$19.99	2	2	
525-1566	Cotton knit top	$14.00	1	8	Assorted
555-1234	Dress slacks	$29.95	1	10	Black
936-3477	All-star leather tennis	$42.99	2	0	
936-9087	Blackmon's leather tennis	$35.00	2	0	
212-6335	Safari dress	$37.99	1	2	Brown
280-1897	Knit dress	$29.75	1	6	Blue, Red
277-1789	Oversized top	$17.99		10	White, Red
291-5674	Dress blouse	$22.00		12	White
345-9741	Women's designer jeans	$27.99	2	3	
396-1527	Blackmon's women's jeans	$23.00	2	2	
256-9134	Women's dress pants	$21.25	1	4	Assorted
222-0965	Skirt	$22.00	1	4	Assorted
365-8743	Jacket	$47.00	1	0	Yellow

Blackmon's charges tax only to California residents, so Tanya and Jamil will not have to pay tax on the items they order. They have to pay a 5% sales tax on items they purchase from Applebaum's.

Blackmon's does charge shipping costs on all items purchased from their catalog. Jamil and Tanya would have to pay the following shipping rates listed for zone II.

Answer the following questions.

Weight	Zone I	Zone II
0 to 1 lb	$1.39	$1.76
1 lb 1 oz to 3 lb	$1.70	$2.52
3 lb 1 oz to 5 lb	$1.97	$3.20
5 lb 1 oz to 7 lb	$2.17	$3.67
7 lb 1 oz to 9 lb	$2.33	$3.83
9 lb 1 oz to 11 lb	$2.50	$4.01

8. What advantages and disadvantages do you see in catalog shopping?

9. What calculations must Tanya or Jamil make before comparing the price of an item at Applebaum's with the cost of a similar item from Blackmon's?

10. Jamil visits Applebaum's and decides to purchase store-brand jeans because of the price reduction on the tops. He selects three tops that normally sell for $21 and three pairs of jeans. How much do these items cost?

11. What would be the cost of three pairs of store brand jeans and three cotton tops from Blackmon's?

12. The dress slacks Jamil likes at Applebaums's regularly sell for $35. How much will they cost on sale? Taking into consideration sales tax and shipping charges, where will Jamil get the best buy on dress slacks?

13. Assuming Jamil decides to buy the all-star tennis shoes from Blackmon's and to buy three pairs of store-brand jeans, three tops, and the dress slacks from the store with the best price, how much will Jamil spend?

14. Tanya discovered Applebaum's carried the same top-line yellow jacket that she had seen in Blackmon's catalog. It regularly sold for $50 at Applebaum's and $47 from Blackmon's. However, because the jacket was on sale at Applebaum's, she decided to buy it from them. Was this the better choice? Explain.

15. Applebaum's had several other items that Tanya liked. One was a top that normally sold for $26. Another top regularly sold for $27. Applebaum's also carried a white skirt that cost $25 when it was not on sale. If Tanya decides to buy them all at the sale price of 25% off, how much will she have to spend?

16. Tanya also liked two pairs of women's dress pants carried by both Applebaum's and Blackmon's. They normally sold at Applebaum's for $35 but were on sale for 25% off. At Blackmon's they sold for $21.25, but she would have to pay shipping charges. Where would she get the best buy? How much does she save?

17. Tanya decides to complete her wardrobe by purchasing a safari dress, a knit dress, an oversized top, a blouse, and a pair of women's designer jeans from Blackmon's. How much do Tanya's purchases cost if she purchases these items from Blackmon's and purchases the clothing in Questions 14–16 at the least expensive price?

DECIDE FOR YOURSELF

How would you go about deciding on new clothes to buy? What factors would affect your decision? How would you find information about clothing and prices? Summarize how you, and Jamil and Tanya, went about deciding what new clothes to buy.

Chapter 7 Review

VOCABULARY

Consumer Price Index (CPI)   discount, or markdown   sale price

For Exercises 1–3, select the word or words that complete each statement.

1. The _____ is the amount saved by buying an item at a discounted price.

2. The discounted price is called the _____ .

3. The _____ measures inflation, or the cost of consumer goods.

SKILLS

Express as decimals.

4. 16%

5. 46.5%

6. $4\frac{1}{2}\%$

Find each sum.

7. 8 lb 4 oz + 3 lb 14 oz

8. 3 lb 6 oz + 2 lb 8 oz + 15 oz

Write as fractions.

9. $3\frac{2}{3}$

10. $8\frac{5}{8}$

11. $4\frac{5}{6}$

Find each quotient. Round your answer to the nearest hundredth.

12. $13.56 ÷ 8

13. $492 ÷ 18

14. $56.35 ÷ 7

CONSUMER TOPICS

15. Kristi purchased a card table on sale for $19.50. The regular price was $26. What was the markdown?

16. Rick purchased a shirt at 20% off. If the regular price is $12.99, how much did he pay?

17. Dean ordered snowshoes (at $78) and snow goggles (at $44) from a catalog. The sales tax was 6% and the shipping for the 5-pound order came to $2.01. What was the total amount he was billed?

18. Lisa ordered 2 boxes of apples (at $14.75 each) from a catalog. Shipping charges were $5.25 for each box. What was her total cost?

Solve using the table of shipping charges on page 227.

19. Item 1: 2 lb 5 oz
Item 2: 3 lb 7 oz
Item 3: 1 lb 4 oz
Total weight: ▪
Shipping charges
(Zone I): ▪

20. Item 1: 1 lb 14 oz
Item 2: 2 lb 7 oz
Item 3: 5 lb 3 oz
Total weight: ▪
Shipping charges
(Zone II): ▪

21. Item 1: 1 lb 3 oz
Item 2: 1 lb 11 oz
Item 3: 15 oz
Total weight: ▪
Shipping charges
(Zone II): ▪

22. Roy wanted to mail a first-class letter weighing 3.2 ounces. If the first ounce was 25¢ and each additional ounce (or fraction thereof) was 20¢, what was the total cost?

23. Marla sent a certified letter weighing 4 ounces. First-class postage was $.85, the charge for certified mail was $.80, and the charge for a return receipt was $.90. What was her total cost?

Solve using the table of postal rates on page 231.

24. Package weight: 2 lb 5 oz
Zone I
Insurance value: $120
Cost of mailing package: ▇

25. Package weight: 5 lb 7 oz
Zone IV
Insurance value: $250
Cost of mailing package: ▇

Solve.

26. For a costume, Steve needs $2\frac{1}{2}$ yards of 44-inch-wide fabric (at $2.68 per yard), a zipper (at $2.19), buttons (at $1.89 for six), and thread ($.79). What will his total cost be?

27. Find the total cost of two jackets on sale for half price if the original price of the first is $37 and the original price of the second is $45.

Solve. Use the ad on page 238 for Problems 28–30.

28. Women's casual wear:
  2 cotton tank tops
  2 cotton sweaters
  Total: ▇

29. Men's casual wear:
  2 cotton knit shirts
  2 cotton shorts
  Total: ▇

30. Women's casual wear:
  2 cotton knit tops
  2 wool sweaters
  Total: ▇

31. Justin found a stepladder on sale for $69.99. The regular price was $87.50. He also found a humidifier that was originally $37.99. It was marked down 20%. Find his total savings.

32. Geri went to a sale that offered one pair of shoes at half price with the purchase of a pair at the regular price. If the regular price was $37.50 and Geri got the second pair at half price, what was the total amount of her purchase, including 6% sales tax.

33. Dale found a $599.99 sofa on sale at a department store for half price. He found the same sofa on sale at a furniture store for 40% off, but the regular price was $560. Which store had the lower price and how much was it?

Use the CPI graph on page 242 to solve.

34. Determine the CPI for a suit that costs $210 now and cost $88 in 1967.

35. In 1970 a skirt cost $16.35. Find its cost now with a rate of inflation of 1.52.

Chapter 7 Test

Solve.

1. Rita purchased a telephone on sale for $23.40. The regular price was $39. What was the markdown rate?

2. Don bought a leather jacket that originally cost $265. The markdown was 25%. What was the sale price?

3. Item: Lamp
Regular price: $49.99
Markdown: 18%
Sale price: ■

4. Item: Watch
Regular price: $64.50
Markdown: ■
Sale price: $51.60

5. Starla ordered a skirt ($37) and a blouse ($21.50) from a catalog. Shipping charges came to $1.62. What was the total amount she was charged?

6. Wendy ordered an afghan that weighed 2 pounds 12 ounces and a serving tray that weighed 24 ounces. What was the total weight of her order?

Use the table of postal rates on page 231 to find the cost of first-class postage for each letter in Problems 7–9.

7. 2.2 oz

8. 4.9 oz

9. 8 oz

10. A package weighing 5 pounds 3 ounces is sent parcel post to Zone IV. How much is the postage? (Use the table on page 231.)

11. Garth needs $3\frac{1}{8}$ yards of 44-inch-wide fabric to sew a pair of slacks. If the fabric costs $4.29 per yard, how much will his purchase cost?

12. In Problem 11, Garth also needs a zipper (at $2.59), a pattern (at $3.50), and thread (at $1.25) in addition to the fabric. What will the total cost of the slacks be?

13. Garth saw a similar pair of slacks in a store for $48. How much will he save by making them himself?

15. Tam bought 3 rolls of film on sale. How much did she save?

14. Dameon located a $22.99 backpack on sale for 25% off. If there was 5% sales tax added to the purchase price, what was his total purchase amount?

16. Mallory found board games on sale for $7.99 each. The regular price was $9.95. She could save even more money by buying 3 games for $22. If she bought three, what would her savings be?

17. Determine the CPI for a jacket that costs $68.79 now and cost $34.95 in 1967.

Use the CPI graph on page 242 to solve.

18. A pair of slacks cost $18.95 in 1975. How much would they have cost in 1980?

FILM

Regularly 3 rolls for $6.50

SALE

3 rolls for $4.99

Cumulative Mixed Review

1. Margaret purchased a $395 electronic typewriter on the installment plan. She paid 10% down. The finance charge on the remainder was 18%. She was given 12 months to pay off the balance. What was her monthly payment?
   a. $29.63 b. $35.95
   c. $39.50 d. $34.96

2. Carl ordered 2 shirts (at $19.50 each) and a wool vest (at $28) from a catalog. Sales tax was 5%, and shipping charges came to $1.76. What was the total amount of his order?
   a. $70.35 b. $72.11
   c. $68.76 d. $71.11

3. Barbara charged a $232 purchase on her credit card. The first month she paid $50. The second month's statement included a 1.5% monthly finance charge, computed with the unpaid balance method. What was the total amount due on the second statement?
   a. $184.73 b. $235.48
   c. $185.76 d. $50.75

4. Joanne needs $6\frac{1}{8}$ yards of 36-inch-wide fabric to sew stuffed animals. If the fabric costs $4.35 per yard, what will her cost be?
   a. $25.64 b. $23.12
   c. $26.64 d. $27.52

5. Determine the monthly payment under an add-on plan, where simple interest is charged on the amount borrowed: $1,200 for 12 months at 8% interest.
   a. $108 b. $110
   c. $96 d. $92

6. Russ fixed a bowl of cereal containing 2 servings. The nutrition label on the box indicated that each serving had 110 calories. If the milk he added contained 40 calories, how many calories in total did he consume?
   a. 260 b. 280
   c. 150 d. 300

7. Barnaby prepared fried chicken, green beans, and a glass of milk for dinner. The fried chicken contained 60 IU of vitamin A, the green beans contained 680 IU of vitamin A, and the milk contained 350 IU of vitamin A. What percentage of the U.S. RDA of vitamin A was provided by his meal if he needs 1000 IU of vitamin A per day?
   a. 89% b. 109%
   c. 98% d. 92%

8. Determine the CPI for a bicycle that costs $229 now and cost $89 in 1967.
   a. 155 b. 198
   c. 234 d. 257

9. Bob had the following telephone bills: March, $145.21; April, $154.32; May, $132.86. What is his average monthly expense for the telephone?
   a. $149.18 b. $140.89
   c. $144.13 d. $142.53

10. Brenda wants to knit a wool sweater that would cost $43 if she bought it. She will need 5 skeins of wool at $4.80 per skein and a pattern at $4. How much will she save by making the sweater?
    a. $24 b. $28
    c. $16.50 d. $15

CHAPTER 8
Buying a Car

Diane is shopping for her first car. She has saved $3,000 to use in buying the car. She has found one used car she likes, which costs slightly more than she has saved. However, she has also found a new car that she likes for almost three times what she has saved.

- What factors should she consider in her decision about which car to buy?

- What are some of the advantages of buying a new car? What are some of the disadvantages?

- What are some of the advantages of buying a used car? What are some of the disadvantages?

- What are some of the costs related to car ownership not included in the actual price of the car?

If you were buying a car, what would be your most important considerations?

8-1 Shopping for a New Car

When you decide to buy a new car, you can read consumer magazines, consumer guides, and newspaper ads to learn as much as possible about the performance, features, fuel efficiency, cost of maintenance, safety test results, prices, and so on of different makes and models of cars. Once you have decided upon the kind of car you want, you can visit dealers to see what cars and prices they have to offer.

All new cars are labeled with stickers like the one shown on the right. These stickers give information about the cost of the car. The **sticker price** is the total of the **base price,** the **options,** and the **destination charge.**

Extra features such as air conditioning and radio

Price of the car with only the standard equipment

Sedan 4400		Base Price $8,127.00
	Options	
ABK	Automatic Speed Control and Tilt Steering Column	$295.95
HAJ	Air Conditioning	$757.80
RAD	Radio–AM & FM Prem. Stereo w/Cassette	$279.20
TBB	Conventional Spare Tire	$ 82.55
WHB	Road Wheels–Cast Aluminum 14"	$232.50
	Destination Charge	$398.00

Cost of shipping the car from the factory to the dealer

EXAMPLE 1

Naomi is interested in purchasing the sedan 4400 whose sticker is shown. What is the sticker price of the car?

Step 1. Find the total cost of the options.

$295.95 + $757.80 + $279.20 + $82.55 + $232.50 = $1,648

Step 2. Find the sticker price.

base price + cost of options + destination charge = sticker price
$8,127   + $1,648   + $398   = $10,173

The sticker price of the sedan is $10,173.

Many dealers are willing to settle for a price somewhat below the sticker price. Dealer's profit is often expressed as a percentage of the sticker price and is called the **margin of profit.** The margin of profit varies with make, size, and type of car and with the number and type of options. The margin on a large luxury car is about 22% but on a compact car it can be as low as 12%. A wise consumer will try to estimate the dealer's cost and make an offer that is between the dealer's cost and the sticker price.

EXAMPLE 2

Naomi wanted to make an offer on the sedan that had a sticker price of $10,173. She had read that the dealer's margin of profit is about 18% on this car. She decided to make an offer of $500 over the dealer's cost. Use estimation to find how much she offered.

Skill Review

To compute sticker prices, you need to be able to add money amounts.

Find each sum.

1. $2,356.45 + $198 + $12,765.76

2. $295.30 + $387.10 + $8,441.97

3. $12,765.84 + $1,600 + $375.95 + $4,529.73

4. $725.19 + $3,000 + $21,346.87

(For additional help, see page 544.)

Step 1. Estimate the dealer's profit.

profit margin × **sticker price = dealer's profit**
    18%   × $10,000   =   ■

Think: 18% × $10,000 = 0.18 × $10,000 = $1,800

Step 2. Estimate the dealer's cost.

sticker price − **dealer's profit = dealer's cost**
  $10,000   − $1,800   = $8,200

Step 3. Find how much Naomi offered.

dealer's cost + $500 = Naomi's offer
  $8,200   + $500 = $8,700

Naomi offered $8,700.

With a calculator and mental math, you can
find the exact answer to Example 2.

Key: $\boxed{\text{CE}^{\text{C}}}$ 10173 $\boxed{\text{M+}}$ $\boxed{\times}$ 18 $\boxed{\%}$ $\boxed{\text{M−}}$ 500 $\boxed{\text{M+}}$ $\boxed{\text{MC}^{\text{R}}}$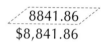
                                                 $8,841.86

Class Exercises

Complete the table by computing the missing values.

Base Price	Price of Options	Destination Charge	Sticker Price
$5,472	$1,610	$298	**1.** ■
$8,100	$1,100	$200	**2.** ■
$9,837	$2,015	$375	**3.** ■

Complete the table by estimating the missing values.

Sticker Price	Profit Margin	Dealer Profit	Dealer Cost	Amount Offered over Estimated Cost	Total Amount Offered
$5,496	12%	**4.** ■	**5.** ■	$200	**6.** ■
$7,118	18%	**7.** ■	**8.** ■	$300	**9.** ■
$8,962	17%	**10.** ■	**11.** ■	$400	**12.** ■

13. Explain how mental arithmetic can be used to find the answer
to Exercise 2.

EXERCISES

Complete the table by computing the missing values.

Base Price	Price of Options	Destination Charge	Sticker Price
$5,000	$1,400	$350	1. ■
$6,200	$1,750	$225	2. ■
$9,912	3. ■	$349	$11,159

Complete the table by estimating the missing values.

Sticker Price	Profit Margin	Dealer Profit	Dealer Cost	Amount Offered over Estimated Cost	Total Amount Offered
$ 4,945	11%	4. ■	5. ■	$100	6. ■
$14,994	19%	7. ■	8. ■	$500	9. ■
$21,952	20%	10. ■	11. ■	$600	12. ■

Solve.

13. A Wizard 222 has a sticker price of $9,920 and the dealer's profit margin is 16%. Would the dealer be likely to accept an offer of $8,000?

14. Karl made an offer on a Wizard 222 (Problem 13) of $8,923, which he thought was $350 over dealer cost. The dealer said, "That's $965 less profit than I usually make!" What is the dealer's usual margin of profit?

15. Choose two new cars you would like to buy. Find out how much the cars cost at two dealers and what options are available. Compare your answers with your classmates' answers.

Consumer Note: *Shopping for a Car*

Buying a car involves time, money, and patience. Doing a little homework before actually getting into the driver's seat can make a big difference in the car-buying process, the amount of money you spend, and your future driving pleasure. As a wise consumer you should decide upon your transportation needs, compare the kinds of cars available priced within your budget, and narrow the choices down to a couple of models.

For a small fee some independent car-buying services and automobile clubs offer detailed computer printouts, which list the wholesale vehicle price plus the cost of the options you specify. These services will put you in touch with dealers willing to sell cars for a low markup over the wholesale price.

You can also gather information by consulting consumer publications buyer's guides for test ratings of the new model-year cars. With this kind of information in hand, you can compare the prices at dealer showrooms and be in a better position to get the best possible deal when buying a car.

8-2 Financing a Car

Once you and a new-car dealer have agreed on a price for the car you want, you may want to finance some or all of the cost of the car. The money that you need can be borrowed from a bank, a credit union, an independent credit company, a savings and loan company, or even the car dealership. Dealers usually require between 20% and 30% of the price of the car to be paid as a **down payment.**

EXAMPLE 1

The price of Bruce's car was $5,237. The dealer required a 20% down payment. How much did Bruce have to borrow or finance?

Step 1. Find the down payment.

down payment rate × price = amount of down payment
$$20\% \quad \times \$5,237 = \quad \blacksquare$$

Think: 20% = 0.20

$$\begin{array}{r} \$5,237 \\ \times \ 0.20 \\ \hline \$1,047.40 \end{array}$$

Key: $\boxed{C^C_E}$ 5237 $\boxed{\times}$ 20 $\boxed{\%}$ ⟋1047.4⟋
$1,047.40

Step 2. Find the amount financed.

price − down payment = amount financed
$$\$5,237 - \quad \$1047.40 \quad = \quad \$4,189.60$$

Bruce financed $4,189.60.

Problem Solving Strategy: Solving another way.

You can use mental math and percents to solve Example 1 another way.

total cost of car	−	down payment	=	amount financed
100% of total cost	−	20% of total cost	=	amount financed
		80% of total cost	=	amount financed
		0.8 × $5,237	=	$4,189.60

Skill Review

To find down payment amounts, you need to be able to find a percent of a number.

Find each percent.
1. 18% of 4,000
2. 25% of $3,500
3. 28% of 35,295
4. 20% of $7,624

(For additional help, see page 551.)

EXAMPLE 2

Bruce repaid the loan of $4,189.60 in 36 months. His monthly payments, which included the finance charge, were $128.20. Find the finance charge and the final cost of the car.

Step 1. Find the finance charge.

$$\begin{matrix} \text{amount of} \\ \text{monthly} \\ \text{payment} \end{matrix} \times \begin{matrix} \text{number of} \\ \text{monthly} \\ \text{payments} \end{matrix} - \begin{matrix} \text{amount} \\ \text{financed} \end{matrix} = \begin{matrix} \text{finance} \\ \text{charge} \end{matrix}$$

$$\$128.20 \quad \times \quad 36 \quad - \quad \$4,189.60 \quad = \quad \blacksquare$$

```
    $128.20   amount of monthly payments
  ×      36   number of monthly payments
     769 20
   3 846 0
  $4,615.20
  −4,189.60   amount financed
    $425.60   finance charge
```

The finance charge is $425.60.

Step 2. Find the final cost of the car.

cash price + finance charges = final cost
$5,237   + $425.60   = $5,662.60

The total cost of the car was $5,662.60.

With a calculator, the problem in Example 2 can be streamlined through the use of memory keys.

Key: $\boxed{\text{C}^{\text{C}}_{\text{E}}}$ 128.2 $\boxed{\times}$ 36 $\boxed{\text{M+}}$ Find the total amount paid in 36 months; place in memory.

4189.6 $\boxed{\text{M−}}$ Enter the amount financed; subtract from memory.

5237 $\boxed{\text{M+}}$ $\boxed{\text{M}^{\text{R}}_{\text{C}}}$ 5662.6 Enter the cash price; add to memory; recall the total cost from
          $5,662.60   memory.

Class Exercises

Use the information about the Spirit 2000.

1. What is the down payment?

2. What is the amount to be financed?

3. What is the finance charge?

4. What is the final cost of the car?

> Buy the SPIRIT 2000!
> Cash price: $4,318
> Down payment: 25%
> Monthly payments: $144.11 for 24 mo

EXERCISES

Use the information about the Marsel 1000.

1. What is the down payment?

2. What is the amount to be financed?

3. What is the finance charge?

4. What is the final cost of the car?

Use the information about the Knockout 650.

5. What is the down payment?

6. What is the amount to be financed?

7. What is the finance charge?

8. What is the final cost of the car?

9. If 36 payments of $198.86 were made instead of the 48, what would the final cost of the car be?

Buy the MARSEL 1000!
Cash price: $6,429
Down payment: 22%
Monthly payments: $164.37 for 36 mo

Buy the KNOCKOUT 650!
Cash price: $9,000
Down payment: 30%
Monthly payments: $154.02 for 48 mo

10. Explain how mental arithmetic can be used to find the answer to Exercise 6.

Solve.

11. Model: Compact
Cash price: $5,137
Down payment amount: ■
Amount financed: $3,737

12. Model: Midsized
Cash price: $7,380
Down payment percentage: 25%
Amount financed: ■

13. Romaine agreed to pay $8,250 for a midsized car. The dealer added 5% sales tax to this price but allowed a $2,500 trade-in for her old car. If she paid 25% of the remainder down and financed the rest, how much did she have to finance?

14. Nelbert settled on a price of $5,400 for a compact car. The dealer had to add 5% sales tax to this price but allowed a $1,400 trade-in for Nelbert's old car. Would $1,000 be enough for a 30% down payment?

Mental Math: Using Fractions to Find Percents

There is an easy way to find a percent of a number when the percent is 20%, 25%, or 50%, for example.

Find 20% of $425.

Think: 20% = $\frac{1}{5}$. So, 20% of $425 = $\frac{1}{5}$ of $425.
$\frac{1}{5} \times \$425 = \$425 \div 5 = \$85$ Multiplying by $\frac{1}{5}$ is the same as dividing by 5.

Find each of the following using mental arithmetic.

1. 25% of $600

2. 50% of $388

3. 20% of $428

4. 10% of $2,298

5. 25% of $3,000

6. 20% of $998

8-3 Car Insurance

Insurance companies use tables, like the one shown, to determine the **premium,** or annual cost, of your insurance protection. The annual insurance base premium shown in the table is then multiplied by the driver rating factor. The **driver rating factor** is determined by your age, driving record, and other factors.

Annual Base Premiums for Liability/Property Insurance			
Liability		**Property Damage**	
Limit	**Premium**	**Limit**	**Premium**
10/20	$75	$5,000	$31
25/50	$78	$10,000	$35
50/100	$81	$25,000	$39
100/300	$84	$50,000	$43

There are several types of insurance protection, or coverage.

- *Liability insurance* covers injury or harm the driver may do to people not in the driver's car. A liability limit of 50/100 means the limits of liability are $50,000 per injured person and $100,000 per accident.
- *Property damage insurance* covers damage done by the driver to any vehicle or property of others. The limit of liability for this insurance is often given with the liability insurance limits. For example, 50/100/25 means that the insurance has a limit of liability of $25,000 for property damage.
- *Medical coverage* covers the cost of medical expenses for those in the driver's car.
- *Uninsured motorist insurance* covers injuries or damage to occupants of the driver's car, if it has been an accident caused by an uninsured motorist.
- *Collision insurance* covers damage done to one's own car in a collision caused by the driver.
- *Comprehensive insurance* covers any damage done to the car from causes other than collisions.

EXAMPLE 1

Determine the insurance premium for 100/300 liability insurance for a driver having a rating factor of 2.85.

Step 1. Find the base premium for 100/300 liability in the table above: 100/300 has a premium of $84.

Skill Review

Computing the annual cost of insurance protection requires knowing how to multiply with decimals.

Find each product.
1. 2.8 × 5.6
2. 7.91 × 0.32
3. $28.50 × 1.6
4. 9,000 × 0.00043

(For additional help, see page 545.)

Step 2. Find the annual premium.

base premium × rating factor = annual premium
$$\$84 \quad \times \quad 2.85 \quad = \quad \blacksquare$$

Estimate: $\$84 \times 2.85 = \blacksquare \rightarrow \$80 \times 3 = \$240$

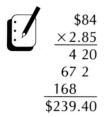
$$\begin{array}{r} \$84 \\ \times 2.85 \\ \hline 4\ 20 \\ 67\ 2 \\ 168 \\ \hline \$239.40 \end{array}$$

Key: $\boxed{C_E^C}$ 84 $\boxed{\times}$ 2.85 $\boxed{=}$ 239.40
$$\$239.40$$

The answer $239.40 is reasonably close to the estimate $240 and is a sensible answer.

The annual premium is $239.40.

EXAMPLE 2
Lucy wants 50/100/10 liability and property damage coverage. Her driver rating factor is 1.90. What is her total premium?

Step 1. Find the cost of liability coverage.

base premium × driver rating factor = premium
$$\$81 \quad \times \quad 1.90 \quad\quad = \$153.90$$

Step 2. Find the cost of property damage coverage.

base premium × driver rating factor = premium
$$\$35 \quad \times \quad 1.90 \quad\quad = \$66.50$$

Step 3. Find the total premium.

$\$153.90 + \$66.50 = \$220.40$ Add the cost of liability and property damage coverage.

The total premium is $220.40.

With a calculator, the three-step problem in Example 2 can be simplified.

Key: $\boxed{C_E^C}$ 81 $\boxed{\times}$ 1.9 $\boxed{M+}$ liability coverage
$\quad$ 35 $\boxed{\times}$ 1.9 $\boxed{M+}$ property damage coverage
$\quad \boxed{M_C^R}$ 220.4   total premium
$\quad\quad \$220.40$

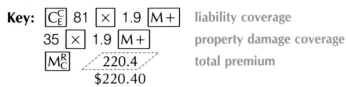

Assessment visit guaranteed within 24 hours!

Class Exercises

Determine the total premium for the insurance coverage indicated. Use the chart on page 262 to find the base premium for each coverage.

Liability Insurance	Property Damage	Driver Rating Factor	Total Premium
10/20	$ 5,000	1.00	**1.** ■
25/50	$10,000	1.75	**2.** ■
100/300	$50,000	2.15	**3.** ■

Determine the total premium.

Liability	Property Damage	Medical Coverage	Uninsured Motorist	Collision	Comprehensive	Total Premium
$150	$75	$10	$15	$125	$50	**4.** ■
$256	$71.50	$12	$14.50	$215.75	$54.30	**5.** ■
$198.75	$67.93	$13.45	$7.85	$243.91	$52.50	**6.** ■

EXERCISES

Determine the total premium for the insurance coverage indicated. Use the chart on page 262 to find the base premium for each coverage.

Liability Insurance	Property Damage	Driver Rating Factor	Total Premium
10/20	$10,000	1.15	**1.** ■
50/100	$ 5,000	1.50	**2.** ■
50/100	$50,000	2.00	**3.** ■

Determine the total premium.

Liability	Property Damage	Medical Coverage	Uninsured Motorist	Collision	Comprehensive	Total Premium
$120	$ 50	$10	$10	$100	$50	**4.** ■
$250	$ 75	$13	$16	$205.05	$53	**5.** ■
$214.62	$107.39	$11.75	$ 9.98	$207.54	$67.85	**6.** ■

7. Explain how mental arithmetic and pencil and paper can be used to solve Exercise 5.

Solve. Use the chart on page 262 to find the base premium for the coverage.

8. Gracie Thurmond
Coverage: 50/100/50
Rating factor: 1.75
Premium: ■

9. Wally Imholt
Coverage: 25/50/10
Rating factor: 2.65
Premium: ■

10. Janet Stahl
Liability: 10/20
Rating factor: ■
Premium: $161.25

11. A male under 21 years old has a factor of 2.50. If he drives to work more than 20 miles, the factor is increased by 1.50. If he has had an accident, the factor is increased by 0.25. What would the premium be for minimum liability coverage (10/20) for a 19-year-old male who drives more than 20 miles to work and who has had one accident?

12. Emmy has a rating factor of 1.75 and wants 100/300/50 coverage. Her medical coverage premium is $10.15, her uninsured motorist protection is $8.63, her collision premium is $193.56, and her comprehensive premium is $88.46. Estimate her total premium.

13. Jollie has a rating factor of 2.42. Her insurance premiums are paid in four equal payments every 3 months. She has premiums of $24.50 for medical coverage, $12.48 for uninsured motorist premium, $225.80 for collision, and $60.51 for comprehensive. What is the maximum liability and property damage coverage she can obtain and still keep her quarterly payments under $150?

14. Ask an insurance agent to describe how the rating factors are determined for various drivers. Compare your findings with those of others in your class.

Reading in Mathematics: *Insurance Terms*

Match each of the following terms with its definition.

1. Comprehensive insurance
2. Medical coverage
3. Driver rating factor
4. Collision insurance
5. Liability insurance
6. Uninsured motorist coverage
7. Premium
8. Property damage insurance

a. Covers injury or harm drivers may do to people not in their car.
b. Covers injuries or damage in an accident caused by an uninsured motorist.
c. A factor determined by the driver's age and driving record used to determine insurance costs.

d. Covers damage done to cars from causes other than collisions.
e. Covers the cost of medical expenses for those in the driver's car.
f. Cost of insurance.
g. Covers damage done by the driver to property of others.
h. Covers damage done to the driver's car by the driver.

8-4 Maintenance Costs

Proper maintenance on your car is very important as it makes the car safer to drive. It may also help your car to last longer if you maintain it. You can have maintenance done at the dealership where you purchased the car or at one of the service stations or auto maintenance shops in your area. You can also do some of the maintenance yourself. By shopping around, you can often save money on maintenance costs.

QUICK CHANGE

We'll drain the old oil and install up to 5 qt of new oil and a new oil filter.
$15.95

EXAMPLE 1

Charlene has driven 3,000 miles since the oil and oil filter in her car were changed. She saw these newspaper ads.

Charlene's car requires 5 quarts of oil. How much would Charlene save by changing the oil and oil filter herself?

A&W AUTO REPAIR

Oil Filter $4.62

1 qt Oil $1.28

Sales tax 6%

Step 1. Find the cost of the materials.

$$
\begin{array}{ll}
\$1.28 & \\
\times \quad 5 & \\
\hline
\$6.40 & \text{cost of 5 qt of oil} \\
+ \ 4.62 & \text{cost of the filter} \\
\hline
\$11.02 & \text{total cost of materials}
\end{array}
$$

Step 2. Calculate the tax on the cost of the materials.

Think: 6% = 0.06

$$
\begin{array}{ll}
\$11.02 & \\
\times \quad 0.06 & \\
\hline
\$.6612 & \\
\$.66 & \text{Round to nearest cent.}
\end{array}
$$

Step 3. Add the tax to the cost of the materials.

$$
\begin{array}{l}
\$11.02 \\
+ \quad 0.66 \\
\hline
\$11.68
\end{array}
$$

Step 4. Find the difference between the cost of changing the oil and filter herself and having it done at Quick Change.

$$
\begin{array}{ll}
\$15.95 & \text{cost at Quick Change} \\
- \ 11.68 & \text{cost of doing it herself} \\
\hline
\$4.27 & \text{savings}
\end{array}
$$

Charlene will save $4.27 by changing the oil and filter herself.

With a calculator, the solution to Example 1 can be simplified.

Key: $\boxed{C^C_E}$ 1.28 $\boxed{\times}$ 5 $\boxed{+}$ 4.62 $\boxed{M+}$ Calculate the cost of materials; add to memory.

$\boxed{\times}$ 6 $\boxed{\%}$ $\boxed{M+}$ Calculate the tax; add to memory to determine the total.

15.95 $\boxed{-}$ $\boxed{M^R_C}$ $\boxed{=}$ ⟋ 4.2688 ⟍ Calculate the savings.

$4.27   Round to nearest cent.

EXAMPLE 2

Norman took his car to the auto shop to have the air conditioner pump replaced. The car also needed two air conditioner hoses and 2 quarts of air conditioner fluid. How much did it cost him?

THE AUTO SHOP

	Price	Labor
Air cond. pump	$54.62	3 h
Air cond. hose	$12.23 ea	$\frac{1}{4}$ h
Air cond. fluid (qt)	$ 5.45	---

Labor $24.00 per hour
Sales tax 8% on parts

Step 1. Find the cost of the parts, including tax.

```
  $54.62    pump
   24.46    hoses (Think: $12.23 × 2 = $24.46)
+ 10.90    fluid (Think: $5.45 × 2 = $10.90)
  $89.98    total cost of parts
×   0.08    Think: 8% = 0.08
  $7.1984
  $7.20     tax (Round to nearest cent.)
```

Step 2. Find the cost of labor.

labor for pump + labor for hoses = total labor hours

$$3 \quad + \quad (2 \times \tfrac{1}{4}) \quad = \quad ■$$

Think: $3 + (2 \times \frac{1}{4}) = 3 + \frac{1}{2} = 3\frac{1}{2}$ h

$$3\frac{1}{2} \times \$24 = \frac{7}{\underset{1}{\cancel{2}}} \times \frac{\overset{12}{\cancel{24}}}{1} = \$84 \quad \text{cost of labor}$$

Step 3. Find the total cost.

```
  $89.98    cost of parts
    7.20    tax
+ 84.00    cost of labor
 $181.18    total cost
```

Norman paid $181.18 to have his car repaired.

Class Exercises

Complete the table by finding the missing values. Assume sales tax is 5%.

Parts Needed for Repair	Price	Do-it-yourself Cost	Cost of Repair at Auto Shop	Amount Saved
1 air filter	$5.25	**1.** ■	$17.95	**2.** ■
2 qt brake fluid	$1.73/qt	**3.** ■	$16.95	**4.** ■
2 gal antifreeze	$4.46/gal	**5.** ■	$15.95	**6.** ■

Use the following information and the price list for A & A Auto Repair for Exercises 7–9.

A tune-up for a 6-cylinder car requires a tune-up kit and 6 spark plugs and takes about 2 hours.

7. How much would the labor cost for the tune-up at A & A Auto Repair?

8. What is the cost of the parts at A & A Auto Repair?

9. What is the total cost of the tune-up at A & A Auto Repair?

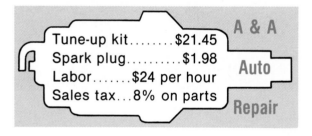

A & A Auto Repair

Tune-up kit........$21.45
Spark plug.........$1.98
Labor.......$24 per hour
Sales tax...8% on parts

EXERCISES

Complete the table by finding the missing values. Assume sales tax is 5%.

Parts Needed for Repair	Price	Do-it-yourself Cost	Cost of Repair at Auto Shop	Amount Saved
3 qt transmission fluid	$3.16/qt	**1.** ■	$22.95	**2.** ■
8 spark plugs	$1.98 each	**3.** ■	$18.95	**4.** ■
tune-up kit, 4 spark plugs	$21.45, $1.98 each	**5.** ■	$42.95	**6.** ■

Use the following information and the price list for A & A Auto Repair for Exercises 7–14.

An engine job requires a new engine, oil filter, and 5 quarts of oil.

7. What is the labor cost of an engine job?

8. What is the cost of the parts of an engine job?

9. What is the entire cost of an engine job?

10. A brake job requires 2 brake pads, 2 brake shoes, and 2 quarts of brake fluid. What is the total cost of a brake job?

11. What is the cost of replacing a water pump?

12. How much would it cost to have four new tires put on a car?

13. A radiator job requires the installation of a radiator, a water pump, and 2 gallons of antifreeze. How much would it cost?

A&A AUTO REPAIR

Part	Price	Labor
Antifreeze (gal)	$4.46	—
Brake fluid (qt)	1.73	—
Oil (qt)	1.28	—
Oil filter	4.62	—
Brake pads	17.50 (ea)	1½ h
Brake shoes	10.25 (ea)	½ h
Engine	572.00	10 h
Muffler	46.00	1 h
Radiator	183.62	4 h
Tailpipe	16.34	½ h
Tire	62.50	¼ h
Water pump	37.95	¾ h
Labor: $24 per hour	Sales tax: 6% on parts	

14. A muffler job requires the installation of a muffler and two tailpipes. Estimate what percent the labor charge is of the total cost.

Solve.

15. In a certain repair job, labor was 41% of the total cost. If the cost of parts was $28.08 more than the cost of labor, what was the total cost of the repair?

Consumer Note: *Repair Scams*

If you own or use a car regularly and are responsible for its maintenance, you need to find an honest, reputable mechanic to help keep it running smoothly. This isn't always as easy as it sounds. At one time or another, most people have had to deal with incompetent or dishonest mechanics.

For instance, one anxious car owner took her sputtering foreign car to the nearest garage. When she asked about the garage's services, the mechanic said that he worked on cars like hers all the time. Two days later he had taken the motor apart but was unable to diagnose the problem and put it back together. The woman took him to small claims court and won a decision to cut his final bill in half.

Some garages regularly use deceitful practices to make more money. The mechanics tell people that they need a special, expensive service or repair when a minor adjustment is needed. If the car owner appears to know little about cars, he or she may end up paying for a major tune-up when new spark plugs are needed, or the mechanic may suggest new tires when the old ones only need to be rotated. Some discount muffler shops regularly replace the entire exhaust system when a new muffler is all that is needed.

If a mechanic you do not know suggests major work, get a second opinion before agreeing. By being alert and aware, you may be able to save money on repairs.

8-5 Used Cars

Rather than purchasing a new car, you may decide to buy a used car. When you purchase a used car, you do not have a choice of options—you find a used car you like, and then buy it as is.

When buying a used car, you need to be able to decide about what the car should be worth. Then, based on the condition of the car you have chosen, you have to decide if that value is reasonable. The value of a used car depends on the **depreciation,** or decrease in value, of the car as well as the condition of the car.

The line graphs on these two pages show the costs of depreciation and repair and maintenance over a period of 10 years for full-sized, midsized, and compact cars.

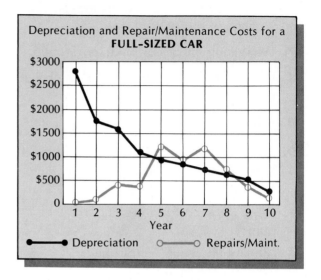

EXAMPLE 1

Kevin wants to buy a full-sized used car that is 3 years old. He knows that the dealer's cost of that model, when it was new, was $10,965. Find the value of the car now.

Step 1. Find the total depreciation.

> **Problem Solving Strategy: Finding information.**
> You can find information about depreciation from the graphs.
> First year's depreciation: $2,900
> Second year's depreciation: $1,800
> Third year's depreciation: $1,550

$$\$2,900 + \$1,800 + \$1,550 = \$6,250$$

Step 2. Find the value of the car.

$$\text{original price} - \frac{\text{total}}{\text{depreciation}} = \text{value of car}$$

$$\$10,965 \quad - \quad \$6,250 \quad = \quad \blacksquare$$

The car is now worth about $4,715.

Skill Review

To compute costs associated with used cars, you need to be able to add whole numbers.

Find each sum.

1. $1,100 + $400 + $600

2. $2,350 + $1,875 + $534

3. 11,978 + 456 + 39 + 923

4. 2,543 + 299 + 673 + 100

·(For additional help, see page 542.)

In order to get a picture of the cost of operating the full-sized car Kevin wants to buy, he considers the **variable cost,** or the depreciation plus the cost of repairs and maintenance.

EXAMPLE 2

What is the variable cost of a full-sized car in its fourth year?
Find the depreciation cost and the repair and maintenance cost in the graph for full-sized cars.

depreciation cost	+	repair/maintenance cost	=	variable cost
$1,050	+	$500	=	$1,550

The variable cost will be $1,550.

Class Exercises

Complete the table by finding the missing values. Use the graphs on pages 270 and 271.

Type of Car	Year	Depreciation Cost	Maintenance Cost	Variable Cost
Compact	3	**1.** ■	**2.** ■	**3.** ■
Midsized	4	**4.** ■	**5.** ■	**6.** ■
Compact	5	**7.** ■	**8.** ■	**9.** ■
Full-sized	2	**10.** ■	**11.** ■	**12.** ■

13. A 3-year-old used midsized car is purchased for $5,375. What is the value 2 years later?

14. A 2-year-old full-sized used car is operated for 3 additional years. What is the total variable cost of operating the car for these 3 years?

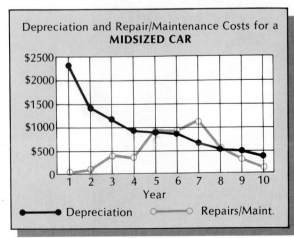

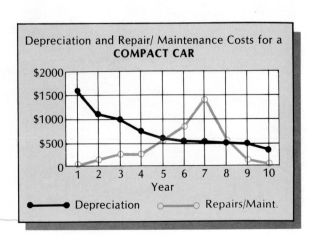

EXERCISES

Complete the table by finding the missing values. Use the graphs on pages 270 and 271.

Type of Car	Year	Depreciation Cost	Maintenance Cost	Variable Cost
Full-sized	4	1. ■	2. ■	3. ■
Compact	2	4. ■	5. ■	6. ■
Compact	7	7. ■	8. ■	9. ■
Midsized	9	10. ■	11. ■	12. ■
Full-sized	3	13. ■	14. ■	15. ■
Full-sized	8	16. ■	17. ■	18. ■
Compact	3	19. ■	20. ■	21. ■
Midsized	2	22. ■	23. ■	24. ■

Solve.

25. Used car type: full-sized
Age when purchased: 2 y
Purchase price: $6,825
Value 2 y later: ■

26. Used car type: compact
Age when purchased: 4 y
Purchase price: $3,580
Value 2 y later: ■

27. Used car type: midsized
Age when purchased: 6 y
Purchase price: $2,375
Value 2 y later: ■

28. Used car type: compact
Age when purchased: 2 y
Purchase price: $4,362
Value 3 y later: ■

29. A used midsized car is 4 years old when purchased. What are the total variable costs of operating it for 2 years?

30. Kit bought a 4-year-old used full-sized car for $5,713. The cost of the car when it was brand new was $12,620. Estimate how much profit the dealer made on the used car, assuming that the dealer had originally paid the correct value for the car.

31. How much more is the cost of operating a new full-sized car for 2 years than one that is 4 years old when purchased?

32. Make a line graph that shows the total variable cost of a midsized car over a 10-year period. In which three years are the costs the greatest?

33. The graphs on pages 270 and 271 show large increases in maintenance costs when cars are several years old. What reasons can you give for these increases?

34. The fixed costs (insurance, gas and oil, fees, parking, tolls, and so on) for operating a 3-year-old midsized car for 1 year are about $1,750. Find the total cost of operating the car for that year and the average cost per mile if the car was driven 12,000 miles during the year.

35. Fred bought a compact used car for $3,375 and sold it 3 years later for $1,719. Assuming the car depreciated according to the graph for a compact car, how old was the car when he sold it?

Critical Thinking: *Ordering Information (Ranking)*

When you put items or information in order, you arrange them in a sequence according to some characteristic of the items or information. For instance, clothes in a store are usually arranged in order of size.

Four used cars are for sale:

Compact	Full-sized	Midsized	Compact
Freedom 700	Hampstead 215	Lightning 902	Dancer 230M
2 y old	3 y old	5 y old	5 y old

1. Rank (order) these cars in descending order according to the probable cost for maintenance and repairs during the next 3 years (use the graphs on pages 270 and 271).

2. Describe your thought processes as you were ranking the cars.

3. What mathematical calculations did you perform in order to rank the cars?

4. What are some other characteristics of these cars that you could use to rank them?

Career
Auto Mechanic

About 1 million **auto mechanics** service the 170 million cars and trucks in the United States. Most of a mechanic's work is routine checking and maintenance to keep vehicles in good operating order.

Profile of an auto mechanic. Most mechanics have some special training beyond high school, but some are not high school graduates. Most have a keen interest in motors and electrical systems. Many like to work with their hands, use tools, and repair or improve machines.

The auto mechanic's work environment. Mechanics are employed by service stations, by owners of fleets of cabs, buses, and trucks, by construction and other companies that provide their own transportation, and by auto dealerships. Many work in small shops with one or two other mechanics and a supervisor. Mechanics may provide their own tools, but the shop owner often provides them along with heavy equipment for lifting cars and electronic equipment for testing systems. Mechanics use math in reading instruments and preparing cost estimates for customers.

All in a day's work. Jane had done minor repairs to the electrical and heating systems of her own car and had studied auto mechanics in high school. She got a job at a local gas station, where she pumped gas and made simple repairs.

1. Carburetor replacement parts and a rebuilt water pump were provided for the Brown's automobile. Parts came to $42 and labor was 5 hours at $21 per hour. The car was filled with 8 gallons of gas at $1.11 per gallon. What was the total bill?

2. Jane's boss usually charged $8 for rotating tires, but he charged the Acme Cab company only $6.50 per cab. He also gave them a discount of 5% on all business over $750 per month. Each month, Acme paid their gasoline bills and costs of any repairs or other purchases made that month. Complete their bill for April:

   a. Rotating tires on 4 cabs @ $6.50 ■
   b 924 gallons of gasoline @ $1.11 ■
   c. Wiper blades—two sets @ $6.40 ■
   d. Gas tank lock caps 4 @ $11 ■

   Total ■
   5% Discount ■
   Amount Payable ■

8-6 Leasing a Car

One alternative to buying a car is to **lease** one. When you lease a car, you pay the automobile dealer a monthly fee in exchange for the use of the car for a specified period. At the end of that time, you may return the car to the dealer or you may purchase it.

Leasing payments are generally lower than finance payments on a given car if you finance all or most of the cost of the car. You do not have to make a down payment on a leased vehicle, and you pay only for the portion of the car's useful life that you actually use. However, at the end of the leasing period, the dealer owns the car and you have no asset in exchange for your investment.

LEASE YOUR NEXT CAR!

Roadmaster $259/mo
5-y lease

Venture $199/mo
60-mo lease

Bravo $298/mo
48-mo lease

EXAMPLE 1

Samantha saw the above ad in a newspaper. After some investigation, she decided to lease a Roadmaster. How much will it cost her to lease the car?

Hidden Question: How many monthly payments would you have to pay over 5 years?
$$5 \text{ y} = 5 \times 12 = 60 \text{ mo}$$

monthly payment × number of payments = leasing cost
$259 × 60 = ■

Estimate: $259 × 60 = ■ → $300 × 60 = $18,000

$259   monthly payment
× 60   number of payments
$15,540   leasing cost

 Key: $\boxed{C^C_E}$ 259 $\boxed{\times}$ 60 $\boxed{=}$ 15540
$15,540

The answer $15,540 is reasonably close to the estimate $18,000 and is a sensible answer. Samantha's leasing cost will be $15,540.

To determine if leasing a car is worthwhile, compare the cost of leasing with the cost of purchasing a similar car. Include the depreciation and finance charges on the purchased car.

Skill Review

In order to compute leasing charges, you need to be able to multiply whole numbers.

Find each product.
1. $399 × 36
2. 24 × $209
3. $156 × 45
4. 2,308 × 154

(For additional help, see page 543.)

EXAMPLE 2

Seth leased a new car for 3 years and was charged $218 per month. The finance charge on the purchase of such a car would be about $425. Use the graph on page 270 to find the depreciation of the car over 3 years. Determine if Seth saved money by leasing rather than purchasing a similar full-sized car.

Renter pays a monthly fee for an agreed upon number of years. Renter also pays for gasoline, insurance, maintenance, and most other fees.

E-Z LEASING

Step 1. Find the cost of leasing a car.

monthly payment × number of payments = leasing cost
$218 × 36 = $7,848

Step 2. Find the cost of owning the car.

depreciation + finance charge = cost of owning
($2,900 + $1,800 + $1,550) + $425 = $6,675

Step 3. Compare the cost of leasing with the cost of owning.

$7,848   cost of leasing
− 6,675   cost of owning
$1,173

It cost $1,173 more to lease the car for 3 years than to purchase the car.

With a calculator, you can simplify the computation in Example 2.

Key: $\boxed{C_E^C}$ 218 $\boxed{\times}$ 36 $\boxed{M+}$ 2900 $\boxed{+}$ 1800 $\boxed{+}$ 1550 $\boxed{+}$ 425 $\boxed{M-}$ $\boxed{M_C^R}$ / 1173 /
$1,173

Class Exercises

Complete the following table.

Monthly Payment	Number of Payments	Leasing Cost
$279	48	1. ■
$199	60	2. ■
$345	30	3. ■

4. Which of Exercises 1–3 could be done mentally? In which would pencil and paper be appropriate? Which could best be done by using a calculator?

5. Describe a mental math strategy you could use to find the answer to Exercise 2 without using pencil and paper.

Solve.

6. Find the total cost of a 30-month car lease at $198.50 per month.

7. Estimate the cost of a 4-year lease at $203.75 per month.

EXERCISES

Complete the following table.

Monthly Payment	Number of Payments	Leasing Cost
$344	48	**1.** ■
$158	60	**2.** ■
$400	30	**3.** ■
$313	60	**4.** ■

Solve. Round to the nearest dollar.

5. 48-month lease
Monthly payment: $328
Total cost: ■

6. 5-year lease
Monthly payment: $299
Total cost: ■

7. 3-year lease
Monthly payment: $299.58
Total cost: ■

8. Sara leased a compact car for 4 years at $142.50 per month. Would it have cost less to purchase a similar car if the finance charges on such a purchase were about $385? (Use the graph on page 271 to find the depreciation of the car.)

9. Over a 3-year period, which would cost less, the lease of a midsized car for $171.18 per month, or the purchase of a midsized car with finance charges of $395? (Use the graph on page 271 to find the depreciation of the car over 3 years.) How much less would the cheaper plan cost?

10. Show how you would use a calculator to help streamline the computation for Problem 9.

11. For what reasons might large companies lease their cars rather than purchase them outright? Would an individual or family have the same reasons?

12. Find out some information about leasing costs in your community. Are short-term as well as long-term leases available? Share your answers with your classmates.

Mixed Review

1. Ramon's annual net income is $11,675. He budgets 29% of his net income for food. How much does he have to spend each week on food?

2. Ramon always waits for a sale to buy his clothes. He saw a jacket that originally sold for $49.95 but was marked down 15%. What was the sale price?

8-7 Traveling by Car

Many people who take vacations travel by car. If you decide to take a vacation in your car, you will probably want to use a map to plan your route.

EXAMPLE 1

The Johnstons are traveling by car through South Dakota. Amy Johnston estimates the distances between towns by using the scale on the map. She estimates the distances between Aberdeen and Redfield to be 40 miles. Amy knew that it took them $2\frac{1}{2}$ hours to drive the first 125 miles. Approximately how long will it take the Johnstons to drive from Aberdeen to Redfield?

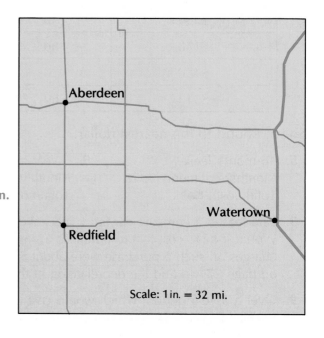

Scale: 1 in. = 32 mi.

$$\frac{\text{1st distance}}{\text{1st time}} = \frac{\text{2nd distance}}{\text{2nd time}}$$

$\dfrac{125 \text{ mi}}{2\frac{1}{2} \text{ h}} = \dfrac{40 \text{ mi}}{\blacksquare \text{ h}}$ Write a proportion.

$\dfrac{125}{2\frac{1}{2}} = \dfrac{40}{x}$ Let x be the second time.

$125 \times x = 40 \times 2\frac{1}{2}$ Cross multiply.

$125x = 100$

$x = \frac{100}{125} = \frac{4}{5}$

Think: $\frac{4}{5}$ of 60 min = 48 min

It will take them about 50 minutes.

EXAMPLE 2

Estimate the distance between Redfield and Watertown.

The scale is 1 in. = 32 mi. The map distance between the two towns is about $2\frac{1}{4}$ inches.

$\dfrac{1 \text{ in.}}{32 \text{ mi}} = \dfrac{2\frac{1}{4} \text{ in.}}{\blacksquare \text{ mi}}$ Write a proportion.

$\dfrac{1}{32} = \dfrac{2\frac{1}{4}}{x}$ Let x be the second number of miles.

$1 \times x = 2\frac{1}{4} \times 32$ Cross multiply.

$x = 72$ Think: $(2 \times 32) + (\frac{1}{4} \times 32) = 64 + 8 = 72$

The distance between Redfield and Watertown is approximately 72 miles.

Class Exercises

Determine the distances using the given map measurements and scales.

Map Measurement	Scale 1 in. Equals:	Distance in Miles
$2\frac{3}{4}$ in.	28 mi	**1.** ■
$1\frac{1}{2}$ in.	30 mi	**2.** ■

Use proportions to find the missing values.

1st Distance	1st Time	2nd Distance	2nd Time
145 mi	3 h	321 mi	**3.** ■
200 mi	5 h	159 mi	**4.** ■
275 mi	$5\frac{1}{2}$ h	**5.** ■	3 h

6. How can you use mental arithmetic to solve Exercise 2?

EXERCISES

Determine the distances using the given map measurements and scales.

Map Measurement	Scale 1 in. Equals:	Distance in Miles
$1\frac{1}{2}$ in.	20 mi	**1.** ■
$4\frac{1}{2}$ in.	12 mi	**2.** ■
$3\frac{3}{4}$ in.	28 mi	**3.** ■
$9\frac{5}{8}$ in.	32 mi	**4.** ■

Use proportions to find the missing values.

1st Distance	1st Time	2nd Distance	2nd Time
140 mi	3 h	280 mi	**5.** ■
129 mi	$3\frac{1}{2}$ h	81 mi	**6.** ■
189 mi	2 h	**7.** ■	$4\frac{1}{2}$ h
8. ■	$3\frac{1}{4}$ h	129 mi	$2\frac{1}{2}$ h
250 mi	**9.** ■	˙73 mi	$1\frac{1}{2}$ h

10. Find the approximate distance between Brookings and Sioux Falls.

11. Find the approximate distance between Mitchell and Sioux Falls.

12. The Strecks drove 388 miles on 13.2 gallons of gasoline. Round to estimate how many gallons they will need to drive the next 179 miles.

13. Carroll drove 200 miles and used 8 gallons of gasoline. How far can she drive on a full tank of 12 gallons?

14. Saul left Sioux Falls and drove for $4\frac{1}{2}$ hours at an average speed of 50 miles per hour. Then he drove for $3\frac{1}{2}$ hours at 60 miles per hour. Find his average rate of speed for the trip.

Scale: 1 in. = 32 mi.
Huron
Brookings
Madison
Mitchell
Sioux Falls
Ethan
Lennox
Parkston

15. Brinette used her calculator to change 3.27 hours into hours, minutes, and seconds. Study her keystrokes and answer the questions.

Key: 3.27 $\boxed{-}$ 3 $\boxed{=}$ $\boxed{\times}$ 60 $\boxed{-}$ 16 $\boxed{=}$ $\boxed{\times}$ 60 $\boxed{=}$ ⟋ 12 ⟋

Her conclusion: 3.27 hours = 3 hours, 16 minutes, 12 seconds.
a. Explain her procedure.
b. Which keystroke(s) would change if she were converting 4.27 hours to hours, minutes, and seconds?
c. Use your calculator to convert 2.56 hours to hours, minutes, and seconds.

Using a Calculator: Solving Proportions

You can use your calculator to solve proportions.

Example: Solve $\dfrac{4\frac{1}{2}}{9} = \dfrac{18}{n}$

$$4\tfrac{1}{2} \times n = 9 \times 18$$

Think: $4\frac{1}{2} = 4.5$

Key: $\boxed{C_E^C}$ 9 $\boxed{\times}$ 18 $\boxed{\div}$ 4.5 $\boxed{=}$ ⟋ 36 ⟋

Use your calculator to solve each proportion.

1. $\dfrac{x}{1\frac{1}{2}} = \dfrac{8}{3}$

2. $\dfrac{2}{5} = \dfrac{x}{200}$

3. $\dfrac{n}{100} = \dfrac{28}{16}$

Computer:
IF/THEN Statements

Irene spent $8,560 for her compact car and wants to keep it for at least 5 years. She placed the depreciation and maintenance costs for the first 5 years in the DATA statements in the following program. The statement below will allow her to determine if these costs exceed 15% of the price (P) of the car.

50 IF D + M > .15 * P THEN PRINT "YEAR #";Y, "COST = $"; D+M

If D + M is greater than (>) 0.15 × P, the computer executes the command following the word THEN. That is, it prints the cost for that year. Otherwise, it does *not* execute the command but proceeds to the next step.

Her program is as follows:

10 HOME	Clears the screen.
20 P = 8560	Sets original price of the car to $8,560.
30 FOR Y = 1 TO 5	Opens FOR/NEXT loop to count from 1 to 5.
40 READ D, M	Reads next (first) set of values of D and M.
50 IF D + M > .15 * P THEN PRINT "YEAR #"; Y, "COST = $"; D+M	Tests to determine if D+M exceeds 15% of P; prints the information if it does.
60 NEXT Y	Closes the FOR/NEXT loop.
100 DATA 1600, 50	5 DATA statements (one for each year) setting values for Depreciation and Maintenance (from the figure for compact cars on page 271).
110 DATA 1100, 125	
120 DATA 1000, 300	
130 DATA 800, 300	
140 DATA 700, 550	
200 END	

Enter and RUN the program.

EXERCISES

1. What do you think the output would be if line 30 were changed to the following?
>   30 FOR Y = 1 TO 2

2. If the depreciation and maintenance costs in the following statements were inserted into the program, what one line would have to be changed to process them?
>   150 DATA 600, 800
>   160 DATA 525, 1450

Decision Making:
Choosing a Car

Carolyn rode a bus to work every day, but she disliked waiting for the bus in bad weather. Also, she believed she would enjoy driving on weekends to visit some friends who had moved away, rather than using buses and planes. A car would make her life much more flexible, she decided.

THE COST OF A NEW CAR

Carolyn realized that a car would be one of the most expensive purchases she would make. She noticed that car prices ranged from $100 for very old used cars up to $40,000 or more for new cars. Many cars were listed in the range of $6,000 to $12,000. Carolyn knew that used cars sometimes require expensive and unexpected repairs. She preferred to buy a new compact car if possible.

Carolyn first figured out what it would cost her to buy a new car. If she bought a $6,000 car and used her savings of $2,135 as a down payment, she could pay the rest in installment payments over several years. From her credit union, she learned that she could pay $118 for 36 months or $92 for 48 months.

Carolyn knew there would also be expenses for operating the car. She did some research by using the figure on page 270 and talking to an insurance agent. She made a table of her estimated costs:

Expense	Notes	Monthly Cost
Car payments	Paid over 48 mo	$92
Maintenance and repairs	$200 per year	$17
Insurance; registration	$290 per year; $150 per year	$37
Gasoline	1,000 mi per month, 30 mi per gallon, $.90 per gallon	$30
Total		$176

Thus her estimated monthly cost for the new car would be $176 if she paid for the car over 48 months.

Answer the following questions.

1. What might be some reasons why someone who has never owned a car might want to buy one?

2. If the cost of gasoline goes up to $.95 per gallon, how will Carolyn's estimate change?

3. Can you think of any costs Carolyn has overlooked in her estimation of what it will cost to own and operate a new car?

4. Would you prefer to pay $118 for 36 months or $92 for 48 months? Explain your thinking process in making your choice.

PAYING FOR A NEW CAR

Carolyn looked carefully at the records of her expenditures to decide if she could afford $176 per month.

- She was willing to use $50 of the $75 she saved each month to buy a car.

- Bus fare of $30 per month could be used toward car payments.

- About $50 per month from plane and long-distance bus fares would now be available.

She would still need $46 more for payments for a new car. She determined that she could spend less on clothes and entertainment to make $26 more available per month.

Carolyn considered the fact that she could save money by packing her lunch instead of buying it in the company cafeteria. She decided it was realistic for her to plan to bring her lunch some days but not every day. She calculated that packing her lunch as often as 10 days a month would save her $30.

If she did this, she would have more than enough to pay $176 per month for a new car. Perhaps she could consider paying for the car in 36 months or even buying a more expensive car.

Answer these questions.

5. Do you think $25 per month is enough for Carolyn to save? Has Carolyn allowed enough for unexpected expenses?

6. Which of your own present expenditures would you be willing to change if you wanted money for something else?

IDENTIFYING IMPORTANT FEATURES IN A CAR

Carolyn decided to buy a compact car. She visited several car agencies and saw many different compact cars. She also asked friends and relatives how they had selected their cars.

Carolyn developed the following list of important factors:

size of car and engine	color
4 doors	inside space
price	mileage rating (miles per gallon)
safety record	manufacturer's warranty
handling	comfortable seats
options available (such as radio and air conditioning)	

She quickly realized that all factors were not equally important. She decided to rank the factors in the order of their importance to her. Since she had already decided on a price range, she did not include price on the list. Her list, from most important to least important, is as follows:

1. safety record	6. handling
2. manufacturer's warranty	7. inside space
3. mileage rating (miles per gallon)	8. 4 doors
4. comfortable seats	9. color
5. options available (such as radio and air conditioning)	

Answer these questions.

7. Why might a person rank 4 doors as most important?

8. Why might a person rank size as most important?

FINDING INFORMATION

Carolyn went to the library to consult consumer publications for objective information about safety records and mileage. She visited automobile dealers to find out about warranties and the colors and options available for different models, as well as whether these models were available in 4-door styles. She test drove many cars, comparing how much room there was inside the cars, how comfortable the seats were, and how well the car handled at various speeds in various situations.

Answer these questions.

9. Can you suggest other sources of information Carolyn might use?

10. What other information should Carolyn seek if she were buying a used car?

INTERPRETING INFORMATION

Carolyn chose three cars to consider for her final choice. To help her compare these cars according to her ranked list of desired features, she constructed a chart. She rated the cars first, second, and third for each feature, giving 3 points to the best car, 2 points to the second best, and only 1 point to the lowest-rated car. In some cases, where the cars were the same, she gave each car 3 points.

Carolyn showed the importance of each feature by *weighting* it. Since safety record was the most important of the nine features, she gave it 9 points and multiplied the ranking of each car by 9. For warranties, she multiplied the rankings by 8. She continued in this way down to color, where the rankings were multiplied by 1.

MAKING THE CHOICE

Using her chart, Carolyn found it easy to see which car had most of the features she considered most important. Carolyn decided to buy a Dancer and felt certain she had chosen the car that was best for her.

CAROLYN'S CHART

Features (ranked by importance)	Freedom	Hummingbird	Dancer
1. Safety record (3 = best)	$1 \times 9 = 9$	$2 \times 9 = 18$	$3 \times 9 = 27$
2. Warranties (3 = longest warranty for most parts)	$3 \times 8 = 24$	$1 \times 8 = 8$	$2 \times 8 = 16$
3. Mileage (3 = highest miles per gallon)	$2 \times 7 = 14$	$1 \times 7 = 7$	$3 \times 7 = 21$
4. Comfortable (3 = most comfortable)	$1 \times 6 = 6$	$2 \times 6 = 12$	$3 \times 6 = 18$
5. Options (3 = air conditioner available)	$3 \times 5 = 15$	$3 \times 5 = 15$	$3 \times 5 = 15$
6. Handling (3 = handles best)	$2 \times 4 = 8$	$1 \times 4 = 4$	$3 \times 4 = 12$
7. Inside space (3 = roomiest)	$1 \times 3 = 3$	$3 \times 3 = 9$	$2 \times 3 = 6$
8. 4 doors (3 = 4 doors available)	$3 \times 2 = 6$	$3 \times 2 = 6$	$3 \times 2 = 6$
9. Color (red or yellow available)	$3 \times 1 = 3$	$1 \times 1 = 1$	$2 \times 1 = 2$
	88	80	123

Answer these questions.

11. When did Carolyn rank information as she was deciding which car to buy?

12. Describe the two other kinds of decisions where ranking items or information would be helpful to you.

13. How would a chart like Carolyn's be helpful to someone choosing a college?

14. Identify the small decisions Carolyn made in the larger process of selecting a car.

15. How would you illustrate or diagram the steps Carolyn used in deciding what car to buy?

16. Compare and contrast buying a car with choosing a job.

DECIDE FOR YOURSELF

Suppose you were buying a car. How would your decision making strategy be like Carolyn's? How would it be different?

Chapter 8 Review

VOCABULARY

base price
depreciation
destination charge
down payment

driver rating factor
lease
margin of profit
options

premium
sticker price
variable cost

For Exercises 1–6, select the word or words that complete each statement.

1. The price of a car with only standard equipment is called the
_____ .

2. The _____ is the base price plus the options plus the destination charge.

3. The _____ is determined by the driver's age, driving record, and other factors.

4. The amount you pay annually or semiannually for insurance coverage is called the _____ .

5. The value of a used car depends in part on the _____ , or decrease in value.

6. You can _____ a new car, or sign a long-term arrangement to use the car, as an alternative to buying one.

SKILLS

Find each percent.

7. 19% of 6,000

8. 23% of $4,300

9. 27% of $9,381

Solve each proportion.

10. $\dfrac{n}{8} = \dfrac{6}{24}$

11. $\dfrac{15}{18} = \dfrac{10}{a}$

12. $\dfrac{225}{15} = \dfrac{x}{2}$

CONSUMER TOPICS

Solve.

13. Corinne wants to purchase a new car with a base price of $10,872. The options she has chosen cost $132.58, $396, $72.30, and $790.45. The destination charge is $256. Find the sticker price.

14. Lynn wanted to make an offer on a new car with a sticker price of $10,809. If the dealer's margin of profit was 17% and Lynn wanted to offer $600 more than the base price, calculate the amount of her offer to the nearest dollar.

15. The cash price for Isaac's new car was $7,854. The dealer required a 20% down payment. How much did Isaac have to finance?

16. In Problem 15, Isaac agreed to repay the loan in 36 monthly payments. The monthly payments included the finance charge and came to $195.48. What was the total cost of his car?

Solve using the table on page 262.

17. Determine the annual insurance premium for 50/100 liability insurance for a driver having a rating factor of 2.85.

Solve.

18. Howard had his car serviced by his mechanic, who charges $19 per hour for labor. The mechanic put in new spark plugs ($8), a condenser ($3.45), a fuel filter ($5.95), and an air filter ($10.60). The labor took $1\frac{1}{2}$ hours. What was Howard's total bill?

19. Howard (Problem 18) could save 18% on parts and all the labor by doing the work himself. How much could he save?

20. Map measurement: $2\frac{1}{2}$ in.
Scale: 1 in. = 25 mi
Distance in miles: ■

Use the graph on page 270 to solve.

21. Eric wants to buy a full-sized used car that is 2 years old. The dealer's cost of the car, when it was new, was $12,775. Find the value of the car now.

22. What is the variable cost of a full-sized car in its third year?

Solve.

23. Sara leased a new full-sized car for 5 years for $239 per month. What was her total cost?

24. Which would cost less, the lease in Problem 22 or purchasing the same car over a 5-year period with finance charges of $3,575? (Use the graph on page 270 to find the depreciation over 5 years.) How much less would the cheaper plan be?

25. If it takes 3 hours to drive 165 miles, how long will it take to drive 247.5 miles at the same rate?

26. Marissa used 6 gallons of gas driving 168 miles. She had 126 miles left to complete her trip. How many more gallons of gas will she use?

Chapter 8 Test

Solve.

1. Car: Axis 180; Base price: $5,340;
   Options: $639; Destination charge: $156;
   Sticker price: ■;   Profit margin: 14%;
   Dealer profit: ■

2. Car: Silverado; Sticker price: $12,345;
   Profit margin: 19%; Dealer cost: ■;
   Amount offered over cost: $600;
   Total amount offered: ■

3. Tom bought a new car with a sticker
   price of $10,852. He paid 18% of the
   cost as a down payment. What amount
   did he finance?

4. Tom (Problem 3) repaid his loan in 48
   monthly payments. Each payment,
   including the finance charge, was
   $207.64. Find the total cost of his car.

5. Ruppert's Auto Repair charges $19.95 for
   an oil change. If Phyllis changes the oil
   herself and can buy the 4 quarts she
   needs for $1.25 each on sale and the oil
   filter for $4.79, how much money can
   she save?

6. Kelly had her car serviced. The mechanic
   charged $18 per hour for labor. The charge
   for new parts was $39. The mechanic also
   changed the oil (5 quarts at $2 each) and
   put in a new oil filter ($5.95). If the
   mechanic worked on her car for 4 hours,
   what was the total bill?

7. Find the annual premium for 25/50 liability insurance for a
   driver with a rating factor of 2.85 if the base premium is $78.

Solve. Use the graphs on pages 270 and 271 if necessary.

8. A 3-year-old midsized car was purchased
   for $7,248. What is the value 2 years
   later?

9. A 2-year-old midsized car is operated for
   3 years. What is the total variable cost of
   operating the car for these 3 years?

10. Find the cost of a 36-month car lease at $219.50 per month.

11. Over a 2-year period, which would cost less: the lease of a
    full-sized car for $258.50 per month or the purchase of a full-
    sized car with finance charges of $475. Use the graph on
    page 270 to find the depreciation over 2 years. How much less
    would the cheaper plan be?

12. Jeffrey is driving from St. Paul to Milwaukee. He estimates the
    distance to be 330 miles. If he averages 50 miles per hour,
    how long will the trip take him?

13. Mike drove 216 miles and used 8 gallons of gasoline. How far
    could he drive on a full tank of 14 gallons?

14. The distance on a map from Centerville to Cactus is $3\frac{1}{2}$ inches.
    If the scale is 1 inch = 50 miles, how far apart in miles are
    the two towns?

Cumulative Mixed Review

Select the letter corresponding to the correct answer.

1. Martina wanted to make a set of towels. She needed $8\frac{1}{4}$ yards of 36-inch-wide fabric. If the fabric cost $3.19 per yard, what was her total cost?
   a. $22.80
   b. $28.56
   c. $25.30
   d. $26.32

2. Determine the CPI for a shirt that costs $32 now and cost $15.79 in 1967.
   a. 203
   b. 189
   c. 207
   d. 195

3. Julian bought a new car with a sticker price of $9,760. If he paid 5% sales tax, traded in his old car for $1,700, and made a 15% down payment, calculate the total amount of the purchase price that he financed.
   a. $8,548
   b. $7,265.80
   c. $1,282.20
   d. $7,482

4. Sydney receives a net pay of $585.60 biweekly. She has $160 withheld from her pay each pay period. What is her annual gross salary?
   a. $17,175.60
   b. $17,655.30
   c. $15,225.60
   d. $19,385.60

5. Carlos made the following purchases: an alarm clock for $8.99, a flashlight for $5.49, and a humidifier for $18.99. He paid 5% sales tax. Compute the total cost.
   a. $1.67
   b. $33.47
   c. $38.28
   d. $35.14

6. Joyce deposited $3,000 in a savings account at a rate of $8\frac{1}{2}$% compounded monthly. How much was in her account after 3 months?
   a. $3,064.20
   b. $3,068.60
   c. $3,063.75
   d. $64.20

7. Charles earns $52,000 annually and pays $10\frac{1}{2}$% for state and local taxes. How much tax does he pay annually?
   a. $5,220
   b. $7,800
   c. $5,460
   d. $6,140

8. Kip drove 216 miles on 9 gallons of gas. He had 180 miles left to complete his trip. How many more gallons of gas would he need?
   a. 4
   b. 7.5
   c. 36
   d. 8.3

9. Margo budgeted $90 a month for eating out. At an estimated $6 per meal, that allows her 15 meals per month. She would like to eat 21 meals out per month. How much more would she have to budget?
   a. $48
   b. $126
   c. $36
   d. $112

10. A 2-pound block of cheese costs $7.35. An 8-ounce package of the same cheese costs $1.95. What is the difference in price per 2-ounce serving?
    a. $.03
    b. $.68
    c. $.23
    d. $1.73

Public Transportation

Zach is planning to travel from Northfield, Minnesota, to San Diego, California, to visit his grandparents for 2 weeks.

- What forms of public transportation might Zach consider using?

- What might be some of the factors that would affect his decision?

- Where could he get the information about public transportation that he needs?

Discuss trips you or your friends have taken. What factors did you consider in deciding how to travel?

9-1 Air Travel

If you decide to travel by air, you usually have choices. You may be able to fly nonstop, your plane may make one or more stops, or you may need to change planes. Airlines generally have several rates: first class, business class, coach, excursion, and economy. Less expensive fares are not always available on all flights; travel restrictions often apply to these fares.

Airline schedules show local times. When you travel, you may go from one **time zone** into another. To compute the travel time between departure and arrival times, you must *subtract* 1 hour for each time zone you enter if you fly east. If you fly west, you must *add* 1 hour for each time zone you enter.

The table below gives the scheduled flights leaving Salt Lake City. First-class fare is 30% higher than coach fare. Economy fares are 10% lower than coach fare. There is an 8% federal excise tax on all air fares.

From Salt Lake City Airport						
Destination	**Departs**	**Arrives**	**Direction**	**Miles**	**Time Zones Entered**	**One-Way Coach Fare (Including Tax)**
Atlanta, GA	11:05 A.M.	5:36 P.M.	E	1,583	2	$185
Boston, MA	8:50 A.M.	3:51 P.M.	E	2,099	2	$246
Chicago, IL	12:17 P.M.	4:42 P.M.	E	1,260	1	$147
Denver, CO	9:15 A.M.	10:19 A.M.	E	371	0	$ 44
Los Angeles, CA	5:45 P.M.	6:41 P.M.	W	579	1	$ 68
New Orleans, LA	8:28 A.M.	1:32 P.M.	E	1,434	1	$168
New York, NY	10:25 A.M.	5:01 P.M.	E	1,972	2	$231
Seattle, WA	9:35 P.M.	10:54 P.M.	W	701	1	$ 82
Washington, DC	9:18 A.M.	4:42 P.M.	E	1,848	2	$216

EXAMPLE 1

Mamie planned a trip from Salt Lake City to Washington, DC. How long will her flight take?

Problem Solving Strategy: Finding information.

Use the table of flight information to find the flight from Salt Lake City to Washington. It leaves at 9:18 A.M. and arrives at 4:42 P.M.

Step 1. Compute the elapsed time.

9:18 A.M.—12 noon = 2 h 42 min
12 noon—4:42 P.M. = 4 h 42 min
6 h 84 min 84 min = 1 h 24 min
7 h 24 min

Step 2. Account for the time zones.
Mamie will enter 2 time zones. Since she is traveling from west to east, subtract 1 hour for each time zone entered.

7 h 24 min − 2 h = 5 h 24 min

The flight time is 5 hours 24 minutes.

EXAMPLE 2
How much would a first-class ticket cost Mamie?

coach fare + 30% of coach fare = first-class fare
$216   +   30% of $216   =   ∎

Think: 30% = 0.3

Estimate: $216 + 0.3 × $216 = ∎ → $200 + 0.3 × $200 = $200 + $60 = $260

216
× 0.3
64.8

 Key: $\boxed{C_E^C}$ 216 $\boxed{M+}$ $\boxed{×}$ 30 $\boxed{\%}$ $\boxed{+}$ $\boxed{M_C^R}$ $\boxed{=}$ 280.8
$280.80

$216 + $64.80 = $280.80

The answer $280.80 is reasonably close to the estimate $260 and is a sensible answer.
A first-class ticket would cost $280.80.

Class Exercises

Complete the table below to determine the travel time.

Flight Number	Departs	Arrives	Direction	Time Zones Entered	Travel Time
387A	8:28 A.M.	3:10 P.M.	E	2	**1.** ∎
92	7:15 P.M.	9:45 P.M.	W	1	**2.** ∎
840	11:45 A.M.	3:21 P.M.	W	3	**3.** ∎

Skill Review

In order to find travel times, you need to be able to compute elapsed time.

Find the elapsed time.

1. 3:35 P.M. to 9 P.M.

2. 12 noon to 8:45 P.M.

3. 6:15 A.M. to 2:40 P.M.

4. 5:15 P.M. to 12:05 A.M. the next day

(For additional help, see page 552.)

4. Explain how mental arithmetic can be used to find the answer to Exercise 2.

5. What is the cost of an economy fare between Salt Lake City and Denver?

EXERCISES

Use the table on page 292 for information about the flights. Complete the table to determine the travel time.

Destination	Travel Time	Destination	Travel Time
Atlanta, GA	1. ■	Seattle, WA	2. ■
New York, NY	3. ■	Chicago, IL	4. ■
Los Angeles, CA	5. ■	Boston, MA	6. ■

In Exercises 7–12, determine the total cost for the fares indicated.

Destination	Fare Type	Total Cost
New Orleans, LA	Coach	7. ■
Denver, CO	First class	8. ■
Atlanta, GA	First class	9. ■
Chicago, IL	Coach	10. ■
Washington, DC	Coach	11. ■
New York, NY	First class	12. ■

Solve. Use the table on page 292.

13. Jackie
Destination: Seattle
Fare type: Economy
Fare: ■

14. Rico
Destination: Atlanta
Fare type: Supersaver
(28% less than coach)
Fare: ■

15. Willie is going from Los Angeles, CA, to Boston, MA, with a 45-minute stop in Salt Lake City. If his departure time in Los Angeles is 9:45 A.M., what is his expected time of arrival in Boston?

16. Portia used her calculator to compute the total cost of a first-class ticket between Salt Lake City and Seattle, WA. Study her keystrokes and answer the questions below.

$$\boxed{C_E^C} \quad 1.3 \quad \boxed{\times} \quad 82 \quad \boxed{=} \quad \cancel{106.60}$$

a. Explain her procedure.

b. What keystroke(s) would have changed if she were computing the cost between Salt Lake City and Chicago?

c. How would her procedure have changed if she were calculating the cost of economy fare, which is 10% less than coach fare?

Critical Thinking: *Judging the Reliability of Information*

Your travel agent has sent you the following information about the flight you plan to take from Pasadena, CA, to Boston, MA.

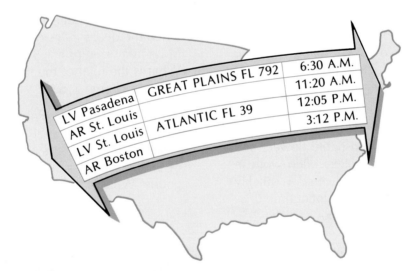

LV Pasadena	GREAT PLAINS FL 792	6:30 A.M.
AR St. Louis		11:20 A.M.
LV St. Louis	ATLANTIC FL 39	12:05 P.M.
AR Boston		3:12 P.M.

You would like to know how long you will actually be in the air on your trip.

1. List three ways you could find out in how many time zones you will travel on the flight from Pasadena to Boston.

2. Which way will give you the most reliable information?

3. Explain what you thought about in answering Question 2.

4. In how many time zones will you travel on the flight from Pasadena to Boston?

5. How long will you be in the air during this trip?

You would like to let a friend know when to meet you at the Boston airport.

6. How reliable is the ticket, which says you will arrive at 3:12 P.M.?

7. What did you think about in answering Question 6?

8. What will you tell your friend about meeting you?

Career
Truck Driver

About 2.5 million **truck drivers** work in the United States. They are part of a big industry that many other industries and consumers depend upon. Their work is governed by federal, state, and local regulations.

Profile of a truck driver. Truck drivers need not be high school graduates. Potential drivers may have to pass physical and written tests to receive a chauffeur's license, and interstate drivers must be over 21. Federal regulations limit drivers to 60 hours of work in a 7-day period. Some truckers may load and unload merchandise or serve as salespeople on the routes they serve. A trucker should be good at estimating loads, distances, gas mileage, and time.

The trucking environment. The loads truckers haul are as diverse as perishable flowers and automobiles or cattle. Truckers often work in teams in order to get loads delivered as quickly as possible. A trucker spends a lot of time driving and may sleep in a berth above a cab while a teammate drives. The trucker experiences a variety of driving situations and must be able to handle a large truck in all kinds of weather and traffic conditions.

All in a day's work. Roberta has just started working for an express company. She needs to be able to plan how long her routes will take and to be able to complete billing forms for the items she delivers.

1. Roberta leaves at 7:30 A.M. to take a load to Hadleyville, a distance of 200 miles. If she averages 50 miles per hour and allows 75 minutes to unload and have lunch, when will she get back?

2. Roberta will be taking one load to Capitol City and another to Prairie City. Capitol City is 120 miles away, and Prairie City is 140 miles away. Road conditions to Capitol City allow an average truck speed of 40 miles per hour, and those to Prairie City allow an average speed of 50 miles per hour. If she returns to her dispatching center between trips, how many hours must she allow for the two trips?

3. Roberta delivers 25 television sets costing $298 each to a dealer in Capitol City. Since the dealer pays cash for the sets, Roberta gives him a 1.5% discount. What is the total of the invoice if the trucking charge is $75?

4. On another delivery, Roberta delivers a refrigerator costing $698 and a sofa costing $475. There is a trucking charge of $30 and a sales tax of 6% on the goods. What is the total of the invoice?

9-2 Traveling by Bus or Train

Travel by bus or train is generally less expensive than travel by airplane, but such travel is usually slower as well. Buses serve many more cities than either trains or planes, so travel by bus is often more convenient. Buses stop more often than trains, but if you have to change from one bus or train to another, you may have to wait several hours.

You can estimate the distance you will have to travel by using a mileage chart like the one shown below.

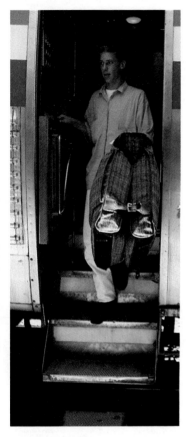

	Albuquerque	Atlanta	Baltimore	Cheyenne	Chicago	Denver	Houston	Kansas City	New York	Reno	St. Louis
Albuquerque, NM		1404	1890	538	1312	437	853	777	1997	1022	1042
Atlanta, GA	1404		654	1482	708	1430	791	822	854	2410	565
Baltimore, MD	1890	654		1669	717	1643	1404	1070	199	2615	828
Cheyenne, WY	538	1482	1669		981	101	1111	683	1754	966	942
Chicago, IL	1312	708	717	981		1021	1091	542	809	1947	289
Denver, CO	437	1430	1643	101	1021		1034	606	1794	1029	863
Houston, TX	853	791	1404	1111	1091	1034		743	1610	1880	780
Kansas City, MO	777	822	1070	683	542	606	743		1233	1653	257
New York, NY	1997	854	199	1754	809	1794	1610	1233		2711	976
Reno, NV	1022	2410	2615	966	1947	1029	1880	1653	2711		1892
St. Louis, MO	1042	565	828	942	289	863	780	257	976	1892	

EXAMPLE 1

Jon planned to visit his grandfather in Cheyenne, Wyoming. The bus he would take goes from his home in Saint Louis, Missouri, to Denver, Colorado, where Jon would change buses and catch one to Cheyenne. Use the mileage chart to find the total distance Jon would travel by bus. How much farther is it going by bus than traveling directly by car?

$$
\begin{array}{ll}
863 \text{ mi} & \text{St. Louis to Denver} \\
+101 \text{ mi} & \text{Denver to Cheyenne} \\
\hline
964 \text{ mi} & \text{total distance by bus}
\end{array}
$$

The direct distance from St. Louis to Cheyenne is 942 miles.

$$964 \text{ mi} - 942 \text{ mi} = 22 \text{ mi}$$

The bus trip is 22 miles longer.

Bus and train services provide **schedules** that give the routes, distances, and times of service for the cities they serve. A sample schedule for train service between St. Louis and Kansas City is shown on page 298.

on page 298.

Skills Review

In order to compute mileages, you should be able to add whole numbers.

Find each sum.

1. 455 + 498

2. 856 + 209 + 376

3. 700 + 56 + 392

4. 1,286 + 745 + 479

(For additional help, see page 542.)

EXAMPLE 2

Clarissa wants to travel from St. Louis to Kansas City. How far is it by train? How long does the trip take on the *Comet*?

$$\begin{array}{r} 565 \\ -282 \\ \hline 283 \end{array}$$ mileage at end of trip
mileage at start of trip

The *Comet* departs St. Louis at 5:05 P.M. and arrives in Kansas City at 10:30 P.M. No time zones are crossed.

5:05 P.M.–6 P.M. = 55 min
6 P.M.–10:30 P.M. = 4 h 30 min
　　　　　　　4 h 85 min   85 min = 1 h 25 min
　　　　　　　5 h 25 min

The distance is 283 miles and the elapsed time is 5 hours 25 minutes.

Train Name ▶			The Mustang	The Tower	The Comet	The Lincoln	The Southern	The Truman
Train Number ▶			100	105	112	26	73	133
Days of Operation ▶			Daily	ExSu	Daily	ExSa	Daily	Daily
	Mile	Symbol						
Chicago, Il–Union Sta. (CST)	0	Dp		8 15A	11 35A	3 30P	5 00P	5 15P
Pontiac, IL	92			9 47A		5 03P		6 44P
Normal, IL	124			10 16A				
Bloomington, IL	127			10 23A	1 41P	5 46P		7 25P
Lincoln, IL	156	↓		10 47A	2 07P	6 12P		7 51P
St. Louis, MO	282	Ar			4 45P	8 50P		10 40P
St. Louis, MO	282	Dp	8 05A		5 05P			
Jefferson City, MO	407		10 12A		7 18P			
Sedalia, MO	471		11 16A		8 25P			
Lee's Summit, MO	541		12 42P		9 38P			
Independence, MO	555	↓	1 02P		9 54P			
Kansas City, MO (CST)	565	Ar	1 30P		10 30P			
Kansas City, MO (CST)	0	Dp					12 35A	
Albuquerque, NM (MST)	901	Ar Dp					4 37P 4 57P	
Flagstaff, AZ (MST)	1249	↓					9 08P	
Los Angeles, CA (PST)	1795	Ar					7 45A	

EXAMPLE 3

Find the average speed of the *Comet* from St. Louis to Kansas City.

distance ÷ time = average speed
283 ÷ 5 h 25 min = ■

Hidden Question: How many hours is 5 h 25 min?
$$5\text{ h }25\text{ min} = 5\tfrac{25}{60}\text{ h} = 5.42\text{ h}$$

$$\begin{array}{r} 52.21 \rightarrow 52.2 \quad \text{Round to nearest tenth.} \\ 5.42\overline{)283.0000} \end{array}$$

The average speed is about 52.2 miles per hour.

With a calculator, the computation for Example 3 can be simplified.

Key: $\boxed{C_E^C}$ 25 $\boxed{\div}$ 60 $\boxed{+}$ 5 $\boxed{M+}$ 283 $\boxed{\div}$ $\boxed{M_C^R}$ $\boxed{=}$ ⟋⟋52.246154⟋⟋

52.2　　　**Round to nearest tenth.**

Class Exercises

Use the chart on page 297 to find the total distance between cities.

Starting City	Ending City	Via	Distance
Reno	Kansas City	Direct	1. ■
Cheyenne	Chicago	Denver	2. ■
New York	Houston	Atlanta	3. ■

4. Use the train schedule on page 298 to determine the distance from Pontiac, IL, to Sedalia, MO.

5. Use the train schedule on page 298 to determine the travel time and average speed on the *Lincoln* between Chicago and St. Louis.

6. The bus trip between Albuquerque and Denver takes 12 hours. The bus trip between Denver and Cheyenne takes 3 hours. What is the average speed for the bus ride between Albuquerque and Cheyenne through Denver?

EXERCISES

Use the mileage chart on page 297 to find the distance between cities.

Starting City	Ending City	Via	Distance
Chicago	Kansas City	Direct	1. ■
Baltimore	Albuquerque	Chicago	2. ■
Houston	St. Louis	Direct	3. ■
Reno	New York	Chicago	4. ■
Cheyenne	Atlanta	Houston	5. ■
New York	Denver	Chicago	6. ■

7. Use the train schedule on page 298 to determine the distance from Lincoln, IL, to Independence, MO.

8. Use the train schedule on page 298 to determine the distance from Albuquerque, NM, to Flagstaff, AZ.

9. Use the train schedule on page 298 to determine the distance between Jefferson City, MO, and Albuquerque, NM.

10. Use the train schedule on page 298 to determine the total trip time and average speed on the *Comet* between Bloomington, IL, and St. Louis, MO.

11. The one-way bus fare for the trip from New York to Kansas City is $115.15. What is the cost per mile?

12. A train from New York to Baltimore costs 11.3¢ per mile. What is the total cost of the trip?

13. A round-trip ticket is double the price of a one-way fare less 6%. What is the cost of a round-trip ticket if the cost of a one-way ticket is $37.85?

14. A round-trip ticket is double the one-way fare less 6%. Find the cost of a round-trip ticket between Atlanta and Houston if it costs 10.4¢ per mile one way.

15. A round-trip ticket is twice the price of a one-way ticket less 6%. Darby used his calculator to figure the round-trip cost of a ticket for which the one-way price was $73.85. Study his keystrokes and answer the questions that follow.

$$\boxed{C_E^C}\ 2\ \boxed{\times}\ 94\ \boxed{\%}\ \boxed{\times}\ 73.85\ \boxed{=}$$
138.838

a. Explain his procedure.
b. What keystrokes would he change if the cost of a one-way ticket was $43.25?
c. What keystrokes would he have changed if the discount had been 8% instead of 6%?

16. Heather is traveling from St. Louis to Flagstaff. She begins her trip on the *Comet* and must change at Kansas City. How much time will she spend waiting for the change at Kansas City? How much travel time will she spend if she enters 1 time zone heading west?

Consumer Note: *Public Transportation*

If you have ever ridden on a subway, bus, train, or airplane, you have used public transportation. Some of these modes of travel are publicly owned and operated, while others are privately owned. What do you think the difference is for the consumer?

Examples of publicly owned transportation systems are the subways and bus lines operated by most large cities. These systems are designed to move thousands of people around the city as rapidly and efficiently as possible. They are relatively inexpensive to use, and their rates are usually fixed for each route or line.

Trains and airlines are examples of privately owned transportation companies. These businesses work hard to attract the largest number of customers possible. Consumers benefit from the competition among the various companies by being able to choose from different classes of service, competitive rates, and schedules.

9-3 Renting a Car and Using a Taxi

When you travel by public transportation you may need to find a way to get from the airport or station to your final destination. If the distance is not great, using a taxi is often convenient. If the distance is greater or if you will be traveling around during your stay, it may be more convenient to rent a car.

Pamela is on a business trip and is trying to decide whether to rent a car or take a taxi from the airport. She has a copy of the taxi rate schedule shown at the right.

Taxi Rate Schedule	
First $\frac{1}{6}$ mile (or fraction)	$1.10
Each additional $\frac{1}{6}$ mile (or fraction)	$ .20
Passenger pays any tolls	

EXAMPLE 1

The distance from the airport to Pamela's hotel is $4\frac{1}{2}$ miles. What is the round-trip taxi fare?

Step 1. Find the one-way fare.

6 × (number of miles − $\frac{1}{6}$) × $.20 + $1.10 = total fare
6 ×   ($4\frac{1}{2}$ − $\frac{1}{6}$)   × $.20 + $1.10 =   ■

$$6 \times 4\frac{1}{3} \times \$.20 + \$1.10 = 6 \times \frac{13}{3} \times \$.20 + \$1.10$$
$$= 26 \times \$.20 + \$1.10$$
$$= \$5.20 + \$1.10 = \$6.30$$

Step 2. Find the round-trip fare.

Think: $6.30 × 2 = $12.60

Pamela's round-trip fare would be $12.60.

EXAMPLE 2

How much would it cost Pamela to rent a compact car for the same trip if the gasoline cost about $.42 and she needed the car for only one day? (Use the table of car rental rates on page 302.)

$$\left(\begin{matrix} \textbf{daily} \\ \textbf{rate} \end{matrix} \times \begin{matrix} \textbf{number} \\ \textbf{of days} \end{matrix} \right) + \left(\begin{matrix} \textbf{mileage} \\ \textbf{rate} \end{matrix} \times \begin{matrix} \textbf{number} \\ \textbf{of miles} \end{matrix} \right) + \begin{matrix} \textbf{gasoline} \\ \textbf{cost} \end{matrix} = \textbf{total cost}$$
($22.75 ×   1)   +   ($.17 ×   9)   + $.42   =   ■

$22.75	rental rate
1.53	$.17 × 9
+ 0.42	gasoline cost
$24.70	

The rental car would cost her $24.70.

Skill Review

In computing taxi fares, you will need to be able to multiply fractions.

Find each product.

1. $4\frac{1}{2} \times 8$
2. $6\frac{2}{3} \times 12$
3. $5\frac{1}{3} \times 7\frac{3}{4}$
4. $2\frac{4}{7} \times 6\frac{5}{6}$

(For additional help, see page 548.)

Car Rental Rates		
Type of Car	Daily Charge	Mileage Rate
Compact	$22.75	$.17 per mile
Midsized	$25.98	$.22 per mile
Full-sized	$29.75	$.26 per mile

EXAMPLE 3

If it were 15 miles from the airport to Pamela's meeting place, which mode of travel would be less expensive, taxi or rented compact car? Assume $1.25 for gasoline and 1 day's use of the rented car.

Step 1. Find the cost of the taxi.

$6 \times$ **(number of miles** $- \frac{1}{6}$) $\times$ **$.20 + $1.10 = total fare**
$6 \times \qquad (15 - \frac{1}{6}) \qquad \times \ $.20 + $1.10 =$ ■

$$6 \times (15 - \tfrac{1}{6}) \times \$.20 + \$1.10 = 6 \times 14\tfrac{5}{6} \times \$.20 + \$1.10$$
$$= 89 \times \$.20 + \$1.10$$
$$= \$17.80 + \$1.10 = \$18.90$$

Round-trip fare: $2 \times \$18.90 = \$37.80$

Step 2. Find the cost of the rental car.

$$\left(\begin{array}{c} \textbf{daily} \\ \textbf{rate} \end{array} \times \begin{array}{c} \textbf{number} \\ \textbf{of days} \end{array} \right) + \left(\begin{array}{c} \textbf{mileage} \\ \textbf{rate} \end{array} \times \begin{array}{c} \textbf{number} \\ \textbf{of miles} \end{array} \right) + \begin{array}{c} \textbf{gasoline} \\ \textbf{cost} \end{array} = \textbf{total cost}$$

$(\$22.75 \times \quad 1) \quad + \quad (\$.17 \times \quad 30) \quad + \ \$1.25 \ = \ $ ■

$$
\begin{array}{ll}
\$22.75 & \text{rental rate} \\
5.10 & \$.17 \times 30 \\
+ \quad 1.25 & \text{gasoline cost} \\
\hline
\$29.10 &
\end{array}
$$

The difference is $\$37.80 - \$29.10 = \$8.70$, so Pamela would save $8.70 by renting a car.

Class Exercises

1. Use the table of taxi rates on page 301 to determine the one-way taxi fare for a ride of $1\frac{1}{6}$ miles.

2. Use the table of taxi rates on page 301 to determine the cost of a round-trip taxi fare for a ride of $3\frac{5}{6}$ miles each way.

3. Use the table of car rental rates on this page to determine the cost of renting a midsized car for 1 day to drive 26 miles. Assume the cost of gasoline is $1.50.

4. Use the table of car rental rates on this page to determine the cost of renting a full-sized car for 1 day to drive 38 miles. Assume the cost of gasoline is $2.

5. Which is less expensive for a one-way ride of 18 miles, taking a taxi (table of taxi rates, page 301) or renting a compact car (table of car rental rates, page 302) for 1 day, spending $.85 for gas?

EXERCISES

Determine the one-way taxi fare using the table of taxi rates on page 301.

1. 8 miles

2. $5\frac{1}{2}$ miles, $1.20 in tolls

3. $6\frac{2}{3}$ miles

4. $12\frac{5}{6}$ miles, $2.45 in tolls

Determine the round-trip taxi fare using the table on page 301.

5. 3 miles each way

6. 4 miles each way, $.85 in tolls each way

7. $5\frac{2}{3}$ miles each way

8. $15\frac{1}{6}$ miles each way, $.90 in tolls each way

Use the table of car rental rates on page 302 to complete the chart by finding the cost of renting a car for 1 day.

Car Type	Number of Miles	Cost of Gas	Total Cost
Full-sized	29	$1.75	**9.** ▬
Compact	38	$1.90	**10.** ▬
Midsized	15	$ .80	**11.** ▬
Compact	125	$5.25	**12.** ▬

Solve.

13. Renèe has to travel 13 miles from the airport to her meeting. She must return later to the airport. Determine whether she should take a taxi or rent a midsized car for 1 day. Assume that the cost of gas is 5¢ per mile.

14. Maurino wants to travel 25 miles from the airport and return the next day. Would it cost him less to take a taxi both ways or to rent a compact car for 2 days? Assume that the cost of gas is 5¢ per mile.

15. Justin has a meeting at a conference center that is 4 miles from the airport. At the conclusion of the meeting, he wants to visit a store 2 miles from his meeting and then return $2\frac{1}{2}$ miles to the airport. Would it be less expensive for him to take a taxi for the three trips or to rent a full-sized car for 1 day? Assume that the cost of gas is about 6¢ per mile.

16. Charlotte, Michelle, and Donna travel together by taxi from the airport to a hotel. The distance is $4\frac{1}{6}$ miles one way and they must pay $3.28 in tolls each way. They will return to the airport the next day using the same route. If they split the cost equally, how much will it cost each of them?

17. How far can you travel in a taxi for $8?

18. How far could you travel in a rented compact car for $35? Assume that the cost of gas is 5¢ per mile and you rent the car for only 1 day.

19. The full-sized car at the rental company gets an average of 16 miles per gallon of gasoline. If gasoline costs $.98 per gallon, how much does it cost per mile for gas?

20. How much does it cost to take a taxi in your city? Do different companies have different rates? Are there other options, such as limousine services, available for airport trips? How much do they cost? Report your findings to the class.

21. Under what other circumstances might you rent a car?

Using a Calculator: Multiplying Fractions

Sometimes you can use your calculator to find products involving fractions. For example, to find the product of $4\frac{1}{3}$ and 6,

Key: $\boxed{\text{C}^\text{C}_\text{E}}$ $\boxed{3}$ $\boxed{\times}$ $\boxed{4}$ $\boxed{+}$ $\boxed{1}$ $\boxed{=}$ $\boxed{\div}$ $\boxed{3}$ $\boxed{\times}$ $\boxed{6}$ $\boxed{=}$ 25.999999

26   **Round to nearest whole number.**

1. Explain the keystrokes above.

2. How would the keystrokes differ if you wanted to find the product of $5\frac{2}{3}$ and 6?

Find each product.

3. $12 \times 3\frac{1}{6}$ **4.** $8 \times 2\frac{1}{2}$ **5.** $9 \times 7\frac{2}{3}$

9-4 Comparing Travel Costs

When you go on a vacation, you may want to compare travel costs to decide if you would rather take public transportation instead of driving. Airplane travel usually has the greatest initial expense, but less travel time is needed and meals may be provided as part of the fare.

Bus or train fare would be less costly than plane fare, but you would have to purchase meals separately. If you use public transportation, you will have to consider travel costs to and from the airport or station and your destination.

If you drive, you will have costs for gasoline, tolls, maintenance of your car, and food and lodging while traveling.

Marie is planning a trip for four members of her family. In deciding which form of transportation to use, she made a table summarizing travel costs.

Summary of Travel Information

	Car	Plane	Bus	Train
Round–trip distance	1500 mi	1500 mi	1500 mi	1500 mi
Fare or car expenses	$368.85	$956.00	$780.40	$498.00
Other transportation	none	$70.00	$50.00	$50.00
Travel time	4 da	12 h	3 da	2 da
Lodging ($72 per night)	$216.00	none	none	none
Meals ($80 per day)	$320.00	included	$240.00	$160.00

EXAMPLE 1

Find the total cost if Marie's family travels by train.

Estimate: $498 + $50 + $160 = ■ → $500 + $50 + $150 = $700

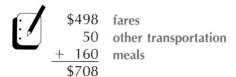

$498 fares
 50 other transportation
+ 160 meals
$708

 Key: $\boxed{C_E^C}$ 498 $\boxed{+}$ 50 $\boxed{+}$ 160 $\boxed{=}$ ⟋708⟋
$708

The answer $708 is reasonably close to the estimate $700 and is a sensible answer. It will cost $708 to travel by train.

EXAMPLE 2

Which is less expensive for Marie's family, travel by car or by train?

Step 1.   Find the cost of travel by car.

$368.85   car expenses
  216.00   3 nights' lodging
+ 320.00   4 days' food
$904.85

Step 2.   Compare travel costs.

It costs $708 to travel by train and $904.85 to travel by car, so it is more expensive to travel by car.

EXAMPLE 3
What is the average cost per passenger-mile traveled if Marie's family travels by train?

Step 1.   Find the number of passenger miles traveled.

number of passengers × miles traveled = passenger-miles
           4   ×   1,500   =   6,000

Step 2.   Find the cost per passenger-mile.

total cost ÷ passenger-miles = average cost per passenger-mile
   $708   ÷   6,000   = $.118

The average cost per passenger-mile is $.118, or 11.8¢.

Class Exercises

Use Marie's information to solve these problems.

1. What is the average cost per passenger for automobile travel?

2. What is the average cost per mile for automobile travel?

3. What is the average cost per passenger-mile for automobile travel?

4. Why might Marie's family prefer to drive even if it costs more than taking the train? What other factors besides cost make taking the train attractive?

EXERCISES

1. Determine the total travel cost if Marie's family travels by bus for their vacation.

2. What is the average cost per passenger if Marie's family travels by bus?

3. What is the average cost per mile if Marie's family travels by bus?

4. What is the average cost per passenger-mile if Marie's family travels by bus?

5. Determine the total travel cost if Marie's family travels by plane for their vacation.

6. What is the average cost per passenger if Marie's family travels by plane?

7. Which way of travel do you think Marie's family should choose? Explain your answer.

Use the information in the table below for Problems 8–13. Assume that three passengers are traveling, that lodging for all three costs $54 per night, and that 3 meals cost $17.50 per person per day.

Summary of Travel Information				
	Car	Plane	Bus	Train
Round-trip distance	1,900 mi	1,900 mi	1,900 mi	None
Fare or car expenses	$475.96	$758.35	$518.67	
Other transportation	none	$65	$45	
Travel time	5 da	8 h	2 da	
Lodging	_____	none	none	
Meals	_____	included	_____	

8. How much would be spent for lodging and meals if this trip were made by car and the passengers needed 4 nights lodging and 3 meals per day for 5 days?

9. Show how you would use a calculator to help streamline the computation for Problem 8.

10. How much would be spent for meals if this trip were made by bus?

11. Find the total cost per passenger-mile if this trip were made by car.

12. Find the total cost per passenger-mile if this trip were made by plane.

13. Find the total cost per passenger-mile if this trip were made by bus.

14. What are some of the disadvantages of making a long trip by car even if it is the least expensive way to travel?

15. What are some advantages to traveling by plane, even though it might cost more? What are some disadvantages?

Challenge

Carolyn and Bob are trying to decide whether to drive or to fly to visit friends. They have a week to travel.

1. If they drive their own car, they will spend about $100 for gasoline. They will have to pay for lodging for 2 nights at $52.50 per night plus 8% room tax. Meals will cost about $90. Tolls will cost $15. How much will it cost to drive?

2. If they fly, it will cost $189.50 each. The trip would take only 3 hours each way. The taxi fare to the airport in their own city would cost them $18.50. They could use their friend's car while they are visiting. What will it cost to fly?

3. A rental car would cost them $199.99 plus $.12 per mile for 300 miles, plus the cost of gasoline, $20. How much will a rental car add to the cost of their trip if they fly?

9-5 Commuting to Work

If you commute to work, you may have several options. You may be able to take a bus or train, or you may drive your own car. If you own a car, you may wish to form a **car pool** with other workers.

Ron commutes $2\frac{1}{2}$ miles each way to work. If he drives to work, he must pay $2.75 per day for parking in addition to paying for gas. If he uses public transportation, the bus fare is $1.35 each way. He can purchase a commuter pass for $45.95 per month, which allows unlimited bus use each month. Or, he could form a car pool with two co-workers. This means he would drive only once every 3 days, but when he drives, he would have to drive $1\frac{1}{4}$ miles further each way to pick up and drop off his passengers.

Skill Review

In order to compute commuting costs, you need to be able to multiply decimals.

Find each product.

  1. 5 × $2.38
  2. 12 × $4.86
  3. 1.4 × $56
  4. 22 × $.45

(For additional help, see page 545.)

EXAMPLE 1

Ron's car averages 16 miles per gallon in the city. He pays an average of $1.03 per gallon for gas. Determine his monthly commuting cost if he drives to and from work 22 days a month.

Step 1.   Find the cost per mile for gasoline.

cost per gallon ÷ miles per gallon = cost per mile
  $1.03   ÷   16   =   ■

$$\frac{\$.0643}{16)\overline{\$1.0300}} \rightarrow \$.064$$
Round to nearest 0.1 cent.

 Key: $\boxed{C_E^C}$ 1.03 $\boxed{÷}$ 16 $\boxed{=}$ 0.064375
$.064
Round to nearest 0.1 cent.

Step 2.   Find the daily cost.

Think: $2\frac{1}{2} \times 2 = 5$ miles per day

number of miles × **cost per mile** + **parking fee** = **daily cost**
  5   × $.064   + $2.75   =   ■
      $.32   + $2.75   = $3.07

Step 3.   Find the monthly cost.

daily cost × 22 = monthly cost
  $3.07   × 22 = $67.54

His monthly cost is $67.54.

With a calculator, the solution to Example 1 can be streamlined.

Key: $\boxed{C_E^C}$ 1.03 $\boxed{÷}$ 16 $\boxed{×}$ 2 $\boxed{×}$ 2.5 $\boxed{+}$ 2.75 $\boxed{=}$ $\boxed{×}$ 22 $\boxed{=}$ 67.58125
$67.58

The $.04 difference in answers occurs because the rounding occurs in different places in the computation.

EXAMPLE 2

If Ron rides the bus to work, how much will he save (in 22 round trips) by buying a commuter pass instead of paying the full fare?

Step 1. Find the cost by the trip.

cost per trip $\times$ **number of trips per day** $\times$ number of days $=$ **monthly cost**

$1.35 $\times$ 2 $\times$ 22 $=$ $59.40

Step 2. Compare the costs.

$$\$59.40 - \$45.95 = \$13.45$$

It costs $13.45 more to pay full fare.

EXAMPLE 3

How much would it cost Ron per month if he joined a car pool with two other workers and drove every third day? Assume an average of 22 work days per month.

Step 1. Find the added cost of carpooling if Ron drove every day. Ron would have to drive an extra $1\frac{1}{4}$ miles each way.

Think: $2 \times 1\frac{1}{4} = 2\frac{1}{2} = 2.5$

cost per mile $\times$ **number of miles per day** $\times$ number of days $=$ **added cost per month**

$.064 $\times$ 2.5 $\times$ 22 $=$ $3.52

Step 2. Find the cost of carpooling per month if Ron drove each day.

$67.54   cost of driving to work each month
+   3.52   extra cost per month of carpooling

$71.06

Step 3. Find the cost to Ron if he drives every third day. Since Ron drives $\frac{1}{3}$ of the days, his cost is $\frac{1}{3}$ of what it would be if he drove every day.

$71.06 $\times$ $\frac{1}{3}$ = $23.686 \rightarrow$ $23.69   **Round to nearest cent.**

It would cost Ron $23.69 if he carpooled with two other workers.

Class Exercises

Find the cost of commuting by car to work.

Miles Each Way	Cost per Mile	Daily Parking	Number of Days	Monthly Cost
20	$.25	$3.00	20	1. ■
11.6	$.262	$2.95	21	2. ■

Solve.

3. Find the cost of commuting to work by bus for 22 days and find the savings by purchasing a commuter pass if the one way fare is $1.15 and the commuter pass costs $39.95.

4. Which of the Exercises 1–3 can be done mentally? In which would the use of pencil and paper be more appropriate? Which could best be done by using a calculator?

EXERCISES

Find the cost of commuting by car to work.

Miles Each Way	Cost per Mile	Daily Parking	Number of Days	Monthly Cost
3.0	$.26	$4.00	20	**1.** ■
10	$.25	$2.50	20	**2.** ■
14.7	$.211	$3.95	23	**3.** ■

Find the cost of commuting to work by bus and find the savings.

One-way Fare	Number of Days	Monthly Cost	Commuter Pass	Savings
$1.00	22	**4.** ■	$35.00	**5.** ■
$1.05	21	**6.** ■	$36.85	**7.** ■
$1.75	23	**8.** ■	$67.45	**9.** ■

10. How much will Ron (Example 1) save if he carpools to work?

11. Manuel drives 3.7 miles each way to work at a cost of $.171 per mile. He pays $4.72 each day to park and works an average of 21 days per month. If he joins a car pool with two others, what will his average monthly cost be?

12. Golda is in a car pool with three other workers. She drives 4.2 miles each way at a cost of $.196 per mile and pays $2.65 each day to park. In a month (22 days) how much will she save by carpooling instead of driving alone?

Mental Math: *Multiplying by 22*

You can do some computations mentally by using properties of numbers. For example, to multiply $4.24 by 22, think of 22 as 20 + 2:

Think: $4.24 × 20 = $84.80 $4.24 × 2 = $8.48 $84.80 + $8.48 = $93.28

So, $4.24 × 22 = $93.28.

Find each product mentally.

1. 34 × 22   **2.** 16 × 22   **3.** $3.20 × 22   **4.** $6.18 × 22

Computer:
DATA Statements

Deborah, who lives in Atlanta, GA, is planning a vacation. She has written a program to give her some travel information. She uses the mileage table on page 297. The name of each city and mileage to that city are placed in DATA statements. Her program READs these DATA statements and computes and PRINTs the approximate driving time and cost to each city. In line 110, the expression TAB(24) tells the computer to tab, or skip, to the 24th position in the screen to print the next characters.

10 HOME	Clears the screen.
20 RT = 51	Sets the average rate in miles per hour.
30 GS = .98	Sets the average cost of a gallon of gasoline.
40 MPG = 26	Sets the average number of miles per gallon.
50 CPM = GS / MPG	Computes the cost per mile: cost per gallon ÷ miles per gallon.
60 PRINT "CITY", "MILES "; "TIME (HRS) "; "COST ($)"	Prints the heading (the punctuation and blank spaces within quotation marks are important!)
70 FOR N = 1 TO 7	Opens the loop to read, compute, and print data.
80 READ C$, M	Each time through the loop, captures the "next" city name and miles to that city.
90 T = M / RT	Computes the driving time to that city.
100 C = M * CPM	Computes the cost of gasoline to that city.
110 PRINT C$, M; TAB(24); T; TAB(37); C	Prints the city name and data for that city.
120 NEXT N	Closes the loop
130 DATA ALBUQUERQUE, 1404, BALTIMORE, 654, CHEYENNE, 1482	DATA statements that hold the data set from the mileage chart on page 297.
140 DATA CHICAGO, 708, DENVER, 1430, HOUSTON, 791	
150 DATA ST. LOUIS, 565	
160 END	Tells the computer to end the program.

Enter this program into your computer and RUN it.

EXERCISES

1. What one statement in the program would have to be changed if the cost of gasoline were $1.05 per gallon instead of $.98?

2. Make the change suggested in Exercise 1. RUN the program and observe the output.

Decision Making:
Planning a Trip

"I'm going to spend the evening planning my trip to Florida," Jeannine remarked. Maps, timetables, magazines, brochures, guidebooks, and letters were spread about on the table in front of her. Jeannine added Volume F of the encyclopedia to the pile.

"That sounds like a good idea," said Jeannine's roommate Gloria.

"Some of my planning is done," Jeannine said. "I have decided on the flights I want. Also, I plan to rent a car at the airport. I think I'll take my two weeks in April, because I've heard the weather is nice in April and costs aren't as high."

Answer the following questions.

1. Jeannine is using various kinds of printed information to plan her trip. For which of these is the date of publication important to Jeannine? Explain your answer.

2. What problems might Jeannine have if she uses an out-of-date map to plan her trip?

3. Where could Jeannine obtain reliable information about the weather in Florida in April? Which would be the most reliable source of this information?

4. Explain how you thought in judging that this source of information about Florida weather would be the most reliable.

MAKING PLANS

Jeannine and her cousin Karen planned to go camping in the Everglades. Several people had commented that they'd heard there were poisonous snakes all over the walking paths, so Jeannine had written to Joan Deming, a friend who is studying biology at the University of Miami and does field work in the Everglades. Joan wrote back to Jeannine and stated that there were few snakes along the paths and that they were not likely to be poisonous.

Answer the following questions.

5. Jeannine has heard about the snakes from two sources. Which of the two is likely to be more reliable?

6. Explain the reasoning that led to your answer for Question 5.

7. Suppose you wanted to buy new equipment for a camping trip. What qualifications would a person need to have in order to give you reliable advice about what to buy? What questions could you ask that person to assess his or her reliability?

CHOOSING A PLACE TO STAY

After the camping trip, Karen and Jeannine planned to go to Disney World. Gloria asked Jeannine where they planned to stay.

"I'm not sure. That's the main thing I want to decide about tonight. I have a newspaper ad here for a motel that sounds wonderful. Look! And it even has a pool!" Jeannine held out the ad.

"I can remember being so disappointed in a motel once," Gloria remarked. "It just wasn't as good as it sounded and looked in the travel brochure I had."

Jeannine looked at the ad. "I wonder how much I should rely on the information in this ad. What I really need is some first-hand information about this motel. I wish I knew someone who had stayed there. Since I don't, maybe I'll phone the motel."

Answer the following questions.

8. Which statements in the advertisement are exact? Which are vague?

9. What is the purpose of the writer of the advertisement?

10. What advice would you give a high school student about judging the reliability of advertisements?

12. If you called the motel, what questions would you ask to obtain reliable information about the motel?

CASTLEMOUNT MOTEL.
RESORT CENTER.
3500 Vine Parkway

Only 10 minutes from Disney World!

Luxury accommodations!
Low rates!

Your best bet at
the resorts!

Call 305-555-9000
for reservations

11. Would Jeannine get reliable information by talking with someone who had stayed at the motel? Explain your answer.

13. What factors will determine how reliable this information will be?

USING OTHER SOURCES

"How about your travel guidebook?" Gloria asked. "The Castlemount Hotel is probably listed there."

Jeannine picked up a booklet entitled *Griffin's Guidebook: Florida*. She found 21 listings for hotels and motels in the immediate area of Disney World. Castlemount Motel was among them. The listing read:

> **Castlemount Resort Motel**   **Rates Guaranteed**
>
> 12/1 to 4/15 & 6/16 to 8/31:   1P 79.00   2P/2B 79.00–105.00
>
> 4/16 to 6/15 & 9/1 to 11/30:   1P 65.00   2P/2B 65.00–90.00
>
> 255 units. On US 192; $5\frac{1}{2}$ miles east of intersection with
> Route I-4. A/C; C/CATV; radios; phones. Coin laundry. Pool.
> Lighted tennis court. Playground. Reserve deposit required.
> Dining rm; 7 am to 10 pm.

Jeannine realized that the Castlemount Motel charged varying rates according to the time of year. She consulted a key at the front of the guidebook. Here she learned that "2P/2B" referred to a room for two persons with two beds. "Units" meant the number of rooms in the motel. "A/C" means air conditioned rooms.

"It looks pretty good," Jeannine remarked. "I'll save money by going the last two weeks of April rather than the first two weeks."

"What about location?"

Jeannine unfolded her map of Florida and found the intersection of Routes US 192 and I-4. "It's close enough," she said. "I guess the ad was right about the motel being minutes away."

Answer the following questions.

14. If Jeannine and Karen stay for three nights in the lowest-priced room with two beds for two people, how much do they save by taking their vacation after April 16 rather than before April 16?

15. If the entrance to Disney World is on US Route 192, $1\frac{1}{4}$ miles west of the intersection of US 192 and I-4, and if it is $1\frac{3}{4}$ miles from the entrance to the Disney World parking lot, how far will Jeannine and Karen have to drive to go from their hotel to their parking place at Disney World each morning?

"How do I know this guidebook is more reliable than the ad?" asked Jeannine.

"Why don't you see how information is obtained for the book?" Gloria suggested.

Reading the introduction, Jeannine found that Griffin Guidebooks, Inc. accepted no money for listings and inspected the places it listed at least once a year. The stars in each listing were also explained: one meant the accommodation met basic standards, two and three were used for medium and high ratings, and four meant outstanding.

Answer the following questions.

16. Judge the reliability of the guidebook information about the Castlemount.

17. Describe the thinking steps you used in answering Question 16.

MAKING A DECISION

"This information seems based on a pretty thorough examination," Jeannine said. "I'd say it's about as reliable as I can hope for."

She turned again to the descriptions of accommodations near Disney World. "Look!" she said. "Here are two motels that charge *less* than Castlemount and are even *closer* to Disney World! Dinsmore Park Motel has four stars. That's clearly the best place to stay."

"Well, I think it's getting late," said Gloria as she rose. "Do you still have a lot of planning to do?"

"I want to figure out my budget for the trip and write a detailed itinerary," replied Jeannine. "And I want to read about Florida. But those tasks can wait for another time. I've made the main decision I wanted to make tonight. And I'm comfortable about my decision," she said, "because it's based on reliable information."

Answer the following questions.

18. How could Jeannine get additional reliable information about the Dinsmore Park Motel?

19. State some general procedures for thinking when you want to judge the reliability of information.

DECIDE FOR YOURSELF

Suppose you are planning a vacation and want to find a place to stay. How would you go about finding a place? Summarize how you, and Jeannine, went about deciding on a place to stay.

Chapter 9 Review

VOCABULARY

car pool   schedules   time zone

For Exercises 1–3, select the word or words that complete each statement.

1. You sometimes pass from one _____ to another when you travel.

2. _____ can help you plan your travel itinerary.

3. Many workers form a _____ to share driving to work.

SKILLS

Find the elapsed time.

4. 2:35 P.M. to 8 P.M.

5. 12 midnight to 4:50 A.M. the next day

Find each product.

6. $3\frac{1}{2} \times 6$

7. $5\frac{3}{5} \times 8$

8. $10\frac{2}{3} \times 3\frac{1}{4}$

Find each product.

9. 6 × $3.10

10. 14 × $2.08

11. 42 × $.43

CONSUMER TOPICS

Solve using the table on p. 292.

12. Joey Wilms
Destination: New Orleans
Fare type: coach
Cost per mile: ■

13. Carla Martine
Destination: Denver
Fare type: first class
Cost of round trip ticket: ■

14. Lena is going from Seattle to New York, with a 35-minute stop in Salt Lake City. If her departure time in Seattle is 10:30 A.M., what is her expected time of arrival in New York?

15. Use the mileage chart on page 297 to find the distance between Baltimore, MD, and Houston, TX.

Solve using the schedule on p. 298.

16. Louis planned to go from Bloomington, Illinois, to Independence, Missouri. Calculate the number of miles he will travel.

17. In Problem 16, if Louis makes the trip on the *Comet*, find his total travel time.

18. The *Truman* leaves Chicago at 5:15 P.M. and arrives in St. Louis, Missouri, at 10:40 P.M. The distance is 289 miles. There are no time changes. Find the average speed.

19. The one-way train fare from Chicago to St. Louis is $43. The distance is 289 miles. What is the cost per mile of the trip?

20. Determine the cost of a taxi trip of $9\frac{2}{3}$ miles if the fare is $1.10 for the first $\frac{1}{6}$ mile and $.20 for each additional $\frac{1}{6}$ mile.

Solve. Use the table on page 302 for Problems 21 and 22.

21. Guisseppi rented a midsized car for a 2-day business trip. He drove 8 miles each way to his hotel. Gasoline cost $1.75. If a taxi costs $1.10 for the first $\frac{1}{6}$ mile and $.20 for each extra mile, how much more or less would a taxi have cost?

22. Josephine rented a compact car for a 4-day trip of 270 miles. The rental agency gave her 25 free miles per day and she paid for her additional miles. Gas cost $12.92. Find the total cost of the rental car.

23. Malcolm and Roberta had to choose between making a 1,600-mile round trip by car or plane. Round-trip airfare was $253 for each of them and would take 3 hours. Round-trip cab fare to the airport would add $12. Driving their car would take 2 days each way and would add the cost of gas, food, and lodging. Roberta estimated that gas would cost $75, that food would be $25 per day (4 days) for each of them, and that lodging would be $42 for each of the 2 nights they would stay in a motel. Find the total costs for each mode of transportation.

24. In Problem 23, which means of transportation would be less expensive? What would the savings be?

25. In Problem 23, find the average cost per passenger-mile of flying.

26. In Problem 23, find the average cost per passenger-mile of driving.

27. Percy's car gets an average of 18 miles to the gallon in the city and he pays an average of $1.01 per gallon of gas. What is his monthly commuting cost if he drives 12.5 miles round-trip 22 days a month for work?

28. In Problem 27, Percy pays $108 per month to park his car in an indoor underground garage. If you include his monthly gasoline cost, what is the average daily cost (22 days per month) of driving his car to work?

29. Percy could ride the bus to and from work for $.75 each way. If he rode the bus 22 days per month, how much could he save each month?

30. If Percy joins a carpool with two other people who split all the costs, what will his average monthly cost be?

Chapter 9 Test

1. Cory's flight leaves Los Angeles at 9:15 A.M. and arrives in Salt Lake City at 11:56 A.M. He leaves Salt Lake City at 12:41 P.M. for New York. He arrives in New York at 6:47 P.M. He has 3 time zone changes. Find the time he spends flying.

2. One-way coach fare from Salt Lake City to Atlanta is $185. If a first-class ticket is 30% higher, find the cost of a round-trip first-class ticket.

3. Use the mileage chart on page 297 to find the distance from Denver, CO, to Atlanta, GA.

4. Find the average speed of a train if it leaves St. Paul at 8:15 A.M. and arrives in Chicago, a distance of 400 miles, at 4 P.M. There are no time zone changes.

5. Beth is traveling by train from Springfield, Illinois, to Kansas City, Missouri. She leaves Springfield at 2:50 P.M. and arrives in Kansas City at 10:30 P.M. Find her total travel time.

6. The distance from Bryan's hotel to the airport is $8\frac{1}{2}$ miles. If the cab driver charges $1.10 for the first $\frac{1}{6}$ miles and $.20 for each additional $\frac{1}{6}$ mile (or fraction), what will the fare be if Bryan takes a cab from the hotel to the airport?

Use the table on page 302 to solve.

7. Dick rented a full-sized car for 3 days. He drove 42 miles. Gas cost $2.79. Find the total cost of renting the car.

8. Which is less expensive for a round trip of 13 miles each way, taking a taxi (table of taxi rates, page 301) or renting a midsized car (table of car rental rates, page 302) for 1 day, if gas costs $1.20?

9. José and Dolores planned to fly from Phoenix to San Diego, a distance of 353 miles. Round-trip airfare was $238 each. Find their cost per passenger-mile.

10. In Problem 9, if they drove their car, José estimated that it would take 2 days for the round trip and would cost $42 for gas plus approximately $50 for meals. Find their cost for the trip if they went by car.

11. Use Problems 9 and 10 to find the less expensive mode of travel.

12. Elsie drives 3.6 miles each way to work at a cost of $.18 per mile. She pays $3.80 to park each day and works an average of 22 days per month. Find her average monthly cost of driving to work.

13. In Problem 12, if Elsie joins a car pool with two other workers, what will her average monthly cost be?

14. In Problem 12, how much would Elsie save if she takes a bus to work ($1.50 each way)?

Cumulative Mixed Review

1. Beau settled on a price of $6,280 for a compact car. The dealer had to add 6% sales tax to this price but allowed a $1,500 trade-in for Beau's old car. If the dealer required a 20% down payment, calculate the amount of the purchase price that Beau financed.
   a. $4,125.44   **b.** $1,031.36
   c. $6,656.80   **d.** $5,156.80

2. Determine the annual insurance premium for 100/300 liability insurance for a driver having a rating factor of 1.75 if the base premium is $84.
   a. $149   **b.** $253
   c. $147   **d.** $128

3. Lynne has a net monthly income of $1,582.46. She spends 25% of that on rent and 21% on food. How much money does she spend each month on rent and food?
   a. $395.62   **b.** $727.93
   c. $332.32   **d.** $729.46

4. Lloyd has an annual salary of $36,582. He is paid semimonthly. What is his semimonthly pay?
   a. $1,524.25   **b.** $18,291
   c. $3,048.50   **d.** $762.13

5. Samantha earns $282.25 each week. The federal government withholds 15% of that for federal income tax. How much is withheld from her pay annually for federal income tax?
   a. $12,486.76   **b.** $42.38
   c. $240.13   **d.** $2,201.55

6. Tessa allocated 15% of her net monthly income of $1,851.21 for clothes. She found she was spending too much for clothing. She wanted to reduce her total monthly clothing expense to $200 and put the extra money in savings. How much money could she put in savings each month by doing that?
   a. $157.42   **b.** $77.68
   c. $277.68   **d.** $54.61

7. Cary had an average daily balance of $330.01 in his charge account. He paid 1.5% interest on that amount. Compute his finance charge.
   a. $495   **b.** $334.96
   c. $3.30   **d.** $4.95

8. Maureen is flying from Salt Lake City to New York, a distance of 1,972 miles. Her one-way coach fare is $231. Compute the cost per mile of her flight.
   a. $8.54   **b.** $.23
   c. $2.50   **d.** $.12

9. Determine the cost of a taxi trip of $10\frac{1}{3}$ miles if the fare is $1.10 for the first $\frac{1}{6}$ mile and $.20 for each additional $\frac{1}{6}$ mile (or fraction).
   a. $12.40   **b.** $13.30
   c. $13   **d.** $12.20

10. Wendell borrowed $2,800 for the purchase of a computer. He paid back 12 monthly payments of $266 each. How much interest did he pay?
    a. $3,192   **b.** $266
    c. $392   **d.** $402.25

CHAPTER 10
Renting an Apartment

Marilyn is looking in the classified ads of her local newspaper for an apartment. She has decided to move out of her parents' house now that she is working full time.

- What factors should she consider when looking for apartments?

- What decisions can she make about the apartment strictly from reading the ads?

- Can you think of any decisions she would have to make that would require seeing the apartments?

If you were looking for an apartment, what factors would you take into consideration?

10-1 Finding an Apartment

When you first decide to live on your own, you may decide to rent an apartment. You can use newspaper ads to find out what apartments are available and how much the rents are. Many apartment rents include some or all utility costs and some apartments are furnished. You may have to agree to live in the apartment for a specified length of time, such as a year. If the cost of utilities is not covered by the rent, you will also have to make utility payments each month in addition to your rent. If the apartment is not furnished, you will have to buy or rent furniture.

1. DOWNTOWN: 2 BR, 1½ bath, W/D, microwave, $355/mo

2. DOWNTOWN: studio, furnished, W/W, A/C, $285/mo

3. DOWNTOWN: 1 BR, A/C; W/D, W/W, furnished, balcony, $355/mo

4. NORTHEAST: 2 BR, A/C, furnished, gas & elec. incl., W/W, patio, $480/mo

5. WEST: 1 BR, W/W, furnished, private ent., $400/mo

BR: Bedroom

W/D: Washer and dryer

A/C: Air conditioning

W/W: Wall-to-wall carpeting

EXAMPLE 1

Rae's employer asked her to move to a new location to open another office. She looked in the local newspaper and found these ads for apartments that looked as though they would fit her needs. Rae's new job will pay an annual salary of $19,280 and she is willing to pay 26% of her salary for housing. How much is Rae willing to spend on rent each month? Are there any apartments that she may not be able to consider because the rent is too high?

Step 1. Find the amount she is willing to pay annually for rent.

$$\text{annual salary} \times 26\% = \text{annual amount for rent}$$
$$\$19,280 \times 26\% = \blacksquare$$

Estimate: $19,280 × 26% = $\blacksquare$ → $20,000 × ¼ = $5,000

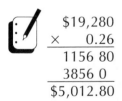
$$\begin{array}{r} \$19,280 \\ \times \quad 0.26 \\ \hline 1156\ 80 \\ 3856\ 0 \\ \hline \$5,012.80 \end{array}$$

 Key:  $\boxed{C^C_E}$ 19,280 $\boxed{\times}$ 26 $\boxed{\%}$ /5012.8/
$5,012.80

Skill Review

To compute rental expenses, you should be able to multiply and divide by whole numbers.

Find each product or quotient.

1. $476.04 ÷ 12

2. $35.26 × 12

3. $523.88 × 18

4. $893.55 ÷ 15

(For additional help, see pages 545 and 546.)

The answer $5,012.80 is reasonably close to the estimate $5,000 and is a sensible answer.

Step 2. Find the monthly rent she can pay.

$$\text{annual amount for rent} \div 12 = \text{monthly amount for rent}$$
$$\$5,012.80 \div 12 = \$417.73 \quad \text{Round to nearest cent.}$$

Step 3. Find out which of the apartments she could rent for $417.73 per month.

Apartments 1, 2, and 3 would fit within her budget, but apartment 4 would not. Since she would have to pay utilities for apartment 5, it would cost too much, too.

EXAMPLE 2

Rae estimates that she would have to pay $12 per month for a telephone, $32.50 per month for electricity and gas, and $10 per month for water. If she chooses apartment 3, will the total cost be above her budgeted amount? Use estimation to decide.

$$\text{rent} + \quad \text{cost of utilities} \quad = \text{total cost}$$
$$\$355 + \$12 + \$32.50 + \$10 = \quad \blacksquare$$

Estimate: $\$355 + \$12 + \$32.50 + \$10 = \blacksquare \rightarrow$
$\$360 + \$10 + \$30 + \$10 = \$410$

The estimated sum is less than her budgeted amount, so she probably can afford apartment 3.

Class Exercises

Estimate the monthly and annual cost for renting each apartment.

Monthly Rent	Utilities per Month	Furnishing per Month	Monthly Cost	Annual Cost
$250	$50	None	1. ■	2. ■
$385	$48	None	3. ■	4. ■
$525	$62.50	$31.50	5. ■	6. ■

7. What would apartment 1 in Example 1 cost per year if utilities cost $38 per month and furniture cost $20 per month to rent?

EXERCISES

Estimate the monthly and annual cost for renting each apartment.

Monthly Rent	Utilities per Month	Furnishing per Month	Monthly Cost	Annual Cost
$275	$45	None	1. ■	2. ■
$315	$50	$15	3. ■	4. ■
$395	$47.25	$22.75	5. ■	6. ■

Refer to the newspaper ad on page 322 to answer the following questions.

7. Which is the most expensive apartment?

8. Which of the apartments includes utility costs in the rent?

9. Which of the apartments have more than one bedroom?

Solve.

10. Hal Angstra
Annual salary: $20,400
Housing budget: 25%
Monthly housing cost: ■

11. Ginger Uhlrecht
Annual salary: $28,514
Housing budget: ■
Monthly housing cost: $570.28

Use the newspaper ad on page 322 to solve Problems 12–14.

12. Determine the total annual cost of apartment 2 if utility bills cost $62.50 per month.

13. Determine the total annual cost of apartment 4.

14. Nick and Trudy want to rent apartment 1. They figure that utilities will cost $55 per month. They will purchase $1,260 worth of furniture for it and plan to stay there for 2 years. What will the total cost of their housing be for the 2-year period? What is the average monthly cost?

15. Harry has budgeted 25% of his annual salary for housing. His company decided to give him a monthly housing allowance of $41.50. Harry finds with this allowance he need budget only 22% of his annual salary to afford the same apartment. What is his annual salary?

16. If Rae's new office (Example 1) is downtown, what additional costs might she have to budget for if she chooses to live in apartment 4?

17. Look in your local newspaper for apartment ads. What kinds of apartments would you consider renting? Describe some of their features, their rents, and their locations. Compare your answers with others in your class. Compile a list of important features to consider in renting an apartment.

Reading in Mathematics: *Reading Apartment Ads*

Many different terms and abbreviations are used in classified ads. Use the ads in this lesson to answer these questions.

1. Which of the apartments have both wall-to-wall carpeting and air conditioning?

2. What is a studio apartment?

3. What is a $\frac{1}{2}$ bath?

4. An ad for an apartment states: 13th mo free w/yrs lease, security deposit. What do you think this means?

10-2 Signing a Lease

When you find an apartment that you like, you may have to sign a *lease* in order to occupy the apartment. A **lease** is a written agreement between the owner and the renter that specifies the conditions for rental, including the monthly rent, the length of the lease, and the rights and responsibilities of both parties.

In addition to the rent, you may have to pay a **security deposit,** a cash deposit to be retained by the owner to cover any damage to the apartment you may cause. Your security deposit is usually returned if there is no damage beyond normal wear and tear. You may also have to pay a utilities deposit in order to have gas and electric service started and an installation fee for a telephone.

EXAMPLE 1

Norton found an apartment to rent and was given the lease agreement shown to sign. If he had to pay a $45 deposit for utilities and a phone installation fee of $28, how much did he have to pay in all?

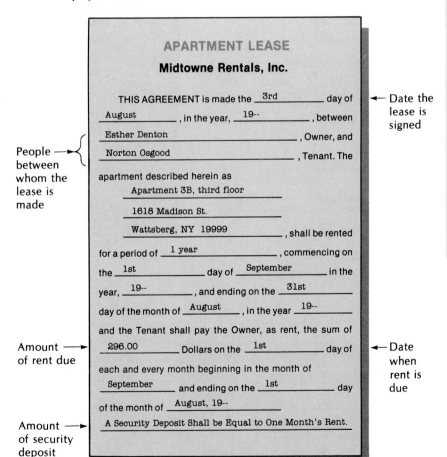

Skill Review

In order to find the total cost of renting an apartment, you should be able to add money.

Find each sum.

1. $354 + $350 + $43

2. $375 + $375 + $46 + $88

3. $1,000 + $400 + $80 + $30

4. $436.50 + $79.25 + $350.95 + $48.92

(For additional help, see page 544.)

Estimate: $296 + $296 + $45 + $28 = →
$300 + $300 + $50 + $30 = $680

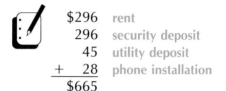

$296	rent
296	security deposit
45	utility deposit
+ 28	phone installation
$665	

Key: $\boxed{\text{C}^\text{C}_\text{E}}$ 296 $\boxed{+}$ 296 $\boxed{+}$ 45 $\boxed{+}$ 28 $\boxed{=}$ *665*
$665

The answer $665 is reasonably close to the estimate $680 and is a sensible answer.
Norton will have to pay $665 initially.

EXAMPLE 2

At the end of the lease period, the owner of the apartment raised Norton's rent by 6%. Norton decides to sign the new lease agreement. How much rent will Norton pay over a period of 1 year?

Step 1. Find the new monthly rent.

old rent + 6% of old rent = new rent
$296 + 0.06 × $296 =
$296 + $17.76 = $313.76

Problem Solving Strategy: Solving another way.
old rent + 6% of old rent = 106% of old rent
$296 × 106% = $296 × 1.06 = $313.76

Step 2. Find the yearly rent.

Hidden Question: How many months in 1 year?
1 y = 12 mo

$313.76 × 12 = $3,765.12

Norton will pay $3,765.12 rent a year at the new rate.

Class Exercises

Complete the table by finding the total initial charges.

Rent	Security Deposit	Utility Deposit	Phone Installation	Initial Charges
$250	$250	$50	$25	1.
$288	$288	$42	$30	2.
$421.50	$475	$74.50	$41.60	3.

4. At the end of Wilma's lease period, the owner raised her rent by 8%. If her previous monthly rent was $308, what is her new rent?

5. Which of Exercises 1–4 can be done mentally? In which would pencil and paper be appropriate? Which could best be done by using a calculator?

EXERCISES

Complete the table by finding the total initial charges.

Rent	Security Deposit	Utility Deposit	Phone Installation	Initial Charges
$200	$200	$30	$20	*1.* ■
$264	$264	$45	$35	*2.* ■
$319.50	$319	$55	$40	*3.* ■
$495.45	$525	$64.75	$38.95	*4.* ■

5. Faye Duncan
Monthly rent: $275
Security deposit: $275
Utility deposit: $50
Phone installation: $25
Initial charges: ■

6. Derak Quinlin
Monthly rent: $345
Security deposit: $345
Utility deposit: ■
Phone installation: $35
Initial charges: $770

7. Danny Halstead
Monthly rent: $315
Security: same as rent
Utility deposit: $65
Phone installation: ■
Initial charges: $723

8. Lois Fallstaff
Monthly rent: ■
Security: same as rent
Utility deposit: $53
Phone installation: $32
Initial charges: $917

9. Valerie signed a 1-year lease for monthly rent of $364. What was her total rent over the 1-year period?

10. Allegra signed a 2-year lease for monthly rent of $388.25. What was her total rent over the 2-year period?

11. Vernon's rent of $425.50 was raised by 9%. What is his new rent?

12. Beth's rent of $375.20 was raised by 11%. What is her new rent?

13. Sid signed a 2-year lease. He paid $314 a month in the first year and 6% more in the second year. How much rent did he pay over the 2-year period?

14. Rebecca was required to make a security deposit of $300 and had to pay 2 months' rent in advance in order to sign her lease. If her monthly rent was $425, her utility deposit was $50, and phone installation was $43, how much were her initial charges?

15. Explain how mental arithmetic can be used to find the answer to Problem 14.

16. Henry rented an apartment for 2 years. The second year his rent was 10% higher than the first. He paid a total of $8,820 over the 2-year period. What was his monthly rent during the first year?

17. Secure a copy of a standard lease form. What kinds of restrictions are spelled out in the lease? Do you have to pay a security deposit? Can you have pets? Talk about various restrictions in the lease and how they benefit the landlord or the tenant.

Consumer Note: *Signing a Lease*

Before signing a lease you have to determine what you can afford to pay for rent. A common rule of thumb is to keep your total monthly housing cost equal to either one week's gross pay or one-third of your monthly salary. Keep in mind that some types of rental housing have additional fees for services such as trash collection or recreational memberships. However, your rent may include the cost of water or other utilities.

You will normally be asked to sign either a lease or a written rental agreement. A lease is a preprinted legal document that records the contract between the owner and the renter. It defines the length of time you will live in the unit, the amount of rent, and the various conditions binding on both parties, such as how many people may occupy the apartment.

A written agreement is a more informal document than a lease. It usually permits month-to-month tenancy and allows the landlord to state his or her own preferences. It also may allow the landlord to change the rent at his or her discretion.

10-3 Renter's Insurance

When you rent an apartment, the owner of the building is responsible for insuring the building from loss or damage by fire, storm, theft, vandalism, and certain other perils. However, this insurance does not cover any of your personal belongings. You may wish to take out **renter's insurance,** a form of insurance for people who live in dwellings owned by someone else. Renter's insurance usually covers the value of personal property (such as clothing, furniture, or appliances) that is damaged or lost and may pay your living expenses if you have to live somewhere else while your building is being repaired. Such insurance may also cover personal liability and medical coverage for someone hurt in your apartment. It may also pay for damage to any additions or alterations you may have made to the apartment.

The following table shows typical coverage of renter's insurance.

Coverage of Renter's Insurance	
Minimum value of property insured	$6,000
Additional living expenses	20% of policy amount
Additions and alterations	10% of policy amount
Personal liability/medical	$25,000

EXAMPLE 1

Art insured his personal property for $15,000. How much coverage did he have for additional living expenses and damage to alterations?

$$\textbf{20\% of policy amount} = \textbf{additional living expenses}$$
$$20\% \times \$15,000 =$$ ■

Think: $20\% = 0.2$
$0.2 \times \$15,000 = \$3,000$

$$\textbf{10\% of policy amount} = \textbf{alterations/additions coverage}$$
$$10\% \times \$15,000 = \$1,500$$

Art has $3,000 available for additional living expenses and $1,500 coverage for damage to alterations or additions.

Factors that may affect your insurance costs are the type of building in which you live (brick, wood, and so on) and the number of families in the building. The table on the next page shows sample premiums for renter's insurance. The class refers to the type of materials used in construction.

Skill Review

In order to figure insurance coverage, you will need to be able to find a percent of a number.

Find each percent.
1. 40% of $3,000
2. 50% of $3,400
3. 15% of $2,400
4. 25% of $1,846

(For additional help, see page 551.)

EXAMPLE 2

Sample Premiums for Renter's Insurance

Policy Amount	Classes 1–8	Classes 9–10		Policy Amount	Classes 1–8	Classes 9–10
	3–4 families				5–20 families	
$10,000	$71	$73		$10,000	$72	$74
15,000	77	78		15,000	79	80
20,000	87	87		20,000	87	87

Karen rented an apartment in a class 5 building that has 12 other families in it. She wants to insure her personal property for $20,000. How much is her premium?

Problem Solving Strategy: Finding information.
Use the table above: Find the row "$20,000" under "5–20 families." Read the premium in the column "Classes 1–8."

Karen's premium is $87 per year.

Class Exercises

Use the table on page 329. Determine the amount for additional living expenses and additions/alterations coverage on a renter's insurance policy.

1. Policy amount: $6,000

2. Policy amount: $21,000

Complete the following by determining the premium on each renter's insurance policy. Use the table at the top of this page.

Policy Amount	Building Class	Number of Families	Premium
$10,000	8	4	**3.** ■
$15,000	3	18	**4.** ■
$20,000	6	10	**5.** ■

EXERCISES

Use the table on page 329. Determine the amount for additional living expenses and additions/alterations coverage on a renter's insurance policy.

1. Policy amount: $10,000

2. Policy amount: $14,000

3. Policy amount: $16,000

4. Policy amount: $46,000

Complete the following by determining the premium on each renter's insurance policy. Use the table on page 330.

Policy Amount	Building Class	Number of Families	Premium
$20,000	4	9	5. ■
$10,000	7	16	6. ■
$15,000	8	3	7. ■
$10,000	9	20	8. ■

9. Lucinda purchased a $26,000 renter's insurance policy. After damage to her building, she lived in another apartment building while hers was being repaired. How much of her rent would the insurance cover?

10. Paul paid $325 per month rent. When his building was damaged by fire, he moved to another building for 9 months at $475 per month. His renter's insurance exactly covered the difference in rent for the time he was in the other building. How much was the policy amount on his insurance policy?

Critical Thinking: Predicting Consequences

Tom's starting salary on his new job is $18,858 per year. He wants to spend no more than 25% of his income on housing. He has rented an apartment that costs $375 per month, including utilities. The payments on his new furniture will be $83 per month for the next year. Tom decided not to purchase renter's insurance.

Tom invited some friends over to see his apartment. One friend commented, "Mike lost everything during a fire in his apartment building. The worst part of it was that he hadn't insured his belongings. I can't believe somebody as smart as Mike didn't have renter's insurance."

Answer the following questions.

1. Predict some consequences of Tom's decision not to purchase renter's insurance.

2. How much over budget are Tom's housing expenses?

3. Assume that Tom's building houses a total of four families and is a class 9 building. Using the table on page 330, determine how much $10,000 of renter's insurance would cost per year.

4. If Tom changes his mind and decides to get the insurance, predict some possible consequences.

10-4 Utility Costs

When you rent an apartment, you will probably have to pay some utility costs. One cost is for electricity. Electricity is measured in **kilowatt-hours.** One kilowatt is equal to 1,000 watts. A kilowatt-hour is the amount of electricity needed to light ten 100-watt bulbs for 1 hour. The cost of a kilowatt-hour of electricity varies from community to community. The cost may also vary with the amount of power you use. The amount of electricity you use is recorded on an *electric meter,* which is read once a month by your utility company.

EXAMPLE 1

Frieda's electric meter read 4381 last month and 4715 this month. Her electric company charges $.064 per kilowatt-hour for electricity. How much is her electric bill for the month?

Step 1. Find the number of kilowatt-hours used.

$$\underset{4715}{\overset{\text{this month's}}{\text{reading}}} - \underset{4381}{\overset{\text{last month's}}{\text{reading}}} = \underset{334}{\overset{\text{number of kilowatt-hours}}{\text{used}}}$$

Step 2. Find the cost of the electricity.

$$\underset{334}{\overset{\text{number of}}{\text{kilowatt-hours}}} \times \underset{\$.064}{\overset{\text{cost per}}{\text{kilowatt-hour}}} = \text{cost of electricity}$$

$$= \begin{array}{l}\$21.376 \\ \$21.38 \quad \text{Round to} \\ \quad \text{nearest cent.}\end{array}$$

Frieda had to pay $21.38 for electricity.

EXAMPLE 2

The oven on Frieda's stove draws 1,350 watts of electricity per hour. How much would it cost her to cook a roast in her oven for $3\frac{1}{2}$ hours at $.064 per kilowatt-hour of electricity?

Step 1. Find the number of kilowatt-hours used.

Think: $3\frac{1}{2} = 3.5$

$$\underset{1,350}{\text{number of watts}} \times \underset{3.5}{\text{number of hours}} \div \underset{\div\,1,000}{1,000} = \underset{4.725}{\overset{\text{number of}}{\text{kilowatt-hours}}}$$

Step 2. Find the cost of the electricity.

$$\begin{array}{ccccc}\textbf{number of} & & \textbf{cost per} & & \\ \textbf{kilowatt-hours} & \times & \textbf{kilowatt-hour} & = & \textbf{cost of electricity} \\ 4.725 & \times & \$.064 & = & \$.302400 \rightarrow \$.30\end{array}$$

It would cost Frieda about $.30 to cook the roast.

Other utilities you might have when renting an apartment are natural gas and water. For instance, your stove and heating system might use gas. Gas and water meters are similar to an electric meter. Natural gas and water, however, are measured in units of **100 cubic feet (CCF).**

You might receive a bill for natural gas like the one shown. Many utilities give information about previous use to help consumers become more aware of their consumption of gas, electricity, or water.

EXAMPLE 3

In one month, Travis's water meter advanced from a reading of 408609 to 409209. His water utility charged $2.76 per 100 cubic feet of water used in addition to a 75% surcharge for sewage treatment. How much was his total water bill for the month?

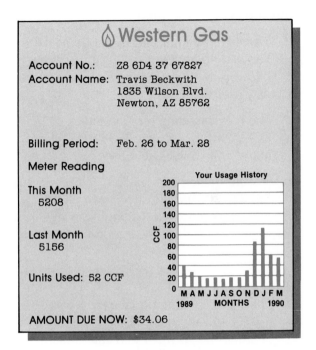

△ Western Gas

Account No.: Z8 6D4 37 67827
Account Name: Travis Beckwith
1835 Wilson Blvd.
Newton, AZ 85762

Billing Period: Feb. 26 to Mar. 28

Meter Reading

This Month
5208

Last Month
5156

Units Used: 52 CCF

Your Usage History

AMOUNT DUE NOW: $34.06

Step 1. Find the number of cubic feet used.

$$\begin{array}{ccccc}\textbf{2nd meter reading} & - & \textbf{1st meter reading} & = & \textbf{units used} \\ 409209 & - & 408609 & = & 600\end{array}$$

Step 2. Find the charge for water.

$$\begin{array}{ccccc}\textbf{units used} \div \textbf{100} \times \textbf{\$2.76} & = & \textbf{charge for water} \\ 600 \quad\div\ 100 \times \$2.76 & = & \$16.56\end{array}$$

Step 3. Find the sewage charge.

$$\begin{array}{ccc}\textbf{charge for water} \times \textbf{75\%} & = & \textbf{charge for sewage} \\ \$16.56 \quad\times 75\% & = & \$12.42\end{array}$$

Step 4. Find the total charge.

$$\$16.56 + 12.42 = \$28.98$$

Travis's water bill was $28.98.

With a calculator and the memory function, you can simplify the computation for Example 3.

Key: $\boxed{C^C_E}$ 409209 $\boxed{-}$ 408609 $\boxed{=}$ $\boxed{\div}$ 100
$\boxed{\times}$ 2.76 $\boxed{M+}$ $\boxed{\times}$ 75 $\boxed{\%}$ $\boxed{+}$ $\boxed{M^R_C}$ $\boxed{=}$ ⟋ 28.98 ⟋
$28.98

Class Exercises

Find the cost of the utility.

1. The meter reading on April 18 was 9128 kilowatt-hours. On May 18 it was 9646 kilowatt-hours. How much electricity was used?

2. An air conditioner uses 1,200 watts of electricity per hour. How much will it cost to run it for 4 hours if the unit cost of electricity is $.061 per kilowatt-hour?

3. The meter reading on June 6 was 3458 CCF. On July 7 it was 3608 CCF. How many units of gas were used?

4. If gas costs $.505 per CCF, what is the gas bill in Problem 3?

5. A water meter was read as 392665 on January 16 and as 395027 on April 12. The town charges $.392 per 100 cubic feet plus a 65% surcharge for sewage treatment. What is the total water bill for the period covered?

EXERCISES

1. The meter reading on January 6 was 3029 kilowatt-hours. The reading on February 6 was 3211 kilowatt-hours. How much electricity was used?

2. The meter reading on April 12 was 8141 CCF. The meter reading on May 11 was 8178. How many units of gas were used?

3. Find the cost of electricity in Problem 1 if the unit cost is $.062 per kilowatt-hour.

4. If gas costs $.60 per CCF, what is the gas bill in Problem 2?

Complete the table to calculate each water bill from the given meter readings.

Beginning Reading	Ending Reading	Cost per 1,000 Cubic Feet	Sewage Surcharge	Total Bill
643781	646992	$4.43	55%	**5.** ■
890002	896002	$4.00	50%	**6.** ■
715628	719331	$3.99	65%	**7.** ■

Solve.

8. Meter readings: 5490; 6002
Cost per unit: $.059
Cost of electricity: ■

9. Meter readings: 6125; 6911
Cost per unit: $.059
Cost of electricity: ■

10. Find the cost of operating an electric iron for $1\frac{1}{4}$ hours if the iron uses 950 watts per hour and the cost of electricity is $.052 per kilowatt-hour.

11. A self-defrosting refrigerator uses 365 watts per hour, and a regular refrigerator uses 210 watts. Each is run 3,450 hours per year and electricity costs $.061 per kilowatt-hour. How much would you save by using a regular refrigerator?

12. Show the keystrokes you would use to do Problem 11 with a calculator. Try to find more than one way to solve the problem.

13. On Todd's gas meter, readings for March, April, May, and June were 2287, 2345, 2404, and 2441. His gas company charges $.58 per unit. What was the total of his bills for April, May, and June?

14. During one quarter Laurie's water meter went from 88626 to 91158. Her town charges $.502 per 100 cubic feet and adds a surcharge of 65% for sewage treatment. She used her calculator to check her bill. Study the keystrokes and answer the questions that follow.

$\boxed{\text{C}^{\text{C}}_{\text{E}}}$ 91158 $\boxed{-}$ 88626 $\boxed{=}$ $\boxed{\div}$ 100 $\boxed{\times}$ .502 $\boxed{\times}$ 1.65 $\boxed{=}$ 20.972556

  a. Explain her procedure.
  b. What keystroke(s) would have changed if her town had charged $.493 per 100 cubic feet?
  c. What keystroke(s) would have changed if her town had a sewage treatment surcharge of 80% instead of 65%?

15. An electric company charges $.45 per unit for the first 10 units of electricity, $.062 per unit for the next 990 units, and $.054 per unit for all units over 1,000. Kent received an electric bill for $85.59. How many units did he use?

16. Find out how many watts some of the appliances in your home use. Estimate how many kilowatt-hours each would use in a day. Compare your answers with those of other students.

Mental Math: *Dividing by Powers of 10*

In order to find the number of kilowatts in a given number of watts, you need to be able to divide a number by 1,000. Dividing by a power of 10 can be done mentally:

$$4{,}920 \div 1{,}000 = 4\underset{\frown}{\,}920 = 4.92 \qquad \text{Move the decimal point one place}$$
$$2.5 \div 100 = \underset{\frown}{02.5} = 0.025 \qquad \text{to the left for each zero in the divisor.}$$

Find each quotient.

  1. 300 ÷ 10   **2.** 3,723 ÷ 100   **3.** 254 ÷ 10,000

Career

Meter Reader

A meter is a measuring device that automatically measures utility use. Companies employ **meter readers** to read utility meters on a regular basis. The companies then use these readings to compute their customers' utility bills.

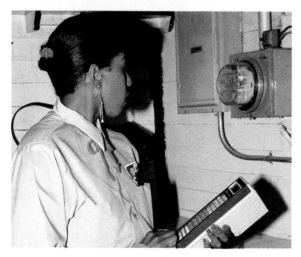

Profile of a meter reader. The meter reader is usually a high school graduate. Reading meters does not require any special training other than learning to read a meter accurately.

The meter reader's environment. Each meter reader has a territory, called a route, that may consist of houses, apartment buildings, offices, schools, and hospitals. After reading meters for much of the day, the reader returns to a central office, files the new readings, and makes a report of any damage to the meters or unusual usage that might indicate a meter is faulty or being improperly used.

All in a day's work. Carol works as a meter reader for Tri-State Water. The meters she reads show consumption in cubic feet, but Carol reads only the first four dials (100,000, 10,000, 1,000, and 100), so that the reading is recorded in hundreds of cubic feet (CCF). Each dial shows the part used of the indicated number of cubic feet shown.

1. The meter below on the left reads 2538. What is the reading of the meter on the right?

2. Carol has to record the consumption of water indicated by the meters below. How many CCF were used during the month shown?

3. Tri-State charges a minimum charge of $4 for 2 CCF. For the next 14 CCF, they charge $1.20 per CCF. For any CCF over 16, they charge $1.45 per CCF. Find the total charge for the usage shown.

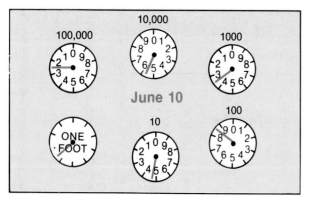

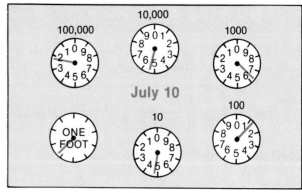

10-5 Telephone Service

When you move into an apartment, you will probably want a telephone. You may rent a phone from your local telephone company or you may buy a phone from a department store or other retail outlet. You must also have the telephone company install service in your apartment. There is usually an initial installation charge and a regular monthly charge that depends upon the amount and type of service the telephone company provides.

EXAMPLE 1

Pat wants to have phone service installed in her apartment. She called her local telephone customer service representative and received the list of available services and costs shown in the table below. If she had service installed and then bought a phone for $29.95 in a discount store, how much would her initial charges be?

$$\begin{array}{ccc} \text{installation} & + & \text{cost of} & = & \text{initial} \\ \text{charge} & & \text{phone} & & \text{charge} \\ \$48.50 & + & \$29.95 & = & \$78.45 \end{array}$$

The initial cost for phone service is $78.45.

If your phone company offers different kinds of services, as in the table, you may need to make a choice about which kind of service is best for you.

Telephone Service and Costs

Service	Cost	Description
Initial installation	$48.50	Brings in basic service for one pulse–dialed (rotary dial) phone
Basic Monthly Charges Economy service	$ 8.95	For people who make few calls. Each local call costs $.09 in addition to the basic charge.
Limited service	$12.45	Each call over 65 calls costs $.09 in addition to the basic charge.
Unlimited service	$20.35	No additional charge for local calls.

EXAMPLE 2

Helga expects to make about 85 calls per month. Which basic service would be best for her?

Step 1. Find the cost of each kind of service.

Economy:

basic charge + number of calls × \$.09 = cost of economy service
    \$8.95   +   85   × \$.09 =   ■

$$\begin{array}{r} 85 \\ \times\,\$.09 \\ \hline \$7.65 \\ +\ 8.95 \\ \hline \$16.60 \end{array}$$
    cost of calls
    basic charge
    cost of economy service

Limited:

basic charge + number of calls over 65 × \$.09 = cost of limited service
   \$12.45   +   (85 − 65)   × \$.09 =   ■

Think: 85 − 65 = 20
        20 × \$.09 = \$1.80

$$\begin{array}{r} \$12.45 \\ +\ \ 1.80 \\ \hline \$14.25 \end{array}$$
    basic charge
    cost of calls
    cost of limited service

Unlimited: From the figure on page 337, the cost is \$20.35.

Step 2. Compare the costs of the three services.
Limited service costs the least and so would be the most economical for Helga.

If you choose a phone service that charges by the call, you will be billed for your individual calls each month. In addition, once you choose a long-distance phone company, you will be billed for these calls. The cost of **long-distance calls,** or calls made outside your local calling area, depends upon the distance over which the call is placed, the length of the call, and the time of day.

Marcus chose a long-distance company from among several available based on its rates and reputation. The table on page 339 shows a sample of this company's rates.

EXAMPLE 3
Marcus called a friend in Dallas at 3 P.M. on Tuesday and talked to the friend for 11 minutes. How much was the cost of the call?

cost for 1 min	+	extra minutes	×	cost per minute	=	total cost
\$.51	+	(11 − 1)	×	\$.35	=	■

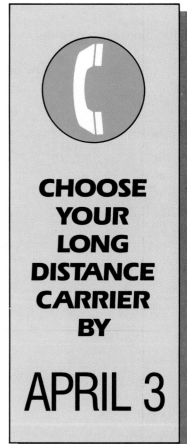

CHOOSE YOUR LONG DISTANCE CARRIER BY

APRIL 3

Think: $(11 - 1) \times \$.35 = 10 \times \$.35 = \$3.50$
$\$3.50 + \$.51 = \$4.01$

Marcus' call cost $4.01.

| City Called | Long-Distance Costs | | | | | |
| | Weekday | | Evening | | Night/Weekend | |
	1st Min.	Each Add'l Min.	1st Min.	Each Add'l Min.	1st Min.	Each Add'l Min.
Atlanta, GA	$.49	$.39	$.31	$.22	$.19	$.13
Boston, MA	.45	.31	.28	.20	.17	.12
Houston, TX	.51	.35	.32	.23	.19	.14
Kansas City, MO	.51	.35	.32	.23	.19	.14
New York, NY	.45	.31	.28	.20	.17	.12
San Francisco, CA	.53	.37	.34	.24	.20	.15

Weekday: 8 A.M.–5 P.M. Monday thru Friday, Evening: 5 P.M.–10 P.M. Monday thru Friday, Night/Weekend: 10 P.M.–8 A.M., Saturday, and Sunday until 5 P.M.

Class Exercises

Use the table on page 337 to find the following.

1. The charges for starting phone service if the cost of the telephone is $35.95.

2. The basic monthly charge for economy service with 60 calls.

3. The basic monthly charge for limited service with 60 calls.

Find the cost of a long-distance call from Marcus' city using the table on this page.

City Called	Type	Number of Minutes	Charge
Atlanta, GA	Night	16	**4.** ■
Houston, TX	Evening	3	**5.** ■
San Francisco, CA	Weekday	14	**6.** ■

EXERCISES

Use the table on page 337 to find the charges for the following.

1. Starting phone service if the cost of the telephone is $16.

2. Starting phone service if the cost of the telephone is $54.75.

3. Limited phone service with 48 calls.

4. Economy phone service with 20 calls.

Determine the cost of a long-distance call from Marcus' city using the table on page 339.

City Called	Type	Number of Minutes	Charge
Kansas City, MO	Weekday	4	5. ■
New York, NY	Weekend	14	6. ■
Boston, MA	Night	21	7. ■
San Francisco, CA	Evening	12	8. ■
Atlanta, GA	Weekday	8	9. ■

Use the tables on pages 337 and 339 to solve Problems 10–15.

10. Zach expects to make 24 calls per month. What would be the most economical basic service for him?

11. Nancy expects to make about 120 calls per month. What would be the most economical basic service for her?

12. For how many calls per month would economy service cost more than limited service?

13. For how many calls per month would limited service be more expensive than unlimited service?

14. How much do you save by calling New York in the evening instead of a weekday morning if you speak for 15 minutes?

15. Marcus wants to call a friend in Boston. How many minutes can he talk at the night rate and be charged no more than $2.50 for the call?

16. Sheila called a friend at 9 A.M. on two different weekdays. On the first day she spoke 10 minutes and was charged $1.94. On the second day she spoke 16 minutes and was charged $3.02. What was her phone company's initial charge and how much was each additional minute?

Using a Calculator: *Computing Long-Distance Costs*

You can use your calculator to streamline computation of long distance costs. For example, to find the cost of a 7-minute weekday call from Marcus' city to Boston:

Key: $\boxed{C_E^C}$ 7 $\boxed{-}$ 1 $\boxed{=}$ $\boxed{\times}$ .31 $\boxed{+}$ .45 $\boxed{=}$ ⟋ 2.31 ⟋
$2.31

Use your calculator to find the cost of each call.

1. To Kansas City, weekend, 48 min

2. To Atlanta, evening, 1 h 15 min

3. To New York, weekday, 23 min

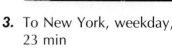

Computer:
INPUT Statements

Rob wrote a program to find the cost of long-distance calls from his city. The user enters a city name and the length of the call in minutes. If the city is in the computer's list, the cost of the call is computed.

10 HOME	Clears the screen.
20 INPUT "WHAT CITY?"; C$	Prompts and accepts input for the name of city.
30 INPUT "HOW MANY MINUTES?"; M	Prompts and accepts input for number of minutes.
40 FOR K = 1 TO 6	Begins loop to match city entered.
50 READ A$, X, Y	Reads first (next) city name and cost data.
60 IF A$ = C$ THEN GOTO 100	Tests to see if city names match; if so, program flow is directed to line 100.
70 NEXT K	If no match is made, the next value of K is computed and the search continues.
80 PRINT "SORRY, THAT CITY IS NOT IN THE LIST."	Loop is terminated and no match is made. A message is posted that the city entered is not on the list.
90 END	The program stops.
100 C = X + (M−1)*Y	The cost is computed.
110 PRINT "CITY: "; C$	The name of the city called is labeled and printed.
120 PRINT "TIME: "; M, " MINUTES"	The number of minutes are labeled and printed.
130 PRINT "COST: $"; C	The cost of the call is labeled and printed.
140 DATA ATLANTA, .49, .39	Six DATA statements containing the name of each city and the costs for the first minute and each minute thereafter.
150 DATA BOSTON, .45, .31	
160 DATA HOUSTON, .51, .35	
170 DATA KANSAS CITY, .51, .35	
180 DATA NEW YORK, .45, .31	
190 DATA SAN FRANCISCO, .53, .37	
250 END	Tells the computer to end the program.

EXERCISES

1. RUN the program. When prompted, enter the following data and observe the output. City: Houston   Time: 11

2. What lines would have to be added or changed to add the following to the list: Seattle, $.53 for the first minute and $.37 for each additional minute? Make the suggested changes. RUN the new program asking for the new city and a 10-minute call.

Decision Making:
Choosing a Roommate

LOOKING FOR AN APARTMENT

Doris Bullock plans to begin teaching in the fall. Her new job will pay $21,000 as a starting salary. She is currently living with her parents and can stay there until she gets established in her new job and saves some money. However, Doris is anxious to have her own apartment.

After giving it a great deal of thought and figuring her anticipated expenses, Doris decides that the most she can spend on housing is 25% of her gross salary. She has $2,000 in a savings account from money she earned while in school. She figures that she will need to use some of this money to pay the initial charges involved in renting an apartment (security deposit, utility deposit, phone installation, and so on).

Doris's new job at Elmhurst Elementary School is in the northwest section of the city. Since she does not have a car, she would prefer to find a nice apartment in the same section of town. Doris circles the following advertisements from the local paper for additional consideration:

1. **NORTHWEST:** 1 BR, DEN, A/C, W/W, balcony, near schools and shopping, $475/mo

2. **NORTHWEST:** 1 BR, A/C, W/W, new kit. appl., balcony, close to bus line, $425/mo

3. **NORTHWEST:** 1 BR, A/C, W/D, microwave, freshly painted, quiet area, $395/mo

4. **NORTHWEST:** 2 BR, A/C, W/W, 1½ bath, patio, near Elmhurst Ele., no pets, $495/mo

None of the apartments includes the cost of gas and electric in the rent. So, Doris estimates that she will spend an additional $50 per month to cover the cost of these utilities. Doris will also need some furniture for any of these apartments.

Answer the following questions.

1. How much of her salary does Doris anticipate spending on housing each month?

2. The initial charges for moving into any of the four apartments Doris is considering consist of the security deposit, which is the same as a month's rent; the first month's rent; a deposit for utilities, which is $75; and the charge for installation of a phone, which is $47.50. Because they are closest to her job, Doris is most interested in apartments 1 and 4. What are the initial charges for moving into each of these apartments?

3. How much will Doris have left in her savings account after paying the initial charges for apartment 1? For apartment 4?

4. Doris considers using the leftover cash for essential furniture such as a bed, chair, and table. If she does this and has no monthly expense for furniture, can she afford the rent and anticipated utility charges for either of the apartments in which she is most interested?

5. Suggest three alternatives Doris might want to consider at this point.

6. What did you think about in coming up with alternatives?

7. Share your answers to Questions 5 and 6 with a classmate. Discuss with your classmate how each of you thought of alternative actions Doris could take.

CONSIDERING SOME OPTIONS

Doris decides to go visit apartments 1 and 4 even though she is sure she cannot afford either of them. In looking at the apartments, Doris realizes that they both are extremely spacious. She wonders if she could find a roommate to share the expense of renting an apartment.

Doris gives a great deal of thought to her personality and preferred lifestyle. Although she enjoys privacy, she doesn't really want to live alone. Doris realizes that finding the right roommate with whom to share an apartment might not only solve her financial dilemma but might also be fun.

Doris makes a list of the characteristics she feels are important in a roommate:

> *− Single woman about my age*
> *− nonsmoker*
> *− Someone whose working hours are similar to mine*
> *− Someone who earns enough to pay half the rent*

Answer the following questions.

8. List the characteristics of your ideal roommate. How did you think of the characteristics that are important to you?

9. Doris developed her list quickly. What, if any, important characteristics did she fail to consider?

CHOOSING A ROOMMATE

By talking with friends and relatives, Doris finds out about three people who might be interested in sharing an apartment with her.

- Diane Cook-Stewart: account executive, age 42, salary $47,000
  She has furniture available, since she has been living on her own. She has savings of $5,700 and a sports car that she lets her friends drive. She has been paying half of a $1,500-per-month mortgage payment. Friends describe her as a workaholic who often works late, a smoker, and a person who is compulsively neat.

- Lydia Travers: teacher, age 23, salary $22,750
  She has been living with her parents. She just bought a new car, so she doesn't have much savings. She doesn't see any problem with spending up to 25% of her salary on housing. She is a nonsmoker and is confident that her parents will let her take some of the extra furniture from their house. She likes to have friends over often.

- Rita Browne: part-time sales clerk, age 18, income $10,000
  She has been living with her parents but wants to move because they complain about her friends hanging around and how messy she is. She is unsure of her plans—whether to work full time or go to secretarial school while working part time. She is a nonsmoker but some of her friends smoke. She is willing to spend up to 30% of her income on housing and all of her $500 savings on initial costs.

Answer the following questions.

10. If Doris is to have a roommate, she would prefer to rent the 2-bedroom apartment near her school. What are the initial charges for this apartment? If Doris is to pay $\frac{1}{2}$ these charges, what is her share?

11. If Doris has a roommate, her housing expense will be less than the 25% of her gross salary that she had anticipated spending. What would you suggest she do with the extra money? Explain how you thought of these suggestions.

12. Which of Doris' prospective roommates can afford to pay the other $\frac{1}{2}$ of the initial charges for the two bedroom apartment?

13. Predict how Doris' life might change if she decides to share an apartment with each of the prospective roommates.

14. If you were Doris, which person would you choose? Explain.

DECIDE FOR YOURSELF

Suppose that you are deciding whether to share an apartment with a roommate. Collect information about possible roommates and use the information, together with what you know about your own personality, to find a possible roommate. Then summarize how you, and Doris, went about finding a roommate.

Chapter 10 Review

CCF (100 cubic feet)   lease   renter's insurance
kilowatt-hours   long-distance calls   security deposit

For Exercises 1–6, select the word that completes each statement.

1. A written agreement between the owner and the renter that specifies the conditions for rental is called a _____ .

2. A _____ is a cash deposit to be retained by the owner to cover any damage to an apartment a renter may cause.

3. _____ is a form of insurance for people who live in dwellings owned by someone else.

4. Electricity is measured in _____ .

5. A unit used to measure natural gas is a _____ .

6. _____ are telephone calls that are made outside your local calling area.

SKILLS

Find each product or quotient.

7. $25.72 × 12

8. $580.50 ÷ 18

9. $246 ÷ 12

Find each sum.

10. $425 + $350 + $95 + $100

11. $35.50 + $125.75 + $95.98

Find each percent.

12. 20% of $1,200

13. 35% of $2,500

14. 17% of $3,825

Find each quotient.

15. 8,297 ÷ 1,000

16. 963 ÷ 1,000

17. 2.98 ÷ 1,000

Compare. Choose the greater number.

18. $325.75, $352.75

19. $63.08, $63.80

20. $208.60, $206.80

CONSUMER TOPICS
Solve.

21. Jerome earns $18,500 per year and has budgeted 26% of his salary for housing. How much can he afford to pay each month for housing?

22. Peggy pays $375 per month rent. Her utilities cost her $72 per month and her furnishings cost her $45 per month. Estimate her annual cost for renting her apartment.

23. Find the total initial charge.
Monthly rent: $325
Security deposit: $325
Utility deposit: $75
Phone installation: $30

24. Use the table on page 330.
Class 5 building
18 families
Policy amount: $15,000
Premium: ■■

Solve.

25. Rachel purchased a $20,000 renter's insurance policy. The policy pays up to 20% of the policy amount for additional living expenses. How much will she have available for additional living expenses if she ever needs them?

26. At the end of Victor's lease period, the owner raised Victor's rent by 7%. If his old monthly rent was $382, what is Victor's new rent?

27. 1st meter reading: 7286
2nd meter reading: 7625
Cost per unit: $.062
Cost of electricity: ■■

28. Use the table on page 337.
For 92 calls per month, which is more economical: economy, limited, or unlimited service?

29. An electric light bulb used 75 watts of electricity per hour. How much will it cost to keep the bulb lit for 5 hours if the cost is $.065 per kilowatt-hour?

30. What is the gas bill for a period in which 136 CCF of gas were used if gas costs $.515 per CCF?

31. A water meter was read as 286455 on May 15 and as 291068 on September 12. The town charges $.278 per 100 cubic feet plus a 60% surcharge for sewage treatment. What is the total water bill for the period covered?

32. The basic charge each month for Rita's phone service is $9.35. She makes an average of 75 calls per month and is charged $.08 per call. What is the cost of her phone service per month?

33. Neda phoned a friend and talked for 13 minutes. If she was charged $.65 for the first 3 minutes and $.15 for each extra minute, how much did the call cost her?

Chapter 10 Test

1. Estimate the monthly cost for renting an apartment if rent is $305, utilities are $115, and furnishings are $65.

Find the total initial charge.

2. Monthly rent: $335
Security deposit: $335
Utilities deposit: $95
Phone installation: $45

3. Monthly rent: $360
Security deposit: $360
Utilities deposit: $65
Phone installation: $30

4. Ray earns $18,750 per year and has budgeted 22% of his income for housing. How much can he afford to pay each month for housing?

5. Michele purchased a $15,000 renter's insurance policy that pays 20% of the policy amount for additional living expenses. How much is available for additional living expenses?

6. At the end of Claire's lease period her landlord raised the rent by 8%. If her old monthly rent was $320, what is her new rent?

7. At the first meter reading, an electric meter read 6245. At the end of the period the meter read 6689. If electricity cost $.061 per kilowatt-hour, what was the cost of the electricity?

8. A hair dryer uses 1,250 watts of electricity per hour. Walter uses his hair dryer an average of 2.5 hours a month. If electricity costs $.055 per kilowatt hour, how much does it cost Walter to operate his hair dryer every month?

9. Use the table on page 330 to find the premium for $20,000 in renter's insurance in a class 7 building containing 12 families.

10. What is the gas bill for a period in which 245 CCF of gas were used if gas costs $.605 per CCF?

11. The basic charge each month for Corey's phone service is $8.95. He makes an average of 80 calls per month and is charged $.09 per call. What is the cost of his phone service each month?

12. Economy phone service is $8.50 plus $.48 for each call. Limited service is $16 plus $.48 for each call over 10. Which service should Sally choose if she expects to make 18 calls per month?

13. If a call to New York costs $1.25 for the first 3 minutes and $.35 for each additional minute, how much will a call to New York cost if you talk for 8 minutes?

14. A water meter was read as 346285 on March 10 and as 348601 on June 15. If the town charges $.315 per 100 cubic feet plus a 65% surcharge for sewage treatment, what is the total water bill for the period covered?

Cumulative Mixed Review

Select the letter corresponding to the correct answer.

1. Lionel has an annual income of $19,500. He has 25% of his gross salary withheld for deductions. What is the net amount of each paycheck if he gets paid biweekly?
   a. $4,875   b. $14,625
   c. $562.50   d. $281.25

2. Carolyn earns an annual gross salary of $21,500. If she has $6,450 withheld annually for deductions, what percent of her salary is withheld for deductions?
   a. 30%   b. 3%
   c. 33%   d. 0.3%

3. Jason's beginning balance in his checkbook was $275.65. He made deposits of $50, $25 and $35.50. He wrote checks for $125.75. He had to pay a bank charge of $3.80. What was his ending balance for the month?
   a. $264.20   b. $256.60
   c. $260.40   d. $294.70

4. Ingrid borrowed $1,200 for 3 months at an annual rate of 9.5% under a single-payment plan. How much interest must she pay?
   a. $114   b. $28.50
   c. $1,314   d. $1,140

5. Creighton deposited $1,500 in a savings account that pays 7.5% interest, compounded quarterly. What was his balance at the beginning of the third quarter?
   a. $1,556.78   b. $112.50
   c. $1,528.13   d. $1,733.44

6. Norma borrowed $800 at 9% for 12 months under a monthly installment plan. She must pay $8.7453 per $100 each month for 12 months. How much is her monthly installment payment?
   a. $72   b. $872
   c. $839.55   d. $69.96

7. Andy makes two payments a year of $450 each for real estate taxes. He makes 4 payments a year of $225 for auto insurance. How much must he budget monthly to cover these fixed expenses?
   a. $56.25   b. $150
   c. $1,800   d. $93.75

8. Pia had an outstanding balance on her credit card account of $468.42 for purchases she made. How much was the finance charge if it was 1.5% per month?
   a. $84.36   b. $.59
   c. $7.03   d. $.50

9. How much will it cost to mail a first-class letter that weighs 2.7 ounces if the rate is $.25 for the first ounce and $.20 for each additional ounce or fraction of an ounce over the first?
   a. $.45   b. $.75
   c. $.60   d. $.65

10. Alvin financed $4,250 to buy a new car. If he made 36 payments of $138.50 each, how much interest did he pay on the loan?
    a. $4,986   b. $4,270.44
    c. $20.44   d. $736

Lynn and Richard are buying their first house. They have lived in an apartment for 5 years and have saved money for a down payment.

- What do you think their primary consideration will be in looking for a house?

- What other considerations will they have?

- How can they determine how much of a mortgage they can afford?

What would be your first step if you decided to buy a house?

11-1 Making a Down Payment on a House

The cost of a home depends on the size and location of the lot, the size of the house, the material from which it is built, and special features of the house and the lot. When you buy a house, you may need to borrow money from a bank or mortgage company. Most lenders require a down payment of between 10% and $33\frac{1}{3}$% of the price of the house.

A *condominium* is a unit in a multiunit building. When you purchase a condominium, you own the unit you live in but not the building.

Irene and Carl Waxter decided to buy their first house. In order to make a good investment, they looked at a lot of different houses.

EXAMPLE 1

The down payment on one house costing $68,500 was 15%. How much would the Waxters need for a down payment?

percent required × **cost of home** = **amount of down payment**
15%   × $68,500   = $10,275

Think: 15% = 0.15
Estimate: 15% × $68,500 = ■ → 0.2 × $70,000 = $14,000

$68,500 × 0.15 = $10,275

The answer $10,275 is reasonably close to the estimate $14,000 and is a sensible answer.

The Waxters need $10,275 for a down payment.

One common rule for deciding how much you can afford to pay for a house or condominium is to multiply your total annual income by $2\frac{1}{2}$. A house costing more than $2\frac{1}{2}$ times your annual income may represent too great a debt.

Skill Review

In order to determine if you have enough for a down payment, you need to be able to compare numbers.

Compare. Choose the greater number.
   1. $5,560; $5,506
   2. $11,067; $10,968
   3. $14,736; $20,100
   4. $11,249; $11,251

(For additional help, see page 539.)

EXAMPLE 2

If the Waxters' combined annual income is $31,600, how much should they be able to afford to pay for a house?

$2\frac{1}{2}$ × **combined annual income** = **suggested cost of house**
$2\frac{1}{2}$ × $31,600   =   ■

Think: $2\frac{1}{2} = 2.5$

$$
\begin{array}{r}
\$31,600 \\
\times \quad 2.5 \\
\hline
15\ 800\ 0 \\
63\ 200 \\
\hline
\$79,000.0 \\
\$79,000
\end{array}
$$

 Key: $\boxed{\text{C}_\text{E}^\text{C}}$ 31600 $\boxed{\times}$ 2.5 $\boxed{=}$ 79000

$79,000

The Waxters should be able to afford as much as $79,000 for a house.

Class Exercises

Complete the table to find the amount of the down payment needed.

Cost of House	Percent for Down Payment	Down Payment
$59,700	16%	1. ■
$80,000	10%	2. ■
$78,900	15%	3. ■
$68,450	$12\frac{1}{2}$%	4. ■

For each of the given family incomes, find the maximum amount the family should be able to spend on a house.

5. $46,200

6. $26,200

EXERCISES

Complete the table to find the amount of the down payment needed.

Cost of House	Percent for Down Payment	Down Payment
$ 50,000	10%	1. ■
$ 65,000	10%	2. ■
$ 83,200	7.5%	3. ■
$ 59,700	16%	4. ■
$ 92,350	12.5%	5. ■
$104,200	15%	6. ■

For each of the given family incomes, find the maximum amount the family should be able to spend on a house.

7. $20,000

8. $33,165

9. $29,400

10. $51,320

Solve.

11. Jacobs family
Amount of savings: $6,500
Cost of house: $58,000
Down payment: 10%
Enough in savings?: ■

12. Aldrige family
Amount of savings: $8,000
Cost of house: $62,500
Down payment: 16%
Enough in savings?: ■

13. Maria Gorden's weekly salary is $362. Rob Gorden's weekly salary is $381. How much should they be able to afford to pay for a home?

14. Tony DeMartino's monthly salary is $1,682. Helena DeMartino makes $1,744 per month. How much should they be able to afford for a house?

15. Dorsey and Mayellen Wilson receive an average of $1,200 per year in interest. Adding this to their combined salaries, they figure that they can afford a house that costs $81,300. What is their combined income?

Critical Thinking: Comparing and Contrasting

Your plans for the future definitely include owning a home as soon as you can afford it. A friend tells you that planning to be a homeowner involves much more than a down payment and the monthly mortgage. "Homeowners and renters," your friend says, "have very different types of personalities."

The comment seems strange to you, but you decide to give it some serious thought. You begin your reflection by answering the following questions.

1. What are some responsibilities that a homeowner and a renter would have in common? What are some responsibilities that would be different?

2. Imagine that you are just starting your professional life. You know that a lot of your time will be spent working. Would this decision affect whether or not you own or rent the place in which you live?

3. How does the answer you gave to Question 2 compare to the answers given by your classmates? Review the similarities and differences among the responses. Do these suggest additional personality traits of owners versus renters? Explain.

4. Do you think there is sufficient evidence to support the claim that "homeowners and renters have very different types of personalities"? Describe how you used your own thinking and the thoughts shared by your classmates to answer this question.

11-2 Mortgage Payments and Closing Costs

Once you have decided to buy a home, you will have to arrange for a loan, or **mortgage**, to pay for it. Several kinds of mortgages are available. You may be able to save a lot in interest by paying back your mortgage over a shorter period of time.

Paying back a mortgage is called **amortizing** the mortgage. Part of each payment goes toward lowering the amount of the principal of the loan. Interest is calculated on the new balance. The table below gives the monthly payments for borrowing $1,000 at different rates of interest. To find a mortgage payment, multiply the payment per $1,000 for the given rate of interest and number of years over which the mortgage is to be amortized by the number of thousands borrowed.

Monthly Mortgage Payments per $1,000 Borrowed					
Interest	15 Years	20 Years	25 Years	30 Years	35 Years
10%	$10.74	$ 9.65	$ 9.08	$ 8.77	$ 8.59
10.5%	$11.05	$ 9.98	$ 9.44	$ 9.14	$ 8.98
11%	$11.36	$10.32	$ 9.80	$ 9.52	$ 9.36
11.5%	$11.68	$10.66	$10.16	$ 9.90	$ 9.76
12%	$12.00	$11.01	$10.53	$10.28	$10.15
12.5%	$12.32	$11.36	$10.90	$10.67	$10.55
13%	$12.65	$11.71	$11.27	$11.06	$10.95

EXAMPLE 1

Robert and Kim borrowed $66,500 to buy a house. If their bank offered a 10.5% interest rate on a 30-year mortgage, how much would their monthly payments be?

Problem Solving Strategy: Finding information.
Refer to the table above. Look across the row labeled 10.5% to the column headed 30 years. The value is $9.14.

table value $\times$ $\dfrac{\text{number of}}{\text{thousands borrowed}}$ = monthly payment

$9.14 $\times$ ($66,500 \div$ $1,000) = ■

Skill Review

To find mortgage payments, you should be able to multiply decimals.

Find the product. Round to the nearest cent.

1. $5.89 × 66.5
2. $14.12 × 78.45
3. $9.67 × 45.9
4. $8.88 × 50.5

(For additional help, see page 545.)

Think: $66,500 \div \$1,000 = 66.5$

$$\begin{array}{r} 66.5 \\ \times \$9.14 \\ \hline 2\ 660 \\ 6\ 65 \\ \underline{598\ 5} \\ \$607.810 \rightarrow \$607.81 \end{array}$$

Key: $\boxed{C_E^C}$ 9.14 $\boxed{\times}$ 66.5 $\boxed{=}$ 607.81
$\$607.81$

Their monthly mortgage payment is $607.81.

EXAMPLE 2

If Robert and Kim pay off their mortgage in 30 years, how much interest will they have paid on the loan?

Step 1. Find the total repaid.

> **Hidden Question:** How many payments in 30 years?
> 30 years $\times$ 12 payments per year = 360 payments

$$\begin{array}{l} \textbf{360} \times \textbf{monthly payment} = \textbf{total paid} \\ 360 \times \quad \$607.81 \quad = \$218,811.60 \end{array}$$

Step 2. Find the amount of interest paid.

$$\begin{array}{l} \textbf{total payments} - \textbf{amount borrowed} = \textbf{interest paid} \\ \$218,811.60 \quad - \quad \$66,500 \quad = \$152,311.60 \end{array}$$

They paid $152,311.60 in interest.

Once you have found a house you like and have arranged for financing, you are ready to take possession. Taking possession of your house is called *settlement*. At the time of settlement, you must pay a number of extra fees called **closing costs.**

- **Points** are charges that a bank usually makes for granting the loan. A point is 1% of the loan amount. The number of points charged varies from bank to bank. Often, a bank will charge more points for a longer-term mortgage or a lower interest rate.

- *Transfer taxes, title stamps,* and *processing fees* are costs that are charged as a percent of the amount borrowed.

EXAMPLE 3

Thom and Marguerita obtained a loan for $52,000. As part of the closing costs, they were charged 2 points, 1% for transfer tax,

356 Chapter Eleven

0.5% for title stamps, and 0.2% for loan processing fees. How much did they pay for the variable part of the closing costs?

Think: 2 points = 2%

sum of rates		× amount of loan	= variable closing costs
(2% + 1% + 0.5% + 0.2%) ×		$52,000	= ■
3.7%	×	$52,000	= $1,924

They paid $1,924 for variable closing costs.

Other closing costs are fixed by the bank, state, or the lawyer who represents you. Total closing costs are fixed costs plus variable costs.

Class Exercises

Use this information and the table on page 355: cost of house: $56,800; down payment: $6,500; length of mortgage: 30 years; interest rate: 12.5%.

1. How much must be borrowed?

2. What is the monthly payment?

3. How much is repaid over 30 years?

4. How much interest is paid in 30 years?

Determine the total closing costs.

Fixed Costs	Variable Costs	Total Costs
$400	$2,000	5. ■
$395	$2,175	6. ■

EXERCISES

Find the monthly mortgage payment using the table on page 355.

Amount Borrowed	Number of Years	Rate of Interest	Monthly Payment
$75,000	15	12%	1. ■
$52,300	25	11.5%	2. ■
$95,000	35	13%	3. ■

Determine the total closing costs.

Fixed Costs	Variable Costs	Total Costs
$300	$1,700	4. ■
$365	$2,295	5. ■
$424.75	$1,933	6. ■

7. Which of Exercises 1–6 could be done mentally? In which would pencil and paper be appropriate? Which could best be done by using a calculator?

Solve.

8. Roney family
Monthly mortgage: $575.38
Number of years: 25
Total repaid: ■

9. Vickers family
Monthly mortgage: $671.56
Number of years: 20
Total repaid: ■

10. Winkler family
Loan: $30,000
Points: 3
Transfer tax: 0.6%
Title stamps: 0.2%
Processing fee: 1.2%
Lawyer fee: $275
Credit check: $48
Title search: $75
Recording fee: $12
Closing costs: ■

11. Nugat family
Loan: $56,000
Points: 2.5
Transfer tax: 0.5%
Title stamps: 0.1%
Processing fee: 1.5%
Lawyer fee: $205
Credit check: $55
Title search: $65
Recording fee: $15
Closing costs: ■

12. In Exercise 10, what percent of the loan is represented by the closing costs that the Winkler family had to pay?

13. Norma needs to borrow $39,300. She can get a rate of 13%. How much more will she repay in all if she gets a 30-year instead of a 20-year mortgage? (Use the table on page 355.)

14. Caleb and Prudence had a 30-year mortgage on the $58,400 loan for their house. Over the 30 years they paid a total of $157,726.72 in interest alone. What was the rate of interest?

Reading in Math: *Vocabulary*

Complete each of the following sentences by unscrambling the underlined words. The scrambled words correspond to words in the following list.

closing costs   mortgage   processing fees   title stamps
down payment   points   settlement   transfer taxes

1. When you purchase a house, you will take out a <u>gamtroeg</u>, or loan to purchase the house, which is the cost of the house minus the <u>nwdo mtaypen</u>.

2. If you have a low interest rate on your <u>tggmaeor</u> your bank may charge you more <u>spniot</u>.

3. At the time of <u>telesttnem</u>, when you take possession of your house, you must pay <u>glsocin sstco</u>, including <u>letti smatsp</u>, <u>crsipgseon efes</u>, and <u>frntsrea etasx</u>.

Career
Police Officer

A **police officer** upholds the laws and protects the people in his or her working area. Police officers also provide safety and health information, work to educate young people, and instruct residents and business people in how to protect their property.

Profile of a police officer. Police departments are made up of men and women over 21 years of age. A high school education is required, and a college education is sometimes preferred. All police departments provide training programs for their officers.

Officers must be in good health, be in good condition, and have good vision and hearing. A lot of police work is routine, but it can be dangerous.

The police department environment. Police officers often work outdoors, but they can also work in a headquarters office, a detention building, a crime laboratory, or a classroom. Police work on foot, on motorcycles, on horses, in cars, and in boats and planes. Officers are assigned to various shifts, so they do not work regular hours. They frequently work in pairs.

All in a day's work. Charlene Thomas was a new police recruit. Before starting her full-time work, Charlene had to spend several weeks at the police academy. While at the academy, she learned the fundamentals of police work. Charlene studied methods for investigating crimes, and she also learned the proper procedure for arresting a suspect.

When she joined the police department, she decided to purchase a home within the city limits. Charlene found a condominium for $79,000 that she liked. She had to make a 10% down payment and pay 1½ points. Other closing costs were 0.5% of the mortgage.

1. How much was Charlene's down payment?

2. How much did Charlene pay in points?

3. How much were total closing costs?

4. Charlene was able to get a 20-year mortgage at 12.5%. Use the table on page 355 to help determine her monthly payment.

5. If she took out a 30-year mortgage at 12.5%, what would be her monthly payment?

6. If Charlene paid off the loan in 30 years instead of 20, how much more interest would she pay?

11-3 Property Taxes

The major source of revenue for many cities is a tax that is levied on all property within the city. This tax is called a **property tax,** or *real estate tax.* It is based upon a percentage of the actual **market value** of the property, or the value at which the property could be sold. This value is called the **assessed value** of the property. The percentage used is the *rate of assessment.*

EXAMPLE 1

Mark and Sun-Lee own a house with a market value of $72,600. In their city the rate of assessment is 63%. What is the assessed value of their house?

market value × rate of assessment = assessed value
$72,600 × 63% = ■

Think: 63% = 0.63
Estimate: $72,600 × 0.63 = ■ → $70,000 × 0.6 = $42,000

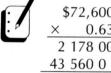

```
    $72,600
  ×    0.63
   2 178 00
  43 560 0
  $45,738.00
```

Key: $\boxed{C_E^C}$ 72600 $\boxed{\times}$ .63 $\boxed{=}$ ⟋ 45738 ⟋
$45,738

The answer $45,738 is reasonably close to the estimate $42,000 and is a sensible answer.
The assessed value of Mark and Sun-Lee's house is $45,738.

A city government sets *tax rates* based upon the amount of money it needs to operate and the total assessed value of property within its boundary. This tax rate is often expressed in **mills,** or tenths of a cent, per dollar of assessed value. One mill is equal to $.001. To express the tax rate in dollars instead of mills, divide the number of mills by 1,000.

EXAMPLE 2

What would be Mark and Sun-Lee's property tax if their city sets a tax rate of 34.19 mills?

Step 1. Express the tax rate in dollars.

mills ÷ 1,000 = tax rate in dollars
34.19 ÷ 1,000 = 0.03419

> ### Skill Review
>
> In order to compute tax rates, you need to be able to divide by 1,000.
>
> Find each quotient.
> **1.** 34.98 ÷ 1,000
> **2.** 5.972 ÷ 1,000
> **3.** 254.87 ÷ 1,000
> **4.** 83.02 ÷ 1,000
> (For additional help, see page 545.)

Step 2. Find the property tax.

assessed value × tax rate = property tax
$45,738   × 0.03419 = $1,563.7822
                    $1,563.78   **Round to nearest cent.**

Mark and Sun-Lee have to pay $1,563.78 in property taxes.

Some towns and counties express their tax rate in dollars of tax per thousand dollars of assessed value. To find the tax rate per dollar, divide the dollars of tax per thousand dollars by $1,000.

EXAMPLE 3

Waldorf County has an assessment rate of 75% and a tax rate of $29.81 per $1,000 of assessed value. What would be the property taxes on a house whose market value is $59,300?

Step 1. Find the assessed value.

market value × rate of assessment = assessed value
$59,300   ×   75%   = $44,475

Step 2. Find the tax rate per dollar.

dollars per thousand ÷ $1,000 = tax rate
$29.81   ÷ $1,000 = 0.02981

Step 3. Find the property tax.

assessed value × tax rate = property tax
$44,475   × 0.02981 = $1,325.79975
                    $1,325.80 **Round to nearest cent.**

The property tax is $1,325.80.

With a calculator and mental math, you can streamline the computation for Example 3.

Think: $29.81 ÷ $1,000 = 0.02981

Key: $\boxed{C_E^C}$ 59300 $\boxed{×}$ 75 $\boxed{\%}$ $\boxed{×}$ .02981 $\boxed{=}$  1325.7997
                                        $1,325.80   **Round to nearest cent.**

Class Exercises

Find the assessed value of each house.

Market Value	Assessment Rate	Assessed Value
$60,000	50%	**1.** ■
$74,300	45%	**2.** ■

Find the property tax.

Assessed Value	Tax Rate	Property Tax
$40,000	30 mills	3. ■
$60,582	$41.60 per $1,000	4. ■

Find the property tax.

Market Value	Assessment Rate	Tax Rate	Property Tax
$90,000	55%	31.5 mills	5. ■
$74,250	63%	$33.71 per $1,000	6. ■

EXERCISES

Find the assessed value of each house.

Market Value	Assessment Rate	Assessed Value
$ 50,000	40%	1. ■
$ 81,000	51%	2. ■
$104,200	72%	3. ■
$123,800	58%	4. ■

Find the property tax.

Assessed Value	Tax Rate	Property Tax
$30,000	40 mills	5. ■
$42,000	30.6 mills	6. ■
$61,385	$26.72 per $1,000	7. ■

Find the property tax.

Market Value	Assessment Rate	Tax Rate	Property Tax
$ 60,000	50%	30 mills	8. ■
$ 95,000	60%	42 mills	9. ■
$ 88,000	71%	29.5 mills	10. ■
$107,300	45%	$26.54 per $1,000	11. ■

Solve.

12. Brunson home
Market value: $79,200
Assessment rate: 42%
Assessed value: ■

13. McDonald home
Market value: $80,200
Assessment rate: ■
Assessed value: $46,516

14. When a house is purchased in the middle of a tax year, the buyer must pay the property tax for the remainder of the tax year. The Wechler family occupied their house on April 1. The previous owner had paid $1,172.54 in taxes the previous September 1. How much did the Wechler's owe the seller for taxes?

15. Show how a calculator could help you streamline the computation for Exercise 14.

16. The Fogler family occupied their house on January 1. The taxes had been paid the previous August 1. The house was assessed for $52,500 and the county tax rate was $41.16 per $1,000. How much did the Fogler's owe the seller for taxes?

17. Roth and Selina's house is assessed for $42,337 and the county's assessment rate is 51%. What is the market value of their home (to the nearest $100)?

18. Art received a property tax bill for $1,262.50. The tax rate for his town is 40.23 mills and the assessment rate is 53%. What is the market value of his house (to the nearest $100)?

19. Find out how the values of houses in your city are determined, what the rate of assessment is, and what the property tax rate is. Compare your answers with others in the class.

Consumer Note: *Factors Affecting the Value of a House*

Many factors are involved in determining the value of a house or condominium. Location, style, condition, size, amenities, and prevailing market conditions all contribute to a property's current value.

Real estate brokers acknowledge that location is the most important factor of all. Is the property located in the city, the suburbs, or the countryside? Is it located in an appreciating, stable, or declining neighborhood? Does it look

out over the water or does it face a factory? The answers to these questions about location help to assess the value of property.

Another important factor affecting the value of a house is the current market. If mortgage interest rates are down, if the supply of property is low or average, and if buyer demand is strong, then the value of most property will rise. If the conditions are reversed, the value of most property will decline.

11-4 *Homeowner's Insurance*

When you buy a home, the bank or mortgage company may require you to insure your home against fire and other perils. A **homeowner's policy** covers perils such as fire, storm, theft, and vandalism. Many insurance companies require you to insure your house for at least 80% of its *replacement value,* or cost of replacing your home at current costs of materials and labor if it were destroyed.

Homeowner's insurance protects several things in addition to the dwelling itself:

- unattached structures (garages, for example)

- the personal property of people in the house

It also covers:

- additional living expenses in case the people in the house must live elsewhere while it is being repaired

- liability insurance and medical payments for someone injured on the property

- damage to the property of others

The following table shows typical coverage by a homeowner's policy.

Coverage by a Typical Homeowner's Policy
House. . . . . .Full policy amount
Unattached structures. . . . . .10% of policy amount
Personal property. .50% of policy amount
Additional living expenses . . . . .20% of policy amount
Liability/medical $25,000

EXAMPLE 1

Clarissa and Van are insured for 80% of the replacement value of their home, which is valued at $72,300. What is the most they can recover for the other items covered in their policy if their policy contains the coverage outlined in the above table?

The policy amount is $72,300 × 0.8 = $57,840.

Unattached structures: 10% of the policy amount

Think: $57,840 × 10% = $57,840 × 0.1 = $5,784

Personal property: 50% of the policy amount

Think: $57,840 × 50% = $57,840 × $\frac{1}{2}$ = $28,920

Additional living expenses: 20% of the policy amount

$$\$57,840 \times 0.2 = \$11,568$$

Clarissa and Van have $5,784 coverage for unattached structures, $28,920 coverage for personal property, and $11,568 coverage for additional living expenses.

Insurance rates are based not only on the policy amount but also on the building material used in the house, the nearness of fire-fighting equipment, the presence of smoke detectors, and other factors. The rate schedule for one company is shown in the table below.

	Annual Insurance Premium Rates							
Policy Amount	**Brick/Masonry Protection Class**				**Wood Frame Protection Class**			
	1–6	**7–8**	**9**	**10**	**1–6**	**7–8**	**9**	**10**
$50,000	$158	$170	$203	$213	$170	$178	$213	$226
$60,000	$183	$197	$237	$247	$197	$216	$241	$261
$70,000	$218	$225	$270	$283	$225	$236	$283	$299
$80,000	$240	$258	$311	$325	$258	$271	$325	$345
$90,000	$270	$292	$351	$362	$292	$306	$363	$390

EXAMPLE 2
Clarissa and Van have a frame house that is in protection class 7. Use the closest value in the table above to find their annual insurance premium.

Problem Solving Strategy: Finding information.
Look across the row for $60,000 (the value in the table above closest to $57,840) to the column under wood frame for classes 7–8.

Their annual premium is $216.

Class Exercises

Find each policy amount.

Value of House	Amount of Coverage	Policy Amount
$ 90,000	80%	*1.* 
$ 53,500	75%	*2.* ■
$107,000	90%	*3.* ■

Use the information below and the tables on pages 364 and 365.

Homeowner: Betty Watson   Value of home: $68,000
Amount of coverage: 90%   Building material: brick
Protection class: 4

4. How much is the policy amount on Betty's house?

5. What is the maximum coverage on Betty's unattached garage?

6. How much in additional living expenses can Betty receive from her homeowner's policy?

7. Use the value in the table on page 365 nearest to the value of Betty's policy to determine her annual premium.

EXERCISES

Find each policy amount.

Value of House	Amount of Coverage	Policy Amount
$80,000	80%	**1.** ■
$75,000	90%	**2.** ■
$62,500	75%	**3.** ■

4. Explain how mental arithmetic can be used to find the answer to Exercise 1.

Use the information below and the tables on pages 364 and 365.

Homeowner: Samuel Strack   Value of home: $90,000
Amount of coverage: 80%   Building material: masonry
Protection class: 9

5. How much is the policy amount on Samuel's house?

6. What is the maximum coverage on Samuel's unattached garage?

7. For how much is his personal property insured?

8. How much in additional living expenses can Samuel receive from his homeowner's policy?

9. Use the value in the table on page 365 nearest to the value of Samuel's policy to determine his annual premium.

10. How much more would it cost Samuel to insure his house for 100% of its value?

Use the information below and the tables on pages 364 and 365.

Homeowner: Sally Perego   Value of home: $78,500
Amount of coverage: 90%   Building material: wood
Protection class: 7

11. How much is the policy amount on Sally's house?

12. What is the maximum coverage on Sally's storage shed in the back yard?

13. For how much is her personal property insured?

14. How much in additional living expenses can Sally receive from her homeowner's policy?

15. Use the value in the table on page 365 nearest to the value of Sally's policy to determine her annual premium.

16. How much more would it cost Sally to insure her house for 100% of its value?

17. The Waldorfs' garage was destroyed by fire and cost $7,821 to replace. They had a homeowner's policy on their $82,000 home, which was insured for 80% of that value. How much of the cost of replacing the garage did the insurance company pay?

18. When the Leonards' $63,000 home was damaged by fire, they had to live in a hotel, which cost $70 per night for the family. If their home was insured for 80% of its value, for how many nights would the insurance company pay for their hotel?

19. By changing her coverage from 80% to 90%, the amount of personal property coverage on Yolanda's homeowner's insurance policy would increase by $4,250. What is the value of Yolanda's home?

Mental Math: *Multiplying by 20%*

One way to find 20% of a number is to multiply the number by 0.2. But it sometimes helps to think of 20% as 2 × 10%. Then, all you have to do to find 20% of a number is find 10% of it and double your answer.

20% of 350 = 2 × (10% of 350) = 2 × 35 = 70

Find each answer.

1. 20% of 800   **2.** 20% of 280   **3.** 20% of 195   **4.** 20% of 7,700

11-5 Home Maintenance and Improvements

Your home is an investment that will probably continue to grow in value. One way to improve your investment in your home is to make repairs and improvements. Home maintenance (painting, repairing and replacing damaged materials, and so on) helps your home maintain its value. Home improvements, however, actually increase the value of your home.

Shelley wants to decorate the living room of her house. The dimensions of her living room are 15 feet long by 12 feet wide.

EXAMPLE 1

Shelley decided to paint the walls of her living room. She measured the room and found it to be 8 feet high. She decided to disregard the areas of windows and doors, since the paint she saves by not painting those areas will help keep her from running out of paint. If the paint costs $12.65 per gallon and 1 gallon covers 500 square feet, how much will it cost to paint her living room?

Problem Solving Strategy: Making a diagram or model.
You can draw a diagram of Shelley's living room to help you find the area of all the walls.

Skill Review

In order to calculate the area that you will paint or carpet, you need to be able to find the area of a rectangle.

Find the area of each rectangle.

1. l = 4 ft, w = 3 ft

2. l = 8.4 cm, w = 5.6 cm

3. l = $9\frac{1}{2}$ yd, w = $6\frac{2}{3}$ yd

4. l = 5.26 km, w = 1.09 km

(For additional help, see page 553.)

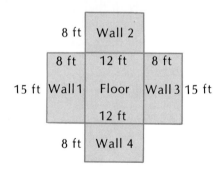

Step 1. Find the area of walls 1 and 3, which are the same size.

$$A = lw \qquad \text{area of one wall}$$
$$A = 15 \text{ ft} \times 8 \text{ ft}$$
$$A = 120 \text{ ft}^2$$

area of 2 walls = 2 × 120 ft² = 240 ft² area of walls 1 and 3

Step 2. Find the area of walls 2 and 4, which are the same size.

$$A = lw \qquad \text{area of one wall}$$
$$A = 12 \text{ ft} \times 8 \text{ ft}$$
$$A = 96 \text{ ft}^2$$

area of 2 walls = 2 × 96 ft² = 192 ft² area of walls 2 and 4

Step 3. Find the total area.

$$\text{total area} = 240 \text{ ft}^2 + 192 \text{ ft}^2 = 432 \text{ ft}^2$$

Step 4. Find the amount of paint needed and its cost.
total area ÷ 500 = number of gallons needed
432 ft² ÷ 500 = ■

Think: $432 \div 500 = 432 \div 1,000 \times 2 = 0.432 \times 2 = 0.864$

Any fraction of a gallon must be rounded up to the next whole gallon, so Shelley will have to buy 1 gallon of paint, which will cost $12.65.

EXAMPLE 2

John wants to build a new fence around his entire property. The type of fencing that he wants costs $95 for 75 feet of fencing. How much will the fence cost if the property is 40 feet wide and 120 feet long?

Hidden Question: What is the perimeter of the property?
perimeter = (2 × *l*) + (2 × *w*)
perimeter = (2 × 120) + (2 × 40) = 240 + 80 = 320 ft

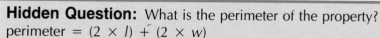

Use proportion to find the cost. Let *C* be the final cost.

$$\frac{C}{320} = \frac{\$95}{75}$$ Write a proportion.

$C \times 75 = 320 \times \$95$ Cross multiply.
$C \times 75 = \$30,400$

$$C = \frac{\$30,400}{75}$$ Divide by 75.

$C = \$405.33$ Round to nearest cent.

The fence will cost $405.33.

   In deciding whether a home improvement is worth the cost, it is helpful to consider the cost over the period of time it will be used.

EXAMPLE 3

Larry and Sabrina remodeled their kitchen. It cost $11,780. They expect the kitchen to last 25 years. How much is the cost per year?

total cost ÷ number of years = cost per year
$11,780 ÷ 25 = $471.20

The kitchen will cost an average of $471.20 per year of use.

Class Exercises

Find the cost of fencing each yard if 11 feet of fencing costs $12.75.

Length of Yard	Width of Yard	Cost of Fencing
95 ft	30 ft	1. ■
80 ft	35 ft	2. ■
105 ft	50 ft	3. ■

Solve.

4. How many gallons of paint will it take to paint the four walls of a room that is 16 feet long, 15 feet wide, and 8 feet high if a gallon of paint covers 500 square feet?

5. Al had his bathroom replaced at a cost of $7,250. He expects that it will last for 30 years. What is the cost per year of the improvement?

EXERCISES

Find the cost of fencing each yard if 8 feet of fencing costs $9.82.

Length of Yard	Width of Yard	Cost of Fencing
20 ft	40 ft	1. ■
24 ft	48 ft	2. ■
45 ft	60 ft	3. ■

Solve.

4. Reed Amity
Improvement: landscaping
Cost per square foot: $4.95
Number of square feet: 102
Cost: ■

5. Name: Arlene Weekins
Improvement: new walkway
Cost per foot: $8.37
Number of feet: 82
Cost: ■

6. Rachel Varga
Improvement: new porch
Cost per square foot: ■
Number of square feet: 144
Cost: $3,283.20

7. Jennifer Trinh
Improvement: storm windows
Cost per window: ■
Number of windows: 18
Cost: $741.60

8. Length of room: 15 ft
Width of room: 11 ft
Height of room: 7 ft
Area of 4 walls: ■

9. Length of room: 14 ft
Width of room: 10 ft
Height of room: 8 ft
Area of 4 walls: ■

10. Find the cost of carpeting the floor of a room that is $11\frac{1}{2}$ feet by 8 feet if the cost of carpeting is $18.55 per square yard.

11. Show how you would use a calculator to streamline the computation for Problem 10.

12. If a gallon of paint will cover 500 square feet, how much will a quart cover?

13. What is the hidden question in Problem 12? Explain how mental arithmetic can be used to find the answer.

14. The Aughberts had a hardwood floor replaced at a cost of $1,250. They expect that it will last for 15 years. What is the cost per year of the improvement?

15. The lumber that Juan and Karla need for the floor of the new deck they are building costs $5.95 for 6 square feet. The floor of the deck will be 12 feet by 9 feet. How much will the lumber cost?

16. The Wessels are having a new garage built on their house at a cost of $9,115. They expect it to last 20 years. What is the cost per year for the improvement?

17. Ceiling tiles cost $1.18 for a 24-inch by 16-inch panel. Bryan and Cindy wish to tile a ceiling that is 14 feet by 12 feet. How much will the tiles cost them?

18. Two rolls of wallpaper cover 61 square feet. How many rolls will Paul and Jasmine need to wallpaper two walls in their hallway that are 15 feet by 11 feet each?

19. A can of paint covers 450 square feet and costs $12.88. How much did it cost to buy paint to apply two coats of paint to the four walls and ceiling of a room 15 feet by 12 feet by 10 feet high?

Using a Calculator: *Finding Permutations*

Many homeowners install security systems. To deactivate some systems, you must enter a numerical code into the system. Numbers can be arranged in different orders to create security codes. Arranging numbers in different orders is called *permuting* them.

If a security system requires a 5-digit code (in which no numbers can be repeated) to deactivate it, what is the probability that someone could enter the code by chance? The first digit of the code can be selected in 10 ways, the second in 9 ways, and so on. To find the number of permutations, use the *counting principle,* which says that to find the number of permutations of several objects, you must find the product of the number of ways each can occur:

Key: $\boxed{C_E^C}$ 10 $\boxed{\times}$ 9 $\boxed{\times}$ 8 $\boxed{\times}$ 7 $\boxed{\times}$ 6
$\boxed{=}$ 30240

The probability of pressing the correct code by chance is

$$\frac{\text{number of successes}}{\text{total number}} = \frac{1}{30,240}$$

Find each probability.

1. Pressing the correct 6-digit code.

2. Pressing the correct 10-digit code.

11-6 Conserving Energy

In your home, you may heat with electricity, gas, or oil. Many appliances use electricity. Your water may be heated with gas or electricity. You may use electricity or gas to cook. All these resources are expensive. By keeping records of your fuel and energy use and attempting to conserve energy, you will save yourself money and also help to conserve your natural resources.

You can save oil or gas by turning down your thermostat in the winter. The table shows typical energy savings for turning your thermostat down if you live in the central states.

Energy Savings for Central States	
Degrees Turned Down	Percent of Heat Saved
3°	10%
5°	16%
8°	23%

EXAMPLE 1

Krystena spends about $1,050 per year in heating costs. How much can she expect to spend if she turns down her heat by 5°?

Step 1. Find the amount of savings.

Problem Solving Strategy: Finding information.
From the table, turning the thermostat down by 5° saves 16%.

$$\text{previous cost of energy} \times \text{percent saved} = \text{savings}$$
$$\$1,050 \times 16\% = \$168$$

Step 2. Find the amount spent after the savings.

$$\text{previous cost of energy} - \text{savings} = \text{new cost of energy}$$
$$\$1,050 - \$168 = \$882$$

Krystena can expect to spend $882.

If you have air conditioning, you can also save energy in the summer by setting your thermostat higher. The table shows estimated percents of increase in energy costs by setting your thermostat lower than 80°.

EXAMPLE 2

Roger spent about $750 to cool his home during the summer. How much more would it have cost him if he had lowered the setting by 2° from 80°?

Energy Cost of Cooling Compared to 80° Setting	
Setting	Increase in Cost
80°	0%
79°	9%
78°	18%
77°	28%
76°	39%
75°	51%

The new setting is $80° - 2° = 78°$. From the table on page 372, 78° uses 18% more energy.

previous cost of energy × percent increase = extra cost

$$\$750 \qquad \times \qquad 18\% \qquad = \qquad \$135$$

It would cost Roger $135 more to turn down his thermostat 2° in the summer.

Class Exercises

Use the table at the top of page 372 to find the new heating costs.

Family	Old Energy Costs	Degrees Turned Down	New Energy Costs
Rohr	$ 700	3°	1. ■
Londaris	$1,165	5°	2. ■

Use the table at the bottom of page 372 to find the cost of air conditioning for the summer at the given temperature settings.

Family	Cost at 80°	New Setting	New Cost
Gosch	$645	77°	3. ■
LaPatin	$500	79°	4. ■

Solve.

5. By turning down the setting on their hot water heater, the Lauers can save about 8% of the cost of heating their water. They estimate that it has cost about $785 per year to heat their water. How much will the new cost be if they turn down the setting?

EXERCISES

Use the table at the top of page 372.

Family	Old Energy Costs	Degrees Turned Down	New Energy Costs
Macki	$ 400	5°	1. ■
Lombard	$1,000	3°	2. ■
Norris	$ 752	3°	3. ■
Billingsly	$ 537	8°	4. ■

Use the table at the bottom of page 372 to find the cost of air conditioning for the summer at the given temperature settings.

Family	Cost at 80°	New Setting	New Cost
Nobel	$ 400	78°	5. ■
Parrish	$ 600	75°	6. ■
Slovik	$ 838.50	79°	7. ■
Krumms	$1,018	77°	8. ■

Solve.

9. By installing storm windows and doors, Carolyn estimates that she can save 10% on her annual heating bills of $1,250. How much can she expect her new annual heating bill to be?

10. By insulating their hot water heater, the Robeson family estimates that they save 7% on their annual cost of heating water. If it regularly cost them about $865, what can they expect their annual bill to be?

11. A TV uses 0.4 kilowatts of electricity per hour and is used every day. How much could be saved per year by using it 1 hour less each day if the cost of electricity is $0.065 per kilowatt hour?

12. The Redrick family found that they could save 11% of their fuel by insulating their attic. The cost of insulating the attic would be $415. If their average annual fuel bill was $1,262, how many years would it take for their savings in fuel to pay for the cost of insulating the attic?

13. Dietrick saved $126 one year by setting his air conditioner up to 77° from 75°. How much more (to the nearest dollar) could he save by setting it up to 80°? (Use the table at the bottom of page 372 in your calculations.)

14. The Detwilers have a leaky faucet that leaks 45 drops a minute. If there are 30 drops to an ounce and 128 ounces to a gallon, how many gallons of water are being wasted in a year by the leaky faucet?

15. Make a list of ways you think you and your family could conserve energy. Compare your list with others' lists.

Challenge

1. Wayne and Patricia are planning to remodel their kitchen. They have a combined annual net income of $24,500. They have budgeted and saved 15% of their net income for the year to finance this project. How much have they saved for this project?

2. Their budgeted amount for utilities for the year was 10%, but by conserving they spent only 7% of their annual net income. They are going to use the money they saved for the kitchen. How much did they save through conservation?

3. How much have they saved for remodeling the kitchen?

Computer:
Mortgage Amortization Schedules

Willy took out a 10-year mortgage for $25,000 at 11% interest. He wrote a BASIC program to compute the monthly payment and print a schedule that would tell him how much of the principal had been repaid after each monthly payment. The BASIC statement 80 MP = P*(RT/(1 − (1/(1 + RT)^YRS))) computes the monthly payment (MP) for any mortgage principal (P), interest rate (RT), and length of time (YRS). The monthly payment is expressed as dollars and cents by the following statement: 90 MP = INT(MP*100)/100

10 HOME	Clears the screen.
20 P = 25000	Sets the principal at $25,000.
30 RT = .11	Sets the interest rate at 11%.
40 YRS = 10	Sets the number of years at 10.
50 PRINT " PRINCIPAL: "; P; "INTEREST: "; RT; " YEARS: "; YRS	Prints the mortgage information.
60 RT = RT/12	Changes the rate (RT) to a monthly rate.
70 YRS = YRS * 12	Changes years (YRS) to number of payments.
80 MP = P*(RT/(1 − (1/(1 + RT)^YRS)))	Calculates the monthly payment (MP).
90 MP = INT (MP*100)/100	Changes monthly payment to dollars and cents.
100 PRINT "MONTHLY PAYMENT: "; MP	Prints the monthly payment amount.
110 PRINT "PAYMENT INTEREST PRINCIPAL BALANCE "	Prints the headings for the amortization schedule.
120 FOR K = 1 TO YRS	Begins the amortization schedule loop.
130 I = P*RT	Calculates the amount of interest for this payment.
140 PP = MP − I	Calculates the amount of principal for this payment.
150 P = P − PP	Calculates the amount of principal remaining.
160 PRINT K; TAB(5); I; TAB(17); PP; TAB(29); P	Prints all the above calculations in the proper columns.
170 IF K/12 = INT(K/12) THEN GOTO 190	Displays 12 lines of the output on the screen until the Enter key is pressed.
180 NEXT K	Terminates the loop.
190 END	Tells the computer to end the program.

EXERCISES

1. Change one line so that the mortgage will be over 15 years instead of 10.

2. Change one line so that the interest rate will be 13.5%.

Decision Making:
Finding and Financing a House

Judy and Eric Bailey have decided that the time is right for them to purchase their first house. After talking with friends, they decide to call the same real estate agent their friends used last year to find their first home.

Kay Wright, the real estate agent, explains to Judy and Eric that they do not pay her directly for her services. Instead, when they purchase their home, she will receive a commission based upon the sale price of the home. Kay explains further that in the Bailey's community, this commission is deducted from the money the sellers receive for their home.

In addition to discussing with Judy and Eric what features they want in a house and what type of home they want, Kay also asks a lot of questions about their financial situation. After completing her questions, Kay does some calculations and tells Judy and Eric that they could probably afford a house that cost about $70,000. This is slightly more than Judy and Eric had estimated by multiplying their family income of $26,000 by $2\frac{1}{2}$.

"My estimate is slightly higher than yours," Kay explains, "because with the $9,500 you have saved and your very low credit card debt, you are in better financial shape than most couples buying their first houses."

"I'm glad to hear we are in good shape financially, but I still really don't know if we will be able to afford the kind of home we've always wanted," Judy remarks.

Answer the following questions.

1. You do not have to have a real estate agent to purchase a home. A buyer and seller can deal directly with each other and use only an attorney to complete a real estate sale. However, most buyers and sellers choose to use the services of a real estate agent. What advantages and disadvantages do you see in using the services of a professional real estate agent?

2. Explain the thinking steps you used to answer Question 1 to a classmate and listen to your classmate's thinking. Compare the way the two of you thought to answer the question.

3. Using the rule of $2\frac{1}{2}$ times their annual income, how much did Judy and Eric estimate they could afford to pay for a home? How does their estimate compare with the estimate given to them by Kay? Which estimate do you think they should use as they look for a house? Why?

FINDING A HOUSE

With Kay's help, Judy and Eric make a list of the characteristics they want in a house. They list the following:

—three bedrooms	— 1.5 or 2 bathrooms
—single-family house with large yard	—finished basement
—fireplace	—wall-to-wall carpet
—no more than a 30 minute drive from our jobs in Town Center	—dining area in kitchen
	—two-car garage

The Baileys decide they are most interested in a house that has the living room, dining room, and kitchen on one floor and the bedrooms upstairs. Kay explains that real estate agents refer to this style house as a colonial. The other type of house they decide to consider is the split level, in which some levels of the house might be separated by only a few steps rather than a full flight of stairs.

Kay then asks Judy and Eric what locations they want. She explains that location is a major determinant of the price of a house. In general, in the Bailey's community, houses closer to downtown are more expensive than houses farther out. In general, houses in more rural parts of the state are less expensive than houses in the suburbs or in the city.

Because they want to get the best buy possible, Judy and Eric decide to be flexible about location. They ask Kay to show them homes in a number of different areas.

After a month of house hunting, Judy and Eric have narrowed their choice down to one of the three houses at the right.

ADDRESS: 1366 Spring Road   PRICE: $71,500
COMMUNITY: West End   SIZE OF LOT: 1/4 Acre
TYPE HOUSE: Split Level   AGE: 2 y
SIZE OF LIVING AREA: 1,500 ft²
NO. OF BEDROOMS: 3   NO. OF BATHS: 1.5
ADDITIONAL FEATURES: fireplace, thermal windows, eat-in kitchen, dishwasher, garbage disposal, central air conditioning, parquet wooden floor in family room
DESCRIPTION: This nearly new home in one of the area's best suburban locations (only a 20-minute drive from Town Center) is situated on a large, well-landscaped, fenced lot.

ADDRESS: 45 E. Second Avenue   PRICE: $73,900
COMMUNITY: Town Center   SIZE OF LOT: 1/10 Acre
TYPE HOUSE: Colonial   AGE: 35 y
SIZE OF LIVING AREA: 1,000 ft²
NO. OF BEDROOMS: 3   NO. OF BATHS: 1.5
ADDITIONAL FEATURES: sun porch, single car garage, partially finished basement, hardwood floors, dishwasher, eat-in kitchen
DESCRIPTION: This recently renovated townhouse is within walking distance of the downtown shopping and business district. The small, fenced backyard is perfect for the homeowner who doesn't want to spend hours on yard work.

ADDRESS: 6225 Horseshoe Pike (Route 123)   PRICE: $69,900
COMMUNITY: Shepherd County   SIZE OF LOT: 1.3 acres
TYPE HOUSE: Colonial   AGE: 15 y
SIZE OF LIVING AREA: 1,900 ft²
NO. OF BEDROOMS: 4   NO. OF BATHS: 2.5
ADDITIONAL FEATURES: wooden deck, central air conditioning, eat-in kitchen, wall-to-wall carpeting throughout, two-car garage, large family room with fireplace
DESCRIPTION: This beautiful custom built home is located on a beautifully wooded lot in the heart of quiet Shepherd County. Enjoy a slower pace of life, away from the hustle of the city and still be less than 45 minutes by car from Town Center.

Answer the following questions.

4. Compare each house with the characteristics Eric and Judy identified as being important to them. Do any of the houses have all the features they want? Identify the features from their list that each house is missing.

5. Do any of the houses listed have extra features that Judy and Eric do not necessarily want? Identify the extra features in each house.

6. In your opinion, which house has the most features for the money? Justify your choice.

MAKING A DECISION

After giving it much thought, Judy and Eric decide to try to purchase the house on Spring Road. Kay secures information on the purchase price of other homes in the neighborhood that have been sold recently. Using this information the Baileys decide to offer the sellers a bid of $68,500 for the house.

The current owners of the house accept the Bailey's bid of $68,500. The Baileys then have to decide which bank to approach about a mortgage loan and decide for what type and length mortgage to apply.

After careful research, the Baileys learn that there are two basic types of mortgage loans for which they could apply, fixed-rate and adjustable-rate:

- The interest rate on a fixed-rate loan remains the same throughout the length of the loan.

- The interest rate on an adjustable-rate loan can go up and down, depending upon market conditions.

How often the interest rate on an adjustable-rate loan can change and the maximum rate that can be charged on the loan are two important issues to consider.

The Baileys learn also that the length of a mortgage loan varies from as little as 5 years to as long as 30 years.

Study this excerpt from a chart comparing the various types of loans offered by banks in the Baileys' community.

Bank	Fixed Rate	Percent Down	Length	Adjustable Rate	Percent Down	Length	Adjustable Period	Maximum Rate
Home	10.0%	10%	25 y	7.5%	10%	25 y	3 y	13.9%
B & L	9.5%	20%	15 y	NONE				
First	11.0%	10%	30 y	7.75%	5%	30 y	5 y	13.75%
State	10.5%	10%	30 y	8.0%	10%	30 y	2 y	14.0%
Central	11.5%	5%	30 y	7.25%	5%	30 y	1 y	14.25%

Answer the following questions.

7. Which bank offers the lowest rate on a fixed-rate loan?

8. Which bank offers the lowest rate on an adjustable-rate loan?

9. What did you have to do to answer Questions 7 and 8?

10. At any given bank, which rate tends to be lower—the rate for an adjustable-rate loan or the rate for a fixed-rate loan?

11. How did the strategy you used to answer Question 10 differ from the strategy used to answer Questions 7 and 8?

12. If the Baileys are able to put down only 10% on the house, how much more will their monthly mortgage payment on a 30-year loan be if they have to take a loan at 10.5% rather than 10%? (Use the table on page 355.)

13. Compare your answer to Question 12 with a classmate's. Discuss how you solved the problem and listen to how your classmate solved it. How were your approaches similar? How did they differ?

14. If the Baileys are able to put down only 10% on the house, how much more will they pay in interest if they have a 30-year loan rather than a 20-year loan at 10%? Use the table on page 355.

15. Compare your answer to Question 14 with a classmate's. Discuss how each of you solved this problem. Compare and contrast your approaches.

16. In addition to loan terms, what other information about banks might the Baileys want to compare before deciding where to go to apply for their mortgage loan?

17. In a short paragraph, explain why the ability to compare and contrast items and/or situations is important for a wise consumer.

DECIDE FOR YOURSELF

How would you go about looking for a house? What features would be important to you?

Chapter 11 Review

VOCABULARY

amortizing	homeowner's policy	mortgage
assessed value	market value	points
closing costs	mill	property tax

For Exercises 1–6, select the term that completes each statement.

1. A _____ is a loan for a home.

2. Paying back the money borrowed for a mortgage is called _____ the mortgage.

3. _____ are the extra fees the borrower must pay at the time of settlement.

4. _____ are charges that a bank makes for granting the loan.

5. The value placed on property for purposes of real estate taxes is called the _____ .

6. A tenth of a cent is a _____ .

SKILLS

Find each product. Round to the nearest cent.

7. $4.50 × 25.5

8. $18.75 × 33.3

9. $39.50 × 15.75

Find each quotient.

10. 856.25 ÷ 1,000

11. 38.7 ÷ 1,000

12. 4.06 ÷ 1,000

Find each value.

13. 15% of $24,500

14. 50.5% of $48,750

15. 43.2% of $87,650

Find the area of each rectangle.

16. length: 16 ft; width: 9 ft

17. length: $4\frac{1}{2}$ yd; width: 3 yd

CONSUMER TOPICS

Solve.

18. Regina and Martin want to purchase a home listed at $63,500. If the down payment required is 20% of the cost of the house, how much would they need for a down payment?

19. Ian and Claudia have a 30-year mortgage. Their monthly payments are $438.50. If they have a $50,000 mortgage, how much will they pay in interest over the life of the mortgage?

20. Armando and Olga purchased a house listed at $72,500. They made a down payment of 20%. What is the amount of the mortgage they must have?

21. A bank offers a 25-year mortgage at 10.5% for a monthly mortgage payment of $9.44 per $1,000 borrowed. What is the monthly mortgage payment on a mortgage of $55,750?

22. Beryl and Dallas have a combined annual income of $28,500. How much can they afford to pay for a house?

23. Determine the total charge for closing costs on a $40,000 loan if 2 points are added, 1% is charged for transfer tax, 0.3% is charged for a title stamp, and 0.5% is charged for a processing fee.

24. How many gallons of paint will it take to paint the four walls of a room that is 18 feet long, 15 feet wide, and $8\frac{1}{2}$ feet high if a gallon of paint covers 450 square feet?

25. Kevin and Maureen own a house with a market value of $84,500. Their rate of assessment is 74%. What is the assessed value of their house?

26. Jerome and Elizabeth own a house with an assessed value of $38,700. What is their property tax if their city sets a tax rate of 27.5 mills?

27. Use the table on page 365 to find the cost of Lena's insurance policy if she has an $80,000 policy and lives in a wood frame house in protection class 7.

28. Replacement value: $80,000
Required insurance: 80%
Amount of policy: ■

29. Amount of policy: $58,700
Additional living expenses:
20% of policy
Amount of additional
living expenses: ■

30. It cost Samantha $4,750 to remodel her bathroom. She expects the bathroom to last 20 years. How much is the cost per year?

31. Ricardo's family can save 10% of their heating costs if they turn down their thermostat 3°. If their heating bills amount to $2,250 a year, how much can the family save by turning their thermostat down 3°?

32. Sally and Rob plan to add a room to their house that will cost $32.50 per square foot. How much will the room cost if it has 228 square feet?

Chapter 11 Test

1. Lani and Guy have a combined annual income of $45,000. How much can they afford to pay for a house?

2. Joseph purchased a house for $82,750. He made a down payment of 30% of the cost of the house. How much was his down payment?

3. A bank offers a 30-year mortgage at 11% for a monthly mortgage payment of $9.52 per $1,000 borrowed. What is the monthly mortgage payment on a mortgage of $35,700?

4. The monthly payments on Jerry and Joan's mortgage are $365.60. Their mortgage is for $40,000. How much will they pay in interest if they have a 30-year mortgage?

5. Determine the total closing costs if the fixed costs are $505.50 and the variable costs are $1,575.

6. Brock's house has a market value of $78,500 and an assessment rate of 80%. What is the assessed value of his house?

7. Rae owns a house with an assessed value of $42,500. Her tax rate is 32.5 mills. What is the amount of her property tax?

8. Linda's mortgage agreement requires that she insure her house for 80% of its replacement value. The replacement value of her house is estimated to be $74,500. What is the required amount of her insurance policy?

9. Linda's insurance policy (Problem 8) pays 50% of her policy amount for damage to personal property. If she loses all her household goods in a flood, how much will her insurance pay if her house is insured for 80% of its value?

10. Use the table on page 365 to find the cost of Linda's insurance (Problem 8) if she lives in a brick house that is in protection class 10.

11. Find the cost of hardwood flooring for a floor that is 18 feet by 12 feet if it costs $12.50 to cover 9 square feet.

12. Tom remodeled his family room at a cost of $2,300. If he expects the remodeling to last for 15 years, how much is the cost per year?

13. Geraldine can save 15% of her energy costs by turning her air-conditioning thermostat up 5° in summer and by turning her heating thermostat down 3° in winter. If her energy bill is now $1,800 a year, how much will she save by changing the settings on her thermostat to conserve energy?

14. Find the cost of painting four walls of a room that is 18 feet long, 12 feet wide, and 8 feet high if the cost of paint is $9.50 per gallon and a gallon covers 500 square feet.

Cumulative Mixed Review

Select the letter corresponding to the correct answer.

1. Jack earns $6.50 an hour with time-and-a-half for hours over 40. How much does he earn for a 47.5 hour week?
   a. $308.75 **b.** $333.13
   c. $269.75 **d.** $463.13

2. Sheila receives a net pay of $486.50 biweekly. If her gross annual income is $18,500, how much is withheld from each paycheck for deductions?
   a. $225.04 **b.** $284.33
   c. $5,851 **d.** $6,824

3. Clay ordered 2 fishing rods (at $49.50 each) from a catalog. He had to pay 6.5% sales tax and a shipping charge of $2.89. What was the total amount he was billed?
   a. $55.61 **b.** $108.33
   c. $93.25 **d.** $646.39

4. Bob ate a container of yogurt that contained 260 calories, a milkshake that contained 325 calories, and an apple that contained 85 calories. How many calories did he consume in all?
   a. 585 **b.** 410
   c. 345 **d.** 670

5. Carla has budgeted 15% of her income for clothing. What is the measure of the central angle she must use to show this item on a circle graph?
   a. 54° **b.** 15°
   c. 45° **d.** 90°

6. Melissa borrowed $1,250. She made 24 payments of $63.50 each. How much did she pay in interest?
   a. $52.08 **b.** $1,313.50
   c. $274 **d.** $1,524

7. Steve bought a stereo that listed for $995. He saved 15% of the original cost by buying it at a sale and paying cash. How much did he pay for the stereo?
   a. $1,009.93 **b.** $149.25
   c. $845.75 **d.** $84.58

8. Kelli makes two payments a year of $450 each for real estate taxes. She makes four payments a year of $225 each for auto insurance. How much must she budget monthly for these two items?
   a. $150 **b.** $56.25
   c. $93.75 **d.** $112.50

9. Molly made a long-distance call that cost her $1.45 for the first 3 minutes and $.35 a minute for each extra minute. If she talked 12 minutes, how much did the call cost her?
   a. $4.20 **b.** $5.65
   c. $1.80 **d.** $4.60

10. Greg signed a 2-year lease for an apartment. If his monthly rent is $325, how much will he pay in rent over the term of his lease?
    a. $3,900 **b.** $650
    c. $7,800 **d.** $780

Paying Taxes

Kurt started working at his first job in February. At the end of the year he began to organize the information he needed to pay his taxes. He knew his employer would send him a W-2 form listing his earnings for the year. In addition, he wanted to assemble the receipts he might need to fill out his tax form.

- What kinds of information would be helpful to Kurt in preparing his tax form?

- Can you think of receipts or records he should save during the year?

- Can you think of deductions that Kurt might be able to take if he has receipts to document them?

What information regarding income or expenses do you think it would be important to keep records of when you have a job?

12-1 Form W-2

When you work for someone else, your employer usually withholds taxes from your earnings. In January of each year, you will receive a **W-2 form** from your employer that gives the total amount of earnings and the taxes withheld during the past year. You will need the information on that form to complete your tax return. Also, copies of the W-2 form must be attached to your federal and state tax forms when you file your tax return.

EXAMPLE 1
Sonya drives a forklift for a construction company. She received the W-2 form below from her employer. Verify that the appropriate amount was withheld by her employer for social security tax if the rate was 7.65%.

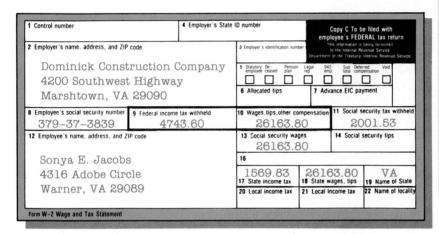

earnings   × tax rate = social security tax withheld

$26,163.80 × 7.65% =

Think: 7.65% = 0.0765

Estimate: $26,163.80 × 7.65% = → $25,000 × 10% = $2,500

```
    $26,163.80
  ×     0.0765
     13 081900
    156 98280
   1831 4660
  $2,001.530700
  $2,001.53      Round to nearest cent.
```

 Key: C$_E^C$ 26163.8 × 7.65 %   2001.5307

$2,001.53   Round to nearest cent.

The answer $2,001.53 is reasonably close to the estimate $2,500 and is a sensible answer.
The correct amount was withheld.

EXAMPLE 2

How much of Sonya's earnings remained after all taxes were withheld?

Step 1. Find the total tax withheld.

federal tax + state tax + social security tax = total tax withheld
$4,743.60 + $1,569.83 + $2,001.53 = $8,314.96

Step 2. Find the income remaining.

total wages − total tax withheld = income remaining
$26,163.80 − $8,314.96 = $17,848.84

Of Sonya's earnings, $17,848.84 remained after taxes were withheld.

With a calculator, you can simplify the computation for Example 2.

Key: $\boxed{C_E^C}$ 4743.6 $\boxed{+}$ 1569.83 $\boxed{+}$ 2001.53 $\boxed{M+}$ 26163.8 $\boxed{-}$
$\boxed{M_C^R}$ $\boxed{=}$ _17848.84_
$17,848.84

You may wish to use the information on your W-2 form to find out how much was withheld from your paycheck each pay period.

EXAMPLE 3

How much was withheld from Sonya's wages each week for federal tax?

Hidden Question: How many weeks in 1 year?
1 y = 52 wk

yearly amount ÷ 52 = weekly amount
$4,743.60 ÷ 52 = ■

$$52\overline{)\$4,743.600} \quad \frac{\$91.223}{} \rightarrow \$91.22 \quad \text{Round to nearest cent.}$$

Each week $91.22 was withheld from Sonya's check.

With a calculator, you can simplify the computation for Example 3.

Key: $\boxed{C_E^C}$ 4743.6 $\boxed{÷}$ 52 $\boxed{=}$ _91.223076_
$91.22 **Round to nearest cent.**

Class Exercises

Use the W-2 form below.

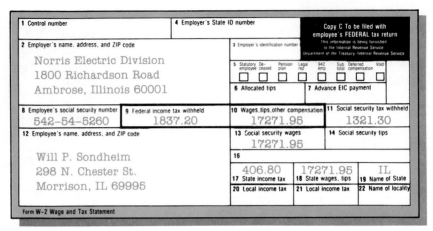

1. What is Will's social security number?	**2.** How much were Will's gross earnings?
3. How much federal tax was withheld from Will's pay?	**4.** How much social security was withheld from Will's gross pay?
5. Determine how much social security should have been withheld from Will's earnings at the rate of 7.65%. Was the correct amount withheld?	**6.** What amount of state tax was withheld from Will's weekly pay?

EXERCISES

Use the W-2 form below.

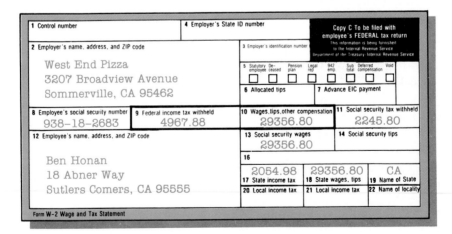

1. What were Ben's gross earnings?	**2.** How much was withheld from Ben's wages for federal tax?
3. How much was withheld from Ben's wages for state income tax?	**4.** How much was withheld from Ben's wages for social security?

5. How much social security does Ben owe at the rate of 7.65%? Was the correct amount withheld?

6. How much was withheld from Ben's pay each month for social security?

7. How much was Ben's monthly gross pay?

8. How much of Ben's annual income was left after taxes had been withheld?

Solve.

9. Employee name: Santos Rosito
Wages, salary, tips: $21,352
Withheld for federal tax: $3,856
Withheld for social security: $1,633
Withheld for state tax: $962
Wages after taxes: ■

10. Employee name: Peggy Boskins
Wages, salary, tips: $28,975.30
Withheld for federal tax: $5,215.50
Withheld for social security: $2,216.60
Withheld for state tax: ■
Wages after taxes: $19,869.70

11. What percent of Sonya's earnings (Example 2) was withheld for taxes?

12. What percent of Peggy's earnings (Exercise 10) was left after taxes were withheld?

13. Santos (Exercise 9) used his calculator to find what percent of his earnings were left after taxes. Study his keystrokes and answer the questions that follow.

$\boxed{C_E^C}$ 21352 $\boxed{M+}$ $\boxed{-}$ 3856 $\boxed{-}$ 1633 $\boxed{-}$ 962 $\boxed{=}$ $\boxed{\div}$ $\boxed{M_C^R}$
100 $\boxed{=}$ ⟋ 69.78737 ⟋
69.8%   **Round to nearest tenth of a percent.**

a. Explain his procedure.
b. What keystroke(s) would have changed if Santos' gross earnings were $22,352?
c. Using Santos' procedure, write the keystrokes Ben (Exercises 1–8) would use to find what percentage of his wages remained after taxes.

14. After taxes were withheld, 63% of Consuela's income remained. Her federal income tax withheld was $4,872.18. This represented 55% of the total withheld. How much was her gross income?

Mixed Review

1. Caleb and Michelle have a combined annual gross income of $39,500. Their deductions amount to 27% of their gross income. What is their net annual income?

2. Caleb and Michelle budget $750 each month for housing, including insurance and taxes. What percent of their combined annual gross income do they budget for housing?

3. Caleb and Michelle want to buy a home. What is the maximum amount they should plan to spend for a house?

12-2 Form 1040

If you earn more than a specified amount of income in one year, you are required to file an **income tax return** by April 15 of the following year. On this return, you give information about your income and any deductions you might have. If you owe money to the government, you pay it when you send in the form. If you are entitled to a refund because more was withheld than you owe, then you indicate this on the form. You can file Form 1040, Form 1040A, or Form 1040EZ.

The following chart will help you decide which form to use.

Use 1040A if:	Use 1040 if:
• Your income is less than $50,000.	• Your income is $50,000 or more.
• Your income was only from wages, salaries, or tips.	• Some or all of your income came from sources other than wages, salaries, tips.
• You have $400 interest income or less.	• You have more than $400 in interest.
• You do not itemize deductions.	• You itemize deductions.
• There are no adjustments to your income.	• You have adjustments to your income.
Use 1040EZ if you qualify for 1040A and are a single taxpayer.	

Len works as a display designer. Here is his W-2 form for last year. Len used Form 1040EZ to file his tax return. He had $55 interest income and owed $1,778 in taxes.

1 Control number	4 Employer's State ID number	Copy C To be filed with employee's FEDERAL tax return
		This information is being furnished to the Internal Revenue Service Department of the Treasury-Internal Revenue Service

2 Employer's name, address, and ZIP code	3 Employer's identification number
Merriman's Department Store 12400 Central Parkway Lewiston, CO 80299	5 Statutory employee / Deceased / Pension plan / Legal rep / 942 emp / Sub total / Deferred compensation / Void
	6 Allocated tips 7 Advance EIC payment

8 Employee's social security number	9 Federal income tax withheld	10 Wages, tips, other compensation	11 Social security tax withheld
318-26-4286	2066.18	16828.75	1287.40

12 Employee's name, address, and ZIP code	13 Social security wages	14 Social security tips
	16828.75	
Leonard Weisendorf 3718 LaJunta Drive Pebbles, CO 80277	16	

17 State income tax	18 State wages, tips	19 Name of State
1178.01	16828.75	CO
20 Local income tax	21 Local income tax	22 Name of locality

Form W-2 Wage and Tax Statement

Skill Review

In order to complete a tax form, you must be able to subtract money amounts.

Subtract.

1. $365.45 − $288.71

2. $3,587 − $2,985.03

3. $1,674.32 − $983.88

4. $2,778 − $2,387.98

(For additional help, see page 544.)

EXAMPLE

Enter the information (including that on the W-2 form) onto Len's Form 1040EZ tax return. Did Len pay tax or get a refund?

Len received a refund of $288.18.

<table>
<tr><td colspan="2">

Form
1040EZ

</td><td>

Department of the Treasury - Internal Revenue Service

Income Tax Return for
Single filers with no dependents (O)

</td><td>

OMB No. 1545-0675

</td></tr>
</table>

Name &
address

Use the IRS mailing label. If you don't have one, please print.

▶ Leonard Weisendorf
Print your **name** above (first, initial, last)

3718 La Junta Drive
Present home address (number and street). (If you have a P.O. box, see instructions.)

Pebbles, CO 80277
City, town, or post office, state, and ZIP code

Please print your numbers like this:

0	1	2	3	4	5	6	7	8	9

Your social security number

3	1	8	2	6	4	2	8	6

Please read the instructions for
this form on the reverse side.

Presidential Election Campaign Fund
Do you want $1 to go to this fund?

Note: Checking "Yes" will
not change your tax or
reduce your refund.   ▶

Yes   No

[ ] [X]

Report
your
income

1 Total wages, salaries, and tips. This should be shown in Box 10
of your W-2 form(s). (Attach your W-2 form(s).)   **1**

Dollars | Cents
16,828.75

2 Taxable interest income of $400 or less. If the total is more
than $400, you cannot use Form 1040EZ.   **2**

55.00

Attach
Copy B of
Form(s)
W-2 here

3 Add line 1 and line 2. This is your **adjusted gross income.**   **3**

16,883.75

4 Can you be claimed as a dependent on another person's return?

[ ] Yes. Do worksheet on back; enter amount from line E here.

[X] No. Enter 2,540 as your standard deduction.   **4**

2,540.00

5 Subtract line 4 from line 3.   **5**

14,343.75

6 If you checked the "Yes" box on line 4, enter 0.
If you checked the "No" box on line 4, enter 1,900.
This is your **personal exemption.**   **6**

1,900.00

7 Subtract line 6 from line 5. If line 6 is larger than line 5,
enter 0 on line 7. This is your **taxable income.**   **7**

12,443.75

Figure
your
tax

8 Enter your Federal income tax withheld. This should be
shown in Box 9 of your W-2 form(s).   **8**

2,066.18

9 Use the **single** column in the tax table on pages 32–37 of
the Form 1040A instruction booklet to find the **tax** on the
amount shown on **line 7** above. Enter the amount of tax.   **9**

1,778.00

Refund
or
amount
you owe

Attach tax
payment here

10 If line 8 is larger than line 9, subtract line 9 from line 8.
Enter the **amount of your refund.**   **10**

11 If line 9 is larger than line 8, subtract line 8 from line 9.
Enter the **amount you owe.** Attach check or money order
for the full amount, payable to "Internal Revenue Service."   **11**

Sign
your
return

I have read this return. Under penalties of perjury, I declare
that to the best of my knowledge and belief, the return is true,
correct, and complete.

Your signature   Date

Leonard Weisendorf   2/1

For IRS Use Only—Please
do not write in boxes below.

For Privacy Act and Paperwork Reduction Act Notice, see page 31.   Form **1040EZ**

Class Exercises

Find the total income.

Gross Earnings	Interest Income	Total Income
$23,553	$266	*1.* ■
$18,439.45	$188.89	*2.* ■
$20,300	$400	*3.* ■

Solve.

4. Robert has earnings of $14,825 and interest income of $265. Find his total income.

5. Beverly had $1,892.16 withheld for income taxes. She owes $1,542.50 in taxes. How much refund will she receive?

EXERCISES

Find the total income.

Gross Earnings	Interest Income	Total Income
$15,602	$300	*1.* ■
$17,890	$125	*2.* ■
$28,956	$356	*3.* ■
$41,672.59	$198.50	*4.* ■

Solve.

5. William Weiss
Tax withheld: $1,452.98
Tax owed: $1,142
Refund due: ■

6. Patty Saunders
Tax withheld: $2,128.14
Tax owed: $2,296.50
Additional amount due: ■

7. Virgil Thomas
Tax withheld: $2,101.16
Tax owed: ■
Refund due: $252.66

8. Betty Hudgens
Tax withheld: ■
Tax owed: $1,292
Refund due: $531.65

9. Show how mental arithmetic can be used to find the answer to Exercise 5.

10. Curtis owed $2,765.80 in federal income tax. He had $2,678.20 withheld. How much did he still owe or receive as a refund?

11. Angela received the W-2 form below. She had $40 interest income and owes $601 federal income tax. Use this information to complete Form 1040EZ.

1 Control number		4 Employer's State ID number	Copy C To be filed with employee's FEDERAL tax return
			This information is being furnished to the Internal Revenue Service Department of the Treasury-Internal Revenue Service
2 Employer's name, address, and ZIP code		3 Employer's identification number	
Klien's Pharmacy 1824 Broadview Road Marysburgh, MD 21099		5 Statutory De- employee ceased □ Pension plan □ Legal rep □ 942 emp. □ Sub total □ Deferred compensation □ Void □	
		6 Allocated tips	7 Advance EIC payment
8 Employee's social security number 282-92-5872	9 Federal income tax withheld 724.85	10 Wages,tips,other compensation 8982.95	11 Social security tax withheld 687.20
12 Employee's name, address, and ZIP code		13 Social security wages 8982.95	14 Social security tips
Angela Yovannah 9717 Hargrove Ave. Sanding Reach, MD 20998		16 528.81	8982.95 MD
		17 State income tax 18 State wages, tips	19 Name of State
		20 Local income tax 21 Local income tax	22 Name of locality

Form W-2 Wage and Tax Statement

12. Melinda's W-2 form is below. She has interest income of $275 and owes $2,498 in income taxes. Use this information to fill in Form 1040EZ.

1 Control number		4 Employer's State ID number	Copy C To be filed with employee's FEDERAL tax return
			This information is being furnished to the Internal Revenue Service Department of the Treasury-Internal Revenue Service
2 Employer's name, address, and ZIP code		3 Employer's identification number	
Pleasant Plains Wicker Works 14000 North Boulevard Pleasant Plains, GA 30099		5 Statutory De- employee ceased □ Pension plan □ Legal rep □ 942 emp. □ Sub total □ Deferred compensation □ Void □	
		6 Allocated tips	7 Advance EIC payment
8 Employee's social security number 442-52-6228	9 Federal income tax withheld 2732.04	10 Wages,tips,other compensation 21412.90	11 Social security tax withheld 1638.09
12 Employee's name, address, and ZIP code		13 Social security wages 21412.90	14 Social security tips
Melinda T. Adkins 4215 Roseview Ave. Warfield, GA 30090		16 1284.77	21412.90 GA
		17 State income tax 18 State wages, tips	19 Name of State
		20 Local income tax 21 Local income tax	22 Name of locality

Form W-2 Wage and Tax Statement

Consumer Note: Tax Forms

Anyone who earns money over an amount that is specified by the Internal Revenue Service (IRS) must file a tax return. The IRS has several tax forms available for workers to use: Forms 1040, 1040A, and 1040EZ. If you need help choosing the right tax form, filling it out, and computing your taxes, several options are open to you.

During the tax season (January to April) you can call a toll-free telephone number and speak directly to an IRS representative about your questions, or you can bring your questions to one of the IRS information booths located in shopping malls and office buildings.

You can also enlist the services of private tax preparers, companies specializing in tax returns, or certified public accountants (CPAs). In addition, many people use current reference books about taxes to help them fill out their income tax forms correctly.

12-3 Using a Tax Schedule

When you file Form 1040, you need to use a **tax table,** which is a table giving amounts of tax owed for various incomes, or a **tax schedule,** which is a schedule of tax rates, like the table below.

Taxpayers are classified by their **filing status.** There are four classifications: single, married filing jointly, married filing separately, and head of household. (Some widows and widowers are permitted to file under the status of married filing jointly.) Most married couples pay less tax by filing jointly.

Taxable income is determined by subtracting your *exemptions* and *deductions* from the total of your gross earnings and other income. The amount that remains after these two amounts have been subtracted is used to determine the amount of tax.

There are three steps in calculating taxes.

1. Calculate the adjusted gross income.

2. Subtract the deductions and personal exemptions to find the taxable income.

3. Find the amount of tax owed by consulting a tax table or compute the tax from a tax schedule.

Taxpayers can itemize deductions or take a standard deduction. The amount of the standard deduction depends upon filing status. The table at the right shows standard deductions for a recent year.

Additional standard deductions are allowed for taxpayers who are over 65, blind, or both. For each **exemption,** or person being supported by the taxpayer, the taxpayer may deduct $2,000.

(*Note:* A person who is claimed as a dependent on another return is not entitled to an exemption for himself or herself.)

EXAMPLE 1

Leota and Rob are married and have decided to file jointly. Leota's gross earnings were $21,298 and she had $2,744.70 withheld from her pay. Rob had gross earnings of $19,982 and had $2,547 withheld from his pay. They earned $428 in interest from a savings account and had no other unearned

Skill Review

To use a tax schedule to compute taxes, you will need to express percents as decimals.

Express as decimals.
1. 15%
2. 12.9%
3. 5.2%
4. 0.3%

(For additional help, see page 550.)

Standard Deductions

Filing Status	Deduction
Single	$3,000
Married filing jointly	$5,000
Married filing separately	$2,500
Heads of household	$4,400

Tax Schedule

Single

Taxable Income	Tax Rate
-0- to $17,850	15%
Over $17,850	28%

Married Filing Jointly/Qualifying Widow(er)

Taxable Income	Tax Rate
-0- to $29,750	15%
Over $29,750	28%

Married Filing Separately

Taxable Income	Tax Rate
-0- to $14,875	15%
Over $14,875	28%

Head of Household

Taxable Income	Tax Rate
-0- to $23,900	15%
Over $23,900	28%

income and no adjustments to their income. Find their taxable income if they take the standard deduction and have three exemptions.

Step 1. Find their adjusted gross income.

earned income	+	unearned income	–	adjustments	=	adjusted gross income
$21,298 + $19,982	+	$428	–	0	=	■

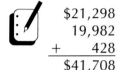

$$\begin{array}{r} \$21,298 \\ 19,982 \\ +\quad 428 \\ \hline \$41,708 \end{array}$$

 Key: 21298 $\boxed{+}$ 19982 $\boxed{+}$ 428

$\boxed{=}$　⟋ 41708 ⟋
$41,708

Step 2. Find their taxable income.

adjusted gross income	–	deduction	–	number of exemptions × $2000	=	taxable income
$41,708	–	$5,000	–	3 × $2,000	=	■
$41,708	–	$5,000	–	$6,000	=	$30,708

Leota's and Rob's taxable income is $30,708.

Taxes owed can be found by using a tax schedule like the one on page 394.

EXAMPLE 2
Leota and Rob decided to use the table on page 394 to determine their taxes. How much tax do they owe?

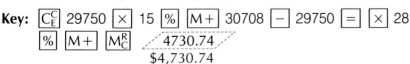

Problem Solving Strategy: Finding information.
Use the table on page 394 to find the tax rate:
　　　　15% on the first $29,750
　　　　28% on the amount over $29,750

tax at 15% rate	+	tax at 28% rate	=	total tax
$29,750 × 15%	+	($30,708 – $29,750) × 28%	=	■
$29,750 × 0.15	+	$958 × 0.28	=	■
$4,462.50	+	$268.24	=	$4,730.74

They owe $4,730.74 in tax.

With a calculator, you can simplify the calculations in Example 2.

Key: $\boxed{C_E^C}$ 29750 $\boxed{\times}$ 15 $\boxed{\%}$ $\boxed{M+}$ 30708 $\boxed{-}$ 29750 $\boxed{=}$ $\boxed{\times}$ 28

$\boxed{\%}$ $\boxed{M+}$ $\boxed{M_C^R}$　⟋ 4730.74 ⟋
$4,730.74

Class Exercises

Determine the taxable income. Assume the basic standard deduction is taken.

Adjusted Gross Income	Filing Status	Number of Exemptions	Taxable Income
$17,320	Married filing separately	2	1. ■
$15,000	Single	1	2. ■
$22,500	Married filing jointly	4	3. ■
$63,495	Head of household	3	4. ■

5. Franklin has taxable income of $36,850.45. Use the table on page 394 to determine his tax. He is married and filing a separate return.

6. Show how you would use a calculator to help streamline the computation for Problem 5.

EXERCISES

Determine the taxable income. Assume the basic standard deduction is taken.

Adjusted Gross Income	Filing Status	Number of Exemptions	Taxable Income
$10,000	Single	1	1. ■
$14,000	Head of household	2	2. ■
$28,300	Married filing jointly	2	3. ■
$43,800	Married filing separately	1	4. ■

Determine the tax from the table on page 394.

Taxable Income	Filing Status	Tax
$ 9,000	Single	5. ■
$14,375	Married filing jointly	6. ■
$31,298	Head of household	7. ■
$24,950	Married filing separately	8. ■

Solve.

9. Status: Married filing jointly
Number of exemptions: 3
Gross income: $38,400
Tax owed: ■■

10. Status: Single
Number of exemptions: 2
Gross income: $13,552
Tax owed: ■■

11. Status: Married filing separately
Number of exemptions: 2
Gross income: $24,398
Tax owed: ■■

12. Status: Head of household
Number of exemptions: 5
Gross income: $56,378
Tax owed: ■■

13. Allison's gross earnings were $25,300 with $3,652.19 withheld for taxes. Jerry's gross earnings were $22,350 with $3,350.60 withheld. They had unearned income of $1,483. They have two children and file jointly. How much tax do they owe? Will they receive a refund or will they have to pay additional tax?

14. Jay's gross earnings were $31,214 with $4,462.39 withheld for taxes. Shelly's gross earnings were $25,382 with $3,842.56 withheld. They had unearned income of $853.28. They have three children and file jointly. How much tax do they owe? Will they receive a refund or will they have to pay additional tax?

15. Allison and Jerry (Problem 13) want to see if they would pay less tax by filing separately. If they each claimed one child as dependent and each claimed half of the unearned income, how much total tax would they owe using the status "married filing separately"?

16. If you do not receive a tax form in the mail or need another, where could you get one? How could you get help filling out a tax form if you needed it? Discuss your answers with your classmates.

Mental Math: *Subtracting by Using Parts*

Sometimes you can subtract large numbers by breaking them into parts. For example, to subtract $11,000 from $41,708:

Think of $41,708 as $41 708
Think of $11,000 as $11 000
The difference is $30 708, or $30,708

Write $30, which is $41 − $11 ————↑ └—Write 708, which is 708 − 0

Find each difference. Break the numbers into parts to help.

1. $34,576 − $5,000

2. $18,534 − $9,000

3. $21,067 − $11,000

4. $40,856 − $12,000

Career
Upholsterer

An **upholsterer** is a person who repairs and re-covers furniture.

Profile of an upholsterer. Upholsterers may be high school graduates and usually have undergone some training or an apprenticeship. Two out of every five upholsterers own their own shops. Upholsterers enjoy working with their hands and usually work on their own.

The upholsterer's environment. An upholsterer works indoors and usually has a large, well-lighted room in which to work. He or she usually has a van or truck to deliver and pick up the furniture needing to be reupholstered. Many upholsterers have storage areas in which they keep springs, webbing, padding, foam rubber, and fabrics. Upholsterers often do their own accounting, ordering of raw materials, estimation of time and cost of jobs, and billing.

All in a day's work. Wendy owned her own upholstery shop. She had a small business with one employee. When it came time to file a business tax return, she used Form 1040 with Schedule C, a form added to the regular 1040.

1. Complete the following partial Schedule C to find Wendy's gross income, total deductions, and profit or loss.

SCHEDULE C (Form 1040)	
Part I Income	
1a. Gross receipts..........1a.	.... $29,000
2. Cost of goods sold..(less) 2.	3,180
5. Gross income..........5.	
Part II Deductions	
6. Advertising................	.....$ 400
7. Bad debts (uncollected).....	700
9. Truck expenses............	1,200
13. Dues and publications......	81
20. Office expense............	1,200
27. Utilities..................	2,400
28. Wages....................	800
30. Other....................	....
a. Night school............	120
Total deductions 31.	
Profit (loss) 32.	

2. What percentage of Wendy's gross income was spent for cost of goods? For advertising? For utilities?

3. Wendy believed she could increase her business by almost 50% by spending four times her current advertising budget. She decided that the cost of goods sold would increase 18%, and all deductions (except advertising) would increase 25%. What profit could she forecast with these changes to her Schedule C?

12-4 *Itemizing Deductions*

Sometimes, when you have a lot of tax-deductible expenses such as interest, high medical payments, large charitable contributions, or taxes, it is worthwhile to **itemize** your deductions. By listing these deductions separately, you may be able to reduce the tax you owe. The standard deduction for a single taxpayer is $3,000. Unless you can list deductions greater than this, you should use the standard deduction. Deductions fall into several classes:

- *Medical and dental expenses:* These include payments to health insurance plans, medicines, hospital and doctor's bills that are not paid for by insurance, and most items that are purchased for health reasons. Only those medical and dental expenses greater than 7.5% of your adjusted gross income can be deducted.
- *Interest paid:* The entire annual interest on mortgage payments for your main home and a secondary home may be deducted. Any other interest paid can be partially deducted (until 1991) according to the following schedule:

Year	Deductible Percent
1987	65%
1988	40%
1989	20%
1990	10%
After 1990	0%

- *Taxes:* State and local income taxes and property taxes are deductible.
- *Charitable contributions:* Any contribution made to a religious, educational, or charitable organization may be deducted.
- *Casualty losses:* Property that was stolen, destroyed, or damaged can be deducted if it is not covered by insurance. A special form must be completed and attached to your return for these deductions.
- *Miscellaneous deductions:* These include union dues, expenses of looking for a new job, tools and items purchased for your job, job-related educational expenses, work clothes and uniforms, professional organization dues, and so on. Only those miscellaneous deductions greater than 2% of your adjusted gross income may be deducted.

EXAMPLE

In 1988 Al had an adjusted gross income of $25,300. He had medical expenses of $835, charitable contributions of $396, taxes of $3,050, mortgage interest of $3,285, other interest expenses of $1,265, and miscellaneous expenses of $618. How much could he have deducted from his adjusted gross income?

Problem Solving Strategy: Organizing information.
Organize your work and results in a table for ease in solving the problem.

Skill Review

To itemize deductions, you need to be able to add money amounts.

Find each sum.

1. $445.23 + $320.97
2. $1,534.70 + $964.09
3. $880 + $462.56
4. $45,829.30 + $38,099.56

(For additional help, see page 544.)

Category	Allowable deduction	Amount deducted
Medical expenses	$835 − (0.075 × $25,300) = $835 − $1,897.50 No deduction, since $1,897.50 > $835	0
Misc expenses	$618 − (0.02 × $25,300) = $618 − $506	$ 112
Interest	$3,285 + (0.4 × $1,265) = $3,285 + $506	$3,791
Taxes paid	$3,050	$3,050
Contributions	$396	$ 396
Total		$7,349

Al could have deducted $7,349. Since this is a larger amount than the standard deduction, he itemized his deductions.

Class Exercises

1. The Wongs had an adjusted gross income of $17,000 and medical expenses of $1,900. How much could they deduct for medical expenses?

2. Leroy had an adjusted gross income of $9,200 and miscellaneous expenses of $318. How much could he deduct for miscellaneous expenses?

3. Toni has mortgage interest of $2,500 and other interest of $950. How much interest can she deduct in the year 1989?

Use this information for Exercises 4 and 5.

> Expenses for the Lamont family
> Medical (in excess of the 7.5% limit): $672
> Taxes paid: $4,982
> Charitable contributions: $298
> Deductible interest: $2,962
> Miscellaneous (in excess of the 2% limit): $195

4. How much can the Lamont family deduct if they itemize deductions?

5. How much more can they deduct by itemizing deductions rather than using the standard deduction for married filing jointly? (See page 394.)

EXERCISES

Find the total itemized deductions. Assume that the amounts for medical and miscellaneous are the amounts in excess of the percentage limits.

Medical	Taxes	Charity	Interest	Miscellaneous	Total
$ 982	$3,575	$318	$2,755	$142	**1.** ■
$ 0	$2,000	$250	$1,000	$ 0	**2.** ■
$1,200	$3,000	$475	$ 295	$325	**3.** ■

Determine how much can be deducted for interest payments.

Year	Mortgage Interest	Other Interest	Total Deductions
1988	$1,200	$ 400	**4.** ■
1989	$3,150	$ 850	**5.** ■
1990	$ 965	$1,454	**6.** ■

7. Which of Exercises 1–6 could be done mentally? In which would pencil and paper be appropriate? Which could best be done using a calculator?

Use the information below for Exercises 8-12.

> The Rosemon family; adjusted gross income: $24,300
> Filing status: married filing jointly; Year: 1989
>   Total medical expenses: $2,600
>   Taxes paid: $2,775
>   Charitable contributions: $418
>   Mortgage interest: $1,300; Other interest: $1,025
>   Miscellaneous expenses: $325

8. How much of their medical expenses can the Rosemons deduct?

9. How much interest can the Rosemons deduct?

10. How much can the Rosemons deduct for miscellaneous expenses?

11. What is the total amount of the Rosemons' itemized deductions?

12. How much more can the Rosemons deduct by itemizing than by taking the standard deduction? (See page 394.)

Use the information below for Exercises 13 and 14.

Tab Kenner; adjusted gross income: $14,295
Filing status: single; Year: 1990
   Total medical expenses: $875
   Taxes paid: $1,156
   Charitable contributions: $293
   Mortgage interest: $0; Other interest: $3,560
   Miscellaneous expenses: $275

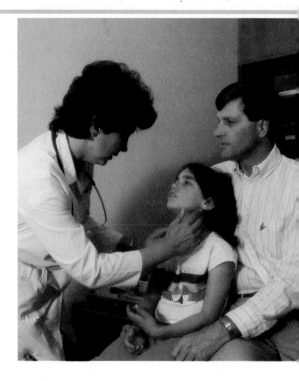

13. How much can Tab deduct if he itemizes deductions?

14. Which will allow Tab to deduct more, itemizing deductions or taking the standard deduction? How much more?

15. Larry had medical expenses one year of $2,375 but he was able to deduct only 12% of them. How much was Larry's adjusted gross income that year?

Critical Thinking: Classifying

Keeping track of all the information needed to file an accurate tax return can be an overwhelming task, especially if the task is approached in a haphazard way.

If you are a working teenager, the effort you must put into filing a tax return is relatively minimal. In most cases all money withheld from your paychecks for taxes is returned when you file a tax return. It is also possible that the money won't be withheld in the first place.

1. Which tax form would a working teenager most likely need to complete in order to receive the tax refund to which she or he is entitled?

2. What categories of information have to be entered on the form you identified in Question 1? How would you locate this information?

3. Is it necessary for you to organize information to get the figures needed for the form? Explain.

4. Select one figure you might enter on the form and describe how you would check its accuracy.

As your earning and buying power increase, you will want to keep accurate records of your deductible expenditures.

5. List the expenditures that can be used to lower your taxable income. Is it possible to group these items into expense categories?

6. How did you think of items to include in Question 5? How did you decide to group certain expenditures into certain categories?

12-5 State and Local Income Tax

Most states and many cities also have income taxes. Counties may also charge income tax based on your state tax. When you complete your federal income tax return, you must also complete one for the state. In most states that have income taxes, the taxable income is found in a manner similar to that of the federal income tax. The adjusted gross income is reduced by deductions and exemptions. The amount allowed for each exemption varies from state to state.

Pearl lives in a state that has an income tax. In her state each exemption is $800. The standard deductions allowed are shown in the table below. Pearl can itemize deductions but she cannot include state or local income tax as a deduction.

EXAMPLE 1
Pearl has an adjusted gross income of $13,280 and will file as a single taxpayer taking the standard deduction. What is her taxable income?

Standard Deduction for Pearl's State Standard deduction is 13% of adjusted gross income but may not exceed the amounts given below.	
Filing Status	**Maximum Deduction**
Single	$1,500
Married filing jointly	$3,000
Married filing separately	$1,500

Step 1. Find Pearl's standard deduction.

$$13\% \times \text{income} = \text{standard deduction}$$
$$13\% \times \$13,280 = \$1,726.40$$

Since $1,726.40 is more than $1,500, Pearl must take the standard deduction of $1,500.

Step 2. Calculate her taxable income.

$$\frac{\text{adjusted gross}}{\text{income}} - \text{deduction} - \frac{\text{number of exemptions}}{\times \$800} = \frac{\text{taxable}}{\text{income}}$$
$$\$13,280 - \$1,500 - (1 \times \$800) = \$10,980$$

Her taxable income is $10,980.

Skill Review

In order to calculate state income taxes, you need to be able to find a percent of a number.

Find each value. Round answers to the nearest cent.

1. 2% of $829
2. 5% of $13,978
3. 8% of $2,098
4. 3% of $465.96

(For additional help, see page 551.)

In many states, the tax rate increases as income goes up. The tax rates for Pearl's state are shown in the following table.

Tax Rate Schedule for Pearl's State		
If your taxable income is		
Over	But not over	Amount of tax is
$ 0	$1,000	2% of taxable income
1,000	2,000	$20 + 3% of excess over $1,000
2,000	3,000	$50 + 4% of excess over $2,000
3,000	—	$90 + 5% of excess over $3,000

EXAMPLE 2

Use the table above to compute Pearl's state income tax.

fixed tax +   percent of excess   = income tax
$90   + 5% × ($10,980 − $3,000) =   ■

Think: $10,980 − $3,000 = $7,980
$7,980 × 5% = $7,980 × 10% × $\frac{1}{2}$ = $798 × $\frac{1}{2}$ = $399

$90   fixed tax
+ 399   percent of excess
$489

Pearl's state income tax is $489.

Class Exercises

Use the table on page 403 to determine the amount of standard deduction allowed.

Filing Status	Adjusted Gross Income	Deduction
Single	$10,000	1. ■
Married filing separately	$16,000	2. ■
Married filing jointly	$26,300	3. ■

Use the tax rate schedule above to determine the amount of tax.

Taxable Income	Tax
$13,000	4. ■
$21,285	5. ■

Solve.

6. Lester has taxable state income of $17,300 and lives in a county that charges a local income tax equal to 50% of his state tax. Use the table on page 404 to find how much he will pay in state and local taxes.

7. Which of Exercises 1–6 could be done mentally? In which would pencil and paper be appropriate? Which could best be done by using a calculator?

EXERCISES

Use the table on page 403 to determine the amount of standard deduction allowed.

Filing Status	Adjusted Gross Income	Deduction
Married filing separately	$ 8,000	1. 
Married filing jointly	$20,000	2. ■
Single	$19,200	3. ■
Married filing separately	$13,280	4. ■

Use the table on page 403 to help determine the taxable income.

Filing Status	Adjusted Gross	Number of Exemptions	Taxable Income
Single	$18,380	1	5. ■
Married filing jointly	$16,300	3	6. ■
Single	$14,290	2	7. ■
Married filing jointly	$31,290	4	8. ■

Use the table on page 404 to determine the tax.

9. Taxable income: $19,325

10. Taxable income: $25,692

11. Taxable income: $51,675

12. Taxable income: $2,192

Solve.

13. Rhonda had taxable state income of $14,288. Her county income tax was 35% of the amount owed for state income tax. What was her total state and local income tax? Use the table on page 404 to determine her state income tax.

14. Caleb had taxable state income of $26,725. His city income tax was 10% of the amount owed for state income tax. What was his total state and local income tax? Use the table on page 404 to determine his state income tax.

15. Geoff had adjusted gross income of $25,000 and is single. He had only one exemption and took the standard deduction. His county charges local income tax equal to 50% of his state income tax. How much total state and local tax did he pay? Use the tables on pages 403 and 404 to figure state income tax.

16. Don and Sandi have two children. His adjusted gross income is $17,300 and hers is $15,480. They will take the standard deduction. Determine how much state tax they will pay by using the status married filing jointly. Then determine how much they will pay by using the status married filing separately and dividing the exemptions equally. How much will they save in taxes by selecting the less costly method? (Use the tables on pages 403 and 404.)

Using a Calculator: *Finding Income Tax*

When you use a tax schedule, the tax rate for a given range of incomes is a constant for all incomes within that range. You can store the tax rate in the calculator's memory and then recall it to do computations.

The city income tax rate in Summerdale is 2.25% of gross income. Find the annual income tax for workers with income $13,974.38

Step 1. Convert 2.25% to a decimal.

Key: $\boxed{C_E^C}$ 1 $\boxed{\times}$ 2.25 $\boxed{\%}$

or

Key: $\boxed{C_E^C}$ 2.25 $\boxed{\div}$ 100 $\boxed{M+}$

2.25% = 0.0225

Step 2. Use $\boxed{M_C^R}$ as a constant to determine the annual city income tax.

Key: 13974.38 $\boxed{\times}$ $\boxed{M_C^R}$ $\boxed{=}$ 314.42355 → $314.42
Round to nearest cent.

Find the city income tax for the following gross incomes. Describe your keystrokes.

1. $19,750 **2.** $72,695 **3.** $112,900

Computer:
BASIC Programming

Dolan has written a BASIC program to help him itemize his deductions. He will file as head of household. The information for interest income is based upon percentages for the year 1988.

10 HOME	Clears the screen.
20 REM INTEREST RATE DEDUCTION 1988	A REM statement that labels the next statement.
30 RT = .40	Sets the 1988 interest rate deduction to 40%.
40 INPUT "ADJUSTED GROSS INCOME?"; G	Prompts and records the adjusted gross income.
50 INPUT "MEDICAL EXPENSES?"; MD	Prompts and records the medical expenses.
60 D1 = MD − (.075 ∗ G)	Computes the deduction for medical expenses.
70 IF D1 < 0 THEN D1 = 0	Sets the medical deduction to zero if it is less than 7.5% of adjusted gross income.
80 INPUT "TAXES PAID?"; TX	Prompts and records the taxes paid.
90 INPUT "CONTRIBUTIONS?"; CH	Prompts and records the charitable contributions.
100 INPUT "MORTGAGE INTEREST?"; MG	Prompts and records mortgage interest.
110 INPUT "OTHER INTEREST?"; IN	Prompts and records the other interest.
120 NT = MG + RT ∗ IN	Calculates the deduction for interest.
130 INPUT "MISC. EXPENSES?"; MS	Prompts and records the miscellaneous expenses.
140 D2 = MS − (.02 ∗ G)	Computes the possible miscellaneous deduction.
150 IF D2 < 0 THEN D2 = 0	Sets the miscellaneous deduction to zero if it is less than 2% of the gross adjusted income.
160 DE = D1 + TX + CH + NT + D2	Computes the total amount to be deducted.
170 PRINT "TOTAL DEDUCTIONS $"; DE	Prints and labels the final total deduction.
180 END	Tells the computer to end the program.

EXERCISES
RUN the program using each set of values for input.

	1.	2.	3.	4.	5.
Adjusted gross income	$20,456	$13,271	$9,192	$31,317	$21,275
Medical expenses	$ 2,037	$ 1,275	$1,613	$ 895	$ 3,045
Taxes	$ 3,728	$ 1,021	$ 925	$ 4,295	$ 2,025
Charitable contributions	$ 325	$ 401	$ 160	$ 1,090	$ 420
Mortgage interest	$ 1,024	$ 2,050	$ 0	$ 4,549	$ 1,875
Other interest	$ 1,538	$ 992	$1,262	$ 3,871	$ 2,056
Miscellaneous	$ 419	$ 58	$ 302	$ 1,291	$ 525

Decision Making:
Itemizing Deductions

Helen Harrison is a science teacher at West High. Last year when she filed her taxes she took the standard deduction. Several of the teachers told her that she would come out much better financially if she itemized her deductions. This year, Helen has decided to look over her records and decide whether or not to itemize her deductions.

Helen was mailed Form 1040EZ because she used that last year. From her bank, she picked up Form 1040 and Schedule A on which to list her deductions. Helen saw that Form 1040 and Schedule A required her to give more detailed information about her expenditures in a number of areas than did the forms she had completed in the past. She realized that completing Form 1040 was going to be more time-consuming than completing Form 1040EZ.

Answer the following questions.

1. What do you think Helen's co-workers mean when they say she will "come out better financially" by itemizing her deductions?

2. From your study of this chapter, what mathematical skills do you think Helen will need to fill out Form 1040?

3. In your opinion, how should Helen proceed in order to determine whether or not she would be better off itemizing deductions?

COLLECTING INFORMATION

Helen decides to begin by going through her checkbook to collect information on how much she spent for various types of expenditures. Helen collected the information shown on page 409 from her checkbook.

Answer the following questions.

4. Helen has listed only those expenditures that she believes to be tax deductible. Examine the items she listed. Are there any items listed that are definitely not tax deductible? Are there any questionable items? How would you go about finding out if these items are tax deductible?

Date	Check Number	For	Amount	Date	Check Number	For	Amount
1/5	406	Payment to dentist	$45	4/30	512	Apartment rent	$395
1/10	415	Donation to charity	$15	5/3	517	Donation to charity	$6
1/13	420	Tagboard for diagram	$11.74	5/13	519	Payment to dentist	$35
		for biology class		5/16	520	Donation to charity	$12.50
1/17	428	Donation to charity	$20	5/17	521	Flowers for biology	$10
1/21	432	Payment to dentist	$135			laboratory activity	
1/21	433	Prescription medicine	$15.78	5/23	524	Donation to charity	$12.50
1/22	436	Renewal, The Science Teacher	$26	5/24	525	Payment to doctor	$35
1/24	441	Donation to charity	$12.50	5/31	528	Apartment rent	$395
1/31	450	Apartment rent	$395	6/6	530	Donation to charity	$15
1/31	451	Donation to charity	$10	6/10	533	Food for school party	$12.48
2/7	460	Donation to charity	$12.50	6/27	541	Donation to charity	$10
2/9	463	Materials for biology	$8.76	6/30	544	Apartment rent	$395
		laboratory activity		7/11	550	Donation to charity	$10
2/14	465	Donation to charity	$14	7/31	564	Apartment rent	$395
2/25	471	Donation to charity	$5	8/29	571	Donation to charity	$20
2/28	475	Donation to charity	$15	8/31	575	Apartment rent	$395
2/28	476	Apartment rent	$395	9/25	591	Donation to charity	$5
3/7	477	Donation to charity	$12.50	9/30	596	Apartment rent	$395
3/9	483	Tropical fish for	$4.20	10/10	615	Donation to charity	$15
		laboratory activity		10/13	620	Tagboard for diagram	$11.96
3/14	485	Donation to charity	$14			for biology class	
3/31	496	Apartment rent	$395	10/17	628	Donation to charity	$20
4/2	499	Renewal, American	$25	10/31	636	Apartment rent	$395
		Biology Teacher		10/31	637	Donation to charity	$15
4/4	502	Donation to charity	$12.50	11/13	647	Payment to dentist	$45
4/8	503	Payment to doctor	$35	11/14	650	Donation to charity	$14
4/8	504	Prescription medicine	$22	11/30	661	Apartment rent	$395
4/18	505	Donation to charity	$25	12/19	671	Donation to charity	$12.50
4/20	507	Seeds for biology	$3	12/20	673	Food for school party	$7.25
		laboratory activity		12/26	682	Donation to charity	$30
4/25	510	Donation to charity	$14	12/31	685	Apartment rent	$395

5. Helen was able to get all of the above information from her checkbook register. What are the advantages to paying expenses by checks?

6. What other records besides her checkbook do you think Helen might need to check before deciding whether or not to itemize?

USING OTHER SOURCES FOR INFORMATION

In talking with co-workers, Helen learns that she also needs some information from her pay stub. The amount she pays for medical insurance can be used in calculating her deduction for medical and dental expenses. Additionally, she can include the amount she pays in union dues in figuring her deduction for miscellaneous expenses. By checking her pay stubs, Helen found out that she pays $18.95 per pay period for medical insurance and $9.79 per pay period for union dues.

Her W-2 form indicates that Helen paid $1,326.31 in state and local income tax. Helen knows that this amount is deductible if she decides to itemize deductions.

Finally, Helen realizes that a number of important financial summary statements came to her during the month of January. They summarized expenses that may be tax deductible. By checking statements such as these, Helen discovers that she has the following additional expenses to consider for this year.

Interest paid on car loan	$1,206.72
Interest paid on credit card	$ 245.89
Interest paid on credit union loan	$ 75.46

Answer the following questions.

7. If medical insurance and union dues are deducted from 20 paychecks, how much does Helen pay per year for medical insurance? For union dues?

8. Now that Helen has collected this information, she should be in a position to determine whether or not to itemize deductions. If the standard deduction for a single taxpayer is $3,000 and Helen has deductions totaling more than that amount, she will save tax dollars by itemizing deductions. Because different types of deductions have different limits, Helen realizes she must classify her deductions before going any further. What categories does she need to include? Explain.

9. Medical and dental expenses greater than 7.5% of adjusted gross income can be deducted. Helen's adjusted gross income is $22,875. How much will she be able to deduct for medical and dental expenses?

10. Explain to a classmate how you figured out an answer to Question 9. Listen to your classmate's strategy. How was your strategy different from your classmate's? Did you both get the same answer?

11. This year, 20% of interest paid on personal loans and charge accounts is deductible. How much will Helen have to deduct in this category?

12. Any contribution to a religious, educational, or charitable organization may be deducted. How much can Helen deduct in this category?

13. Discuss with a classmate how you calculated the answer to Question 12. Look for an efficient way to handle the large number of pieces of data. Discuss both your approach and your answer.

14. Miscellaneous deductions include union dues, expenses of looking for a new job, tools and items purchased for the job, work clothes and uniforms, and so on. What items does Helen have that are deductible under this category?

15. Miscellaneous expenses greater than 2% of gross adjusted income are tax deductible. How much can Helen deduct in this category?

16. Total Helen's deductible expenses. (Do not forget state and local income taxes.) Should Helen itemize her deductions? Explain. Give some reasons why a person in Helen's situation is wise always to examine personal financial records for possible tax deductions.

17. Discuss with a classmate your answer to Question 16. Explain how you thought of reasons to use in answering the last part of this question. Did your partner use a different approach to think of his or her reasons?

18. Discuss with a classmate how a clear understanding of how to do mathematical calculations makes completing a tax return easier. What thinking skills are important in completing a tax return?

DECIDE FOR YOURSELF

How would you go about deciding whether or not to itemize deductions on your tax return? Summarize the steps you, and Helen, used in making this decision.

VOCABULARY

exemption	itemize	tax table
filing status	taxable income	W-2 form
income tax return	tax schedule	

For Exercises 1–5, select the words that complete each statement.

1. The annual statement from an employer that shows the total amount of earnings and taxes withheld during the past year for an employee is called a _____ .

2. A(n) _____ is the form a person is required to file with the government each year giving information about any taxable income and any deductions he or she might have.

3. You determine your _____ when you subtract your exemptions and deductions from the total of your gross earnings and other income.

4. A table of tax rates is called a _____ .

5. If you have many tax-deductible expenses it may be worthwhile to _____ your deductions when you file your income tax return.

SKILLS

Find each quotient. Round to the nearest cent.

6. $5,839.50 ÷ 24

7. $7,842.75 ÷ 26

8. $3,025.78 ÷ 52

Express as decimals.

9. 18%

10. 3%

11. 0.025%

Find each value. Round answers to the nearest cent.

12. 4% of $685

13. 9% of $15,500

14. 2% of $5,683.75

CONSUMER TOPICS

Use the W-2 form on page 413 for Exercises 15–18.

15. How much were Manuela's gross earnings?

16. How much was withheld from Manuela's wages each month for state income tax?

17. How much of Manuela's annual income was left after taxes had been withheld?

18. Manuela did not earn interest income and owed $3,418.29 in federal income tax. Fill in Form 1040EZ for Manuela.

1 Control number		4 Employer's State ID number		Copy C To be filed with employee's FEDERAL tax return
2 Employer's name, address, and ZIP code		3 Employer's identification number		This information is being furnished to the Internal Revenue Service. Department of the Treasury–Internal Revenue Service
Carter Furniture Company 6315 East Fifth Street Promise, IL 60200		5 Statutory De- employee ceased ☐ ☐	Pension plan ☐	Legal rep ☐	942 emp. ☐	Sub total ☐	Deferred compensation ☐	Void ☐
		6 Allocated tips		7 Advance EIC payment				
8 Employee's social security number 542-54-5260	9 Federal income tax withheld 3628.50	10 Wages, tips, other compensation 21640.92		11 Social security tax withheld 1655.13
12 Employee's name, address, and ZIP code		13 Social security wages 21640.92		14 Social security tips
Manuela G. Franco 1489 Ash Lane Promise, IL 60200		16		
		502.14 17 State income tax	21640.92 18 State wages, tips	IL 19 Name of State
		20 Local income tax	21 Local income tax	22 Name of locality

Form W-2 Wage and Tax Statement

Use the table and the tax schedule on page 394.

19. Alicia is a single taxpayer and has taxable income of $22,750. How much tax will she owe?

20. Eric and Bridget are married and have 2 children. Eric's gross earnings were $17,750 and $2,468.92 was withheld for taxes. Bridget's gross earnings were $16,950 and $2,280.70 was withheld for taxes. They earned $506 in interest and had no other unearned income or adjustments. They took the standard deduction of $5,000. How much do they owe in taxes?

21. Will Eric and Bridget receive a refund or do they owe tax?

Solve.

22. Justin had an adjusted gross income of $11,326 and medical expenses of $1,389.50. How much can he deduct for medical expenses if expenses of more than 7.5% of adjusted gross income can be deducted?

23. Clark lives in Pearl's state. His taxable income is $14,690. How much does he owe for state income tax? (Use the table on page 404.)

24. Clark's county (Problem 23) has a piggy-back tax on the state income tax. The local surcharge is based on 35% of the state income tax. How much does Clark owe for local tax?

25. In Ann's state, the standard deduction is 13% of adjusted gross income, not to exceed $1,300. If Ann's adjusted gross income is $23,600, how much is her standard deduction?

Chapter 12 Test

Use the W-2 form for Exercises 1–4.

1 Control number		4 Employer's State ID number		Copy C To be filed with employee's FEDERAL tax return
2 Employer's name, address, and ZIP code		3 Employer's identification number		This information is being furnished to the Internal Revenue Service Department of the Treasury-Internal Revenue Service
Shay's Department Store 600 Main Street Clark, CO 80299		5 Statutory De- employee ceased Pension plan Legal rep 942 emp. Sub total Deferred compensation Void ☐ ☐ ☐ ☐ ☐ ☐ ☐ ☐		
		6 Allocated tips	7 Advance EIC payment	
8 Employee's social security number 381-29-5737	9 Federal income tax withheld 2351.43	10 Wages, tips, other compensation 18456.28	11 Social security tax withheld 1411.91	
12 Employee's name, address, and ZIP code		13 Social security wages 18456.28	14 Social security tips	
Emily Johnson 794 Danson Rd Clark, CO 80299		16		
		1342.76 18456.28 CO 17 State income tax 18 State wages, tips 19 Name of State		
		20 Local income tax 21 Local income tax 22 Name of locality		
Form W-2 Wage and Tax Statement				

1. How much were Emily's gross earnings?

2. How much federal tax was withheld from Emily's pay each week?

3. How much of Emily's annual income was left after taxes had been withheld?

4. Emily had $175 in interest income. She owes $2,696 in federal income taxes. Complete Form 1040EZ for Emily.

Use the table and the tax schedule on page 394 for Problems 5–7.

5. George and Patty are married and have 1 child. Their income was $37,750 and $5,418.25 was withheld for taxes. They earned $785 in interest and had no other unearned income or adjustments. They took the standard deduction of $5,000. How much tax do they owe?

6. Will George and Patty receive a tax refund or do they owe additional tax?

7. Martin's taxable income is $14,350. He files as head of household. Find his tax.

Solve.

8. Becca had an adjusted gross income of $12,690 and medical expenses of $1,176.90. How much can she deduct for medical expenses if expenses of more than 7.5% of adjusted gross income can be deducted?

9. In Rob's state, the standard deduction is 15% of adjusted gross income, not to exceed $1,800. Rob's adjusted gross income is $10,628. Find his taxable income?

10. Don lives in Pearl's state and has a taxable income of $9,675. How much does he owe for state income tax? (Use the table on page 404.)

11. Don's county (Problem 10) has a piggy-back tax of 30% on the state income tax. How much does Don owe for his county taxes?

Cumulative Mixed Review

Select the letter corresponding to the correct answer.

1. Germaine earns $17,500 annually and has 24% of her gross earnings withheld. What is the net amount of her paycheck each pay period if she is paid biweekly?
   a. $161.54   **b.** $175
   c. $511.54   **d.** $554.17

2. Tricia bought 2 sweaters for $19.50 each and a skirt for $17. What was the total amount of her bill if she had to pay a sales tax of 5.25%?
   a. $56   **b.** $2.94
   c. $58.94   **d.** $38.42

3. Tim deposited $1,250 in a savings account that paid 7.5% simple interest. What was the amount in his account at the beginning of the third year of his account?
   a. $1,343.75   **b.** $93.75
   c. $281.25   **d.** $1,437.50

4. Carmela borrowed $1,500 for 3 months at 10.5% interest. How much interest did she pay for the loan?
   a. $39.38   **b.** $157.50
   c. $1,539.38   **d.** $630

5. Byron has an outstanding balance of $135.68 on his credit card account. What is the finance charge for the month if it is calculated at 1.5% per month?
   a. $24.42   **b.** $2.04
   c. $20.35   **d.** $137.72

6. One brand of cereal sells for $1.75 for 12 ounces. What is the unit price per ounce?
   a. $.015   **b.** $.21
   c. $1.46   **d.** $.146

7. Determine the monthly payment under an add-on plan when simple interest is charged on the amount borrowed: $1,500 for 12 months at 12.5% interest.
   a. $2,250   **b.** $15.63
   c. $15   **d.** $140.63

8. Jessica earns $4.50 per hour and 3% commission on the gross amount of her sales. How much did she earn the week she worked 35 hours and sold $4,250 worth of merchandise?
   a. $285   **b.** $127.50
   c. $157.50   **d.** $132.23

9. Ned and Nora purchased a house for $68,500. They had to make a down payment of 10%. What was the amount of the mortgage they obtained?
   a. $54,800   **b.** $6,850
   c. $61,650   **d.** $68,500

10. Tom had new carpet installed in his living room, which measures 12 feet by 15 feet. How much did the carpet cost if the price was $24 per square yard?
   a. $480   **b.** $648
   c. $1,440   **d.** $4,320

CHAPTER 13
Making Investments

Jill found that she was able to save 10% of her net pay. She made monthly deposits in a savings account until she had accumulated more than $1,500. Her savings account paid $5\frac{1}{4}$% interest. Jill did some research and discovered she could earn 5.84% with savings bonds and 5.85% to 6.92% with a certificate of deposit (CD), but her money would not be as readily available to her if she invested it in savings bonds or CDs.

- CDs pay interest depending on the length of the deposit. What factors should Jill consider when deciding how long to invest her money?

- Can you think of advantages one form of investment might have over another? Can you think of disadvantages?

- How would you advise Jill to invest her savings?

What are some factors you would consider when deciding how to invest your savings?

13-1 Certificates of Deposit

A **certificate of deposit** is an account that pays more interest than a regular passbook account but requires you to leave your money on deposit for a fixed period of time. Usually, you also have to deposit a minimum amount of money, such as $500 or $1,000.

Nolan's bank offers certificates of deposit for 6 months or 1, 2, 3, 4, or 5 years. The interest rates offered on these certificates vary depending on economic conditions. When Nolan decided to open a certificate of deposit, the bank was offering the rates shown in the following table.

NOVEMBER	14th	Minimum	Annual Rate %
MONEY MARKET Investor Account		$2,500	**5.65**
MONEY MARKET Investor Account			**5.25**
			.
6 MONTH Certificate		$2,500	**6.00**
6 MONTH Certificate		$10,000	**6.00**
12 MONTH Certificate		$500	**6.40**
12 MONTH Certificate		10,000	**6.40**
24 MONTH		$500	**75**

Term	Minimum Deposit	Interest
6 months	$ 500	6.25%
1 year	$ 500	6.50%
2 years	$1,000	6.75%
3 years	$1,000	7.0%
4 years	$1,000	7.25%
5 years	$1,000	7.50%

The interest on the certificates was compounded daily. If the money is left on deposit for the entire term, the certificate *matures*. Although Nolan can withdraw the interest or have it paid to him directly, he would have to pay a penalty if he withdrew any of the original amount before the certificate matured. The table on page 419 gives the amount of money in a certificate at the time it matures for each dollar invested if the interest is allowed to remain in the account.

EXAMPLE 1

Nolan decided to take out a 3-year certificate and deposited $2,500 at 7% interest. Use the table on page 419 to determine how much interest his account will have earned at its maturity.

Step 1. Find the amount in the certificate account at maturity.

> **Problem Solving Strategy:** Finding information.
> Use the table on page 419 to find the amount in Nolan's account for each dollar invested. The value for $1 invested at 7% for 3 years is $1.23346.

$$\text{amount invested} \times \text{value of \$1} = \text{certificate amount at maturity}$$
$$\$2,500 \times 1.23346 = \$3,083.65$$

Skill Review

In order to find the value of certificate accounts, you need to be able to multiply money amounts by decimals.

Find each product.

1. $4,500 × 2.398
2. $25,000 × 1.28874
3. $1,200 × 1.756
4. $34,650 × 1.0045

(For additional help, see page 545.)

Accumulated Amount for $1.00 Invested						
Interest	6 months	1 year	2 years	3 years	4 years	5 years
6.75%	1.03420	1.06976	1.14439	1.22423	1.30964	1.40100
7.00%	1.03549	1.07244	1.15014	1.23346	1.32282	1.41865
7.25%	1.03679	1.07515	1.15594	1.24281	1.33621	1.43662
7.50%	1.03813	1.07794	1.16196	1.25252	1.35014	1.45537
7.75%	1.03938	1.08054	1.16758	1.26162	1.36324	1.47304
8.00%	1.04069	1.08327	1.17347	1.27119	1.37704	1.49170
8.25%	1.04200	1.08600	1.17940	1.28083	1.39098	1.51061
8.50%	1.04330	1.08872	1.18532	1.29048	1.40498	1.52963
8.75%	1.04455	1.09135	1.19105	1.29986	1.41860	1.54820
9.00%	1.04587	1.09410	1.19707	1.30972	1.43297	1.56781
9.25%	1.04723	1.09696	1.20333	1.32001	1.44800	1.58840
9.50%	1.04849	1.09961	1.20915	1.32960	1.46204	1.60768

Step 2. Find the amount of interest.

$$\begin{array}{ccc} \text{certificate amount at} \\ \text{maturity} \end{array} - \text{amount deposited} = \text{interest}$$

$$\$3,083.65 \quad - \quad \$2,500 \quad = \$583.65$$

There would be $583.65 interest in the account at maturity.

The **annual yield** is the amount of simple interest the bank would have to offer to yield the same amount of interest earned by a certificate account in 1 year. To find the annual yield, divide the amount of interest earned in 1 year by the amount invested and write the result as a percent rounded to the nearest hundredth. There is a shortcut using the table above that is shown in Example 2.

EXAMPLE 2
What is the annual yield on Nolan's certificate of deposit? Use the table above to find the value of $1 after 1 year at 7%.

$$\left(\begin{array}{c} \text{table value of \$1} \\ \text{after 1 year} \end{array} - 1 \right) \times 100\% = \text{annual yield}$$

$$1.07244 - 1 \qquad \times 100\% = \quad \blacksquare$$

Think: $(1.07244 - 1) \times 100\% = 0.07244 \times 100\% = 7.244\%$

7.24%   Round to nearest hundredth.

The annual yield is 7.24%.

The penalty for withdrawing all or part of the original amount deposited in a certificate account before the certificate matures is often equal to 3 months simple interest. To calculate this penalty, determine the annual yield and use it to compute 3 months simple interest.

EXAMPLE 3

Six months after taking out his certificate, Nolan saw another one that offered 8% interest for a 3-year certificate. He felt it would be a better investment. How much would his penalty be if he withdrew the entire amount of his certificate?

The annual yield on the certificate is 7.24%. (See Example 2.) Use the simple interest formula to calculate 3 months' interest.

> **Hidden Question:** 3 months is what part of a year?
> $$3 \text{ mo} = \tfrac{3}{12} = \tfrac{1}{4} \text{ y}$$

$i = p \times r \times t$
$i = \$2,500 \times 0.0724 \times \tfrac{1}{4}$ **Think:** $7.24\% = 0.0724$
$i = \$181 \times \tfrac{1}{4} = \$45.25$

The penalty would be $45.25.

Class Exercises

Use the table on page 419 to help find the interest on the following certificates of deposit.

Amount Deposited	Term	Interest Rate	Interest
$2,600	5 y	8.25%	1. ■
$1,000	6 mo	7.25%	2. ■
$6,500	4 y	9.0%	3. ■

4. What is the annual yield for a certificate of deposit with an interest rate of 8.5%?

5. Hope deposited $3,000 in a 5-year certificate at 7.5% interest. She withdrew her money after 1 year. How much penalty did she pay for early withdrawal?

EXERCISES

Use the table on page 419 to determine the interest on the following certificates of deposit.

Amount Deposited	Term	Interest Rate	Interest
$ 1,000	2 y	8.0%	1. ■
$ 8,000	5 y	9.25%	2. ■
$10,500	3 y	8.75%	3. ■
$11,500	2 y	7.5%	4. ■

Find the annual yield for certificates of deposit having the given interest rate.

5. 9.25%

6. 8.75%

7. 9.5%

Solve.

8. Name: Jaynne Kripp
   Amount deposited: $5,000
   Term: 6 months
   Interest rate: 9.25%
   Amount at maturity: ■

9. Name: Cantrece Levett
   Amount deposited: ■
   Term: 3 years
   Interest rate: 7.75%
   Amount at maturity: $8,198.19

10. Show how to use a calculator to streamline your computation for Exercise 9.

11. Theo deposited $7,500 for 4 years in a certificate of deposit at 6.75% interest. After 6 months he withdrew the entire amount. How much was his penalty for early withdrawal?

12. Dominique had $4,000 to place in a certificate of deposit. She could take a 3-year certificate at 8.25% interest or a 4-year certificate at 9.25% interest. If she took the 4-year certificate, she would have to withdraw the money after 3 years and pay an early withdrawal penalty. Under which plan would she end up with more money? How much more?

Critical Thinking: *Evaluating Information*

Tom thought he wanted to go to college but he knew it would be expensive. He wondered if going to college was worth the sacrifices he had to make to save money. Tom saw the following quote, taken from a book authored by a financial advisor: "Studies show that a college graduate earns $250,000 to $400,000 more during his or her life than does a person with only a high school diploma."

Tom decided college would be a good idea, but he still needed a plan for saving money. He decided to check into different types of investment plans. He went to his bank and requested information on savings accounts. He learned that the interest rate for one type of savings account was 6.25%, compounded quarterly. Tom had $500 in a checking account that he felt he could transfer to savings.

1. What sources of information seem to contribute to Tom's decision to investigate the merits of different investing plans?

2. How would you assess the reliability of the sources of information that Tom incorporated into his decision making?

3. If he put $500 into the savings account described above, how much would he save by the end of one year? (Assume that Tom does not withdraw any money from this account during this year.) How much of this is interest?

4. If Tom purchased a $500 certificate of deposit and left the money on deposit for 1 year, his money would earn 6.75% interest. How much money would Tom have in 1 year?

13-2 Savings Bonds

When federal, state, or local governments or corporations need to borrow large amounts of money, they issue bonds. A **bond** is a promise by the borrower to repay a loan at a specified rate of interest. The government issues savings bonds in various denominations. The interest rates on these bonds are set by the government and change monthly. The interest rate established at the time you purchase a bond is guaranteed for the life of the bond—you may earn more interest than that rate but never less.

The **face value** of a bond is the value printed on the bond itself. It represents the value of the bond at maturity. The initial cost of a savings bond is one-half its face value.

EXAMPLE 1

Camilla decided to have some of her pay withheld in order to purchase U.S. savings bonds. How much will she have to pay for a bond with a face value of $100?

$$\text{face value} \div 2 = \text{cost}$$
$$\$100 \div 2 = \blacksquare$$

Think: $100 \div 2 = $50

The bond will cost $50.

Savings bonds mature after 12 years, but they may be cashed in before they mature. The interest paid on them depends upon how long they are held. A recent issue of bonds has the redemption values shown in the table on page 423. This table gives redemption values for bonds with a face value of $50. To use this table with bonds of differing face values, divide the face value of the bond by $50 and multiply by the redemption value in the table.

EXAMPLE 2

Roberto purchased a $200 bond and cashed it in $2\frac{1}{2}$ years after he purchased it. Use the table on page 423 to calculate the interest on the bond.

Step 1. Find the cash value of the bond.

$$\text{face value} \div \$50 \times \text{redemption value} = \text{cash value}$$
$$\$200 \div \$50 \times \$28.99 = \blacksquare$$

Think: $\$200 \div \$50 = 4$

$$\begin{array}{r} \$28.99 \\ \times \qquad 4 \\ \hline \$115.96 \end{array}$$

 Key: $\boxed{C^C_E}$ 4 $\boxed{\times}$ 28.99 $\boxed{=}$ $\overline{115.96}$
$\$115.96$

Step 2. Calculate the interest on the bond.
The purchase price is the face value divided by 2:
$\$200 \div 2 = \$100$

$$\textbf{cash value} - \textbf{purchase price} = \textbf{interest}$$
$$\$115.96 \quad - \qquad \$100 \qquad = \$15.96$$

Roberto earned $\$15.96$ interest.

Series EE bonds continue to earn interest at the guaranteed rate or higher for up to 40 years. The interest on the mature bonds in the table below is 6% compounded semiannually. To find the value of the bond *n* years after maturity, use this formula:

$$\begin{array}{c} \text{cash value} \\ (n \text{ years after maturity}) \end{array} = \begin{array}{c} \text{cash value} \\ (\text{after 12 years}) \end{array} \times \left(1 + \frac{\text{interest rate}}{q} \right)^{nq}$$

where *n* is the number of years after maturity and *q* is the number of times per year that interest is compounded.

EXAMPLE 3
How much would a $\$200$ Series EE bond be worth after 15 years?

Step 1. Find the cash value of the bond at the end of 12 years.

$$\textbf{face value} \div \$50 \times \textbf{redemption value} = \textbf{cash value}$$
$$\$200 \quad \div \$50 \times \qquad \$50.82 \qquad = \quad \blacksquare$$

Think: $\$200 \div \$50 = 4$

$$\begin{array}{r} \$50.82 \\ \times \qquad 4 \\ \hline \$203.28 \end{array}$$

Step 2. Find the cash value of the bond after 15 years.

> **Hidden Questions:** How many years past maturity is the bond being held? How many times per year is interest compounded?
> $15\text{ y} - 12\text{ y} = 3\text{ y}$; semiannual means twice a year. Therefore, $n = 3$ and $q = 2$.

Face Value: $50	Cost: $25
Redemption Value of Series EE Bond	
After	Redemption Value
6 months	$25.54
1 year	$26.09
1½ years	$26.77
2 years	$27.38
2½ years	$28.99
3 years	$29.72
4 years	$31.06
5 years	$33.60
6 years	$35.64
7 years	$37.81
8 years	$40.12
9 years	$42.56
10 years	$45.15
11 years	$47.90
12 years	$50.82

Think: 6% = 0.06

$$\begin{array}{c}\text{cash value}\\\text{(3 years after maturity)}\end{array} = \begin{array}{c}\text{cash value}\\\text{(after 12 years)}\end{array} \times \left(1 + \frac{\text{interest rate}}{q}\right)^{nq}$$

$$\text{cash value} = \$203.28 \times \left(1 + \frac{0.06}{2}\right)^{3 \times 2}$$

$$\text{cash value} = \$203.28 \times (1.03)^6$$

Key: $\boxed{\text{C}^\text{C}_\text{E}}$ 1.03 $\boxed{\times}$ $\boxed{=}$ $\boxed{=}$ $\boxed{=}$ $\boxed{=}$ $\boxed{=}$ $\boxed{\times}$ 203.28 $\boxed{=}$ 242.72693

$\$242.73$ Round to nearest cent.

The value of the bond would be $242.73 after 15 years.

Class Exercises

Determine the cost of a bond with each given face value.

1. $100   **2.** $550

3. $1,000

Use the table on page 423 to determine the value of each bond at the time of redemption.

Face Value	Length of Time Held	Redemption Value
$ 50	3 y	**4.** ■
$ 25	5 y	**5.** ■
$100	7 y	**6.** ■
$150	10 y	**7.** ■

8. A Series EE bond with a face value of $250 was cashed in after 3 years. Use the table on page 423 to determine the interest on the bond.

9. A Series EE bond whose face value is $100 is held for 14 years. How much is the bond worth at that time?

EXERCISES

Determine the cost of a bond with each given face value.

1. $50   **2.** $200

3. $300   **4.** $500

OVER THE TOP FOR YOU

Buy U.S. Gov't Bonds
THIRD LIBERTY LOAN

Use the table on page 423 to find the value of each bond at the time of redemption.

Face Value	Length of Time Held	Redemption Value
$ 50	2 y	5. ■
$ 100	6 mo	6. ■
$1,000	$2\frac{1}{2}$ y	7. ■
$ 300	5 y	8. ■
$ 500	8 y	9. ■

Solve.

10. Face value: $300
    Time held: $2\frac{1}{2}$ y
    Interest: ■

11. Face value: ■
    Time held: 2 y
    Cash value: $136.90

12. Face value: $300
    Time held: ■
    Cash value: $213.84

13. A Series EE bond with a face value of $200 is held for 13 years. How much is the bond worth at that time?

14. A Series EE bond with a face value of $500 is held for 16 years. How much is the bond worth at that time?

15. A Series EE bond with a face value of $350 is held for $17\frac{1}{2}$ years. How much is it worth at that time?

16. Kevin cashed in a Series EE bond after 6 years. He received $63.84 in interest. Find the face value of the bond.

17. Ivy purchased a $100 savings bond for her daughter's sixth birthday and has purchased another on each birthday since. Her daughter plans to use the bonds to help finance her college education when she reaches 18. Use the table on page 423 to estimate the total worth of the 12 bonds at that time.

Mental Math: *Dividing by 50*

It is easy to divide a number by 50 if you write 50 in a different form. Remember that 50 = 100/2, so dividing by 50 is the same as dividing by 100/2.

$$\$200 \div \$50 = \$200 \div \frac{\$100}{2} = \$200 \times \frac{2}{\$100}$$

So, to divide by 50, divide by 100 and then multiply by 2.

$$\$200 \div \$50 = \$200 \div \$100 \times 2 = 2 \times 2 = 4$$

Find each quotient.

1. $300 ÷ $50

2. $452 ÷ $50

3. $3,850 ÷ $50

4. $12,500 ÷ $50

13-3 Corporate and Municipal Bonds

When large corporations borrow money by issuing bonds, they are often able to pay higher interest than savings accounts or certificates. These bonds, called **corporate bonds,** are issued in units of $1,000 and for periods of from 10 to 30 years. Interest rates are expressed as a percent of the face value of the bond. The face value, or **par value,** is printed on the bond along with its interest rate. At maturity the bond can be redeemed at its par value. The cost of a bond is usually quoted as a percent of its par value. If the **quoted price** is lower than its face value, it is said to sell at a **discount.** If the quoted price is higher than its face value, it is said to sell at a **premium.**

Because owners of bonds often sell their bonds before they mature, most bonds are bought and sold through brokers rather than through the companies that issue them. The **current yield** of a bond is the interest divided by the cost. The result is expressed as a percent.

EXAMPLE 1

Iven purchased a $1,000 bond at a quoted price of $85\frac{1}{4}$. What is the current yield if the interest rate of the bond is $7\frac{1}{2}$%?

Step 1. Find the interest paid.

$$\textbf{par value} \times \textbf{interest rate} = \textbf{interest}$$
$$\$1,000 \quad \times \quad 7\tfrac{1}{2}\% \quad = \quad \$75$$

Step 2. Find the cost of the bond.

$$\textbf{par value} \times \textbf{quoted price} = \textbf{cost}$$
$$\$1,000 \quad \times \quad 85\tfrac{1}{4}\% \quad = \$852.50$$

Step 3. Find the current yield.

$$\textbf{interest} \div \quad \textbf{cost} \quad = \textbf{current yield}$$
$$\$75 \quad \div \$852.50 = \quad \blacksquare$$

Estimate: $75 ÷ $852.50 = $\blacksquare$ → $80 ÷ $800 = 0.1 = 10%

```
            0.0879 → 8.8%   Round to nearest tenth percent.
$852.50)$75.00 0000
        68 20 00
         6 80 000
         5 96 750
           83 2500
           76 7250
            6 5250
```

Key: $\boxed{C_E^C}$ 75 $\boxed{÷}$ 852.5 $\boxed{=}$ ⟋ 0.0879765 ⟍

8.8%   Round to nearest tenth percent.

Skill Review

To find current yield, you must be able to find what percent one number is of another.

Find what percent the first number is of the second.

1. $450, $4,500
2. $98, $1,960
3. $612, $9,000
4. $162.75, $3,875

(For additional help, see page 551.)

426   Chapter Thirteen

The answer 8.8% is reasonably close to the estimate 10% and is a sensible answer.
The current yield is 8.8%.

Municipal bonds are issued by local governments or government agencies. They usually offer lower interest than corporate bonds. The interest income from municipal bonds does not have to be reported for federal, state, or local income taxes.

Many newspapers carry bond market reports every day. A sample of such a report for Thursday is shown at the right.

Daily Bond Market Report Thursday, October 4				
Bonds	High	Low	Closing	Chg
AmMot 8½ 08	92¼	91¾	92⅛	−¼
AmOilCo 7¾ cv 99	101½	101	101	+½
DuMot 10 10	102⅛	101¾	102	...
EnCot 6¼ cv 98	64½	64½	64½	−⅛
Foley 8⅜ 06	91¾	90¾	91⅛	+1

The information for Foley Corp. is as follows:

Foley   Name of the corporation, usually abbreviated.

$8\frac{3}{8}$ Interest rate paid (8.375% of $1,000 = $83.75).

06   Maturity year of the bond; 06 means the year 2006 (cv 98 for EnCot means the interest is convertible to stock in 1998).

High   Highest percentage of par value reached that day.

Low   Lowest percentage of par value reached that day.

Closing   Percentage of par value as of market closing time ($91\frac{1}{8}$% of $1,000 = 0.91125 × $1,000 = $911.25).

Chg   Percent change between Thursday's closing and Wednesday's (Foley gained 1% of $1,000 = $10).

EXAMPLE 2

Laura purchased a DuMot Bond at the closing of the business day on Thursday. What is the current yield of this bond?

Step 1. Find the cost of the bond.

face value × closing percent = cost of bond
$1,000   ×   102%   = $1,020

Step 2. Find the interest from the bond.

face value × interest rate = interest
$1,000   ×   10%   = $100

Corporate and Municipal Bonds   **427**

Step 3. Find the current yield.

interest ÷ cost = current yield
$100 ÷ $1,020 = 0.0980 → 9.8%   Round to nearest
                                   tenth percent.

The current yield is 9.8%.

With a calculator, the computation for Example 2 can be simplified.

Key: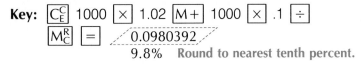
9.8%   Round to nearest tenth percent.

Class Exercises

Determine the current yield (to the nearest tenth of a percent) of each bond.

Quoted Price	Rate	Current Yield
$91\frac{3}{4}$	$9\frac{1}{2}\%$	**1.** ■
90	9%	**2.** ■
$103\frac{1}{2}$	$6\frac{3}{4}\%$	**3.** ■
$66\frac{1}{8}$	$8\frac{1}{4}\%$	**4.** ■

5. Use Thursday's daily bond market report to determine the current yield (to the nearest tenth of a percent) of an AmOilCo bond purchased at closing time.

EXERCISES

Complete the table below by finding the cost of the bond, annual interest of the bond, and current yield of the bond (to the nearest tenth of a percent).

Quoted Price	Cost of Bond	Interest Rate	Annual Interest	Current Yield
100	**1.** ■	9%	**2.** ■	**3.** ■
102	**4.** ■	10%	**5.** ■	**6.** ■
$66\frac{1}{4}$	**7.** ■	$7\frac{3}{8}\%$	**8.** ■	**9.** ■
$79\frac{5}{8}$	**10.** ■	$9\frac{1}{4}\%$	**11.** ■	**12.** ■
$104\frac{3}{8}$	**13.** ■	$10\frac{1}{2}\%$	**14.** ■	**15.** ■

Use Thursday's daily bond market report for Problems 16–24.

16. What is the closing price of EnCot?

17. In what year do AmMot bonds mature?

18. What was the highest selling price of DuMot bonds?

19. What was Wednesday's closing price for AmMot bonds?

20. What was the lowest selling price of AmMot?

21. What is the interest rate of EnCot?

22. Which of the bonds shown can be purchased at a discount?

23. Determine the current yield of AmMot purchased at the closing of the market on Thursday.

24. Determine the current yield of AmOilCo purchased Thursday at the highest selling price of the day.

25. Todd can purchase municipal bonds at $6\frac{1}{4}$% tax-free interest. His other income is taxed at a $35\frac{1}{2}$% combined federal, state, and local rate. What rate of interest (to the nearest tenth of a percent) must he get on a corporate bond in order to have a higher after-tax return than on a municipal bond?

26. Bring a current bond quotation to class and discuss the information given. Choose one bond and follow its closing price for several days. Report your findings to the class.

Using a Calculator: *Changing a Decimal to a Percent*

There is an easy way to use your calculator to write your answer as a percent when you are finding what percent one number is of another. For example, to find what percent $75 is of $852.50:

Key: $\boxed{\text{C}^\text{C}_\text{E}}$ 75 $\boxed{\div}$ 852.5 $\boxed{\times}$ 100 $\boxed{=}$ 8.79765

8.8% Round to nearest tenth and write %.

↑ Multiply by 100 to change to a percent.

Find what percent the first number is of the second.

1. $24, $88   **2.** $38, $250   **3.** $298, $10,340   **4.** $25.50, $997.55

Corporate and Municipal Bonds **429**

13-4 The Stock Market

Selling **stocks** is another method corporations use to raise money. If you buy stock you own a share of the corporation and can, if you want, participate in the company's policy and decision making. The value of a share of stock depends upon many things, including the size and image of the company. The state of the national economy, current interest rates, and even world events all affect stock prices. Stock prices are expressed in eighths of a dollar.

Unlike bonds, stocks do not mature. However, stocks do pay dividends to stockholders; these dividends depend on the profits of the company for the period covered by the dividend.

Stock is usually sold in lots of 100 units. An amount less than 100 units is called an *odd lot*. Most newspapers carry daily stock market reports, such as the one shown below, of stocks bought and sold on the stock exchange.

Daily Stock Market Report							
Thursday, October 4							
Name	**Div**	**PE**	**Sales**	**High**	**Low**	**Last**	**Chg**
ABT	.50	22	51	$33\frac{3}{4}$	$33\frac{1}{4}$	$33\frac{1}{4}$	$-\frac{1}{4}$
AFG	.92	18	350	$33\frac{5}{8}$	$32\frac{7}{8}$	$33\frac{5}{8}$	$+\frac{3}{4}$
AGCCo	1.20	25	225	28	$27\frac{7}{8}$	28	$-\frac{1}{8}$
AlumCo	2.92	10	1769	39	$38\frac{1}{2}$	$38\frac{7}{8}$	$-\frac{1}{4}$
AaFunCo	.98	21	2151	$60\frac{1}{2}$	$59\frac{3}{8}$	$60\frac{1}{4}$	$+\frac{1}{2}$
AraIn	2.10	14	1875	$21\frac{1}{8}$	$19\frac{3}{4}$	$20\frac{3}{4}$	$-\frac{3}{4}$
BaChefs	1.15	35	38	$88\frac{5}{8}$	$87\frac{7}{8}$	$87\frac{7}{8}$	...
BritOil	2.62	15	1650	$77\frac{3}{8}$	76	$76\frac{3}{8}$	$-1\frac{1}{8}$

The information for AGCCo is explained below:

AGCCo   The name of the company (usually abbreviated).

1.20   The current annual dividend based upon latest declaration.

25   PE, the price/earnings ratio. Divide the stock price by the company's latest 12-month earnings.

225   Number of 100 units sold in today's trading; means 22,500 stocks were sold today.

28   The highest price in dollars ($28) for one share today.

$27\frac{7}{8}$ The lowest price ($27.875) for one share today.

28   The last sale of the day ($28).

$-\frac{1}{8}$ The dollar change from yesterday's last sale; $-\frac{1}{8}$ means today's last sale was $.125 less than yesterday's last sale.

EXAMPLE 1

Chrissie wants to buy 200 shares of AlumCo's stock. If she gets them at the closing price, how much will she pay for them?

Problem Solving Strategy: Finding information.
Use the stock market report on page 430 to find the closing price of AlumCo: $38\frac{7}{8}$.

Think: $38\frac{7}{8} = \$38.875$

number of shares × cost per share = total cost
200 × $38.875 = $7,775

Her stock cost $7,775.

The current yield of a stock is the percent of dividend it pays. Current yield is found by dividing the dividend by the cost of a share.

EXAMPLE 2

What is the current yield on the stocks that Chrissie purchased?

Use the table on page 430 to find the dividend for her stock: $2.92.

dividend ÷ unit cost = current yield
$2.92 ÷ $38.875 = ■

```
            0.0751  → 7.5%   Round to nearest tenth percent.
$38 875)$2.920 0000
          2 721 25
            198 750
            194 375
              4 3750
              3 8875
                4875
```

Key: $\boxed{C_E^C}$ 2.92 $\boxed{÷}$ 38.875 $\boxed{=}$ 0.0751125

7.5%   Round to nearest tenth percent.

The current yield is 7.5%.

Chrissie bought her stock through a **stockbroker,** a person who makes a living buying and selling stocks. Every time a stock is bought or sold, the broker receives a commission. The table below gives a typical schedule of commissions for a stockbroker.

Typical Stockbroker Commissions	
Amount of Transaction	Rate of Commission
Less than $1,000	2.0% of sales
$1,000 to $2,500	1.5% of sales
Over $2,500	1.0% of sales

If you sell your stock when the price per share is higher than what you paid, you make a profit on the sale. If you sell when the price per share has dropped, you sell at a loss.

EXAMPLE 3

Several months after Chrissie bought her stock, the price was $46\frac{3}{4}$.
Would she make a profit or loss by selling it at that time?

Step 1. Find the buying price of Chrissie's stock.

$$\begin{array}{ccc} \text{value of stock} + & \text{commission} & = \text{buying price} \\ \$7,775 & + (1\% \times \$7,775) = & \$7,852.75 \end{array}$$

Step 2. Find the selling price of her stock.
The value of her stock is $200 \times 46\frac{3}{4}$.

Think: $46\frac{3}{4} = 46.75$
$200 \times \$46.75 = \$9,350$

$$\begin{array}{ccc} \text{value of stock} - & \text{commission} & = \text{selling price} \\ \$9,350 & - (1\% \times \$9,350) = & \$9,256.50 \end{array}$$

Step 3. Find the profit or loss.
Since she sold the stock for more than it cost her, she made a profit.

$$\$9,256.50 - \$7,852.75 = \$1,403.75$$

She made a profit of $1,403.75.

Class Exercises

Use the table on page 430 to answer the questions below.

1. For which stock(s) were fewer than 5,000 shares sold?

2. Which stock had the greatest advance over yesterday's closing price (last sale)?

3. Which stock was most active (had the greatest number of sales)? How many sales did it have?

4. How much would it cost to purchase 300 shares at the closing price of AaFunCo stock, without the commission?

5. What is the dividend for a share of BaChefs?

6. What is the current yield for ABT stock, purchased at the closing price?

7. Compute the total cost of 400 shares of BritOil stock at the closing price, including the commission.

EXERCISES

Use the table on page 430 to answer the questions below.

1. For which stock(s) were more than 100,000 shares sold?

2. Which stock lost the most in price between yesterday's closing and today's?

3. Which stock was the least active? How many sales did it have?

4. Which stock(s) had a gain of $.50 or more over yesterday's closing price?

5. Which stock had the lowest closing price?

Determine the cost of the stock at the close of the day.

Name	Number of Shares	Cost of Stock
AFG	100	6. ■
AraIn	300	7. ■
AGCCo	500	8. ■

Solve.

9. Explain how mental arithmetic can be used to find the answer to Exercise 6.

10. What is the current yield for AFG stock, purchased at the closing price?

11. What is the current yield for BritOil stock purchased at its highest price for the day?

Use the tables on pages 430 and 431 to complete the following. Assume that all stock is purchased at the close of the day.

Name	Number of Shares	Commission	Total Cost
AraIn	100	12. ■	13. ■
AGCCo	250	14. ■	15. ■
AaFunCo	600	16. ■	17. ■

18. Albert purchased 400 shares of stock at $45\frac{1}{2}$ per share and sold them a year later at $52\frac{1}{4}$. Compute the commissions using the table on page 431 and determine how much profit or loss he made.

19. Keisha purchased 320 shares of stock at $82\frac{1}{4}$ per share and sold them later at $88\frac{1}{2}$. Compute the commissions using the table on page 431 and determine how much profit or loss she made.

20. Tessa purchased 150 shares of stock at $62\frac{3}{4}$ per share. Her stock has been gaining each week. She would like to sell it when she can realize a profit. To what price must the stock rise so that, after paying the commissions, she can begin to get profit on the sale?

21. Many stock quotations list mutual funds. See if you can find out what mutual funds are and why an investor might choose to purchase them. Share your findings with the class.

Consumer Note: *The Stock Market*

A stock market is really a stock exchange, a place where stocks, bonds, or other securities are bought and sold according to fixed regulations. A stockholder is one who owns a share or shares of stock in a company. Stock markets are located in major cities around the world.

A share of what is known as "common stock" represents a part ownership in a corporation. If you buy 10 shares of stock in a company that has issued a total of 100 shares for sale, you actually own 10/100, or 10% of the company.

Career
Electrician

Electricians may work in construction or become supervisors or estimators. About one out of every four electricians is self-employed.

Profile of an electrician. An electrician usually has a high school education and also serves a 3- or 4-year apprenticeship, during which time he or she learns the mathematical and electrical knowledge and skills needed in addition to completing on-the-job training. Electricians read and use intricate meters and other measuring devices in their work.

The electrician's environment. Electricians generally work indoors, but there is some outdoor work. They may repair wiring in an older building or be involved with installing the meters and wiring in a new building. Although the unemployment rate in the construction industry is high, electrical workers are not laid off as often as other construction workers.

All in a day's work. Tina opened her own electrical shop. As profits rose, she decided to invest some of those profits to earn more for her business. With the extra earnings, she felt she would be able to expand her business. As a start, Tina decided to invest $1,000.

1. If Tina took out a 4-year certificate of deposit for $1,000, what would be its value at the end of 4 years? Use the tables on pages 418 and 419.

2. What is the face value of the savings bond Tina could purchase for $1,000?

3. If Tina were to buy a DuMot bond at closing on the day shown in the table on page 427, how much would it cost?

4. Tina could invest her money in a company whose stock was selling at $35\frac{1}{4}$. Disregarding the commission, how many shares of stock could she buy for $1,000 if she had to purchase a whole number of shares?

5. Tina decided to invest conservatively in order to avoid losing money if possible. She decided to invest in "Ginnie Maes," which are mortgages secured by the U.S. Government. They are classified as bonds, and the return on them is fixed. Tina found out she would receive $7 each month for her investment of $1,000. What is the annual rate of interest on this investment?

13-5 Savings Plans

Many workers put a percentage of their earnings into savings over a period of years. Rather than placing money in a savings account yourself, you may have money withheld from your paychecks and deposited in savings automatically. Such a savings plan is called a **payroll savings plan.**

EXAMPLE 1

Julius has an annual salary of $16,380. If he has 4% of his salary deducted for savings, how much is placed in savings each month?

> **Hidden Question:** What is Julius's monthly salary?
> $16,380 ÷ 12 = $1,365

> **monthly salary × percent saved = monthly savings**
> $1,365   ×   4%   = $54.60

Of Julius's monthly salary, $54.60 will be put in savings.

The following table can be used to help determine how much will have accumulated in a savings account through regular savings and interest accumulation. It is based on saving $1 each month at annual yields ranging from 6% to 9.5%. To determine the amount accumulated if more is deposited monthly, multiply the table value for $1 by the regular monthly savings.

Accumulated Value of Regular Savings at $1.00 per Month Saved

Number of Months	Annual Interest Rate							
	6%	6.5%	7%	7.5%	8%	8.5%	9%	9.5%
12	12.336	12.364	12.392	12.421	12.450	12.478	12.507	12.537
24	25.432	25.556	25.681	25.807	25.933	26.060	26.188	26.317
36	39.336	39.632	39.930	40.231	40.535	40.842	41.152	41.466
48	54.098	54.650	55.209	55.776	56.349	56.930	57.519	58.117
60	69.770	70.674	71.592	72.527	73.476	74.441	75.422	76.422
120	163.878	168.404	173.083	177.931	182.944	188.133	193.508	199.080
180	290.817	303.547	316.958	331.113	346.034	361.773	378.392	395.946
240	462.038	490.425	520.919	553.732	589.012	626.972	667.858	711.918
300	692.989	748.844	810.058	877.264	951.010	1032.010	1121.060	1219.050
360	1004.510	1106.190	1219.950	1347.450	1490.330	1650.610	1830.640	2033.010

EXAMPLE 2

If Julius were to save $54.60 every month for 20 years, at 6% interest, how much will be accumulated at the end of that time?

> **Hidden Question:** How many months in 20 years?
> 20 y = 20 × 12 = 240 mo

$$\text{monthly savings} \times \text{table value} = \text{amount accumulated}$$
$$\$54.60 \quad \times \quad 462.038 \quad = \quad \blacksquare$$

└─Look across the row labeled 240 and
under the column labeled 6%.

$$
\begin{array}{r}
462.038 \\
\times \ \$54.60 \\
\hline
277\ 22280 \\
1\ 848\ 152 \\
23\ 101\ 90 \\
\hline
\$25,227.27480 \\
\$25,277.27 \\
\end{array}
$$
Round to nearest cent.

Key: $\boxed{C^{C}_{E}}$ 462.038 $\boxed{\times}$ 54.6 $\boxed{=}$ ⟋⟋ 25227.274 ⟋⟋

$25,227.27   Round to
nearest cent.

Julius's investment will be worth $25,227.27 in 20 years.

The table can also be used to help determine a savings plan designed to reach a specified goal.

EXAMPLE 3

Rebecca would like to have $10,000 saved at the end of 10 years. If she can get 6.5% interest, how much should she deposit every month to achieve this goal?

> **Hidden Question:** How many months are there in 10 years?
> $$10 \text{ y} = 10 \times 12 = 120 \text{ mo}$$

$$\text{savings goal} \div \text{table value} = \text{monthly value}$$
$$\$10,000 \quad \div \quad 168.404 \quad = \quad \blacksquare$$

└─Look in the row labeled 120 under the
column labeled 6.5%.

Key: $\boxed{C^{C}_{E}}$ 10000 $\boxed{\div}$ 168.404 $\boxed{=}$ ⟋⟋ 59.381012 ⟋⟋

$59.38   *Round to nearest cent.*

Rebecca needs to save $59.38 each month to reach her goal.

Class Exercises

Determine the monthly amount deducted for savings for each employee.

Employee Name	Annual Salary	Percent Deducted for Savings	Monthly Deduction
Tess Wilkes	$24,000	5%	**1.** ■
Wendell Norris	$21,500	6%	**2.** ■

Save for a su
day.

Buy U.S. Savings Bonds.

Use the table on page 435 to find the accumulated savings.

Monthly Amount	Interest Rate	Number of Years	Accumulated Savings
$10	9%	10	**3.** ■
$40	6.5%	15	**4.** ■

Use the table on page 435 to determine the monthly savings needed to reach the savings goals.

Savings Goal	Interest Rate	Number of Years	Monthly Amount Needed
$ 5,000	6%	10	**5.** ■
$15,000	7.5%	20	**6.** ■
$90,000	8%	30	**7.** ■

EXERCISES

Determine the monthly amount deducted for savings for each employee.

Employee Name	Annual Salary	Percent Deducted for Savings	Monthly Deduction
Lasha Smith	$12,000	10%	**1.** ■
Nolan Krandall	$18,000	5%	**2.** ■
Selig Daniels	$16,700	4.5%	**3.** ■
Connie Abrams	$26,900	7%	**4.** ■

Use the table on page 435 to find the accumulated savings.

Monthly Amount	Interest Rate	Number of Years	Accumulated Savings
$100	7.5%	10	**5.** ■
$ 65	7%	25	**6.** ■
$ 80	8.5%	30	**7.** ■
$ 18.75	9%	20	**8.** ■

9. Which of Exercises 1–8 could be done mentally? In which would pencil and paper be appropriate? Which could best be done by using a calculator?

Use the table on page 435 to determine the monthly savings needed to reach each savings goal.

Savings Goal	Interest Rate	Number of Years	Monthly Amount Needed
$ 5,000	$6\frac{1}{2}\%$	10	**10.** ■
$ 25,000	7.5%	30	**11.** ■
$100,000	9.5%	30	**12.** ■

Solve.

13. Name: Roger Abraza
Goal: $75,000
Interest rate: 9%
Number of years: 25
Monthly amount: ■

14. Name: Carlton Maris
Goal: $65,000
Interest rate: ■
Number of years: 20
Monthly amount: $132.54

15. Name: Nickie Cransott
Goal: $50,000
Interest rate: 7.5%
Number of years: ■
Monthly amount: $37.11

16. Albert placed $30 in savings each month for 25 years at 7% interest. At the end of that period, how much interest had his money earned?

17. Olivia has placed $45 in savings each month for 30 years at 6% interest. After this time how much interest has her money earned?

18. Ivy has contributed the same amount each month to her savings account for 20 years at an interest rate of 6.5%. Her bank has informed her that her money has earned total interest of $13,465.32. About how much has she contributed each month?

Challenge

ABCBA Corp. offers a savings plan through which an employee can have up to 5% of his or her salary withheld for savings and the company will deposit an equal amount into the account. Employees can often choose to have more than 5% withheld for savings, but the company will match only the first 5%.

Last year Elaine had 10% withheld from her gross annual salary of $23,750 for savings. The company matched 5% of her salary.

1. How much did Elaine contribute to the savings plan?

2. How much did the company contribute to Elaine's account?

3. How much had Elaine and the company contributed to her account by the end of the year?

Computer:
BASIC Programming

Antonio has written a program to calculate accumulated savings from regular deposits over a period of years. The following formula computes the value accumulated for $1: $A = [(1 + I)^N - 1]/I$

    A is the amount accumulated for regular $1 deposits

    I is the annual interest rate divided by number of deposits per year

    N is the number of deposits per year times the number of years

In BASIC raising a number to a power is done using the caret (^) key. The expression $Y = A \char`^ B$ causes the number A to be raised to the power B and to be stored as Y.

10 HOME	Clears the screen.
20 INPUT "WHAT IS THE REGULAR SAVINGS AMOUNT?"; AM	Accepts the amount of the regular deposit.
30 INPUT "WHAT IS THE INTEREST IN DECIMAL FORM?"; IN	Accepts the amount of interest expressed in decimal form.
40 INPUT "HOW MANY DEPOSITS PER YEAR?"; P	Accepts the number of deposits per year.
50 I = IN/P	Divides the annual interest rate by number of deposits per year.
60 PRINT "YEARS", "ACCUMULATED AMOUNT"	Prints the headings.
70 FOR YR = 1 TO 30	Opens the loop to calculate by years.
80 N = YR * P	Converts years to periods.
90 A = ((1 + I) ^ N - 1) / I	Computes the amount accumulated for $1.
100 PRINT YR, A*AM	Prints the year and the total amount.
110 IF YR/15 = INT(YR/15) THEN GOTO 130	Displays 15 lines of the output on the screen until the Enter key is pressed.
120 NEXT YR	Closes the loop.
130 END	Tells the computer to end the program.

EXERCISES

RUN the program above using the following data sets.

Amount Deposited	Interest Rate	Deposits per Year
1. 100	0.07	4
2. 150	0.095	6

Decision Making:
Investing in Tomorrow

Chris has been watching a TV program called *Investment Week*. An investment analyst said that people could become financially independent by making their money work for them. The analyst went on to say that all people, even teenagers, are investors.

The analyst continued, "Money comes either through gifts or through earnings. It may be totally spent on or invested in today's needs and wants or partially invested in today and partially invested in tomorrow. It is through the investments in tomorrow, though, that money is made to work for people. Actually, there is no choice about being an investor or not, but how people choose to invest their money can make all the difference."

Chris was excited because he had just inherited $1,300 from his aunt, and the program was giving him some new ideas about how best to use this gift. However, he was not sure he understood what the analyst meant by investing in today. He asked his friend Rob what he thought the analyst meant.

Rob replied, "I think what she means is that if you decide to buy a stereo, you are investing in your need for entertainment today. If you put savings in a savings account you are investing in tomorrow."

Answer the following questions.

1. Have you ever thought of yourself as an investor? Explain your answer.

2. Given the analyst's idea that all money spent is invested, review what you currently do with your money. List your "investments" for the past 4 weeks under the headings "Today" and "Tomorrow."

3. Does treating each expenditure as an investment make sense to you? Give reasons that support your answer.

4. Review the items listed under the heading "Tomorrow."
   a. What influenced your choice of investments in this list?
   b. Are you satisfied with the quantity of investments in tomorrow?
   c. Would you make any changes in your list for tomorrow? Why or why not?

5. What was your thinking process as you answered each part of Question 4?

SETTING GOALS

Chris realized that investing in tomorrow involves setting goals and making decisions. He also learned from watching *Investment Week* that teenagers have a special advantage because even a small investment at this point in their earning careers has time to grow.

In thinking about his inheritance, Chris decided that he was willing to invest $1,000 in tomorrow. He wanted to keep $300 to use for expenses during the coming year.

Answer the following questions.

6. What are some basic decisions that you might make now about investing in tomorrow?

7. How did you think of these decisions?

8. Discuss your answers to Question 6 with classmates. Make additions to your list, if you wish.

9. How do you think Chris might have arrived at his decision to invest only $1,000? What factors might have influenced his decision?

10. How might Chris decide on the amount to be held out for expenses during the coming year? What thinking steps would he use to determine that amount?

11. Think as Chris might of three things that he would need 5 years from now and that could be paid for in whole or in part through a $1,000 investment. Share your list with two other students.

12. Choose an item on your list as the goal of the investment process. Write a statement that includes the goal, the investment amount, and the term of the investment.

IDENTIFYING OPTIONS

Chris knew that he would have to identify what options were open to him in investing his money. In watching *Investment Week,* he learned that the analyst recommended certificates of deposit (CDs), stocks, municipal bonds, and savings bonds.

Following the recommendations of the analyst, Chris gathered data on actual interest rates and regulations for each type of investment. He obtained the following information for a $1,000 investment.

- CD: 5-year term available; 7.75% interest rate; 3-month simple interest penalty for any early withdrawal.

- Stock: 2% commission for transactions less than $500. From the stock column in the newspaper:

	Div	PE	Sales	High	Low	Last	Chg
Dta Dsg	.24	2.5	9	$10\frac{1}{2}$	$9\frac{3}{8}$	$9\frac{3}{4}$	$-\frac{1}{4}$

  Data Design (Dta Dsg) is a new growth industry that makes computer programs for the production of telephone books and other directories. 100 shares @ $9\frac{3}{4}$; add 2.5% per year, since stock will keep up with the real rate of inflation; add $1 per share after 5 years, since Data Design is a growth industry.

- Municipal Bond: 10-year term is the shortest term available for a $1,000 bond; quoted price = $99\frac{1}{4}$; 5.2%.

- Series EE Savings Bond: $100 bonds available; 6% compounded semiannually; no penalty for early withdrawal.

Answer the following questions.

13. List some contacts that Chris could make to gather information.

For each investment method listed, calculate the earnings on $1,000 for 5 years using Chris's data.

14. Stock   **15.** Municipal bond

16. CD (refer to the table on page 419)

17. Savings bonds (refer to the table on page 423)

COMPARING INVESTMENTS

Chris found he had a lot of information and knew he might have a hard time making a choice. He talked to Rob, expressing his concerns about making the best choice. He said, "Putting my money in a CD seems very safe, but I am not sure it is the best investment. Stocks seem like a good investment, yet the stock market can go down suddenly so that I might not make money—or I might even lose it. Municipal bonds and savings bonds seem very safe, but I wonder if I could make as much money as with other investments." Rob asked, "Have you listed your investing goals? Perhaps you could list what you feel are the pros and cons of each kind of investment."

Answer the following questions.

18. List the goals that Chris might have in creating an investment plan.

19. List the advantages, disadvantages and degree of risk of each type of investment. Share your findings with your classmates.

MAKING A CHOICE

Chris examined the results of his research and decided the CD would be the best investment for meeting his goals. One thing he thought about as he decided was a phrase used on *Investment Week*—"Don't put your eggs in one basket." He recalled that the analyst often advised that it was wise to have a diversified portfolio. However, Chris felt that, for the amount of his investment, the CD was the best choice.

Answer the following questions.

20. Relate the analyst's advice about investing to Chris's investment decision.

21. Will the CD earnings satisfy the goal you stated in Question 12? If not, why not?

22. Would it be wise for Chris to diversify his investment? Find arguments for and against his doing this and share these with the rest of the class.

23. Describe to another student the steps of the thought process which you used to answer Question 22. Have the student write down the steps briefly as you speak. Reverse the tasks of the exercise.

DECIDING FOR YOURSELF

Collect data from local businesses on each type of investment that Chris considered. Which investment would you make, based on your research? Summarize the steps that you, and Chris, followed in deciding on an investment.

Chapter 13 Review

VOCABULARY

annual yield	discount	premium
bond	face value	quoted price
certificate of deposit	par value	stock
corporate bonds	payroll savings plan	stockbroker
current yield		

For Exercises 1–9, select the word(s) that complete each statement.

1. A savings account that pays more interest than a regular passbook account but requires you to leave your money on deposit for a fixed period of time is called a _____ .

2. A _____ is a promise by the borrower to repay a loan at a specified rate of interest.

3. The _____ of a bond is the value printed on the bond itself.

4. The face value of corporate bonds is called the _____ .

5. When the quoted price of a bond is more than its face value, the bond is said to sell at a _____ .

6. The _____ of a bond is the interest divided by the cost.

7. If you buy _____ , you own a share of a corporation.

8. The amount of simple interest the bank would have to offer to yield the same amount of interest as in a certificate account is called the _____ .

9. Bonds issued by corporations are called _____ .

SKILLS

Find each product.

10. $2,500 × 2.54

11. $18,675 × 1.752

12. $48,250 × 1.0065

Find what percent the first number is of the second.

13. $480, $6,000

14. $127.50, $2,500

15. $288.75, $3,850

Express each fraction as a decimal.

16. $\frac{1}{2}$

17. $\frac{3}{8}$

18. $\frac{7}{16}$

Find each percent.

19. 4% of $1,298

20. 38% of $5,469

21. 7.5% of $11,500

CONSUMER TOPICS

Solve. Use the table on page 419.

22. Find the annual yield of a 3-year certificate that pays 8% interest.

23. Gary decided to take out a 3-year certificate of deposit which was paying 6.75%. He deposited $1,500. How much interest will his account have earned at the time of maturity?

24. How much would the penalty be if Gary withdrew the original amount deposited before his certificate matured?

25. Dwayne purchased a savings bond with a face value of $200. What was the cost of the bond?

26. Determine the current yield (to the nearest tenth of a percent) of a bond with a par value of $1,000, if the quoted price is $78\frac{1}{8}$ and the rate is $7\frac{1}{4}$.

Use the information below from a daily Stock Market Report to answer Problems 27 and 28.

Name	Div	PE	Sales	High	Low	Last	Chg
MBDCo	1.15	35	125	$84\frac{5}{8}$	$83\frac{7}{8}$	$84\frac{1}{2}$	$+\frac{1}{4}$

27. Find the current yield of the stock.

28. Marcia bought 100 shares of MBDCo stock at the closing price listed above. How much did the stock cost her?

29. How much did Marcia have to pay for the purchase of the stock if her broker charged her 1% commission?

30. Marcia later sold her stock for $84\frac{3}{4}$. She had to pay a 1% commission on the sale. What was Marcia's profit or loss by selling her stock at that time?

Solve. Use the table on page 435 for Problems 31 and 32.

31. Find the amount you would have to save each month to accumulate $8,000 at 7% interest at the end of 10 years.

32. Determine how much would be accumulated at the end of 5 years at 7% interest if Ignatius saved $40 every month.

33. Brenda has an annual salary of $16,500. If she has 5% of her salary deducted for savings, how much is placed in savings each month?

Chapter 13 Test

Use the table on page 419 for Problems 1–3.

1. Opal decided to take out a 2-year certificate of deposit which was paying 7.25%. She deposited $2,000. How much interest will she have in her account at the time of maturity?

2. What is the annual yield on Opal's certificate of deposit?

3. How much would the penalty be if Opal withdrew the original amount deposited before her certificate matured?

4. Mario purchased a savings bond with a face value of $300. What was the cost of the bond?

Use the table on page 423 for Problems 5 and 6. The interest on the mature bonds in this table is 6% compounded semi-annually.

5. Theo purchased a $300 Series EE bond and cashed it in 5 years after he purchased it. How much was the accrued interest on the bond?

6. How much would a Series EE bond with a face value of $200 be worth after 14 years?

7. Determine the current yield (to the nearest tenth of a percent) of a bond with a par value of $1,000 that has a quoted price of $82\frac{1}{4}$ and a rate of $6\frac{3}{4}$.

8. Naomi bought 200 shares of CBAA at the closing price shown below. How much did she pay for the stock?

Name	Div	PE	Sales	High	Low	Last	Chg
CBAA	.90	15	72	$35\frac{1}{8}$	$34\frac{1}{4}$	$34\frac{7}{8}$	$-\frac{1}{4}$

9. Naomi (Problem 8) had to pay her broker a 1% commission. How much did the stock cost Naomi in all?

10. Naomi (Problems 8 and 9) later sold her stock for $35\frac{1}{4}$ through the same broker. How much profit or loss did she make?

11. Kevin has an annual salary of $21,700. If he has 7% of his salary deducted for savings, how much is placed in savings each week?

12. Lucas has $35 a month deducted through his payroll savings plan. How much will his account be worth at the end of 4 years if he is receiving 6.5% interest? Use the table on page 435.

13. Use the table on page 435 to determine the monthly savings necessary to save $15,000 in 20 years at 7%.

Cumulative Mixed Review

Select the letter corresponding to the correct answer.

1. Jack worked 48 hours for $6.50 an hour and time-and-a-half for overtime (over 40 h). If 25% of his gross earnings were withheld for deductions, what was the net amount of his paycheck for the week?
a. $234
b. $253.50
c. $202.31
d. $84.50

2. Paula bought a sofa for $650 and made 24 payments of $38.45. How much did she pay in interest?
a. $922.80
b. $65.53
c. $27.08
d. $272.80

3. Pete borrowed $3,000 for 3 months at an annual interest rate of 10.5%. How much did he have to repay at the end of 3 months?
a. $78.75
b. $315
c. $3,078.75
d. $3,315

4. Jaime's transportation expenditures for three months were $75.80, $82.50, and $84. What is his average monthly expense for transportation?
a. $20.19
b. $80
c. $80.77
d. $242.30

5. Don makes 6 payments a year of $198.50 for his auto insurance. How much must he budget weekly to cover this fixed expense?
a. $22.90
b. $99.25
c. $1,191
d. $33.08

6. Sheila's phone service costs her $21.50 per month. If she averages $6.50 per month for long-distance calls, what is her annual expense for telephone?
a. $258
b. $168
c. $28
d. $336

7. Fred bought a 24-oz can of juice for $2.30. What was the unit cost?
a. $55.20
b. $9.58
c. $.19
d. $.096

8. Janet and Rick have combined annual gross earnings of $27,500. What is the maximum amount they should consider spending for the purchase of a house?
a. $68,750
b. $6,875
c. $27,500
d. $2,750

9. Lila has a 3-year lease that requires her to pay $325 rent per month. What is the total amount she will pay for rent during the term of her lease?
a. $3,900
b. $11,700
c. $975
d. $1,170

10. Bob's gross income is $19,500. His medical expenses for the year amounted to $746.50. If he can deduct only the amount over $7\frac{1}{2}$% of his gross income for medical expenses, how much can he deduct for medical expenses?
a. $746.50
b. $1,462.50
c. $0
d. $716

CHAPTER 14
Buying Insurance

Russell wants to buy life insurance. He is 34 years old, married, and working as a computer programmer. He called an insurance agent to get information and learned that he had to decide what kind of policy he wanted: ordinary life insurance, term insurance, limited-payment life insurance, or endowment insurance. Russell made an appointment to meet with the insurance agent to discuss his options.

- What factors should Russell be concerned about when buying life insurance?

- What questions do you think he should ask the agent?

- Why do you think it would be important for Russell to have life insurance?

- How should he determine what kind of policy to buy?

What factors would you consider when thinking about buying life insurance?

14-1 Health Insurance

Because of rising medical costs, it is helpful if you have some kind of **health insurance**. If you have health insurance, you or your employer (or both) make payments each month to the insurance company. In return, your insurance company will pay for some or all of the bill if you are hospitalized or have major medical expenses. Most health insurance plans include full or partial payment for hospital rooms and services, surgery, and follow-up visits to the doctor.

Craig's health insurance has a **deductible** clause that requires him to pay the first $150 of covered medical costs for any given year. After that, the insurance company will pay 80% of the remaining cost.

EXAMPLE 1

Craig was in the hospital for 5 days, and his bill was $2,180. If he had not yet paid any deductible for the year, how much of the bill did Craig have to pay?

Think: Insurance pays 80%, Craig pays 100% − 80% = 20%.

deductible	+	20% of remainder	= patient cost
$150	+	20%($2,180 − $150) =	■
$150	+	$406	= $556

Craig had to pay $556 for his hospital stay.

Most employers have a *group health plan* in which an employee and the employee's spouse and family may enroll. Often the employer pays all or part of the health insurance premiums.

EXAMPLE 2

Craig enrolled himself and his wife in his health plan. The premium is $1,280 per year and his employer pays 75%. The remainder is deducted from Craig's weekly wages. How much is deducted each week for health insurance?

Step 1. Find Craig's annual cost.

annual premium	− employer's share	= employee's cost
$1,280	− (75% × $1,280) =	■
$1,280	− $960	= $320

Problem Solving Strategy: Solving another way.
You can think of the employee's cost as 100% − 75% = 25%.
$$25\% \times \$1,280 = \tfrac{1}{4} \times \$1,280 = \$320$$

Step 2. Find the weekly cost.

yearly cost ÷ 52 = weekly cost
$320 ÷ 52 = $6.153 → $6.15   Round to nearest cent.

Each week, $6.15 is deducted from Craig's check.

With a calculator, you can simplify the computation in Example 2.

Key: [C$_E^C$] 1280 [M+] [×] 75 [%] [M−] [M$_C^R$] [÷] 52 [=]   6.1538461
$6.15   Round to nearest cent.

One insurance company offers health insurance for individuals, couples (employee and spouse), and families. Their rate schedule is shown in the following table.

Health Insurance Rate Schedule	
Coverage	**Annual Premium**
Individual	$ 975
Couple	$1,280
Family	$1,850
Maternity benefits	$ 200 extra

EXAMPLE 3

Madge enrolled her family in her health plan. She also added maternity benefits to her coverage. Her employer pays $125 per month towards its employees' health insurance premiums. Using the rate schedule in the table above, determine how much is deducted from her semimonthly wages for health insurance.

> **Hidden Question:** How many pay periods are there? Semimonthly means twice a month: 2 × 12 = 24

Step 1. Find the total premium.

family premium + maternity premium = total premium
$1,850   + $200   = $2,050

Step 2. Find the employer's contribution.

monthly contribution × 12 = employer's contribution
$125   × 12 = $1,500

Step 3. Find the employee cost per pay period.

(total premium − employer's contribution) ÷ 24 = employee cost
($2,050   − $1,500)   ÷ 24 =   ■
$550   ÷ 24 = $22.92   Round to nearest cent.

Each pay period, $22.92 is deducted from Madge's check.

Class Exercises

Determine the patient's share of the hospital bill.

Patient	Hospital Bill	Deductible Amount	Percent Paid by Insurance	Amount Paid by Patient
Clarke	$1,100	$100	80%	1. ■
Stegmeyer	$1,800	$250	80%	2. ■

Determine the amount deducted from each employee's wages per pay period for health insurance. Use the table on page 451.

Employee	Type	Premium	Percent Paid by Employer	Number of Pay Periods	Amount Deducted
Wiggins	Individual	3. ■	60%	12	4. ■
Hope	Couple	5. ■	90%	24	6. ■
Wainwright	Family	7. ■	80%	52	8. ■

EXERCISES

Determine the patient's share of the hospital bill.

Patient	Hospital Bill	Deductible Amount	Percent Paid by Insurance	Amount Paid by Patient
Whipple	$1,000	$200	75%	1. ■
Jeffries	$1,250	$250	65%	2. ■
Carter	$2,450	$150	80%	3. ■
Patterson	$4,380	$200	85%	4. ■

5. Explain how mental arithmetic can be used to find the answer to Exercise 1.

Determine the amount deducted from each employee's wages per pay period for health insurance. Use the table on page 451.

Employee	Type	Premium	Percent Paid by Employer	Number of Pay Periods	Amount Deducted
Wright	Couple	6. ■	50%	12	7. ■
Cheng	Family	8. ■	70%	52	9. ■
Donlan	Individual	10. ■	65%	26	11. ■
Zerheusen	Family	12. ■	88%	24	13. ■

Solve.

14. Amber Shaw
Salary: $15,800
Percent spent on health insurance: 4
Health insurance cost: ■

15. Brandon Olsen
Salary: $14,200
Percent spent on health insurance: ■
Health insurance cost: $781

16. Crystal has a health insurance plan with a premium of $1,400. The plan pays 80% of health costs after a $250 deductible. Her employer pays 70% of her premium. Last year she had one hospital stay that cost $2,800. What were her total personal health expenses for the year?

17. Wylie's share of medical expenses for an operation was $846 including the deductible. His health insurance has a $150 deductible amount and pays 85% of the remainder. How much was Wylie's total hospital bill?

18. Tiffany's health insurance plan requires a $250 deductible amount and pays 75% of the remainder. One year she had medical bills totaling $2,125.95. She used her calculator to compute her share. Study her keystrokes and answer the questions that follow.

Key: $\boxed{C_E^C}$ 2125.95 $\boxed{-}$ 250 $\boxed{=}$ $\boxed{\times}$ 25 $\boxed{\%}$ $\boxed{+}$ 250 $\boxed{=}$ 718.9875

a. Explain her procedure.
b. What keystroke(s) would change if she had a $150 deductible amount instead of $250?
c. What keystroke(s) would change if her insurance company paid 85% of the remainder?

19. Find out about different kinds of available health insurance. List some advantages and disadvantages of each type.

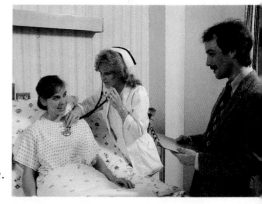

Consumer Note: *Health Care Plans*

Health care plans help offset the high cost of good medical care. Health insurance and health maintenance organizations (HMOs) are two of the best-known types of health care plans available today.

Many people are covered by health insurance plans where they work. These plans are group insurance policies, and the employer and employees share the cost of the insurance premiums. Some people must buy private health insurance and pay much higher individual premiums. Most health insurance plans allow enrollees to choose their own doctors. After a specified deductible, the plans normally pay 80% of the medical bills and the insured pays the remaining 20%.

HMOs are managed health care plans that provide both health insurance and health services through one organization. Consumers pay a fixed monthly fee and a small payment (usually $2 to $5) at the time medical services are rendered. However, participants must use the HMO's doctors and health care facilities in order to be covered.

14-2 Term Life Insurance

Life insurance is designed to provide financial security to your family. The person buying the life insurance names a **beneficiary,** to whom the **face value** of the policy will be paid in the event of the insured person's death.

There are several different kinds of insurance. *Term insurance* provides coverage for a given length of time, usually 5 or 10 years. At the end of that time the policy expires and may be renewed for another term at a higher premium. The premiums are based on the probability of the death of a person at a given age. This probability depends on both the age and sex of the person. It is lower for women than for men because women tend to live longer than men, and it rises as the person grows older. Term life insurance is purchased in units of $1,000. The premium remains fixed for the term of the policy. A sample rate schedule is shown at the right.

Annual Premiums for 5-Year Term Life Insurance		
Age		Premium per $1,000
M	F	
20	23	$ 6.55
25	28	$ 6.88
30	33	$ 7.43
35	38	$ 8.23
40	43	$ 9.76
45	48	$12.03
50	53	$16.55
55	58	$23.80
60	63	$32.19

EXAMPLE 1

Tony and Sally each decide to take out a $15,000, 5-year term life policy. Tony is 25 and Sally is 23. How much is their combined premium?

> **Hidden Question:** How many $1,000s in $15,000?
> $15,000 ÷ $1,000 = 15

	rate per thousand	× number of thousands	= premium
Tony:	$6.88	× 15	= $103.20
Sally:	$6.55	× 15	= + 98.25
			$201.45
			Total premium

Their total premium is $201.45.

EXAMPLE 2

How much will Tony and Sally have paid in premiums over the term of the policy?

annual cost × term of policy = total cost
$201.45 × 5 = $1,007.25

The total cost over the term of the policy will be $1,007.25.

EXAMPLE 3

Tony and Sally expect to keep term insurance for 15 years and then take out another type of life insurance. After each 5-year term, they must renew at the rates for their current ages. How much will they pay in premiums over the 15-year period?

Problem Solving Strategy: Organizing information.
You can organize your work in a table.

5-Year Term	Tony			Sally		
	Age	Premium	5-Year Total	Age	Premium	5-Year Total
1st	25	$6.88	$516.00	23	$6.55	$491.25
2nd	30	$7.43	$557.25	28	$6.88	$516.00
3rd	35	$8.23	$617.25	33	$7.43	$557.25
Totals			$1,690.50			$1,564.50

Together, they will pay

$$\$1,690.50 + \$1,564.50 = \$3,255$$

They will pay $3,255 in premiums.

Insurance companies base their premiums upon highly detailed statistics concerning the *mortality,* or death, rates of the general population. They keep very careful records and develop mortality tables for every year. For males, mortality rates are based upon 10,000,000 live births. For females, they are based upon 10,014,000 live births—the corresponding number of females born. Mortality tables give figures for all ages up to 99 years old. One line of a mortality table for a recent year is shown below.

Age		Number Living	Deaths During Year	Death Rate per 1,000	Years Expected to Live
M	F				
61	64	7,542,106	167,736	22.24	15.44

EXAMPLE 4

Find the probability that a 64-year old female will live until age 65.

number of deaths ÷ number living = probability of dying
167,736 ÷ 7,542,106 = ■

Key: $\boxed{C_E^C}$ 167736 $\boxed{÷}$ 7542106 $\boxed{=}$ ⟋ 0.0222399 ⟋

0.022   Round to nearest thousandth.

$$1 - \text{probability of dying} = \text{probability of living}$$
$$1 - \quad 0.022 \quad = \quad \blacksquare$$

Think: $1 - 0.022 = 0.978$
She has a probability of about 0.978, or about 98 out of 100, of living to be 65.

Class Exercises

Use the table on page 454 to determine the annual premium for term life insurance.

Sex	Age	Face Value	Premium
Female	28	$10,000	*1.* 
Female	43	$18,000	*2.* ■
Male	20	$25,000	*3.* ■
Male	55	$50,000	*4.* ■

Solve.

5. Marcie purchased $25,000 of 5-year term insurance. She was 28 when she purchased it. Using the table on page 454, determine how much she will pay in premiums over the term of the insurance.

6. In a recent year, mortality tables showed there were 9,188,526 living 36-year-old males. Of that number, 25,104 were expected to die that year. What was the probability (to the nearest thousandth) that a 36-year-old man would die within the year?

EXERCISES

Use the table on page 454 to determine the annual premium for term life insurance.

Sex	Age	Face Value	Premium
Male	20	$10,000	*1.* ■
Female	33	$20,000	*2.* ■
Female	58	$45,000	*3.* ■
Female	48	$19,000	*4.* ■
Male	45	$65,000	*5.* ■
Male	25	$50,000	*6.* ■

Use the table on page 454 to determine both the annual premium and the total 5-year premium for term life insurance.

Sex	Age	Face Value	Annual Premium	5-Year Total
Female	23	$13,000	7. ■	8. ■
Female	53	$10,000	9. ■	10. ■
Male	30	$12,000	11. ■	12. ■
Female	43	$15,000	13. ■	14. ■
Male	35	$75,000	15. ■	16. ■

Solve.

17. Bob and Jane Nestor
His age: 25
Her age: 23
Coverage for each: $18,000
Combined annual premium: ■

18. Tim and Eleanor Lopez
Her age: 33
His age: 40
Coverage for each: $35,000
Combined annual premium: ■

19. Krystena and Jon Gulak
His age: 45
Her age: 43
Coverage for each: ■
Combined annual premium: $348.64

20. Sandy and Rudy Castillo
Her age: 28
His age: 30
Coverage for each: ■
Combined annual premium: $286.20

21. Show how you would use a calculator to simplify the computation for Exercise 17.

22. In a recent year, mortality tables showed that out of 883,520 living 52-year-old females, 6,718 would be expected to die within the year. What is the probability of such a person dying within the year?

23. In a recent year, mortality tables showed that out of 912,316 living 44-year-old males, 4,501 would be expected to die within the year. What is the probability of such a person living to age 45?

24. Winona took out a 5-year term life insurance policy when she started working at 23. When the term expired, she renewed the policy and increased the face value by $5,000. After 10 years, she had paid a total of $1,246.40 in premiums. What was the original face value of her policy?

Mixed Review

1. Scott worked 48 hours one week at a regular rate of $6.74 with time-and-a-half for all hours over 40. What was his gross weekly pay?

2. What is Heather's annual gross income if she is paid biweekly and the gross amount she receives per pay period is $450?

14-3 Other Types of Life Insurance

There are other types of life insurance that you might want to consider buying. Term insurance expires at the end of the term, but most other types of insurance cover you for the rest of your life. These types of insurance have other benefits that make them an important part of your financial planning.

There are several types of regular life insurance.

- *Whole-life,* or *ordinary-life,* insurance covers the insured for his or her entire life. The premiums remain fixed and the insurance policy develops a *cash value* as premiums are paid.

- *Limited-payment life* insurance is similar to whole life, but only a limited number of premiums are paid, usually for 20 or 30 years. At that time the insured remains covered; the policy is *paid up.*

- *Endowment life* is similar to limited-payment insurance. Premiums are paid for a limited number of years, usually 20 or 30. At the conclusion of that time, the face value of the policy is paid to the insured.

Should the insured person die while any of these policies are in effect, the insurance company pays the face value of the policy to the insured person's beneficiaries. The table below gives a sample of premiums for different types of life insurance. The premiums, however, may vary with the health and occupation of the insured person.

Sample of Life Insurance Premiums: Annual Premiums per $1,000 of Insurance				
Age			20-Payment Life	20-Year Endowment
M	F	Whole-Life		
20	23	$12.98	$24.75	$44.62
25	28	$15.45	$27.18	$45.13
30	33	$18.04	$30.25	$45.98
35	38	$21.48	$33.61	$46.91
40	43	$25.94	$38.17	$48.88
45	48	$31.86	$44.09	$52.07
50	53	$39.34	$50.92	$56.79
55	58	$49.09	$59.68	$62.75

EXAMPLE 1

Damien purchased a $30,000 whole-life policy when he was 35 years old. How much were his annual premiums?

Step 1. Find the number of $1,000s in $30,000.
Think: $30,000 ÷ $1,000 = 30

Step 2. Find the annual premium.

number of $1,000s × premium per $1,000 = annual premium
$$30 \quad \times \quad \$21.48 \quad = \quad \$644.40$$

Damien's annual premiums were $644.40.

EXAMPLE 2
When Damien reaches 65, how much will he have paid in premiums on his policy?

Hidden Question: For how many years did he pay premiums?
$$65 - 35 = 30$$

annual premium × number of years = total amount
$$\$644.40 \quad \times \quad 30 \quad = \quad \blacksquare$$

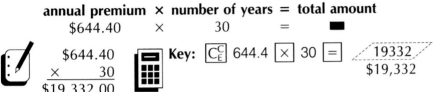

$$\$644.40$$
$$\times \quad 30$$
$$\overline{\$19,332.00}$$

Key: $\boxed{C_E^C}$ 644.4 $\boxed{\times}$ 30 $\boxed{=}$ _19332_
$$\$19,332$$

Damien will have paid $19,332 in premiums.

Besides providing lifelong coverage, whole-life and limited-payment life policies develop *cash* and *loan values* after three years. If the insured cancels the policy, the cash value of the policy will be returned to him or her. Likewise, if the insured needs emergency money, he or she can borrow it at low interest. If the money is borrowed from the policy, the policy remains in effect. However, money still owed is subtracted from any benefits paid to the beneficiary. The following table shows how the cash value of a whole-life policy may grow. The cash value depends upon the amount of premium and the length of time paid and may vary from the values given in the table.

Cash/Loan Value of Whole-Life Policy Cash/Loan Value per $1,000 of Coverage							
Age at Issue		Number of Years Policy Is in Effect				Value of Policy if Cashed at:	
M	F	5	10	15	20	Age 60	Age 65
20	23	$ 29	$ 91	$159	$232	$535	$615
25	28	$ 35	$108	$187	$260	$505	$588
30	33	$ 45	$129	$219	$312	$476	$570
35	38	$ 57	$153	$254	$360	$475	$550
40	43	$ 70	$179	$301	$408	$408	$515
45	48	$ 85	$206	$340	$452	$340	$452
50	53	$101	$237	$381	$498	$237	$381
55	58	$117	$268	$420	$568	$117	$268

EXAMPLE 3

What will be the cash value of Damien's policy at age 65?

Problem Solving Strategy: Finding information.
Use the table on page 459 to find the cash value. Look across the row for 35-year-old males to the column headed "Age 65." The table value is $550.

number of $1,000s × value per $1,000 = cash value
 30   × $550   = $16,500

The cash value of his policy at age 65 is $16,500.

Class Exercises

Use the table on page 458 to determine the annual premium.

Type of Policy	Face Value	Age at Issue	Sex	Annual Premium
Whole-life	$10,000	20	Male	*1.* ■
20-payment	$25,000	33	Female	*2.* ■
Endowment	$42,000	45	Male	*3.* ■

Use the table on page 459 to determine the cash value of each whole-life insurance policy.

Face Value	Sex	Age at Issue	Age Now	Cash Value
$10,000	Female	23	43	*4.* ■
$16,000	Male	40	65	*5.* ■

Solve.

6. Abby purchased a $35,000, 20-payment life insurance policy when she was 48. She is now 68. How much has she paid?

EXERCISES

Use the table on page 458 to determine the annual premium.

Type of Policy	Face Value	Age at Issue	Sex	Annual Premium
20-payment	$10,000	23	Female	*1.* ■
Whole-life	$20,000	25	Male	*2.* ■
Endowment	$45,000	48	Female	*3.* ■

Use the table on page 459 to determine the cash value of each whole-life insurance policy.

Face Value	Sex	Age at Issue	Age Now	Cash Value
$10,000	Male	30	45	**4.** ■
$ 8,000	Male	45	65	**5.** ■
$25,000	Female	53	63	**6.** ■
$32,000	Female	33	53	**7.** ■

8. Name: Wayne Hancock
Policy type: 20-payment
Face value: $36,000
Age at issue: 25
Age now: 40
Total premiums: ■

9. Name: Monica Cambridge
Policy type: Endowment
Face value: $45,000
Age at issue: 48
Age now: ■
Total premiums: $46,863

10. Oliver is 45 and plans to retire at 65. He wants to take out a 20-year endowment policy for $50,000. How much more will he have paid in premiums than he will receive as payment at age 65?

11. Jason took out a whole-life policy for $35,000 when he was 35. He is now 45 and needs to cancel his policy. How much more has he paid in premiums than he will receive in cash value?

12. Dolly is 48 and wants to be covered by $15,000 worth of life insurance for the next 10 years. Which would cost her less, two 5-year term policies (see page 454) or a whole-life policy that she would cancel after 10 years? How much less?

Reading in Mathematics: *Vocabulary*

Match each word in the first column with its definition in the second column.

1. Term insurance
2. Whole-life insurance
3. Limited-payment life insurance
4. Endowment-life insurance
5. Beneficiary
6. Insured person
7. Premium
8. Cash value
9. Face value

a. the person whose life is insured
b. a short-term insurance policy that must be renewed
c. the value of the policy to the insured person
d. life insurance with fixed premiums covering the insured person for life
e. the person to whom benefits are paid
f. life insurance with a limited number of premiums in which the face value of the policy is paid to the insured after all premiums are paid
g. regular payments made to keep a policy in effect
h. value of the policy if paid to the beneficiary
i. life insurance with a limited number of premiums that remains in force when all premiums are paid

14-4 Social Security Benefits

You probably already have a **social security card.** When you begin work, in most cases you give your social security number to your employer, who must withhold money from your paychecks for payments to the social security system. In addition, your employer must make an equal contribution to the system in your name. When you reach age 65, you become eligible for full **social security benefits,** or payments made to you as retirement income. If you retire at age 62, you will receive reduced benefits. You can also receive social security benefits if you are disabled.

In order to be eligible for social security benefits, a worker must have made contributions for a minimum amount of time. This time is counted in quarters, or units of 3 months (or $\frac{1}{4}$ year). For each 3-month period that a worker has earnings of $440 or more and contributes to social security, that worker gets credit for a quarter. The table below gives the minimum number of quarters required to be eligible for social security.

Social Security Eligibility	
If you reach 62 in	**You will need work credit for**
1986	$8\frac{3}{4}$ y = 35 quarters
1987	9 y = 36 quarters
1988	$9\frac{1}{4}$ y = 37 quarters
1989	$9\frac{1}{2}$ y = 38 quarters
1990	$9\frac{3}{4}$ y = 39 quarters
1991 or later	10 y = 40 quarters

EXAMPLE 1

If Leslie has been working full time since July 1, 1984, how many quarters of credit has she gained by December 31, 1988?

Hidden Question: How many years between July 1984 and December 1988?
From July 1, 1984, to July 1, 1988, is 4 years.
From July 1, 1988, to December 31, 1988, is 6 months, or $\frac{1}{2}$ year. The total is $4\frac{1}{2}$ years.

There are 4 quarters in a year.

number of years × 4 = number of quarters
$$4\frac{1}{2} \quad \times\ 4\ = \quad 18$$

She has gained 18 quarters of credit.

Social security retirement benefits are paid to a worker upon retirement at age 62 or older. Benefits can also be paid to the spouse of the worker upon reaching 62 and to unmarried children under 18. When an eligible worker retires at age 62 or older, a formula is used to compute his or her *average indexed monthly earnings* (AIME). From this, the *primary insurance amount* (PIA) is computed. The PIA is the amount a worker who retires at age 65 or older will receive each month. It is computed using a formula like the one below:

PIA = 90% of the first $310
+ 32% of excess over $310 up to $1,866
+ 15% of excess over $1,866

The answer is rounded to the next higher 10¢ if it is between two multiples of 10¢. The values $310 and $1,866 are annual PIA breakpoints and were used in a recent year. They are changed each year to reflect inflation or changes in the economy.

EXAMPLE 2
Sam is 65 and plans to retire. His AIME is $1,956. Using the annual PIA breakpoints above, what is his PIA?

Think: 90% = 0.9, 32% = 0.32, and 15% = 0.15

PIA = 0.9 × $310 + 0.32 × ($1,866 − $310) + 0.15 × ($1,956 − $1,866)
= 0.9 × $310 + 0.32 × $1,556 + 0.15 × $90
= $279 + $497.92 + $13.50
= $790.42 → $790.50   **Round to next higher 10¢**

Sam's PIA is $790.50.

If you retire before age 65, you will receive reduced benefits. For each month before 65, the PIA is reduced by $\frac{5}{9}$ of 1%, or $\frac{5}{9}$%.

EXAMPLE 3
Andrea will reach age 62 this year and plans to retire at that time. Her PIA is $736.90. How much will she receive per month?

Hidden Question: How many months before age 65 is she retiring?
$$65 - 62 = 3 \text{ y}; \ 3 \text{ y} = 3 \times 12 = 36 \text{ mo}$$

Step 1. Find the percent by which her benefits will be reduced.

number of months × $\frac{5}{9}$% = **percent benefits will be reduced**
36   × $\frac{5}{9}$% =   ■

$$\overset{4}{\cancel{36}} \times \frac{5}{\underset{1}{\cancel{9}}}\% = 20\%$$

Step 2. Find her monthly benefit.

PIA — 20% of PIA = monthly benefit
$736.90 − 20% of $736.90 = ■

Think: 20% = 0.2

$736.90	$736.90
× 0.2	− 147.38
$147.380	$589.52
$147.38	$589.60 **Round to next higher 10¢.**

   Key: $\boxed{C_E^C}$ 736.9 $\boxed{M+}$ $\boxed{×}$ 20 $\boxed{\%}$ $\boxed{M-}$ $\boxed{M_C^R}$ 589.52
$589.60   **Round to next higher 10¢.**

Her monthly benefit will be $589.60.

Class Exercises

Determine the number of quarters of social security work credits gained by full employment over the periods given.

1. 3 years

2. 5 years 9 months

3. From August 1, 1990, through January 31, 1992

Use the annual PIA breakpoints given on page 463 to determine the PIA for each worker. Assume each has reached age 65.

Name	AIME	PIA
Gil Mathers	$ 306	**4.** ■
Pahk Cheng	$1,320	**5.** ■
Luann Craigg	$2,024	**6.** ■

Solve.

7. Edith plans to retire 18 months before she reaches 65. If her PIA is $846.20, how much will her monthly benefits be?

EXERCISES

Determine the number of quarters of social security work credits gained by full employment over the periods given.

1. 8 years

2. 6 years 3 months

3. From May 1, 1991, through April 30, 1992

4. From January 1, 1987, through June 30, 1995

Solve.

5. Ramona was 21 years old in 1989 and worked full time from December 1, 1989, through August 31, 1991. How many more quarters does she need to become eligible for social security retirement benefits?

Use the annual PIA breakpoints given on page 463 to determine the PIA for each worker. Assume each has reached age 65.

Name	AIME	PIA
Rosie Long	$ 200	**6.** ■
Durk Wessell	$1,020	**7.** ■
Henry Kreise	$1,315	**8.** ■

Solve.

9. Walter Addison
PIA: $1,632
Retirement age: 64 y 8 mo
Monthly benefit: ■

10. Geri Offitt
PIA: $1,234
Retirement age: 63 y 6 mo
Monthly benefit: ■

11. Nobel retired on his 62nd birthday. His AIME was $1,998. How much were his monthly benefits?

12. Marie retired at age 63 years 7 months. Her AIME was $1,628. How much were her monthly benefits?

13. Sabrina retired on her 62nd birthday. Her PIA was $923.10. If her social security benefits rise each year by an average of 3%, how much will she have earned by the time she reaches 65?

14. If Sabrina (Problem 13) had waited until 65 to retire, her PIA would have been $976.80. At that rate how many years would she have to receive benefits, which rise about 3% per year, to receive the same amount of money as she earned during her retirement years from 62 to 65?

Using a Calculator: *Calculating Percent of Benefits*

You can use your calculator to find the percent by which benefits will be reduced. For instance, if Andrea (Example 3) retires at age 62, her percent of benefits can be found as follows:

Key: $\boxed{C_E^C}$ 65 $\boxed{-}$ 62 $\boxed{=}$ $\boxed{\times}$ 12 $\boxed{\times}$ 5 $\boxed{\div}$ 9 $\boxed{=}$ 20

1. Explain the keystrokes used to find the answer.

2. Find the percent by which benefits will be reduced for a person retiring at 64.

3. Find the percent by which benefits will be reduced for a person retiring at age $63\frac{1}{2}$.

14-5 Retirement Plans

Many companies provide retirement plans for their employees to supplement social security. Usually, employees contribute fixed amounts to the plan, and these amounts are matched by contributions from the employer. Most companies base their benefits on the number of years you have worked for them and your average salary. If you are self-employed, you can participate in private retirement plans that allow you to save money without being taxed on the money or interest until you withdraw it when you retire.

The retirement plan for Ben's company bases its benefits upon the number of years the employee has worked and the average of the four highest annual salaries the employee has earned. A worker's benefits are calculated using the following formula:

average highest salary × number of years ÷ 55 = annual pension

EXAMPLE 1

Mary works at Ben's company. She is retiring after 35 years and her highest four salaries are $27,800, $28,900, $30,300, and $32,600. What is her annual pension?

Step 1. Find her average highest salary.

$$\text{average highest salary} = \frac{\$27,800 + \$28,900 + \$30,300 + \$32,600}{4}$$

$$= \frac{\$119,600}{4} = \$29,900$$

Step 2. Find her annual pension.

average highest salary × number of years ÷ 55 = annual pension

$$\$29,900 \quad × \quad 35 \quad ÷ 55 = \quad \blacksquare$$

$$\begin{array}{r} \$29,900 \\ × \quad 35 \\ \hline 149\ 500 \\ 897\ 00 \\ \hline \$1,046,500 \end{array}$$

$$\begin{array}{r} \$19,027.272 \rightarrow \$19,027.27 \\ 55)\overline{\$1,046,500.000} \quad \textbf{Round to} \\ \textbf{nearest cent.} \end{array}$$

Mary's annual pension is $19,027.27.

With a calculator, you can simplify the computation in Example 1.

Key: $\boxed{C_E^C}$ 27800 $\boxed{+}$ 28900 $\boxed{+}$ 30300 $\boxed{+}$ 32600 $\boxed{=}$ $\boxed{÷}$ 4
$\boxed{×}$ 35 $\boxed{÷}$ 55 $\boxed{=}$ ⟋ 19027.272 ⟍
$\qquad\qquad$ $19,027.27 \quad$ **Round to nearest cent.**

Skill Review

To figure retirement benefits, you should be able to find the average of a group of numbers.

Find the average of each group of numbers.

1. $354; $982; $299
2. $1,982; $3,967; $4,243; $2,297
3. $34,623; $42,867; $48,305; $50,233
4. $28,353; $30,645; $28,132; $29,078; $31,945

(For additional help, see page 552.)

The Nesslerode Manufacturing Company has a pension plan in which the average of the three final years and a rating factor are used to determine annual benefits. The formula is:

$$\frac{\text{3-year}}{\text{average}} \times \frac{\text{number of}}{\text{years}} \times \frac{\text{rating}}{\text{factor}} = \frac{\text{annual}}{\text{pension}}$$

EXAMPLE 2

Brett retired from the Nesslerode Company after 23 years. The company's rating factor is 1.6%. His final three annual salaries were $22,500, $25,600, and $27,500. What is his annual pension?

Step 1. Find his average salary.

$$\text{average salary} = \frac{\$22,500 + \$25,600 + \$27,500}{3}$$

$$= \frac{\$75,600}{3} = \$25,200$$

Step 2. Find his annual pension.

3-year average	×	**number of years**	×	**rating factor**	=	**annual pension**
$25,200	×	23	×	1.6%	=	■

Think: 1.6% = 0.016
Estimate: $25,200 × 23 × 0.016 = ■ →
$25,000 × 20 × 0.02 = $10,000

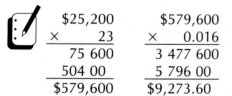

```
   $25,200          $579,600
 ×      23        ×   0.016
   75 600          3 477 600
  504 00           5 796 00
  $579,600         $9,273.60
```

 Key: [C$_E^C$] 25200 [×]
23 [×] 1.6 [%]   9273.6
                 $9,273.60

The answer $9,273.60 is close to the estimate $10,000 and is a sensible answer.
Brett's annual pension is $9,273.60.

Self-employed workers can place money in a savings account under the **Keogh plan,** a plan that allows self-employed workers to provide for their own retirement years. Under a typical Keogh plan, as much as 15% of a worker's annual gross earnings up to a maximum of $30,000 can be placed in such an account. Taxes will not be due on the saved earnings or on the interest until the money is withdrawn, which can be done without penalty at age $59\frac{1}{2}$.

EXAMPLE 3

Timmy is self-employed. He places 12% of his $26,400 annual income in a Keogh plan account. If he is taxed at 22%, how much does he save in taxes per year on his Keogh contributions?

Step 1. Find his annual contribution to the Keogh account.

annual income × percent contributed = amount contributed
$26,400   ×   12%   = $3,168

Step 2. Find his tax savings.

Keogh contribution × tax rate = tax savings
$3,168   ×   22%   = $696.96

Timmy's tax savings are $696.96.

Class Exercises

Determine each annual pension using the information given in the table. Use the formula on page 467.

Annual Salaries to Average	Number of Years Worked	Rating Factor	Annual Pension
$19,400, $23,200, $24,600	14	1.55%	**1.** ■
$15,000, $16,000, $17,000	30	1.5%	**2.** ■

Solve.

3. Use the information in Example 1 to determine the annual pension for a worker with 20 years of service whose highest annual salaries were $31,200, $33,750, $36,210, and $39,840.

4. Jenny is self-employed and has a gross income of $38,600 per year. If she is taxed at a 21% rate and places 13% of her income in a Keogh account, how much does she save on taxes?

EXERCISES

Determine each annual pension using the information given in the table. Use the formula on page 467.

Annual Salaries to Average	Number of Years Worked	Rating Factor	Annual Pension
$10,000, $12,000, $14,000	20	1.5%	**1.** ■
$15,200, $18,900, $21,300	31	1.4%	**2.** ■
$21,200, $23,900, $26,200	28	1.5%	**3.** ■

Solve.

4. Use the information in Example 1 to determine the annual pension for a worker with 12 years of service whose highest annual salaries were $22,345, $23,782, $25,415, and $27,290.

5. Use the information in Example 1 to determine the annual pension for a worker with 22 years of service whose highest annual salaries were $18,250, $19,360, $21,350, and $25,195.

6. Name: Karen Kennedy
Gross income: $29,300
Percent to Keogh account: 13%
Tax rate: 21%
Tax savings: ▬

7. Name: Edward Jones
Gross income: $33,520
Percent to Keogh account: 11%
Tax rate: 18%
Tax savings: ▬

8. Which of Exercises 1–5 could be done mentally? In which would pencil and paper be appropriate? Which could best be done by using a calculator?

9. Barney puts $55 per month into a Keogh account, which earns 6% interest. He is now 30. Use the formula on page 435 to find how much will be in his account when he reaches 60.

10. Normalee is placing money in a Keogh account at the rate of $38.50 per month at 7% interest. She was exactly $44\frac{1}{2}$ years old when she began. Use the table on page 435 to determine how much will be in the account when she is permitted to begin withdrawing it.

11. Frank opened a Keogh account, which he hopes to continue for 25 years. He will save $65 per month and will get 6% interest. For the first 10 years, he will be taxed at a rate of 18%; after that he expects the rate to rise to 25%. How much will he save in taxes over the 25-year period? (Use the table on page 435.)

Critical Thinking: Predicting

Planning your finances requires you to predict what your needs and wants will be at different times in the future. Assume you have just accepted a job with Greenberry, Inc. at a salary of $19,000 per year. Greenberry requires every employee to contribute 3% of his or her salary to the retirement plan, but you may contribute up to 7% of your salary. Greenberry will match the amount you contribute. The contributions accumulate interest until you retire or leave the company. When you retire, you receive a regular income based on the accumulated money. Once a year you may change the percentage of your salary that you contribute.

1. How much money will be deducted from your yearly salary when you contribute 3% to the retirement plan? What will be the total amount contributed by you and the company?

2. How much money will be deducted from your yearly salary if you contribute 7% to the retirement plan? What would be the total amount contributed by you and the company in this case?

3. If you choose the 3% plan instead of the 7% plan for the first year you work at Greenberry, you will have $760 more to spend during that year. Predict what you might need or want to spend the $760 on during your first year of work.

Career

Fish Hatchery Technician

Fish hatcheries in the United States are generally run by the state or federal government. Here fish are raised to stock freshwater lakes, ponds, and streams. People who work in fish hatcheries are called **fish hatchery technicians.**

Profile of a fish hatchery technician. A high school diploma is necessary to work in a fish hatchery, and college education is necessary for advancement. Fish hatchery technicians generally like the outdoors and are interested in conservation.

The hatchery environment. Fish hatcheries are usually located in remote areas near a steady water supply. Technicians work outdoors, often from boats. Some work is done indoors as technicians examine fish or do research on ways to improve living conditions for the fish. Technicians use a variety of mathematics in solving problems, conducting experiments, measuring fish, and so on.

All in a day's work. Tony worked as a fish hatchery technician. One of his jobs was to measure a sample of fish to find the average length. He also worked to develop a special food to feed the fingerlings, or small fish, being raised in the hatchery. When the fingerlings reached a length of 8 inches, Tony released them into a trout-fishing stream.

When Tony went to work for the fish hatchery, he investigated its retirement plan.

1. Tony contributes $7.86 each week to the retirement plan at the fish hatchery. If he works for the hatchery for 25 years, how much will he have contributed?

2. Tony's employer contributes an amount to Tony's retirement fund equal to $1\frac{1}{2}$ times his contribution. After 25 years, how much will his employer have contributed?

3. If the total amount contributed by Tony and his employer is invested in a savings account at an annual interest rate of 7%, how much will the retirement account be worth after 25 years? (Use 4.3 weeks per month.) Use the table on page 435.

Computer:
Nested Loops

Vicky wrote a program to help her estimate social security benefits over a period of years. Her initial payment will be $525 per month and it will increase an average of 4% per year. The program asks for the initial payment, the expected annual increase, and the number of years. Each year's monthly payment is printed and the total amount paid over the period is displayed at the end of the program. The program uses two loops, one inside the other, called *nested loops*.

Program	Explanation
10 HOME	Clears the screen.
20 INPUT "INITIAL PAYMENT?"; PY	Prompts and records input of initial payment.
30 INPUT "ANNUAL INCREASE IN DECIMAL FORM?"; AI	Prompts and records input of expected annual increase.
40 INPUT "NUMBER OF YEARS? "; N	Prompts and records input of number of years.
50 TTL = 0	Initializes the grand total to zero.
60 FOR Y = 1 TO N	Opens the outer loop representing number of years.
70 PRINT "YEAR #"; Y, "MONTHLY PAYMENT = $"; PY	Prints and labels the year and payment for that year.
80 FOR M = 1 TO 12	Opens the inner loop representing months of the year.
90 TTL = TTL + PY	Accumulates the grand total.
100 NEXT M	Closes the inner loop.
110 PY = PY + AI * PY	Adjusts the payment for the next year.
120 NEXT Y	Closes the outer loop.
130 PRINT "TOTAL BENEFITS OVER "; N; "YEARS = $"; TTL	Prints and labels the grand total.
140 END	Tells the computer to end the program.

RUN the program for each of the following sets of data.

	Initial Payment	Annual Increase	Number of Years
1.	$ 386	0.04	15
2.	$ 718	0.05	12
3.	$ 635.40	0.045	14
4.	$ 948.76	0.037	20
5.	$1,072.98	0.0525	25

Decision Making:
Choosing Health Insurance

David Herman accepted a job with a company in a city that was not near his home. He received a packet of information about health insurance benefits and had to let the company know what his choices were. He was not sure about how to choose a health plan, so he decided to talk with his brother Aaron, who had just been in the hospital for 3 days after breaking his leg.

Aaron commented to David that he was glad he had a good health insurance plan. He suggested that David bring over his health insurance information so that they could discuss it together.

Answer the following questions.

1. What health care services might you expect to receive in a year?

2. How might such health care services be paid for?

THINKING ABOUT A HEALTH PLAN

"I have a choice between what is called a traditional health insurance plan and a health maintenance organization, or HMO," David explained to Aaron. "I've read all the information about them. They're similar in many ways. They pay about the same for time in the hospital, for instance. So I listed what I thought were the main differences between the two plans. I also tried to do what you said—think about what it will be like in my new job location. It's not easy to predict what I'm going to want in the future."

Aaron agreed, but suggested that David think about the difference between the two plans. David decided that the HMO would pay for routine physical examinations, immunizations, and visits to the doctor's office, but that the traditional plan would not.

"Do you think those services will be important to you?" asked Aaron. "Do you expect to use them much?"

"Yes," David responded. "I like to stay in shape. And I think I might do some biking outside of the United States. I'd need immunizations for that. So, I guess I can predict that I'll want to have physicals and immunizations paid for by my health insurance."

Answer the following questions.

3. What thinking steps has David already used for making a choice between health plans?

4. What additional information would help David make a sound decision about his health plan?

LOOKING AT DIFFERENCES BETWEEN PLANS

"Any other important differences?" Aaron asked.

"I don't know if you'd call it important," David answered, "but the HMO offers a discount at a local fitness center. Again, that's something I'd really like. The traditional plan has nothing like that."

"Can you predict that your new job will give you enough time to use a fitness center?"

David thought about what he would be doing in the next few months and then listed some ways he might spend his time.

> —Work some overtime hours – longer than the required 8:30 to 5.
> —Phone and write to friends
> —Bowl and do some bicycling
> —Drive home on occasional weekends

Based on his list, David decided he would probably find an hour or so on two or three evenings a week to use a fitness club.

Answer the following questions.

5. Describe the thinking procedures David used to predict whether he will be able to make use of a fitness center.

6. Predict what hobby you might enjoy 2 years from now.

7. Describe the thinking procedures you used to answer Question 6.

8. Predict a hobby your best friend might enjoy 2 years from now.

9. Is it easier to make predictions about yourself or about your friend? Explain your answer.

MAKING A DECISION

David knew that his cost for both plans was about the same. His brother asked what advantages the traditional plan had over the HMO.

David considered. "The important thing with the traditional plan is that you can go to any doctor you want, and with the HMO you go to doctors they employ at their medical center."

"How important do you think it will be to you to be able to choose your own doctor?" Aaron asked.

David thought for a moment.

"Not very important, I guess. It's not as if I were staying here, where we've always gone to Dr. Redman. If I were staying here, I'd want to continue to be his patient. But I won't even know any doctors there. I guess I might be glad to have doctors selected by experts available all the time and in one place. And a dentist, too."

"But what about the question of location?" Aaron asked. "If you can choose any doctor you want in the traditional plan, that means you can choose a doctor that's close to you. The HMO medical center may not be located near where you live."

"I don't think that's going to be very important," David said. "This new city is not very large, and I'll probably be able to drive or ride my bike to the medical center without too much trouble. Considering everything, it seems pretty clear to me that the HMO is the plan I want."

"Are there any other differences between the plans that you ought to consider?"

"No, I don't think so. We've covered everything."

"What if you find out you're wrong?" Aaron asked. "How easily can you change this decision?"

"They have an open enrollment period once each year," David answered. "So I'm certainly not committed to this decision forever."

Answer the following questions.

10. What factors can you think of that could make David change his mind about his decision?

11. List three decisions you can easily change.

12. List three decisions it would be very difficult to change.

OTHER CONSIDERATIONS

As David was putting on his jacket, Aaron said, "Wait a minute! You're going off on a biking trip before you start your new job. What if you break a leg? How will you pay for your medical care?"

"I never thought about that!" David replied. "It's certainly possible that I could have some kind of medical problem between now and the time I start my job. In fact, I'd predict that medical problems would be more likely on a biking trip than here."

"It's possible you still are covered by the health insurance you used in school," Aaron said. "If not, you'd better plan to get some individual insurance to cover you during now and the time your company policy goes into effect."

"Thanks," David said, "that's important. I'll check on it first thing tomorrow. And thanks for listening while I figured out what to do."

Answer the following questions.

13. When might it be important for you to carry individual (rather than group) health insurance?

14. What characteristics of the two health plans did David compare in order to make his choice?

15. How did Aaron help David as he made his decision?

16. What procedures would you use if a friend wanted to talk with you about a decision he or she was making?

17. How did predicting his own needs and wants help David make his decision?

18. List the thinking steps David used in making a choice between the traditional plan and the HMO.

DECIDE FOR YOURSELF

Which of the two health plans would *you* prefer? How did you think in answering that question? In answering the question, did you make predictions? Choose one prediction you made and tell what additional information would make your prediction more certain.

Chapter 14 Review

VOCABULARY

beneficiary   face value   Keogh plan   social security card

deductible   health insurance   life insurance   social security benefits

For Exercises 1–6, select words that complete each statement.

1. If you have _____ , your insurance company will pay for some or all of your expenses if you are hospitalized.

2. If your health insurance plan has a _____ clause, you must pay a specified amount yourself before the insurance company pays anything.

3. _____ is designed to provide financial security to a family in the event of someone's death.

4. The person to whom the value of a life insurance policy is paid is known as the _____ of the policy.

5. The amount that will be paid to a beneficiary is known as the _____ of the insurance policy.

6. Payments made to a person as retirement income are called _____ .

SKILLS

Find each percent.

7. 30% of $7,450   **8.** 13% of $23,618   **9.** 12.7% of $63,428

Find each quotient.

10. $34,000 ÷ 1,000   **11.** $6,023 ÷ 100   **12.** $426,738 ÷ 10,000

Find the average of each group of numbers.

13. $2,146; $1,576; $4,893   **14.** $58,625; $72,500; $63,250

CONSUMER TOPICS

Solve.

15. Sally's deductible clause in her health insurance plan requires her to pay $200 in a given year. The insurance company will pay 80% of the remaining cost. Sally was hospitalized and her stay cost $7,650. How much did Sally have to pay in all?

16. The premium for Larry's health insurance is $1,250 per year. If his employer pays 80% of the premium, how much is deducted each week from Larry's paycheck to cover his share?

Use the information in the table on page 454 to answer Exercises 17 and 18.

17. Otis is 25 years old. He took out a 5-year term life policy for $20,000. How much is his yearly premium?

18. How much will Otis pay in all as premiums on the policy?

Use the information in the tables on pages 458 and 459 to answer Problems 19–21.

19. Reggie purchased a $40,000 whole-life policy when he was 30 years old. How much were his annual premiums?

20. When Reggie reaches 60, how much will he have paid in premiums on his policy?

21. What will be the cash value of Reggie's policy when he reaches 60 years of age?

22. Shawna worked full time from April 1, 1985, through September 30, 1988. How many quarters of credit did she earn for social security eligibility?

Use the information for computing the primary insurance amount (PIA) on page 463 to answer Problems 23 and 24.

23. Joline is 65 and plans to retire. Her average indexed monthly earnings are $2,000. What is her PIA?

24. Matthew is 62 and has decided to retire. His PIA is $864.80. How much will he receive per month?

Solve.

25. The pension plan at Ria's company provides benefits calculated on the average of her four highest annual salaries and uses the following formula:

average salary × number of years ÷ 55 = annual pension

Ria is retiring after 30 years and her average salary is $26,500. What is her annual pension?

26. In a recent year, mortality tables showed that out of 250,000 living 68-year-olds, 61,750 were expected to die within the year. What was the probability of such a person living to age 69?

27. Pauline is self-employed and places 12% of her $24,500 annual income in a Keogh account. If her income is taxed at the 22% tax rate, how much does she save in taxes per year on her Keogh contributions?

Chapter 14 Test

1. Carol's deductible clause in her health insurance plan requires her to pay $150 in a given year. The insurance company will pay 75% of the remaining cost. Carol's hospital stay cost $6,500. How much did Carol have to pay in all for this hospital stay?

2. The premium for Roger's health insurance plan is $1,350 per year. If his employer pays 75% of the premium, how much must Roger pay each year for his share of the premium?

3. How much is deducted each month from Roger's paycheck (Problem 2) to cover his share of the premium?

Use the information on page 454 to answer Problems 4 and 5.

4. Cray is 25 years old. He took out a 5-year term life policy for $30,000. How much is his yearly premium?

5. If Cray renews his policy each year for 5 years, how much will he pay in all as premiums on the policy?

6. In a recent year, mortality tables showed that out of 63,037 living 96-year-olds, 25,250 are expected to die within the year. What is the probability of such a person living to age 97?

Use the tables on pages 458 and 459 to answer Problems 7–9.

7. Marty purchased a $30,000 whole-life policy at age 25. What were his annual premiums?

8. When Marty reaches 60, how much will he have paid in premiums on his policy?

9. What will be the cash value of Marty's policy when he reaches 60 years of age?

10. Brenda worked full time from July 1, 1986, through March 31, 1989. How many quarters of credit did she earn for social security eligibility?

Use the information for computing primary insurance amount (PIA) on page 463 to answer Problems 11 and 12.

11. Peter is 65 and plans to retire. His average indexed monthly earnings are $1,950. What is his PIA?

12. James is 63 and has decided to retire. His PIA is $780.60. How much will he receive per month?

13. The pension plan at Sue's company provides benefits calculated on the average of her four highest annual salaries and uses the formula on page 466. Sue is retiring after 20 years and her average salary is $22,500. What is her annual pension?

14. Marsha is self-employed and has an annual income of $25,000. She puts 10% of her income into a Keogh plan. If her tax rate is 22%, find her tax savings.

Cumulative Mixed Review

Select the letter corresponding to the correct answer.

1. Sheila contributes 8% of her salary to a payroll savings plan. If her annual salary is $16,250, how much is withheld each month for savings?
   a. $25
   b. $108.33
   c. $1,300
   d. $54.17

2. Yuri borrowed $2,500 for 3 months at 11.5%. How much did he have to pay back under an add-on plan?
   a. $287.50
   b. $71.88
   c. $2,571.88
   d. $2,595.83

3. Don had a balance of $315.29 on his department store charge account. How much interest did he have to pay for the month if the rate was 1.5% per month finance charge?
   a. $47.29
   b. $320.02
   c. $4.73
   d. $.47

4. Nellie pays $19.25 per month for her phone service and spends an average of $7.50 per month for long-distance calls. How much does her phone service cost her in all each year?
   a. $231
   b. $321
   c. $26.75
   d. $267.50

5. Trisha budgets 25% of her annual income for housing. If she budgets $450 per month for housing, what is her annual income?
   a. $1,800
   b. $72,000
   c. $7,200
   d. $21,600

6. Michelle bought 500 shares of CBA Corp. for $24\frac{1}{4}$ per share. What was the total purchase price of the stock if she had to pay a 1% commission to her stockbroker?
   a. $121.25
   b. $1,224.63
   c. $12,125
   d. $12,246.25

7. Paul can deduct the amount over 7% of his gross income as medical expenses on his income tax return. If his annual salary is $19,500 and his medical expenses one year were $1,135, how much could he deduct on his tax return?
   a. $0
   b. $1,365
   c. $230
   d. $1,135

8. Lisa bought a 24-ounce box of cereal for $3.15. What was the unit price per pound?
   a. $2.10
   b. $1.58
   c. $.13
   d. $1.30

9. Kathy bought an outfit that cost $62.50. She had to pay 6.25% sales tax. What was the total amount of her purchase?
   a. $62.50
   b. $3.91
   c. $66.41
   d. $62.89

10. Lucy makes 6 payments each year of $115 for her auto insurance. How much must she budget weekly to cover this fixed expense?
    a. $57.50
    b. $13.27
    c. $69
    d. $690

Adriano wanted to buy a computer system. He planned to pay cash for his purchase and had saved $1,800. He had been watching for sales in the newspaper, but he had not decided what brand to purchase.

- How could Adriano get information about the features and reliability of the computer systems he was considering?

- How would you advise him in his decision?

- What are some factors he should consider before making a final selection?

If you decided to buy a computer system, how would you begin your selection process? What factors would enter into your decision making about the kind of system to purchase?

15-1 Buying an Entertainment System

At some time in your life you will probably buy a stereo or video system. These are major purchases that should last many years. In order to get the best buy for your money, it is helpful to read consumer information and newspaper ads as well as to shop in a variety of stores to compare prices.

AM/FM tuner	$245
Turntable	$115
Tape Player	$145
Speakers	$200
Compact disc player	$195

EXAMPLE 1

Maggie wanted to buy a stereo system consisting of the following components: AM/FM tuner, turntable, tape player, speakers, and compact disc player. One newspaper ad contained the prices shown above for these components.

What is the total cost of the stereo system?

$$\$245 + \$115 + \$145 + \$200 + \$195 = \$900$$

The cost of this stereo system is $900.

As a guide to the purchase of the components of her system, Maggie used these figures from a consumer magazine:

Suggested Percent of Total to Spend on Each Component	
AM/FM tuner	27%
Turntable	12%
Tape player	15%
Speakers	25%
Compact disc player	21%

The system advertised in Example 1 comes reasonably close to these percentages.

EXAMPLE 2

If Maggie has budgeted $650 to spend on a stereo system, how much can she spend on each component, using the above table as a guide?

Problem Solving Strategy: Organizing information.
You can organize your information in a table.

Component	Percent ×	Amount Budgeted =	Cost of Component
AM/FM tuner	0.27	$650	$175.50
Turntable	0.12	$650	$ 78.00
Tape player	0.15	$650	$ 97.50
Speakers	0.25	$650	$162.50
Compact disc player	0.21	$650	$136.50

Maggie can spend $175.50 on a tuner, $78 on a turntable, $97.50 on a tape player, $162.50 on speakers, and $136.50 on a compact disc player if she follows the recommendations above.

Like a stereo system, a home video system is a long-term recreational investment. If you already have a color television set, then you can purchase a video cassette recorder for about $250 to complete your home video system.

EXAMPLE 3

The Mao family can rent a video movie for $2.50. It would cost $16.50 to take the family to a movie theater. How much do they save by watching a video movie instead of going to the movie theater?

$$\textbf{cost of movie theater} - \textbf{cost of video rental} = \textbf{savings}$$
$$\$16.50 \quad - \quad \$2.50 \quad = \quad \$14$$

They will save $14.

Class Exercises

Determine the total cost of each stereo system.

AM/FM Tuner	Turntable	Tape Player	Speakers	Compact Disc Player	Total Cost
$245	$118	$137.50	$195	$210	1. ■
$200	$100	$150	$200	$200	2. ■
$275	$125	$175	$200	$175	3. ■
$305.50	$127.45	$192.50	$245.50	$258.75	4. ■

5. Explain how mental arithmetic can be used to find the answer to Exercise 3.

6. Amity has $800 to spend on a stereo system. Use the percents in the table on page 482 to determine how much she could spend on each component.

7. It costs Louis $12 to take a friend to the movies. He can rent a movie for $2. How much does he save by renting films on three evenings instead of taking his friend to the movies three times?

EXERCISES

Determine the total cost of each stereo system.

AM/FM Tuner	Turntable	Tape Player	Speakers	Compact Disc Player	Total Cost
$150	$ 50	$100	$150	$200	1. ■
$250	$100	$125	$150	$225	2. ■
$165	$ 75	$100	$145	$185	3. ■
$218.75	$112.50	$148.25	$175.45	$213.89	4. ■

5. Toni Cheng
Color TV: $315
Video recorder: $275
Total system: ■

6. Carl Myslicki
Color TV: $298.75
Video recorder: $245.25
Total system: ■

7. Sheila Aaron
Color TV: ■
Video recorder: $255.25
Total system: $524.75

8. Terry Reich
Color TV: $389.55
Video recorder: ■
Total system: $695.21

Use the table on page 482 to determine the cost of each component if the total amount to spend is given.

9. $700

10. $840.60

11. $1,080

12. Lenny purchased stereo components for the following amounts: AM/FM tuner: $318.76; turntable: $108.95; tape player: $124.07; and speakers: $275.40. The stereo dealer allowed him $85 for a trade-in on his old system. How much does he owe for the system?

13. Rebecca belongs to a record/tape club that sends her a monthly tape selection unless she directs them not to. She is billed $13.75 for each tape she is sent. How much will she pay in a year if she is sent a tape each month?

14. Wallace can rent a movie for $2.25. It would cost him $18 to take his family to a movie theater. How many such films must he rent instead of going to a movie theater to save enough to cover the cost of his $315 video recorder?

15. Monica followed the table on page 482 exactly when she purchased her stereo system. The AM/FM tuner she purchased cost $83.58 more than her tape player. How much did she spend on each component?

Challenge

Caleb has been saving 3% of his annual net income of $19,500 for a year to buy a new stereo. He earned 5.75% interest on his savings for the year. The stereo store has offered him a trade-in on his old stereo system of $50. He wants to buy an AM/FM tuner for $205.50, a turntable for $125.95, a tape deck for $149.75, and two speakers for $79.50 each. How much more or less does Caleb have than the cost of the system he wants to purchase?

15-2 Buying a Computer

You may decide to purchase a computer for maintaining your personal records or because you need a word processor. Or, you may want a home computer so you can use the wide variety of games and other entertainment software available. Whatever your reason, your purchase of a computer system will require two types of equipment: **hardware,** or the actual computer and its supporting equipment, and **software,** or the sets of instructions that tell the computer what to do. Purchasing a computer is a major expense and you should carefully consider your needs and the type of system that will best meet them. It is also worthwhile to use consumer report magazines for information about available systems.

Most computer systems consist of the following four components:

- The computer itself, consisting of a keyboard and a *central processing unit (CPU),* which holds the memory; circuits for processing data; and the wires, plugs, and connectors that allow the computer to be connected to other pieces of equipment.

- A *monitor,* upon which data are displayed.

- A *disk drive,* which reads information from disks. The disks most commonly used for home computers are called floppy disks. A floppy disk is a flat circular object upon which magnetic information can be stored. When inserted in a disk drive, a disk spins within its jacket and an electronic device resting gently on the surface of the disk reads information from or writes information on the disk. A computer may have one or more disk drives. There are also hard disks, which can store more data.

- A *printer,* which prints copies of material displayed on the screen or stored in the computer.

EXAMPLE

Gina saw the following ad for computer hardware in a local newspaper. If Gina buys this computer system, how much will it cost her?

```
CPU (with 1 disk drive) .............. $900
Monitor ............................. $225
Extra disk drive..................... $125
Printer ............................. $300
```

Think: $900 + $225 + $125 + $300

$900 + $350 + $300 = $900 + $650 = $1,550

The system will cost her $1,550.

The computer's *memory* holds the data that the computer processes as well as the instructions that it uses to process the data. A single unit of memory is called a **byte.** A unit of 1,024 bytes of memory is called a **kilobyte** and is symbolized by 1K.

Input devices allow the user to send information, or input, to the computer. The keyboard and disk drive are input devices. Any information that the computer transmits is called output. *Output devices* include the monitor screen, disk drive, and printer.

One part of the computer's memory contains instructions that cannot be changed. These instructions, called *read-only memory* (ROM), are built into the computer when it is manufactured. When the computer is initially turned on, it is under the control of ROM.

The other part of the computer's memory can be accessed for reading existing information and writing new information. Such memory is called *random-access memory* (RAM). All information that comes from an input device goes to RAM, where it is instantaneously available to the computer.

Class Exercises

1. Name the four major components of Gina's computer.

2. Identify each of the following as an input device, output device, or both: printer; keyboard; disk drive; monitor.

3. What advantage do you think a printer has over a TV monitor as an output device?

4. How many times as much memory does a 512K computer have than one with 128K?

5. Doris wants to purchase a computer with 512K memory, two disk drives, and a printer. She can attach the computer to her TV screen at home. Use the price list at the right to determine how much her system will cost.

CPU, with 1 disk drive and 256K memory	$950
Additional disk drive	$200
256K additional memory	$120
Printer	$400

EXERCISES

1. What advantage do you think a TV monitor or TV screen has over a printer as an output device?

2. What is the difference between ROM and RAM?

3. Name three output devices.

4. Name two input devices.

5. What is meant by ROM?

6. What is in a CPU?

7. How many times as much memory does a 896K computer have than one with 128K?

Use the price list below for Exercises 8–12.

Bytemaster Electronics Computer Price List			
CPU, with 1 disk drive and 128K memory	$675	TV screen	$195
Extra disk drive	$225	High-resolution TV monitor	$350
128K memory package	$ 62.50	Printer	$375
Maintenance policy	12% of purchase price		

8. Rosa purchased a 128K system with 1 disk drive and a TV screen. How much did it cost?

9. Loretta needs a 512K system with two disk drives, a high-resolution monitor, and a printer. How much will it cost?

10. Donna wants to do graphics work on her computer. For this she needs three disk drives, 1,024K memory, a high-resolution TV monitor, and a printer. How much will this system cost her?

11. A *maintenance policy* covers the cost of maintenance of a computer. How much would a maintenance policy cost on the computer system Loretta (Problem 9) purchased?

12. How much is a maintenance policy for Donna's computer system (Problem 10)?

13. Some people lease computer systems instead of purchasing them. Not only are leased systems covered by a maintenance policy, but the person leasing can easily change computer systems as the present one becomes out of date. Bytemaster Electronics Computer charges an annual leasing fee of $\frac{1}{3}$ the purchase price. How much would it cost to lease Donna's system (Problem 10) for 1 year?

14. Do some comparison shopping and choose a computer system you think would fit your needs. Be prepared to justify your choice to the class.

Critical Thinking: *Recognizing Part-Whole Relationships*

You have decided to buy a home computer system for word processing. You see the ad at the right in the newspaper:

1. If you buy all the components of this system separately, how much will they cost?

2. How is the CPU related to the whole computer system?

3. For which part or parts of the advertised ABC computer system could you readily substitute something else? What would these substitutes be?

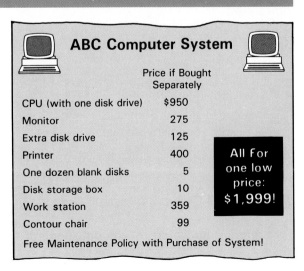

ABC Computer System

	Price if Bought Separately
CPU (with one disk drive)	$950
Monitor	275
Extra disk drive	125
Printer	400
One dozen blank disks	5
Disk storage box	10
Work station	359
Contour chair	99

All For one low price: **$1,999!**

Free Maintenance Policy with Purchase of System!

15-3 Buying Software

Without software, your computer will not be of much use to you. You can purchase educational software, financial software, software that allows you to do word processing, and games that can be used in your leisure time. If you plan a budget for software and shop carefully, you should be able to get a good selection for a reasonable price.

Marcus plans to buy some software from MicroVendors. Their price list is shown below.

MicroVendors Software Store
Software Price List

Program Name	Type of Program	Price
SimpleTyper	Typing practice	$32
SimpleWriter	Word processor	$45
Home Budget	Home finances	$40
Home Filer	Database system	$50
SimpleCalc	Spreadsheet	$52
Spanish Teacher	Foreign language drill	$35
Grapher	Bar, line, circle graphs	$29
SimpleMath	Math skill practice	$33
SimpleSpeller	Spelling checker	$33
Checkmate	Chess game	$25
Spacebattles	Space game	$27

EXAMPLE 1

Marcus budgeted $200 for software. He wants to buy SimpleTyper, SimpleWriter, Home Budget, Spanish Teacher, and Spacebattles. How much will he have left to spend after he makes his purchases?

Step 1. First find the total spent.

$32	SimpleTyper
45	SimpleWriter
40	Home Budget
35	Spanish Teacher
+ 27	Spacebattles
$179	

Key: $\boxed{\text{CE}^{\text{C}}}$ 32 $\boxed{+}$ 45 $\boxed{+}$ 40 $\boxed{+}$ 35 $\boxed{+}$ 27
$\boxed{=}$ 179
$179

Step 2. Find the amount remaining in his budget.

amount budgeted − amount spent = amount remaining

$200 − $179 = ■

Estimate: $200 - $179 = \blacksquare \rightarrow $200 - $180 = 20
Think: $200 - $179 = 21

The answer $21 is close to the estimate $20 and is a sensible answer.
He will have $21 left.

Word processing software, such as SimpleWriter, allows you to write a document and make corrections on your computer. When the document has been completed and is free of errors, a printed copy can be made. All documents written on a word processor can be saved and stored on disks. A spelling checker can be used with some word processors to locate and help correct spelling errors.

EXAMPLE 2

Mitchell's computer has 256,000 bytes of memory. His word processor needs 25,000 bytes of memory to hold the program. The memory remaining in the computer can be used to store written documents. If a page of writing uses 3,000 bytes, how many pages can Mitchell's computer hold?

total memory − **memory needed for program** = **memory available**
256,000 bytes − 25,000 bytes = 231,000 bytes

memory available ÷ **memory needed for each page** = **number of pages**
231,000 bytes ÷ 3,000 bytes/page = 77 pages

The computer's memory will hold 77 pages.

Schools and businesses often need many copies of a single software program. Software companies usually offer discounts when large numbers of the same software package are purchased. MicroVendors Software Store offers a 25% discount on purchases of 10 or more copies of a single title.

EXAMPLE 3

The Laurel Language School is buying 15 copies of Spanish Teacher from MicroVendors. What is the total cost of the software?

Step 1. Find the discount price of the software.

100% − **discount rate** = **discount percent**
100% − 25% = 75%

Think: 75% = 0.75

discount percent × **regular price** = **discount price**
0.75 × $35 = $26.25

Step 2. Find the total cost.

$$\text{discount price} \times \text{number of copies} = \text{total cost}$$
$$\$26.25 \quad \times \quad 15 \quad = \$393.75$$

The total cost of the software is $393.75.

With a calculator and mental math, the solution to Example 3 can be streamlined.

Think: 100% − 25% = 75%

Key: $\boxed{C_E^C}$ 35 $\boxed{\times}$ 75 $\boxed{\%}$ $\boxed{\times}$ 15 $\boxed{=}$ ⟋⟋393.75⟋⟋
$\qquad\qquad\qquad\qquad\qquad\qquad$ $393.75

Class Exercises

Use the MicroVendors Software Store price list.

1. What is the cost of one copy each of Home Filer, SimpleCalc, and Grapher?

2. What is the cost of one copy each of Grapher, SimpleMath, Checkmate, and Spacebattles?

3. Eric budgeted $150 for software and needs Home Budget, Home Filer and Grapher. How much of his budget will he have left after these purchases?

4. The Cipher Accounting Company needs 12 copies of SimpleWriter for its secretaries. If it gets a discount of 25% on this many copies, what will be the total cost of the software?

EXERCISES

Use the MicroVendors Software Store price list.

1. What is the cost of one copy each of Home Budget and SimpleCalc?

2. What is the cost of one copy each of Home Filer, SimpleWriter, and SimpleMath?

3. What is the cost of one copy each of SimpleWriter, SimpleSpeller, Home Filer, and Checkmate?

4. What is the cost of one copy each of Checkmate and Spacebattles?

5. Lorrilea Simons
Software budget: $200
Software wanted: Home Budget; Grapher; SimpleSpeller
Amount left: ■

6. Dennis Nollert
Software budget: $250
Software wanted: Home Filer; SimpleWriter; Grapher
Amount left: ■

7. Macklin Harding
Software budget: $300
Software wanted: SimpleTyper; SimpleWriter; SimpleSpeller; SimpleCalc; Home Budget
Amount left: ■

8. Debbi Fuller
Software budget: ■
Software wanted: Checkmate; Spacebattles
Amount left: $57

9. Franklin Games
Software: Checkmate, Grapher
No. of copies: 13 each
Discount: 25%
Total cost: ■

10. First Bank
Software: SimpleCalc
No. of copies: ■
Discount: 25%
Total cost: $546

11. Show how you would use a calculator to help streamline the computation for Problem 9.

12. Arlene's computer has 128,000 bytes of memory left after loading her word processor. How many pages of writing can fit in the remaining memory if each page uses 3,000 bytes?

13. Marni paid $1,225 for her computer and printer. She needs SimpleWriter and SimpleSpeller to complete her word processing system. How much will her complete system cost?

14. An *integrated* system is a program that consists of a word processor, database system, and spreadsheet. MicroSolid Software Systems offers an integrated system for $81. How much less does it cost to buy this system than to buy the individual programs SimpleWriter, Home Filer, and SimpleCalc from MicroVendors?

15. Nora does typing at $.95 per page on her word processor. If her computer cost $1,400, her software cost $200, and her supplies cost $.02 per typed page, how many pages must she type to recover the cost of her word processing system?

Using a Calculator: *Choosing a Way to Solve*

There are often various methods you can use to solve a problem with the help of a calculator. Here are three methods you could use to solve Example 3.

a. Key: $\boxed{C^C_E}$ 35 $\boxed{\times}$ 15 $\boxed{M+}$ $\boxed{\times}$ 25 $\boxed{\%}$ $\boxed{M-}$ $\boxed{M^R_C}$ ⟋393.75⟋

b. Key: $\boxed{C^C_E}$ 35 $\boxed{\times}$ 25 $\boxed{\%}$ $\boxed{M-}$ 35 $\boxed{M+}$ $\boxed{M^R_C}$ $\boxed{\times}$ 15 $\boxed{=}$ ⟋393.75⟋

c. Key: $\boxed{C^C_E}$ 100 $\boxed{-}$ 25 $\boxed{M+}$ 35 $\boxed{\times}$ $\boxed{M^R_C}$ $\boxed{\%}$ $\boxed{\times}$ 15 $\boxed{=}$ ⟋393.75⟋

1. Explain each method shown above.

2. Can you find another way to use your calculator to solve this problem?

3. How can mental math help shorten the calculator work in Method C?

4. Use the method of your choice to find the cost of 40 copies of SimpleMath if there is a 20% discount for buying more than one copy.

Career
Camp Counselor

One of the jobs available for summer employment is that of **camp counselor** at a camp for young people.

Profile of a camp counselor. Many camp counselors major in recreation, physical education, or teaching in college and work as camp counselors for the summer. A college education, however, is not required, but a first aid certificate is often necessary. Camp counselors enjoy working with young people and generally enjoy a variety of sports.

The camp counselor's environment. The environment of a camp depends upon its location and purpose—there are camps in the mountains, by the seashore, for music training, and so on. Camp counselors spend the whole day with the campers. Unless the camp emphasizes computers or tutoring, you will not need many math skills.

All in a day's work. Sheila and Tom worked at a summer camp every year during college. Sheila was in charge of the waterfront equipment and activities. Tom was supervisor for the arts and crafts activities.

One year, they had to order supplies for the camp. They knew there would be 45 children at the camp for each of two 4-week periods.

1. They estimated that it would cost $50 per week to feed each child. How much will the food cost for the two sessions?

2. They planned to have each child make a craft project from plastic strips. If it takes 3 yards of plastic for each project, how much should Sheila and Tom order?

3. Sheila had to replace $\frac{2}{3}$ of the 45 life preservers. How many life preservers did she have to purchase?

15-4 *Joining a Health Club*

One way to keep fit is to join a health club. Most health clubs have swimming pools, handball courts, exercise equipment, and other facilities. If you join a health club, you also have a chance to meet other people sharing your interest in health and fitness.

EXAMPLE 1

The Downtown Spa health club is having a membership drive. Anyone who joins during the month can join for $18 per month by signing up for at least 12 months. How much will it cost Katrina if she signs up during the month for 1 year?

> **Hidden Question:** How many months in 1 year?
> 1 y = 12 mo

cost per month × number of months = membership cost
$18   ×   12   = $216

It will cost Katrina $216 to join.

By using the facilities of the club frequently, Katrina lowers the cost per visit.

EXAMPLE 2

If Katrina visits her club 62 times during her year of membership, how much does it cost her per visit?

total fee ÷ number of visits = cost per visit
$216   ÷   62   =   ■

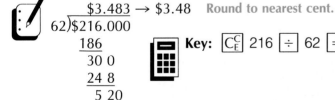

$$\begin{array}{r} \$3.483 \rightarrow \$3.48 \quad \text{Round to nearest cent.} \\ 62)\overline{\$216.000} \\ \underline{186} \\ 30\ 0 \\ \underline{24\ 8} \\ 5\ 20 \\ \underline{4\ 96} \\ 240 \\ \underline{186} \\ 54 \end{array}$$

Key: $\boxed{C_E^C}$ 216 $\boxed{÷}$ 62 $\boxed{=}$ 3.4838709
$3.48   Round to nearest cent.

It will cost her $3.48 per visit.

EXAMPLE 3

If Katrina swam 26 laps on one afternoon she visited the club, how far did she swim? (A lap is 75 ft long.)

length of a lap × number of laps = distance swam

75 × 26 = 1,950

She swam 1,950 feet.

Class Exercises

Complete the table.

Club Name	Monthly Cost	Number of Months	Total Cost
Polar Health Club	$23	8	**1.** ■
Eastside Spa	**2.** ■	12	$180
Fitness, Inc.	$17.50	**3.** ■	$157.50

Complete the table.

Name	Annual Fee	Number of Visits	Cost per Visit
Jerome Hill	$195	45	**4.** ■
Alice Fain	$265	80	**5.** ■

6. Morris swam 104 laps in his health club's pool. If a lap is 75 feet long, how far did he swim?

EXERCISES

Complete the table.

Club Name	Monthly Cost	Number of Months	Total Cost
Pat's Health Club	$20	10	**1.** ■
Roger & Pam's Spa	$15	**2.** ■	$120
Solar Health Spa	$21	**3.** ■	$504
Health-for-All	**4.** ■	16	$384
StayFit Club	$22.50	12	**5.** ■
Great Health Club	**6.** ■	9	$281.25

Complete the table by filling in the missing information.

Name	Annual Fee	Number of Visits	Cost per Visit
Maas Dreyfuss	$250	7. ■	$2.50
Roger Waslo	$285	60	8. ■

9. Which of Exercises 1–8 could be done mentally? In which would pencil and paper be appropriate? Which could best be done by using a calculator?

10. Barrie Holdt
Length of lap: 56 ft
No. of laps: 36
Distance: ■

11. Rena Gold
Length of lap: ■
No. of laps: 62
Distance: 2,952 ft

12. Derek is a member of a health club. His annual membership dues are $265. If he renews his membership for another year, he can get a 15% discount on the fee. How much will the discounted membership cost him?

13. Barry can join a spa for $280 per year or he can use its facilities for an annual fee of $75 and $5 per visit. If he expects to visit the club 35 times during the year, which plan would be more economical for him? How much would he save by using the more economical plan?

14. Sue has paid $205 for her annual health club membership. In the first 11 months of membership, she has visited the club 46 times. How many visits must she make in the twelfth month to bring her cost per visit to $3.75 or less?

15. Investigate the cost of joining a health club in your area. Share your findings with the class.

Consumer Note: *Joining a Health Club*

If you're thinking about joining a health club, you'll want to review your goals and finances and find out what is available in your area before choosing the best membership for you.

First, determine your needs. Are you interested in aerobics, Nautilus training, racquetball, or swimming? Are you a fitness athlete, or are you training for serious competition? What time of day do you want to work out? Do you need instructions in a particular activity?

Next, determine what types of clubs are available. Some clubs offer a wide variety of facilities, activities, classes, and events. Others cater to clients interested in only one activity, such as tennis or body building.

To find out what types are in your area, consult your local yellow pages or fitness publications. Then you can visit the clubs and ask for a guided tour or a pass to use the facilities for one time only. Ask questions about membership or court costs, the schedule and use of the various facilities, and what kinds of instruction or classes are offered.

Making the right choice in a health club will go a long way toward helping you achieve your fitness goals.

15-5 *Continuing Your Education*

There are a variety of reasons why you might choose to continue your education: You might like to get training or education for another type of job, you might wish to get background that would enable you to move up in your present job, or you might simply wish to learn more about subjects that interest you.

EXAMPLE 1

Van is enrolled at a local college in an economics course. He has gotten the following grades on four tests. What is his average?

73, 84, 81, 86

sum of items	÷	number of items	=	average
(73 + 84 + 81 + 86)	÷	4	=	■
324	÷	4	=	81

His test average is 81.

You can use the formula for finding average another way. By multiplying an average by the number of items, you can find the sum of these items. Example 2 shows how to use this to find out what score is needed on a test to raise an average.

EXAMPLE 2

In the first three tests in his writing course, Van's average is 78. What does he need on his next test to bring his average up to 80?

average × number of items = sum of items
78 × 3 = 234

Van's target average is 80, so he will need the following sum:

average × number of items = sum of items
80 × 4 = 320

Van needs to score the difference between the two sums on his next test:

320 − 234 = 86

Van will need to score an 86 on his next test.

The college Van attends charges a tuition fee of $75 for each credit plus a laboratory fee of $35 for a science or computer course.

EXAMPLE 3

Next semester, Van must take a 4-credit course in computer programming. How much will this course cost?

(cost per credit × number of credits) + lab fee = total fee

($75 × 4) + $35 = ■

Think: ($75 × 4) + $35 = ($75 × 2 × 2) + $35 = ($150 × 2) + $35
= $300 + $35 = $335

His total fee will be $335.

Class Exercises

Complete the table by finding each average.

Test 1	Test 2	Test 3	Test 4	Average
90	80	100	None	1. ■
87	68	75	81	2. ■

Complete the table by finding the test score needed to reach the target average.

Average Now	Number of Tests	Target Average	Score Needed Next Test
77	4	75	3. ■
68	3	70	4. ■

Complete the table by finding the total cost of each course.

Course Name	Cost per Credit	Number of Credits	Lab Fee	Total Cost
College math	$100	3	0	5. ■
Chemistry	$ 80	4	$50	6. ■

EXERCISES

Complete the table by finding each average.

Test 1	Test 2	Test 3	Test 4	Average
75	85	80	None	1. ■
70	60	70	60	2. ■
78	76	80	None	3. ■
86	78	72	83	4. ■
91	83	77	None	5. ■
88	67	91	83	6. ■

Complete the table by finding the test score needed to reach the target average.

Average Now	Number of Tests	Target Average	Score Needed Next Test
75	2	80	**7.** ■
80	4	75	**8.** ■
77	3	80	**9.** ■

Complete the table by finding the total cost of each course.

Course Name	Cost per Credit	Number of Credits	Lab Fee	Total Cost
Computer science	$ 50	4	$50	**10.** ■
German	$125	4	$55	**11.** ■

12. Explain how mental arithmetic can be used to find the answer to Exercise 11.

13. Brice Kanton
Test 1: 67; Test 2: 71
Test 3: 75; Test 4: 81
Average: ■

14. Ruth Diemack
Test 1: 83; Test 2: ■
Test 3: 78; Test 4: 88
Average: 84.75

15. Belinda needs 48 more credits to complete her degree. She has three 4-credit courses to complete. The rest of her courses are all 3 credits. How many more courses must she take?

16. George estimates that his college degree will cost him $8,500 from the City Community College. If it takes him 8 years to earn his degree, what is the average cost per year?

17. After he gets his degree, Larry expects to earn an average of $3,500 more per year for the remainder of his working career. If the total 8-year cost of his degree was $16,400, how many years will it take to recover the cost of his education?

Mental Math: *Estimating by Clustering*

It is often possible to estimate sums needed to find an average by *clustering*.
For example, estimate the sum 45 + 38 + 42 + 31 + 49.
Observe that each of the numbers is near 40. Therefore, an estimate of the sum is 40 × 5 = 200.

Estimate each sum using clustering.

1. 69 + 82 + 68 + 73 + 71 + 65

2. 95 + 103 + 104 + 97

Computer:
Software Evaluation Checklist

The following evaluation checklist can be used to help evaluate software.

SOFTWARE EVALUATION FORM

Name of Program: _____

Name of User: _____

I. Is the software easy to use?

_____ 1. Is it self-booting?

_____ 2. Does it display a menu upon booting?

_____ 3. Does it prompt all input?

_____ 4. Does it allow easy correcting of mistakes?

_____ 5. Can you always return to the menu?

_____ 6. Is there always a way to exit the program?

_____ 7. Does it let you call for help?

II. Does the software perform well?

_____ 1. Does the program perform all the tasks listed in the menu?

_____ 2. Are all calculations accurate and all answers correct?

_____ 3. Does it complete its tasks quickly?

_____ 4. When you must wait while the program performs long tasks, does it explain what is happening?

III. Does the software handle errors well?

_____ 1. Is the program free of errors?

_____ 2. If you enter data incorrectly, does the program give you a chance to re-enter the information?

_____ 3. Can you press keys randomly without causing the program to crash?

_____ 4. Does the program run smoothly even when you give it wrong answers and bad data?

IV. Does the software have good documentation?

_____ 1. Is the manual easy to read?

_____ 2. Are all of the program's operations explained clearly?

_____ 3. Are examples given and explained?

_____ 4. Is there a complete index and/or a quick reference sheet?

V. Do you like the software?

_____ 1. Did it capture and hold your interest?

_____ 2. Did it do what you wanted it to do?

_____ 3. Would you recommend it to others?

Summary
21-22 YES Responses .... Excellent
18-20 YES Responses .... Good
15-17 YES Responses .... Fair
Fewer than 15 YES Responses........... Poor

Decision Making:
A Health and Fitness Plan

Caroline Flinner spent her first weekend of summer vacation at a lake resort near her home and was upset to find that she could swim only part of the way around the lake—much less than the summer before. After seeing her physician for her annual checkup, she decided that her weight and blood pressure were higher than she wanted them to be. So, she got some information from her physician about diet and fitness. She decided she was pretty well informed about how to control her calorie intake and how to cut down on salt and fat.

Answer the following questions.

1. What initial steps do you think Caroline has taken to develop her health and fitness plan?

2. What other things should Caroline include in her plan besides good nutrition?

CUTTING DOWN ON CALORIES

Caroline kept track of the number of calories that she ate for several days. She realized she was getting about 2,300 calories per day. She decided she could have fruit instead of a sweet dessert and cut out the snack she always had during her midmorning break. By doing these things, she estimated she would eat about 400 fewer calories per day and still have food from the basic four food groups discussed in her booklet.

Answer the following questions.

3. Assume Caroline needs 2,300 calories per day to maintain her present weight. If she reduces her caloric intake to 1,900 calories each day, how long will it take her to lose 1 pound? (One pound is equivalent to 3,500 calories.)

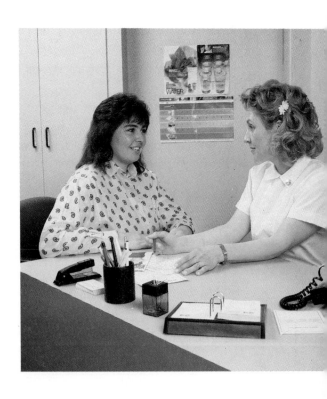

4. Do you think it is realistic for Caroline to plan to eat 400 fewer calories each day? Explain your answer.

5. If Caroline reduces her caloric intake by 600 calories per day, how long will it take her to lose 10 pounds?

6. How could you improve your own nutrition?

DECIDING ON A FITNESS PLAN

Caroline decided she needed to develop a fitness plan to help lower her blood pressure and to help her lose weight. She also decided she would feel better if she exercised more. She planned to swim at the lake each weekend but felt she needed something else to do as well. Caroline listed some possible exercises she could do during the week.

- Jog 1/2 hour per day
- Bicycle 45 minutes per day
- Do aerobics 1/2 hour per day
- Jump rope 20 minutes per day

She decided to jog for $\frac{1}{2}$ hour per day.

Answer the following questions.

7. What factors do you think Caroline might want to consider when deciding what other type of exercise she could do in addition to the swimming?

8. What other kind of exercise can Caroline do if bad weather prevents her from jogging?

9. How much regular exercise do you get? What additional exercise could you plan for yourself?

A COMPLETE FITNESS PLAN

Caroline realized that her fitness plan included several parts besides diet and exercise:

> *—not smoking or using harmful substances,*
> *—having regular medical and dental checkups,*
> *—getting enough sleep*

Answer the following questions.

10. Caroline's health and fitness plan includes several parts. Which parts are most important? Explain your answer.

11. Choose one part of Caroline's plan and explain how omitting that part would change the overall plan.

12. How is good nutrition related to Caroline's whole health and fitness plan?

13. Describe how you thought to answer Question 12.

14. How is good nutrition related to exercise in Caroline's plan?

THINKING ABOUT THE FITNESS PLAN

Caroline thought about the process of developing a fitness plan. She noted that she first had to make the basic decision to have a health and fitness plan and to follow the rules she set up for herself in the plan. Then she had to make decisions about what to include in her plan: nutrition, exercise, checkups, and so on. She had to get information on all these parts. Finally, she had to decide how to cut out calories and how to exercise—and to say no to sweet desserts and snacks. She felt she had started with a big decision and then followed it with many smaller decisions.

Answer the following question.

15. What are some other situations where you make an overall decision that must then be followed with many smaller decisions?

STAYING WITH THE PLAN

One day at work, Caroline had two sweet desserts at a party for a co-worker who was leaving. She was very discouraged because she had not stuck with her plan. But a couple of days later she noticed that she had not gained any weight and decided she would just have to be more careful in the future.

Answer the following question.

16. In this case, when Caroline did not follow all of her plan, it did not affect her overall plan. Identify a different situation that is affected when a small part is missing.

EVALUATING THE PLAN

At the end of the summer, Caroline saw her doctor again. She had lost 9 pounds and her blood pressure was at the level it should be. She also found she could swim around the lake. She decided that she could modify her plan a little.

For instance, Caroline felt she could start to eat a few more calories each day. However, she felt it was still important to continue to pay attention to all parts of her plan and to find some kind of exercise to replace the swimming at the lake. She decided a good health and fitness plan had been worth the planning and decisions she had to make.

Answer the following questions.

17. How is making a decision about a health and fitness plan different from making a decision about buying a personal computer?

18. Why is it important to recognize the relationship between the whole and its parts as you make decisions?

DECIDE FOR YOURSELF

Use the same steps as Caroline to develop a health and fitness plan that you could use yourself. Summarize the steps you, and Caroline, took to develop a health and fitness plan.

Chapter 15 Review

VOCABULARY

byte

kilobyte

hardware

software

For Exercises 1–4, select the word that completes each statement.

1. The actual computer and its supporting equipment is called _____ .

2. _____ are the sets of instructions that tell the computer what to do.

3. A single unit of memory in a computer is called a _____ .

4. A _____ is a unit of 1,024 bytes of memory.

SKILLS

Find each difference.

5. 594 − 326

6. $400 − $267

7. $2,050 − $961

Find each product.

8. $32 × 12

9. $45 × 24

10. $225 × 36

Find the average.

11. 24, 36, 48, 62

12. 85, 76, 99, 110

13. 75, 250, 325, 400, 90, 100

CONSUMER TOPICS

Solve.

14. AM/FM tuner: $250
   Turntable: $125
   Tape player: $150
   Speakers: $200
   Compact disc player: $300
   Total cost:

15. Erik bought a color TV for $399.95 and a video recorder for $249.95. How much did the complete system cost him?

Lincoln has $900 to spend on a stereo system. How much can he spend on each component if he uses the following percentages, suggested by a consumer guide?

16. AM/FM tuner: 27%

17. Turntable: 12%

18. Tape player: 15%

19. Speakers: 25%

20. Compact disc player: 21%

21. Marcus can rent a movie for $2.50. It would cost him $12 to take his family to a movie. How many movies must he rent instead of going to a theater to cover the cost of his $250 video recorder?

22. How many times as much memory does an 896K computer have than one with 256K?

23. Carla bought a computer with two disk drives for $895, a monitor for $350, a printer for $425, and an integrated software package that cost $125. What was the total amount of her purchase?

24. Thom budgeted $500 for software. How much was left in his budget if he bought software costing $321.50 and $78?

25. Karla's computer has 128,000 bytes of memory. Of that amount, 35,000 bytes are used to hold a word processing program. If a page of writing uses 3,000 bytes, how many pages can Karla's computer hold?

26. Bret bought 25 copies of SimpleCalc. If he receives a 20% discount and the price of the software was $52, how much did he spend on software?

27. Patrice joined a health club on a special 18-month plan. If she paid $25 to register and then paid $20 per month, what was her total cost for the membership?

28. Jason paid $250 for a 1-year membership in a health club. If he visited the club an average of 3 times a week during the year, how much did each visit cost him?

29. The pool in Emily's health club is 50 meters long. How far did she swim the afternoon she swam 30 lengths?

30. Jeff enrolled in a technical school that charges $60 per credit for courses. He also had to pay a $25 registration fee. He enrolled in a 3-credit course in electrical repairs, and a 4-credit course in plumbing. How much did he have to pay to enroll in his two classes?

31. Clayton had 4 tests in his automotive class. If his scores were 88, 85, 87, and 90, what was his average for the class?

32. Deborah had scores of 65, 83, 92, and 88. What score would she need on the fifth test so her average would be 80?

1. Find the total cost of a system consisting of an AM/FM tuner at $220, a turntable at $150, a tape player at $170, speakers at $300, and a compact disc player at $250.

Matt has $700 to spend on a stereo system. How much can he spend on each component if he uses the following percentages, suggested by a consumer guide?

2. AM/FM tuner: 27%

3. Turntable: 12%

4. Tape player: 15%

5. Speakers: 25%

6. Compact disc player: 21%

7. David bought a color TV for $299.95 and a video recorder for $249.95. How much did the complete system cost?

8. How many times as many bytes of memory does a 640K computer have than one with 128K?

9. Amy can rent a movie for $2. It would cost her $10 to take her family to a movie. How many movies must she rent instead of going to a theater to cover the cost of her $300 video recorder?

10. Jessica bought a computer with two disk drives for $795, a monitor for $250, a printer for $350, and an integrated software package that cost $100. What was the total amount of her purchase?

11. Carl bought software costing $211.50 and $399.95. How much was left in his software budget of $900?

12. Rob bought 20 copies of SimpleWriter. If he receives a 20% discount and the price of the software was $45, how much did he spend on software?

13. Elaine's computer has 256,000 bytes of memory. Of that amount, 40,000 bytes are used to hold a word processing program. If a page of writing uses 3,000 bytes, how many pages can Elaine's computer hold?

14. Mesha joined a health club on a special 15-month plan. She paid $50 to register and then paid $15 per month. What was her cost per visit if she used the health club an average of 8 times per month?

15. The pool in Maura's health club is 50 meters long. How far did she swim the afternoon she swam 20 lengths?

16. Bob had 4 tests in his automotive class. If his scores were 88, 85, 88, and 92, what was his average for the class?

17. Dawn had test scores of 73, 55, and 54. What score would she need on the fourth test to raise her average to 65?

18. Luke enrolled in a technical school that charges $70 per credit for courses. He also had to pay a $25 registration fee. He enrolled in a 3-credit course, and a 4-credit course. How much did he have to pay to enroll in his two classes?

Cumulative Mixed Review

Select the letter corresponding to the correct answer.

1. Laura and Ken had dinner in a restaurant. The dinner bill was $17.50. They had to pay an 8% food tax and they left a 15% tip on the dinner bill for the waiter. What was the total amount they paid for dinner that night?
- **a.** $17.50
- **b.** $21.53
- **c.** $4.03
- **d.** $2.15

2. Deidra earns $19,500 per year. If she has 25% withheld for deductions, what is the net amount of her biweekly paycheck?
- **a.** $187.50
- **b.** $609.38
- **c.** $14,625
- **d.** $562.50

3. Sam borrowed $2,500 for 4 months at 10.5% simple interest. What was the total amount he had to repay?
- **a.** $2,565.63
- **b.** $2,587.50
- **c.** $2,762.50
- **d.** $262.50

4. Ginger budgets 25% of her income for housing and 20% of her income for food. If she earns $16,000 per year, how much must she budget monthly for housing and food?
- **a.** $7,200
- **b.** $138.46
- **c.** $600
- **d.** $4,000

5. Zeke bought a truck for $17,962. He had to pay 6.25% sales tax on the purchase. What was the total amount he had to pay for the truck?
- **a.** $19,084.63
- **b.** $16,839.37
- **c.** $1,122.63
- **d.** $11,226.25

6. Joanne earns $4.50 per hour, time-and-a-half for overtime, and 5% commission on gross sales. What were her earnings the week she worked 44 hours and sold $2,500 worth of goods?
- **a.** $207
- **b.** $323
- **c.** $311.75
- **d.** $332

7. Henry paid $3.49 for a 12-ounce bag of cookies. What was the unit cost per pound?
- **a.** $4.65
- **b.** $.29
- **c.** $6.96
- **d.** $2.90

8. Warren bought $38.50 worth of items through a catalog. If he had to pay 6.5% sales tax and a shipping charge of $2.50, what was the total amount of the purchase?
- **a.** $5
- **b.** $41
- **c.** $38.50
- **d.** $43.50

9. Cory bought a car for $11,500. She made a down payment of $3,000 and financed the rest. If she made 48 payments of $210 each, how much interest did she pay?
- **a.** $1,420
- **b.** $1,580
- **c.** $10,080
- **d.** $158

10. Matilda bought 200 shares of stock at $35\frac{1}{2}$. She had to pay a 1% commission to her broker. What was the total price of the stock?
- **a.** $7,171
- **b.** $7,100
- **c.** $717
- **d.** $71

Emma learned that 47% of her high school classmates scored lower than the national average on the standardized physical fitness tests given in physical education class. For a special credit project she decided to find out how her classmates scored in specific events, such as running and sit-ups. She needed to compile some statistics.

- What statistics do you think Emma would need to compare the performance of her class to the performance of students nationwide?

- How could she determine how her school compared to other schools in her district?

- How would she find her class median compared to the national median? How would she find the mode?

If you wanted to gather similar information at your school, where would you start? Name several sources of information for statistics that you would use.

16-1 Health Statistics

If you decide to join a health club or you take up a sport for fitness, you may hear about the probability of injury or about the chance of winning. The **probability** of an event is a measure of the likelihood that it will occur. The probability of an event is found by comparing the number of favorable outcomes to the total number of outcomes.

Mary Pat plays tennis with her friends Roger, Dennis, Sam, Lois, and Arlene at her health club. Each week they draw lots to determine their opponents. Mary Pat often tries to guess her opponent and the probability she will be right. To determine the probability that she will get a particular opponent, she makes a **sample space** of all possible events, or pairs of opponents. For Mary Pat's entire group, the sample space is:

(Arlene, Dennis)	(Arlene, Lois)	(Arlene, Mary Pat)
(Arlene, Roger)	(Arlene, Sam)	(Dennis, Lois)
(Dennis, Mary Pat)	(Dennis, Roger)	(Dennis, Sam)
(Lois, Mary Pat)	(Lois, Roger)	(Lois, Sam)
(Mary Pat, Roger)	(Mary Pat, Sam)	(Roger, Sam)

EXAMPLE 1

What is the probability that Mary Pat's opponent will be a man? Mary Pat appears in 5 of the matches. In 3, her opponent is a man.

$$P(\text{male}) = \frac{\text{number of matches with male opponents}}{\text{number of Mary Pat's matches}}$$

$$P(\text{male}) = \tfrac{3}{5}, \text{ or } 0.6$$

The probability that Mary Pat's opponent will be a man is $\tfrac{3}{5}$.

Playing tennis or participating in sports provides you with good ways to exercise. In addition to contributing to your general health, exercising helps to reduce body weight by burning off excess calories. The following table shows the calories used for various forms of exercise.

Calorie Use for Certain Activities			
Activity	Calories per 15 Minutes	Activity	Calories per 15 Minutes
Bicycling	100	Jogging	180
Bowling	100	Running	225
Golf	65	Swimming	100
Handball	150	Walking (briskly)	75

Skill Review

To find the probability of an event, you must be able to express fractions in simplest terms.

Express each fraction in simplest terms.

1. $\frac{7}{28}$

2. $\frac{121}{33}$

3. $\frac{15}{24}$

4. $\frac{36}{100}$

(For additional help, see page 546.)

EXAMPLE 2

Mary Pat played handball for 25 minutes. How many calories did she use playing handball?

To find the calories used per minute, divide calories per 15 minutes by 15.

time spent × **(calories per 15 min ÷ 15)** = **calories used**
25 min × (150 calories per 15 min ÷ 15) = ■

Think: 150 ÷ 15 = 10
25 × 10 = 250

She used 250 calories.

In order to lose 1 pound of weight, it is necessary to burn 3,500 calories. An adult female takes in and uses about 2,100 calories per day in normal activities. Usually, the best way to lose weight is by both reducing calorie intake and exercising.

EXAMPLE 3

How long would Mary Pat have to bicycle to lose 1 pound of body weight?

3,500 ÷ (calories per min) = time needed
3,500 ÷ (100 ÷ 15) = ■

Think: $3{,}500 \div (100 \div 15) = 3{,}500 \div \frac{100}{15}$
$= 3{,}500 \times \frac{15}{100} = 35 \times 15$

$35 \times 15 = 525$

The time needed is 525 minutes.

Hidden Question: How many minutes in 1 hour?
1 h = 60 min

To change 525 minutes to hours, divide by 60.

$$60\overline{)525.00} \quad 8.75$$

She would have to bicycle 8.75 hours to lose 1 pound.

With a calculator, you can simplify the computation in Example 3.

Key: $\boxed{C_E^C}$ 3500 $\boxed{\times}$ 15 $\boxed{\div}$ 100 $\boxed{\div}$ 60 $\boxed{=}$ ⟋ 8.75 ⟋

Class Exercises

1. Use the sample space in Example 1. What is the probability that Dennis will be in the match being played?

Use the table on page 510 to find the calories burned off during the given exercises.

Type of Exercise	Time Spent	Calories Used
Bicycling	30 min	2. ■
Jogging	45 min	3. ■
Walking	60 min	4. ■
Running	20 min	5. ■

6. Explain how mental arithmetic can be used to find the answer to Exercise 2.

7. How many hours would a person have to run in order to lose 1 pound of body weight?

EXERCISES

Use the sample space in Example 1.

1. Find the probability that Dennis' opponent in the tennis match will be a man.

2. Find the probability that Roger's opponent in the tennis match will be a woman.

Solve.

3. Sally wrote the names of sports she enjoys—tennis, volleyball, basketball, and swimming—on cards, one to a card. If she draws a card at random, what is the probability that the sport listed will involve using a ball?

Use the table on page 510 to find the calories burned off during the given exercises.

Type of Exercise	Time Spent	Calories Used
Swimming	30 min	4. ■
Walking	2 h	5. ■
Golf	3 h	6. ■
Jogging	35 min	7. ■
Handball	50 min	8. ■
Bowling	1 h 45 min	9. ■

10. Which of Exercises 1-9 can be done mentally? In which would pencil and paper be appropriate? Which could best be done by using a calculator?

Solve.

11. Activity: Handball
Time spent: 45 minutes
Calories used: ■

12. Activity: Walking
Time spent:
Calories used: 525

13. How many hours of walking are necessary to lose 1 pound of body weight?

14. How much time spent bowling is needed to lose 1 pound of body weight?

15. Louis Pettinger spent 3 hours playing golf. How much body weight did he lose in that time?

16. Stacie Wiggins spent 75 minutes jogging. How much body weight did she lose in that time?

17. Show how to use your calculator to streamline the computation for Problem 16.

18. Jessie wants to lose 1 pound per week over the next several weeks. She will do this by eating less on several days and exercising more on others. If she jogs for 1 hour on 4 days in the week, by how many calories should she reduce her food intake on the other days of the week in order to lose the pound?

19. Keep track of any of the activities in the table on page 510 that you do in one week and the amount of time you spend doing each one. Calculate the number of calories you burn in one week.

Challenge

The **odds** for success of an event are found by dividing the probability of the event's success (a favorable outcome) by the probability of its failure (an unfavorable outcome). If P(S) stands for the probability of success and P(F) stands for the probability of failure, then you can find the odds for success by using the following formula.

$$\text{odds} = \frac{P(S)}{P(F)} \text{ where } P(F) = 1 - P(S)$$

In Example 1, what are the odds that Mary Pat will draw a male opponent? The probability that she will draw a male opponent is $\frac{3}{5}$ and the probability that she will draw a female opponent is $1 - \frac{3}{5} = \frac{2}{5}$.

$$\text{odds} = \frac{\frac{3}{5}}{\frac{2}{5}} = \frac{3}{2}$$

The odds that she will draw a male opponent are 3 to 2.

1. Find the odds that Dennis's opponent will be a man.

2. Find the odds that Roger's opponent will be a woman.

16-2 Sports Statistics

If you participate in or watch sports, you probably keep statistics about your performance or that of others. Baseball statistics show how well players do. A player's **batting average** is a decimal fraction that tells how often a player hits the ball, and the **fielding average** describes the player's success in the field.

EXAMPLE 1

Lisa has been at bat 128 times this season and has gotten 38 hits. What is her batting average?

number of hits ÷ **number of times at bat** = **batting average**

    38   ÷   128   =   ■

Estimate: $38 \div 128 = \blacksquare \rightarrow 40 \div 120 = \frac{1}{3} = 0.333$

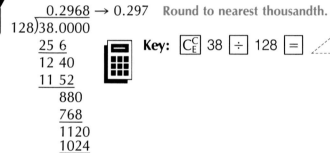

```
        0.2968 → 0.297   Round to nearest thousandth.
128)38.0000
    25 6
    12 40
    11 52
       880
       768
      1120
      1024
        96
```

Key: C^C_E 38 ÷ 128 = 0.296875
0.297   Round to nearest thousandth

The answer 0.297 is reasonably close to the estimate 0.333 and is a sensible answer.

Lisa's batting average is 0.297, which is usually written as .297.

Many teams keep records on the performance of individual batters. This helps them predict how well a batter may do in the future.

EXAMPLE 2

Lisa has batted against Beth 18 times in her softball career. She has gotten 5 hits and walked 3 times. What is the probability of her getting a hit or a walk the next time she bats when Beth is pitching?

Step 1. Find the probability of each event.

$$\text{probability of a hit} = \frac{\text{number of hits}}{\text{times at bat}} = \frac{5}{18}$$

$$\text{probability of a walk} = \frac{\text{number of walks}}{\text{times at bat}} = \frac{3}{18}$$

Step 2. Find the probability of a hit or a walk.

A hit and a walk cannot both happen at the same time. They are called **mutually exclusive events.** For such events, the probability of one *or* the other is the sum of their individual probabilities.

$$\underset{\frac{5}{18}}{\overset{\textbf{probability}}{\textbf{of a hit}}} + \underset{\frac{3}{18}}{\overset{\textbf{probability}}{\textbf{of a walk}}} = \underset{\frac{8}{18} = \frac{4}{9}}{\overset{\textbf{probability of}}{\textbf{a hit or walk}}}$$

The probability that Lisa will get a hit or walk is $\frac{4}{9}$.

Class Exercises

Find each batting average.

Name	Times at Bat	Hits	Batting Average
Louise Ansell	40	10	***1.*** ■
Maurice Delcose	150	42	***2.*** ■
Bandell Magee	139	37	***3.*** ■

4. Jamis has faced pitcher Hank Register 35 times and gotten 8 hits and 4 walks. What is his probability of getting a hit or a walk the next time he bats when Hank is pitching?

EXERCISES

Find each batting average.

Name	Times at Bat	Hits	Batting Average
Brandon Walker	80	20	***1.*** ■
August Martucci	100	38	***2.*** ■
Kitty Foster	145	48	***3.*** ■
Heloise DeSylvia	94	27	***4.*** ■

Solve.

5. Hitter: Sam; pitcher: Wade
At bat: 40 times
Hits: 9; walks: 3
Probability of hit or walk against Wade:

6. Hitter: Lana; pitcher: Sue
At bat: 28 times
Hits: 9; walks: 2
Probability of hit or walk against Sue:

7. Hitter: Eric; pitcher: Frank
At bat: 40 times
Hits: 11; walks: ■
Probability of hit or walk against Frank: $\frac{3}{8}$

8. Hitter: Valerie; pitcher: Don
At bat: ■ times
Hits: 7; walks: 3
Probability of hit or walk against Don: $\frac{5}{16}$

9. Crandell plays basketball for a local team. He has made 106 baskets in 162 tries. What is his percentage of baskets?

10. May Lee plays basketball for a recreation center team. She has made 97 baskets on 135 tries. What is the probability that she will miss a basket on her next try?

11. George, an infielder, has just finished his second year playing professional baseball. In his first year he had a batting average of .256 and had 64 hits. In his second year he had a batting average of .275 and had 22 hits. What is his career batting average for the two years?

12. Matt, an outfielder, began his baseball career at the same time as George (Problem 11). In Matt's first year he had 62 hits in 249 times at bat. In his second year, he got 87 hits in 318 times at bat. Who had the higher batting average the first year, George or Matt? Who had the higher average the second year? Whose overall average was better for the two years?

Critical Thinking: *Identifying Assumptions*

You are at a ball game with your friend, Tony. Your team is two runs ahead. Rich Crowner, a rookie, strikes out. Tony remarks, "I wish they'd trade Rich Crowner! His batting average is only .231. He'll never be much of a hitter!"

In the seventh inning, with a tie score and bases loaded, the opponents send in their new, left-handed pitcher. "The manager better not let Magee bat against *that* pitcher," Tony says. "Magee's batting average is .317 against right-handed pitchers, but it's only .253 against left-handed pitchers."

The manager sends in a pinch hitter instead of Magee.

1. What assumption has Tony made when he predicts Rich's future as a hitter?

2. How did you think to recognize that assumption?

3. What events might occur to make Rich's future different from what Tony predicts?

4. On what assumption do you think the manager has based his decision?

5. Can the manager be *certain* that Magee will get only one hit during the next four times he bats against a left-hander?

6. Compare the assumption Tony made about Rich Crowner with the assumption the coach made about Magee.

7. Why is it important to be able to recognize assumptions?

16-3 Opinion Polls

Opinion polls tell you about everything from favorite movie stars to the number of telephones in U.S. homes. When a poll is taken, care must be exerted to be sure the sample of people interviewed is random. Results of polls are used to get a better picture of people's preferences. Once data are collected, they may be organized and shown by using the **mean** (the average of a group of numbers), **median** (the middle number in a group of numbers), or **mode** (the most frequently occurring number in a group of numbers) of the data.

Radio stations are especially interested in obtaining information about the people who listen to the stations.

EXAMPLE 1

Kerri conducted a telephone poll to find out which daytime radio shows were favored. The ages of the people who were sampled are shown below. Find the mean, median, and mode of the ages.

18, 25, 61, 19, 24, 35, 27, 25, 31, 25, 27, 30

There are 12 ages in the sample.

To find the mean, divide the sum of the ages by the number of people in the sample.

$$\text{mean} = \frac{\text{sum of ages}}{\text{number in sample}}$$

$$= \frac{(18 + 25 + 61 + 19 + 24 + 35 + 27 + 25 + 31 + 25 + 27 + 30)}{12}$$

$$= \frac{347}{12} = 28.9 \quad \text{Round to nearest tenth.}$$

The mean is 28.9.

To find the median and mode, arrange the ages in order from smallest to largest:

18, 19, 24, 25, 25, 25, 27, 27, 30, 31, 35, 61

Since the number in the sample is even, the median is the average of the two middle ages, the sixth and seventh numbers.

$$(25 + 27) \div 2 = 52 \div 2 = 26$$

The median is 26.

Skill Review

In order to organize data, you need to know how to find the mean of a group of numbers.

Find the mean.

1. 23, 87, 46

2. 45, 92, 56, 38

3. 35, 36, 32, 34

4. 56, 74, 38, 47, 52

(For additional help, see page 552.)

The mode is the item with the greatest number of responses. In this sample, three people are 25.

The mode is 25.

In describing a group of numbers, any of the values can be used.

- Use the *mode* if most of the numbers are the same.

- Use the *median* if a few of the numbers are extremely high or extremely low compared to the others.

- Use the *mean* otherwise.

EXAMPLE 2
Using the results of Example 1, determine which of the values (mean, median, or mode) best represents the sample.

In this sample the median gives the best representation. One number in the sample, 61, is very much higher than the rest. This will make the mean too high. It does not affect the median, however. The median gives a more accurate picture of the group.

In opinion polls, the mode is used to determine the most popular response.

Class Exercises

Use the numbers in the following sample for Exercises 1–6.

37, 34, 51, 42, 34, 42, 34, 29, 50, 34, 14, 49, 29

1. Find the mean.   **2.** Find the median.   **3.** Find the mode.

4. Which of the values (mean, median, or mode) would give the best representation of the sample?

5. If the smallest number were removed from the sample, what would be the new mean and median?

6. If the smallest number were removed from the sample, which of the values (mean, median, or mode) would best represent the new sample?

EXERCISES

Use the numbers in the following sample for Exercises 1–6.

One of Kerri's opinion polls showed the family incomes of the people sampled as follows:

$14,000; $28,000; $19,000; $16,000; $74,000;
$21,000; $19,000; $29,000; $20,000; $19,000

1. Find the mean.   **2.** Find the median.   **3.** Find the mode.

4. Which of the values (mean, median, or mode) would give the best representation of the sample?

5. If the largest number were removed from the sample, what would be the new mean and median?

6. If the largest number were removed from the sample, which of the values (mean, median, or mode) would best represent the new sample?

Use the information below for Exercises 7–10.

Kerri took an opinion poll to test the popularity of the following five types of radio shows: (1) talk show; (2) rock music; (3) sports; (4) big bands; (5) news.

The following responses were gathered on the first day's sample.

5, 5, 2, 3, 2, 2, 3, 1, 3, 1, 2, 2, 5, 5, 1, 5, 1, 5, 4, 5,
3, 4, 4, 4, 2, 2, 3, 1, 3, 4, 1, 4, 2, 4, 3, 5, 3, 1, 1, 1

7. Find the mode(s).

8. What percentage preferred talk shows?

9. What percentage preferred sports?

10. What percentage preferred big bands?

11. Of the 15 vacation cottages around a lake, the median value of the cottages is $68,500, the mean value is $72,000, and the mode is $54,000. If the highest priced cottage were increased in value by $8,000, what would be the new mean, median, and mode of the cottages in the group?

12. Take a survey of your classmates to find out their favorite class, TV show, or food from among five choices. Find the mean, median, and mode of your data.

Since the start of modern survey techniques, public opinion polls have played an increasingly important role in the politics, public policy, and economy of our country. Pollsters conduct surveys in rural and urban areas, among rich and poor, and the old and young. Interviewers ask a sample of people to express their attitudes or opinions on the vital issues of the day, often by telephone. Then the interviewers analyze the responses, tabulate the results, and submit them to the news media.

An important requirement of any sample is that it be as representative as possible of the entire group from which it is taken. When the group is uniform, a random sample will represent the group within certain measurable limits of accuracy. If the group is not uniform, then controlled or selective sampling must be used in order to ensure that each part of the group, or subgroup, is represented. If faulty techniques are used and a group is not well represented, then the results are not valid.

16-4 *Statistics in Advertising*

Many manufacturers use statistics to help convince the consumer that their products are better than others. Often the statistics come from data collected from testing manufactured items as they are produced. When the data have been collected, the results are often expressed in terms of the mean, median, or mode of the data. The company will try to use the statistic in their advertising that makes their product appear the best. A **frequency table** can be used to help find mean, median, and mode.

EXAMPLE 1

The NeverLinger Battery Company tested the battery lives of 30 of their batteries. The number of hours each battery lasted is shown below:

13	16	12	18	11	12	15	18	12	13
20	14	15	12	18	16	16	17	12	15
15	14	15	12	17	13	11	15	16	12

> **Problem Solving Strategy:** Organizing information.
> Make a frequency table to show the results and find the mean of the numbers.

In order to find the sum of the items, add a column to the frequency table showing the product of each number times its frequency.

Skill Review

In order to find the mean from a frequency table, you need to be able to multiply whole numbers.

Find each product.

1. 8×56

2. 11×23

3. 14×35

4. 21×84

(For additional help, see page 543.)

Number	Tally	Frequency	Frequency × Number
11	/ /	2	22
12	//// //	7	84
13	/ / /	3	39
14	/ /	2	28
15	//// /	6	90
16	/ / / /	4	64
17	/ /	2	34
18	/ / /	3	54
19		0	0
20	/	1	20
Totals		30	435

sum of the numbers ÷ number of items = mean

435　　　　÷　　　　30　　　=　　■

Estimate: $435 \div 30 = \blacksquare \rightarrow 420 \div 30 = 14$

$$
\begin{array}{r}
14.5 \\
30\overline{)435.00} \\
\underline{30} \\
135 \\
\underline{120} \\
15\ 0 \\
\underline{15\ 0}
\end{array}
$$

Key: $\boxed{C_E^C}$ 435 $\boxed{\div}$ 30 $\boxed{=}$ ⟋ 14.5 ⟋

The answer 14.5 is reasonably close to the estimate 14 and is a sensible answer.

The mean battery life is 14.5 hours.

EXAMPLE 2

Find the median and mode battery life using the numbers in Example 1.

The median is the middle number. Count down the numbers in the frequency table until you find the middle two numbers, since there is an even number of items. Both numbers are 15, so the median is 15.

The mode is the most frequently occurring item: mode = 12.

The median is 15 hours and the mode is 12 hours.

EXAMPLE 3

Which of the values (mean, median, or mode) would the NeverLinger Battery Company probably use in their advertising?

The median makes the battery life appear longer than either the mean or the mode. The company would probably use the median in their advertising.

Class Exercises

The Madewell Automobile Company kept records on the mileage ratings of 25 of its new cars. The results are shown in miles per gallon of gas:

18 21 17 19 18 21 24 25 35 18 22 24 19
19 17 18 16 19 22 19 21 23 19 19 17

Use these numbers in Exercises 1–5.

1. Make a frequency table for the data.

2. Find the mean of the numbers.

3. Find the median of the numbers.

4. Find the mode of the numbers.

5. Would mean, median, or mode be more likely to be used by the Madewell Automobile Company in its advertising?

EXERCISES

The Stapleton Manufacturing Company is advertising to hire some new employees. They have 12 employees currently, whose salaries are shown below:

$19,500 $28,000 $11,000 $11,000 $13,000 $14,000
$11,000 $15,000 $11,000 $14,500 $12,500 $11,000

Use these numbers in Exercises 1–5.

1. Make a frequency table for the data.

2. Find the mean of the numbers.

3. Find the median of the numbers.

4. Find the mode of the numbers.

5. Would mean, median, or mode be more likely to be used by the Stapleton Manufacturing Company in its advertising?

The Trustworthy Automobile Dealership advertises that it sells more cars than any other in their area. Its car sales for the past 12 months are shown below:

31   27   29   26   31   40   42   42   43   31   26   27

Use these numbers in Exercises 6–11.

6. Make a frequency table for the data.

7. Find the mean of the numbers.

8. Find the median of the numbers.

9. Find the mode of the numbers.

10. Of the mean, median, and mode, which is the Trustworthy Automobile Dealership most likely to use in its advertising?

11. Of the mean, median, and mode, which would probably be most useful to a consumer?

The Lyon Department store surveyed their customers to see how long each was in the store. The number of minutes for each person is shown below:

11   28   16   12   29   41   12   12
12   16   30   15   19   12   18

Use these numbers in Exercises 12–15.

12. Make a frequency table of the data.

13. Find the mean of the numbers.

14. Find the median of the numbers.

15. Find the mode of the numbers.

The Speedy Pizza Delivery advertises that it averages less than 18 minutes in making a pizza delivery. The numbers of minutes taken for 20 recent deliveries are shown below:

18   17   17   21   45   30   29   17   16   16
22   24   19   17   16   36   15   13   12   17

Use the numbers at the bottom of page 522 to solve Exercises
16–21.

16. Make a frequency table of the data. **17.** Find the mean of the numbers.

18. Find the median of the numbers. **19.** Find the mode of the numbers.

20. Of the mean, median, and mode, which is the Speedy Pizza
Delivery most likely using in its claim?

21. Of the mean, median, and mode, which would probably be
most useful to a consumer?

Identify whether the following claims are based upon the mean,
the median, or the mode.

22. The Better Granola Company advertises
that its product is preferred by more
people than any other leading brand of
granola.

23. The Citywide Automobile Company
boasts that the cars it sells last 10.5
years.

24. The Rapidlube Automobile Service
advertises that most cars will take 15
minutes or less to receive its full
lubrication service.

25. What is the probability of purchasing a
NeverLinger battery (Example 1) that will
last 18 hours?

Using a Calculator: *Finding the Mean*

You can use your calculator to streamline the computation of the
mean from a frequency table. To find the mean of the numbers in
Example 1:

Key: [C$_E^C$] 11 [×] 2 [M+] 12 [×] 7 [M+] 13 [×] 3 [M+] 14 [×]
2 [M+] 15 [×] 6 [M+] 16 [×] 4 [M+] 17 [×] 2 [M+] 18
[×] 3 [M+] 20 [×] 1 [M+]
2 [+] 7 [+] 3 [+] 2 [+] 6 [+] 4 [+] 2 [+] 3 [+] 1
[=]   30
[M$_C^R$] [÷] 30 [=] *14.5*

1. Find the mean in Exercise 2 using your
calculator.

2. Find the mean in Exercise 7 using your
calculator.

16-5 Misuse of Statistics

The way that statistics are presented can be very important in how they are interpreted. Sometimes people give statistics based on a very small or a biased sample. Other times, people draw graphs in such a way as to present a distorted picture.

Allan read an advertisement from a travel agency that listed some facts about a city in India. Among the facts mentioned was an average monthly rainfall of 15.3 inches. Allan discovered that the average monthly rainfall was indeed 15.3 inches, but that the median rainfall was 1 inch and the mode was 0 inches! He concluded that the information given in the advertisement was misleading. According to the almanac that Allan read, the monthly rainfall for the city advertised by the travel agency is shown in the table below.

Month	J	F	M	A	M	J	J	A	S	O	N	D
Rain	0	0	0	0	2	53	69	41	30	5	0	0

EXAMPLE 1

Draw a bar graph using the information in the table above.

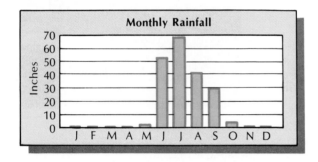

The bar graph is a better way to present statistics here because it gives the entire picture. It shows that nearly all the rainfall comes in a 4-month period. The mean, median, and mode do not show this important fact.

The travel agency did not give any incorrect information in their ad—they just failed to give important information.

Rosemary saw the advertisement at the right about a data processing school she was thinking of attending. Rosemary called the school and learned that while 90% of their graduates do get jobs, only 25% of the students who enroll complete the program.

EXAMPLE 2

What percentage of the students who enrolled in the Brookside Data Processing School actually got high-paying jobs after graduation?

percent of students who graduate	×	percent of graduates who get jobs	=	percent who enroll that get jobs
25%	×	90%	=	0.225 → 22.5%

Only 22.5% of those who enroll get high-paying jobs.

EXAMPLE 3

Marc found the bar graph below in a magazine. He realized that sometimes the information in a graph can be misleading. What was the actual increase in production and why does the increase pictured on the graph seem so great?

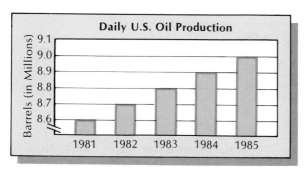

1985 production − 1981 production = increase in production

9.0 million barrels	−	8.6 million barrels	=	0.4 million barrels

The actual increase is 0.4 million barrels out of 8.6 million. The base line of the graph starts at 8.6 million barrels, so the increase seems much greater than it is. To be accurate, the graph should start at 0 barrels.

Class Exercises

Use the figure below for Problems 1–6.

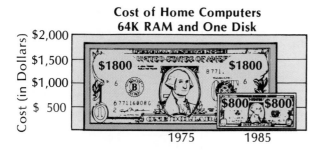

1. What was the approximate cost of home computers in 1975?

2. What was the approximate cost of home computers in 1985?

3. The 1975 cost of home computers was about how many times as great as the cost of 1985 computers?

4. The figure that represents the cost of 1975 computers is about how many times taller than the figure representing 1985 computers?

5. The figure representing the cost of 1975 computers is about how many times *wider* than that representing 1985 computers?

6. Why do the figures appear to show a much greater difference than the actual numbers?

EXERCISES

Use the figures in the following table for Problems 1–6.

Monthly Normal Temperatures of Plains City											
Month	J	F	M	A	M	J	J	A	S	O	N	D
Temp	10	16	21	45	60	78	82	80	78	61	45	18

1. What is the mean temperature?

2. What is the median temperature?

3. Make a bar graph of the information in the table like that in Example 1.

4. What is the mean temperature for the months June, July, August, and September?

5. What is the mean temperature for the months December, January, February, and March?

6. Why would the mean temperature or the median temperature give a misleading picture of Plains City's actual climate?

Use the figure shown at the right for Problems 7–12.

7. About how much oil was imported from Mexico each day in 1978?

8. About how much oil was imported from Mexico each day in 1985?

9. The 1985 amount of oil imported from Mexico is about how many times as great as the 1978 amount?

10. The figure that represents the amount of 1985 imports is about how many times taller than the figure representing 1978 imports?

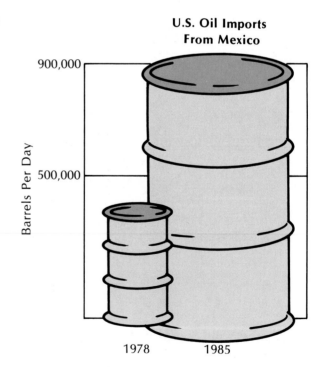

U.S. Oil Imports From Mexico

11. The figure representing the 1985 imports is about how many times *wider* than that representing 1978 imports?

13. A storekeeper advertised that everything in his store was on sale at 25% off. Just before the advertisement appeared, however, he raised the prices of everything by 20%. What is the actual percentage of savings after both the increase and reduction?

Use the figure below for Problems 14–19.

A salesperson gave the report for sales over a 4-year period in the form of a bar graph.

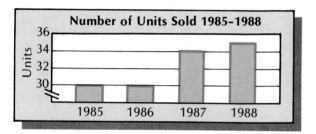

14. How many units did the salesperson sell in 1986?

16. What was the total increase in sales from 1986 to 1987?

18. About how much longer does the bar representing 1987 sales appear to be than that representing 1986 sales?

12. Why do the figures appear to show a much greater difference than the actual numbers?

15. How many units did the salesperson sell in 1987?

17. What was the percentage of increase in sales between 1986 and 1987?

19. Why does the bar graph make the increase in sales appear so much larger than the actual numbers?

Mixed Review

1. Sandy earns $19,500 annually. She is paid monthly. What is the gross amount of her paycheck each pay period?

3. Roberto deposited $250 in a savings account that pays 7% annually, compounded quarterly. What is the principal amount in his savings account at the beginning of the fourth quarter?

2. Kurt saves 15% of his net salary. He receives $1,550 net per month. How much will he have saved at the end of 1 year?

4. Pat and Peggy have fixed annual expenses for life, auto, and home insurance that amount to $2,368.50. How much should they save monthly to cover these annual fixed expenses?

Career
Desktop Publisher

Desktop publishing is used to describe the in-house publishing activities of small businesses and organizations who publish their own brochures and newsletters or who provide printed copy for other organizations. The new publishing technology has brought many changes. Even the small office environment is affected. These changes allow offices to make and produce documents quickly and efficiently and for less money. This means that information can be tailored to meet the specific needs of customers, sales people and in-house staff in an attractive and professional-looking format. Companies can personalize their sales messages for individual clients. They believe this helps them to be more competitive in the marketplace. The **desktop publisher** is a person who is trained to use a personal computer and produce materials that are similar to conventionally printed materials in quality.

Profile of a desktop publisher. A desktop publisher may be an employee from any department of a business. He or she has probably been trained in the use of the computer to publish materials. A high school education is essential, as are good language skills and the ability to use a computer effectively. A person doing this type of work will learn about the various sizes and weights of type the equipment can reproduce and how best to use these. A sense of design and color is also useful.

The desktop publishing environment. The desktop publisher works at a computer station using a computer that may be upgraded for publishing work. The printer available must be a laser or some other high-quality printer. The equipment should be capable of creating graphics and possibly using color.

All in a day's work. Abe and Mary Anne were working on a newspaper that was being set up on a computer. They had worked out the schedules for the athletic program and were trying to fit them into a 22-inch by 12-inch page with 64 square inches of unusable space. They had entered the schedules into the computer in a space that was 12 inches wide by 36 inches long.

1. How many square inches of usable space are there on the page?

2. If Abe and Mary Anne reduced the schedules to 18 inches in length, how wide would they be?

3. How many square inches would the reduced schedules occupy?

4. How much space would be left on the page for other information?

Computer:
BASIC Programming

Norris has written a computer program to find the mean of a sample of numbers. The program first asks how many numbers are in the sample and then prompts the input of the numbers one at a time. At the conclusion of the input, the mean is computed and the result is printed.

10 HOME	Clears the screen.
20 INPUT "HOW MANY NUMBERS IN THE SAMPLE?"; N	Prompts and records the size of the sample.
30 SUM = 0	Initializes the sum to zero.
40 FOR K = 1 TO N	Opens the loop to allow input and accumulates the sum of the sample entries.
50 INPUT "NEXT NUMBER?"; X	Prompts and records the next entry in the sample.
60 SUM = SUM + X	Adds the current entry to the sum.
70 NEXT K	Closes the loop.
80 MEAN = SUM / N	Computes the average by dividing the sum by the sample size.
90 PRINT "SAMPLE SIZE = "; N	Prints and labels the number of entries in the sample.
100 PRINT "THE MEAN IS "; MEAN	Prints and labels the mean of the sample.
110 END	Tells the computer to end the program.

Type the program into your computer.

EXERCISES

1. RUN the program. At the prompts, enter the following data:
Sample size (N) = 5
Sample entries (X); 79, 38, 54, 99, 56

RUN the program for each of the data samples below:

2. Sample size: 8
Sample entries: 55, 18, 92, 16, 73, 54, 55, 89

3. Sample size: 13
Sample entries: 192, 138, 176, 92, 377, 526, 313, 191, 310, 229, 101, 230, 79

4. Sample size: 9
Sample entries: 8.9, 5.7, 2.2, 3.9, 5.7, 2.9, 4.4, 8.2, 9.1

Decision Making:
Using Statistical Information

Todd Doering is 21 years old. He has lived in Hoffman City since taking a job there 15 months ago. During much of that time his knee, which he hurt playing baseball in high school, has continued to give him pain. His surgeon, Dr. Andrews, told Todd he needed to have an operation on his knee. He was given the following information:

- The surgery is a simple procedure.

- There is a very low percentage of complications after surgery.

- More than 95% of people with the same symptoms are cured after the surgery.

Todd considered what the surgeon had said. "Exactly what happens during this kind of surgery?" he asked.

After he had explained the operation in detail, Dr. Andrews added, "You don't have to do this immediately. If you decide on the operation, you can then choose the date and the hospital. The operation can be done at any of the three hospitals in this area."

Answer the following questions.

1. What statistical information given by Dr. Andrews is relevant to Todd's decision about whether to have the operation?

2. Think of some decisions made about your medical care. Who made them?

3. Choose one decision made about your medical care. Think carefully about this decision. Was it an easy or difficult decision to make? Explain your answer.

GETTING ANOTHER OPINION

Todd was not certain what he wanted to do. He decided that it would be wise to get another medical opinion. "Dr. Andrews is a highly recommended expert," he thought. "But if I follow his recommendation without further investigation, I'm assuming that he could not possibly make a mistake. Yet even experts can be wrong."

Todd found that his medical insurer would pay for a second opinion and even recommended another surgeon he could consult.

When the second doctor agreed with Dr. Andrews, Todd decided to have the operation. Next he would have to decide at which hospital he would have the operation.

A week later the *Hoffman City Sentinel* began a series on the three hospitals in the area. The Hospital Assessment Advisory Group, a national organization, had studied the results of treatment of different illnesses at the hospitals. Each part of the *Sentinel* series dealt with the statistics about the treatment of one illness.

Just after he had gotten to work one morning, Todd's friend, Lisa, approached him with a newspaper in her hand.

"Look at this!" Lisa said. "You'd better not go to Central Hospital for your operation. Look at these statistics."

Todd read the following article and carefully studied the graph.

RATE OF COMPLICATIONS VARIES FOR KNEE OPERATIONS

Central Hospital's rate of complications after knee surgery is higher than would normally be expected, a study by the Hospital Assessment Advisory Group shows.

Knee surgery complications at the Lloyd Engle Hospital and at the Thirty-Fifth Street Medical Center were within expected limits.

The number of statistically predicted complications was determined by studying specific cases and considering the diagnosis and such other factors as the severity of the impairment, age of the patient, sex of the patient, and his or her other health problems.

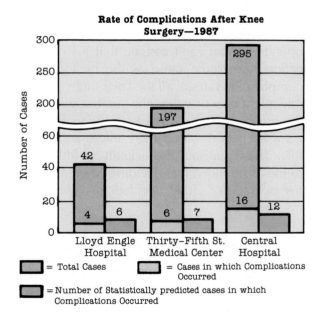

Answer the following questions.

4. What does this graph tell you about the three hospitals?

5. Nine of 238 operations at one hospital result in complications. What percent of the operations result in complications?

INTERPRETING THE DATA

Todd asked Lisa how she interpreted the graph.

"I think you are in more danger of having complications at Central than at other hospitals," she replied promptly.

"I don't think it means that," said Todd. "Their rate of complications is a little higher than the expected rate. But I think you are making some assumptions if you conclude that *I* am in more danger of having complications there than in the other hospitals.

Answer the following questions.

6. Identify some assumptions Lisa is making.

7. Describe how you thought to identify Lisa's assumptions.

GETTING MORE INFORMATION

"There are many things these statistics don't tell and that we can't assume from this general information," Todd continued. "They don't tell the number of complications for people my age. You can't assume it's the same as the rate for people of all ages. They don't tell what happens when it's Dr. Andrews doing the operation. You can't assume that his complication rate is the same as the mean of the complication rates of *all* the knee surgeons. His rate might be worse than the number shown on the graph, though I'll bet with his reputation, it's a lot better! I need more information than this. These statistics are actually of little help to me as an individual deciding where to have my operation." Todd decided to write down his questions:

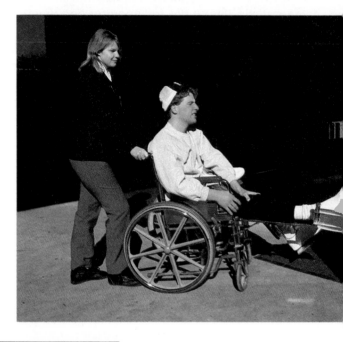

> – How does Dr. Andrews' record for knee surgery at Central Hospital compare with the record of all the surgeons at that hospital as a group?
> – What is the rate of complications for people my age compared with the overall rate of complications?
> – Exactly how did the Hospital Assessment Advisory Group conduct the study?
> – How did the advisory group measure how severe a case was? (After all, they're reading about the case after its all over.)

Answer the following questions.

8. What other questions about the study might Todd ask?

9. What can Todd do to get information about the hospitals?

10. What characteristics would you look for in a surgeon?

MAKING A DECISION

With his questions clearly in mind, Todd talked with Dr. Andrews and other physicians, the local medical society, his medical insurer, and several co-workers. He found that Central Hospital had a Sports Medicine Department that specialized in the kind of operation he needed. Because of this specialization, severe knee problems from all over the world were treated there. Todd also determined that Dr. Andrews had had extensive experience with knee surgery and a very low rate of complications following his work. Several physicians had had Dr. Andrews care for members of their families.

When Todd also learned that Central Hospital had the most modern equipment for knee operations, he decided to have Dr. Andrews perform the operation at that facility.

There were no complications after Todd's surgery, and he felt he had made a wise health care decision. That summer he played second base on his office team and helped them win the company pennant.

Answer the following questions.

11. Is choosing a hospital harder than choosing a course of study? Explain your answer.

12. How is Todd a good model for making effective decisions about health care?

13. How did Todd use the interpretation of statistics in making his decision about the hospital?

14. How did identifying assumptions help Todd make his decision?

15. What would you advise a friend about using statistics in making decisions?

DECIDE FOR YOURSELF

Read an article about a health topic in a popular newspaper or magazine. Interview a scientist or medical worker about his or her interpretation of the same article. Compare this person's interpretation with yours. Find out how you would get information about doctors and hospitals in your community.

Chapter 16 Review

VOCABULARY

batting average   mean   mutually exclusive events
fielding average   median   probability
frequency table   mode   sample space

For Exercises 1–5, select the word or words that complete each statement.

1. The _____ is the average of a group of numbers.

2. The middle number in a group of numbers is called the _____ .

3. The most frequently occurring number in a group of numbers is called the _____ .

4. A player's _____ is a decimal fraction that tells how often a baseball player gets a hit.

5. Two events that cannot occur at the same time are called _____ .

SKILLS

Express each fraction as a decimal.

6. $\dfrac{3}{5}$ **7.** $\dfrac{9}{50}$ **8.** $\dfrac{402}{1,000}$

Find the mean.

9. 28, 64, 35, 42, 17   **10.** 126, 438, 91, 615, 651, 581

Find each percent.

11. 15% of 64   **12.** 39% of 316   **13.** 5.2% of 359

CONSUMER TOPICS

Solve.

14. Jeanne can play tennis or racquetball with Bob, Sally, or Manuel. What's the probability she will play tennis with a man?

15. Handball uses 150 calories in 15 minutes. How many calories does Tricia use if she plays handball for 30 minutes?

16. In order to lose 1 pound of weight, it is necessary to burn up 3,500 calories. How long would Rod have to swim to lose 3 pounds if swimming uses 100 calories in 15 minutes?

17. Adrienne has been at bat 76 times this season and has gotten 23 hits. What is her batting average?

18. Tim has batted against Roger 24 times this season and has gotten 7 hits. What is the probability of his getting a hit when he faces Roger for the 25th time?

Use the numbers in the following sample for Problems 19–23:
80, 82, 80, 80, 84, 86, 90, 86, 92

19. Make a frequency table of the data.   **20.** Find the mean.

21. Find the median.   **22.** Find the mode.

23. Which value (mean, median, or mode) best represents the data?

The members in a diet/exercise program lost the following numbers of pounds in the program: 12, 10, 10, 15, 11, 8, 24, 12, 9, 20, 10, 12, 13, 14, 12, 16, 18, 8, 12, 22. Use this information for Problems 24–28.

24. Make a frequency table to show the results and find the mean.

25. Find the median of the weight loss.   **26.** Find the mode of the weight loss.

27. Which value do you think would be used to advertise the program's success?   **28.** Make a bar graph to show the results of the diet/exercise program.

29. Paige read that 75% of the students surveyed in a music store one Saturday morning preferred cassette tapes over record albums. What other information should Paige get before accepting the results of this survey as meaningful?

Use the bar graph below to answer Problems 30 and 31.

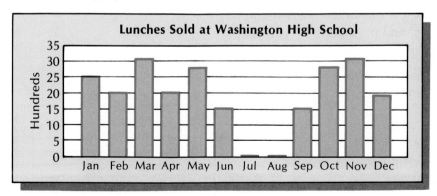

30. Why would the mean not be a proper value to use to interpret the data from this graph?   **31.** How would you revise this bar graph to give an accurate picture of the average number of lunches bought by students during the school year?

Chapter 16 Test

1. Bill can play tennis with Carol, Elaine, Sam, Jack, or Ron. What is the probability his partner will be male?

2. In order to lose 1 pound of weight, it is necessary to burn up 3,500 calories. How long would Tom have to run to lose 2 pounds if he burns 225 calories in 15 minutes?

3. Shiela has been at bat 54 times this season and has gotten 18 hits. What is her batting average?

4. Ginny has batted against Steve 16 times this season and has gotten 7 hits. What is the probability of her getting a hit when she faces Steve for the 17th time?

Use the numbers in the following sample for Problems 5–8:
24, 76, 28, 34, 32, 26, 28, 30, 28.

5. Find the mean. **34**   6. Find the median.   7. Find the mode.

8. Which value best represents the data?

Users of a water-saving device saved the following number of gallons of water in one week: 50, 75, 60, 100, 80, 75, 40, 95, 55, 70, 75, 90, 80, 75, 100, 105. Use this information for Problems 9–12.

9. Make a frequency table and find the mean.   10. Find the median.   11. Find the mode.

12. Which value do you think the company selling the device would use to advertise the success of their program?

13. In June, 28,500 people rode the bus in Summerville. In July, 29,300 people rode the bus, and in August, 27,100 people rode it. Make a bar graph to show the data.

14. A high school advertised that "Of the students taking the Achievement tests, 60% scored 500 or higher." They did not mention that only 70% of their students actually took the test. What percentage of the entire student body scored 500 or higher on the test?

15. The manufacturer of a child's toy argued from this graph that sales of the toy were not down substantially since the beginning of the year. Do you agree? Why?

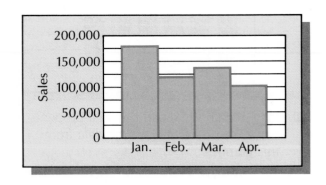

Cumulative Mixed Review

Select the letter corresponding to the correct answer.

1. Jessy's net earnings are $14,250 per year. If she has 28% withheld, what is her gross income?

   a. $3,990   **b.** $50,893

   c. $19,792   **d.** $39,900

2. Sally is paid semimonthly. The net amount of each paycheck is $645.50. What is her net annual income?

   a. $15,492   **b.** $16,783

   c. $7,746   **d.** $3,873

3. Martina's gross income is $19,500. What is the maximum amount she should expect to pay to purchase a house?

   a. $19,500   **b.** $39,000

   c. $58,500   **d.** $48,750

4. Larry bought a computer system for $1,795. He put $400 down and financed the rest. He made 36 payments of $54.50 each. How much interest did he pay?

   a. $167   **b.** $567

   c. $1,962   **d.** $196

5. Lauren purchased a computer system for $1,550 and an integrated software package for $295. If she had to pay a sales tax of 6.25%, what was the total amount of her purchase?

   a. $1,845   **b.** $1,964.93

   c. $1,960.31   **d.** $115.31

6. Ozzie bought a 2.5-kilogram package of cheese for $14. What is the unit price per kilogram?

   a. $5.60   **b.** $8.96

   c. $10   **d.** $14

7. Priscilla budgets 25% of her income for housing. What is the measure of the central angle she must use to show this item on a circle graph?

   a. 120°   **b.** 72°

   c. 45°   **d.** 90°

8. Travers has a balance of $305.42 on his department store charge account. The finance charge is 1.25% on the unpaid balance per month. How much is the monthly finance charge on his balance?

   a. $4.58   **b.** $.38

   c. $3.82   **d.** $309.24

9. Lisa makes four payments a year of $175.50 for car insurance. How much must she budget weekly for this fixed expense?

   a. $3.38   **b.** $13.50

   c. $702   **d.** $27

10. Paula bought a house for $68,900. She made a down payment of 20%. How big a mortgage did she have?

   a. $41,340   **b.** $13,780

   c. $55,120   **d.** $68,900

Skills File

SKILL 1: *Writing Word Names for Numbers*

EXAMPLE

Write $432,000 in words.

$432,000

four hundred thirty-two thousand dollars

Write the word names.

1. $56

2. $309

3. $412

4. $821   **5.** $780   **6.** $1,970

7. $45,000   **8.** $3,400   **9.** $19,000

10. $320,000   **11.** $455,342   **12.** $3,978,034

SKILL 2: *Rounding Whole Numbers*

EXAMPLE

Round 347,562 to the nearest thousand.

347,562   Look at the digit in the place to the right.
    ↓   It is 5 or more. Add 1 to the thousands digit
348,000   and replace the other digits with zeros.

Round.

1. 76 to the nearest ten

2. 842 to the nearest ten

3. 6,851 to the nearest hundred   **4.** 7,070 to the nearest hundred

5. 2,483 to the nearest thousand   **6.** 36,417 to the nearest thousand

7. 72,862 to the nearest hundred   **8.** 548,933 to the nearest hundred thousand

---

SKILL 3: *Rounding Money Amounts*

EXAMPLE

Round $25,874.253 to the nearest cent.

$25,874.253   Look at the digit in the place to the right.
    ↓   It is less than 5. Drop the digit and any
$25,874.25   digits to the right.

Round.

1. $7.562 to the nearest cent

2. $83.738 to the nearest cent

3. $467.895 to the nearest cent

4. $1.84 to the nearest 10¢

5. $4.28 to the nearest 10¢   **6.** $57.96 to the nearest dollar

7. $305.25 to the nearest dollar   **8.** $8,641.09 to the nearest $10

SKILL 4: *Rounding Fractions and Mixed Numbers*

EXAMPLE

Round $2\frac{6}{10}$ to the nearest half.
Use a number line to help.

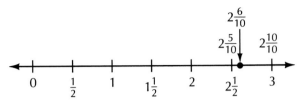

$2\frac{6}{10}$ is closer to $2\frac{1}{2}$ than to 3. So $2\frac{6}{10} \rightarrow 2\frac{1}{2}$

Round each to the nearest half.

1. $\frac{3}{8}$ **2.** $\frac{9}{11}$ **3.** $\frac{5}{16}$

4. $3\frac{8}{12}$ **5.** $2\frac{7}{9}$ **6.** $6\frac{1}{25}$

Round each to the nearest whole number.

7. $3\frac{1}{7}$ **8.** $\frac{7}{11}$ **9.** $18\frac{5}{6}$

10. $20\frac{2}{9}$ **11.** $15\frac{1}{8}$ **12.** $33\frac{2}{3}$

SKILL 5: *Comparing Numbers*

EXAMPLE

Compare. Use >, <, or =.
876.32 ■ 867.23

876.23   Compare places: 7 > 6
↓↓
867.32   So, 876.23 > 867.32

Compare. Use >, <, or =.

1. 29 ■ 92   **2.** 318 ■ 381

3. 360 ■ 3,600   **4.** 7,001 ■ 702.0

5. 47.9 ■ 4.79   **6.** 503.2 ■ 503.20

7. 2,846 ■ 2,845   **8.** 945.02 ■ 949.02   **9.** 6,321.45 ■ 6,321.54

10. 600.030 ■ 600.03   **11.** 20.679 ■ 2.679   **12.** 8.070 ■ 8.0070

SKILL 6: *Ranking Numbers*

EXAMPLE

Rank the following numbers in descending order (greatest to least):

45, 32, 54, 34, 65, 38, 42, 44, 45, 56

Begin with the greatest number. Write the next greatest, and so on, until all numbers are ranked.

65, 56, 54, 45, 45, 44, 42, 38, 34, 32

Rank each group of numbers in descending order (greatest to least).

1. 35, 39, 45, 64, 20, 35, 48, 35

2. 128, 243, 564, 239, 412, 229, 342

3. 12.9, 14.3, 23.5, 19.3, 12.6, 14.7

4. 0.4, 0.7, 0.08, 0.2, 0.4, 0.03, 0.4

Rank each group of numbers in ascending order (least to greatest).

5. 45, 98, 94, 34, 57, 23, 98, 96, 90

6. 0.03, 0.009, 0.044, 0.04, 0.23, 0.008

7. 23,243; 25,983; 31,439; 13,735; 34,287

8. 1,290; 989; 2,198; 3,142; 1,534; 3,392; 899

SKILL 7: *Estimating Sums of Whole Numbers*

EXAMPLE

Estimate the sum: 3,650 + 4,593

$$
\begin{array}{r}
3,650 \rightarrow 4,000 \\
+4,593 \rightarrow +5,000 \\
\hline
9,000
\end{array}
$$

Estimate each sum.

1. 44 + 27

2. 19 + 72

3. 237 + 451

4. 105 + 309

5. 555 + 602

6. $316 + $297

7. 950 + 250

8. 5,408 + 2,978

9. 26,498 + 29,406

10. $314 + $479 + $156

11. 72 + 63 + 95 + 9

12. 125 + 75 + 39 + 61

SKILL 8: *Estimating Differences of Whole Numbers*

EXAMPLE

Estimate the difference: 7,942 − 2,368

$$
\begin{array}{r}
7,942 \rightarrow 8,000 \\
-2,368 \rightarrow -2,000 \\
\hline
6,000
\end{array}
$$

Estimate the difference.

1. 49 − 32

2. $87 − $43

3. 95 − 36

4. 281 − 104

5. 706 − 368

6. $1,760 − $920

7. 2,148 − 1,097

8. 5,041 − 3,289

9. 33,749 − 14,986

10. $25,796 − $9,946

11. 362,148 − 75,428

12. 199,968 − 99,968

SKILL 9: *Estimating Products of Whole Numbers*

EXAMPLE

Estimate the product: 2,408 × 63

$$
\begin{array}{r}
2,408 \rightarrow 2,000 \\
\times \quad 63 \rightarrow \times \quad 60 \\
\hline
120,000
\end{array}
$$

Estimate each product.

1. 36 × 3

2. 24 × 7

3. $49 × 19

4. 308 × 9

5. 275 × 26

6. $652 × 8

7. 2,403 × 12

8. 3,098 × 82

9. 236 × 126

10. $5,289 × 27

11. 4,536 × 239

12. 25,468 × 518

SKILL 10: *Estimating Quotients of Whole Numbers*

EXAMPLE

Estimate the quotient: 7,480 ÷ 24

$$24\overline{)7,480} \rightarrow \overset{300}{25\overline{)7,500}}$$

Estimate each quotient.

1. 115 ÷ 4	**2.** $93 ÷ 9	**3.** 243 ÷ 8
4. 486 ÷ 12	**5.** 416 ÷ 19	**6.** $752 ÷ 25
7. 4,156 ÷ 98	**8.** 3,243 ÷ 29	**9.** 2,658 ÷ 32
10. $8,750 ÷ 286	**11.** 35,680 ÷ 893	**12.** 63,500 ÷ 925

SKILL 11: *Estimating Sums of Decimals*

EXAMPLE

Estimate the sum: $536.84 + $218.28

$$\begin{array}{rcr} \$536.84 & \rightarrow & \$500 \\ + \ 218.28 & \rightarrow & + \ 200 \\ \hline & & \$700 \end{array}$$

Estimate each sum.

1. $7.40 + $9.80	**2.** 26.82 + 43.75	**3.** 15.25 + 10.97
4. 32.5 + 9.75	**5.** $19.98 + $17.75	**6.** $135.50 + $57.95
7. $604.76 + $219.25	**8.** 2,795 + 502.5	**9.** $3,219.64 + $2,706.43
10. $29,475.96 + $67,450.50	**11.** $394.62 + $105.46 + $98.14	**12.** 2,486 + 46 + 98.5

SKILL 12: *Estimating Differences of Decimals*

EXAMPLE

Estimate the difference: 7,582.95 − 604.75

$$\begin{array}{rcr} 7,582.95 & \rightarrow & 7,600 \\ - \ 604.75 & \rightarrow & - \ 600 \\ \hline & & 7,000 \end{array}$$

Estimate each difference.

1. $29.75 − $9.68	**2.** 46.85 − 27.5	**3.** $189.50 − $77.50
4. $308.46 − $116.72	**5.** 498.83 − 425	**6.** $550.50 − $275.95
7. $2,487.95 − $983.25	**8.** $8,463.18 − $2,046.94	**9.** $1,945 − $896
10. 63.5 − 22.5	**11.** 82.168 − 3.792	**12.** 609,595.8 − 49,802.234

SKILL 13: *Estimating Products of Decimals*

EXAMPLE

Estimate the product: 8,546.95 × 27

$$\begin{array}{r} 8{,}546.95 \rightarrow 8{,}500 \\ \times 27 \rightarrow \times 30 \\ \hline 255{,}000 \end{array}$$

Estimate the product.

1. $7.62 × 8	**2.** 23.4 × 4	**3.** $46.25 × 7
4. $79.75 × 6	**5.** $53.95 × 9	**6.** 218.451 × 7
7. 450.3 × 11	**8.** $675.50 × 18	**9.** $2,428.95 × 36
10. $328.96 × 75	**11.** $57,482.95 × 115	**12.** 183.75 × 12

SKILL 14: *Estimating Quotients of Decimals*

EXAMPLE

Estimate the quotient: $24,695.72 ÷ 12

$$12\overline{)\$24{,}695.72} \rightarrow 12\overline{)\$24{,}000}\overset{\$\,2{,}000}{}$$

Estimate each quotient.

1. $23.95 ÷ 4	**2.** 56.894 ÷ 3	**3.** 42.5 ÷ 6
4. $94.25 ÷ 6	**5.** $208.95 ÷ 9	**6.** 89.095 ÷ 15
7. 480.357 ÷ 11	**8.** $236.24 ÷ 12	**9.** $612.98 ÷ 21
10. $3,342.36 ÷ 319	**11.** $59,072.50 ÷ 625	**12.** $64,216.35 ÷ 29.75

SKILL 15: *Adding Whole Numbers*

EXAMPLE

Add: 3,698 + 247 + 16

$$\begin{array}{r} 1\,2 \\ 3{,}698 \\ 247 \\ + 16 \\ \hline 3{,}961 \end{array}$$

Check:

$$\begin{array}{r} 16 \\ 247 \\ +3{,}698 \\ \hline 3{,}961\,\text{✓} \end{array}$$

Add and check.

1. 84 + 97	**2.** 213 + 88	**3.** $457 + $360
4. 794 + 507	**5.** 2,314 + 635	**6.** 7,860 + 5,148
7. $10,241 + $3,592	**8.** 27,863 + 7,907	**9.** 56,740 + 23,285
10. $332,574 + $41,925	**11.** 435,681 + 7,962 + 508	**12.** 5,693 + 12,007 + 258 + 3,699

SKILL 16: *Subtracting Whole Numbers*

EXAMPLE

Subtract: 86,042 − 27,385

```
  15 9 13
 7 5 10 312
 8 6, 0 4 2        Check:    58,657
−2 7, 3 8 5                 +27,385
 5 8, 6 5 7                  86,042✔
```

Subtract and check.

1. 79 − 46

2. 84 − 27

3. $178 − $60

4. 523 − 87

5. 764 − 534

6. $606 − $295

7. 1,324 − 431

8. 5,302 − 3,791

9. $47,298 − $6,279

10. 60,438 − 21,241

11. 841,593 − 742,604

12. 907,800 − 388,945

SKILL 17: *Multiplying Whole Numbers*

EXAMPLE

Multiply: 4,086 × 1,352

```
    4,086      Check:       1,352
  ×1,352                  ×4,086
    8 172                   8 112
  204 30                  108 16
 1 225 8                  5 408 0
 4 086                    5,524,272✔
 5,524,272
```

Multiply and check.

1. 61 × 16

2. $83 × 20

3. 87 × 48

4. 200 × 13

5. $454 × 52

6. 821 × 88

7. 473 × 140

8. $529 × 306

9. 780 × 468

10. 1,203 × $500

11. 4,593 × 676

12. 7,687 × 6,081

SKILL 18: *Dividing Whole Numbers*

EXAMPLE

Divide: 5,558 ÷ 23

```
              241 R15      Check:      241
          23)5,558                   ×  23
             4 6                       723
              95                      4 82
              92                      5,543
              38                    +   15
              23                      5,558✔
              15
```

Divide and check.

1. 258 ÷ 6

2. $1,988 ÷ 28

3. 14,735 ÷ 35

4. $126,198 ÷ 513

5. 386 ÷ 7

6. 9,685 ÷ 34

7. 54,963 ÷ 231

8. 15,838 ÷ 52

9. 7,406 ÷ 80

10. 31,046 ÷ 408

11. 63,750 ÷ 550

12. 482,192 ÷ 3,214

SKILL 19: *Adding Decimals*

EXAMPLE

Add: 0.257 + 0.38

$$\begin{array}{r} 0.257 \\ +\,0.38 \\ \hline 0.637 \end{array}$$

Check:

$$\begin{array}{r} 0.38 \\ +\,0.257 \\ \hline 0.637 ✔ \end{array}$$

Add and check.

1. 0.3 + 0.2 + 0.4

2. 0.4 + 0.9 + 0.3

3. 0.05 + 0.02 + 0.01

4. 0.09 + 0.07 + 0.02 + 0.01

5. $.15 + $.34 + $.08 + $.24

6. 0.6 + 0.21 + 0.59

7. 0.17 + 0.23 + 0.93 + 0.84

8. 7.2 + 4.4 + 2.3

9. 8.9 + 5.2 + 4.3 + 5.5

10. $7.86 + $5.18 + $8.55

11. $6.92 + $5.50

12. 3.74 + 0.6 + 1.8 + 0.58

SKILL 20: *Subtracting Decimals*

EXAMPLE

Subtract: 1.7 − 0.48

$$\begin{array}{r} 1.70 \\ -\,0.48 \\ \hline 1.22 \end{array}$$

Check:

$$\begin{array}{r} 1.22 \\ +\,0.48 \\ \hline 1.70 \end{array} = 1.7 ✔$$

Subtract and check.

1. 0.8 − 0.3

2. $.65 − $.53

3. 0.84 − 0.67

4. 0.05 − 0.03

5. $.99 − $.39

6. 4.6 − 2.7

7. 0.573 − 0.285

8. $32.70 − $5.90

9. 0.9312 − 0.7728

10. 8.572 − 0.8579

11. 67.842 − 18.965

12. 19.714 − 18.836

SKILL 21: *Multiplying Decimals by Powers of 10*

EXAMPLE

Multiply 43.6 by 1,000

3 zeros

43.6 × 1,000 = 43.600 = 43,600

Move the decimal point 3 places to the right.

Find each product.

1. $54 × 10

2. 76.3 × 100

3. $40.23 × 1,000

4. 0.06 × 100

5. 0.005 × 1,000

6. 2,354.98 × 10

7. $376.09 × 1,000

8. 0.003 × 10

9. 0.007 × 10,000

10. 35.9 × 10,000

11. 5.3 × 100,000

12. 9.8 × 1,000,000

SKILL 22: *Multiplying Decimals by Whole Numbers*

EXAMPLE

Multiply: 35.4 × 23

```
      35.4        Check:      23
    ×   23                  ×35.4
    106 2                     9 2
    708                     115
    814.2                    69
                            814.2✔
```

Find each product.

1. 23.9 × 6 × 5.3

2. $128.34 × 9

3. 1,328.1 × 4

4. 43.8 × 12

5. 70.2 × 45

6. 165.9 × 18 × 34.8

7. $634.29 × 54

8. 445.98 × 38

9. 1,435.2 × 201

10. 2.335 × 421

11. 0.00345 × 1,243

12. $43,645.05 × 188

SKILL 23: *Multiplying Decimals*

EXAMPLE

Multiply: 5.72 × 0.98

```
    5.72       Check:    0.98
  ×0.98               × 5.72
  4576                   196
  5 148                  686
  5.6056               4 90
                      5.6056✔
```

Multiply.

1. 0.8 × 0.8

2. 0.74 × $35

3. 0.547 × 8.1

4. $769.40 × 0.5

5. 0.344 × 2.75

6. 0.06 × $77

7. 2.2 × 0.03

8. 0.0006 × 1.7

9. 0.7 × 0.8

10. $.98 × 0.6

11. 23.4 × 0.005

12. 0.174 × 81.25

SKILL 24: *Dividing Decimals by Powers of 10*

EXAMPLE

Divide 387.44 by 100

2 zeros

387.44 ÷ 100 = 387.44 = 3.8744

Move the decimal point
2 places to the left.

Find each quotient.

1. 38.2 ÷ 10

2. $23,000.60 ÷ 100

3. 2,365.9 ÷ 1,000

4. 76.02 ÷ 10

5. 34.98 ÷ 100

6. 398.15 ÷ 1,000

7. $.80 ÷ 10

8. 0.25 ÷ 100

9. 3.987 ÷ 1,000

10. 365.92 ÷ 10,000

11. 5,000.4 ÷ 100,000

12. 365,200.4 ÷ 1,000,000

SKILL 25: *Dividing Decimals by Whole Numbers*

EXAMPLE

Divide 45.32 by 40

```
        1.133
  40)45.320
      40
       5 3
       4 0
       1 32
       1 20
         120
         120
```

Check: 1.133
         ×   40
          45.320✔

Find each quotient.

1. $38.4 \div 4$

2. $\$25.92 \div 3$

3. $48.9 \div 5$

4. $463.2 \div 12$

5. $392.5 \div 25$

6. $\$798.84 \div 42$

7. $5{,}823.2 \div 58$

8. $3{,}403.4 \div 143$

9. $21{,}471.48 \div 81$

10. $8.5772 \div 1{,}046$

11. $256.386 \div 2{,}249$

12. $318{,}809.56 \div 1{,}594$

SKILL 26: *Dividing Decimals*

EXAMPLE

Divide: $0.9112 \div 0.68$

```
          1.34
  0.68)0.91 12
        68
        23 1
        20 4
         2 72
         2 72
```

Check: 1.34
         × 0.68
          1072
           804
          0.9112✔

Divide.

1. $\$.76 \div 0.04$

2. $\$7.77 \div 0.37$

3. $1.328 \div 0.83$

4. $2.106 \div 0.27$

5. $1.1564 \div 0.49$

6. $17.7666 \div 0.06$

7. $0.0969 \div 0.05$

8. $0.34314 \div 0.42$

9. $\$87.48 \div 1.62$

10. $384.285 \div 5.61$

11. $162 \div 0.06$

12. $\$42 \div 0.48$

SKILL 27: *Simplifying Fractions*

EXAMPLE

Express $\frac{27}{42}$ in simplest form.

$$\frac{27}{42} = \frac{\overset{1}{\cancel{3}} \times 3 \times 3}{2 \times \underset{1}{\cancel{3}} \times 7} = \frac{9}{14}$$

Express each fraction in simplest form.

1. $\frac{25}{100}$

2. $\frac{16}{20}$

3. $\frac{15}{75}$

4. $\frac{30}{42}$

5. $\frac{33}{88}$

6. $\frac{250}{450}$

7. $\frac{78}{1{,}000}$

8. $\frac{198}{220}$

9. $\frac{84}{126}$

10. $\frac{100}{225}$

11. $\frac{326}{815}$

12. $\frac{4{,}000}{24{,}800}$

SKILL 28: *Changing Mixed Numbers to Fractions*

EXAMPLE

Express $4\frac{5}{8}$ as a fraction.

$$4\frac{5}{8} = \frac{4 \times 8 + 5}{8} = \frac{37}{8}$$

Express each mixed number as a fraction.

1. $3\frac{1}{2}$ **2.** $6\frac{2}{3}$ **3.** $2\frac{5}{8}$ **4.** $1\frac{6}{11}$ **5.** $7\frac{4}{5}$ **6.** $21\frac{2}{3}$

7. $18\frac{5}{6}$ **8.** $10\frac{7}{9}$ **9.** $7\frac{9}{16}$ **10.** $29\frac{16}{100}$ **11.** $11\frac{7}{50}$ **12.** $36\frac{275}{1,000}$

SKILL 29: *Adding Fractions and Mixed Numbers*

EXAMPLE

Add: $13\frac{7}{8} + 4\frac{1}{5}$

$$
\begin{array}{r}
13\frac{7}{8} = \quad 13\frac{35}{40} \\
+ \ 4\frac{1}{5} = +\ 4\frac{8}{40} \\
\hline
17\frac{43}{40} = 18\frac{3}{40}
\end{array}
$$

Add. Express in simplest form.

1. $\frac{3}{7} + \frac{1}{7}$ **2.** $\frac{7}{9} + \frac{8}{9}$ **3.** $\frac{4}{5} + \frac{11}{15}$

4. $\frac{3}{5} + \frac{5}{6}$ **5.** $\frac{2}{9} + \frac{6}{15}$ **6.** $9 + \frac{3}{4}$

7. $3\frac{3}{14} + 6\frac{4}{14}$ **8.** $8\frac{1}{10} + 4\frac{9}{10}$ **9.** $46\frac{7}{12} + 8\frac{11}{12}$

10. $41\frac{2}{7} + 6\frac{1}{3}$ **11.** $7\frac{2}{5} + 13\frac{3}{8}$ **12.** $23\frac{9}{14} + 26\frac{5}{6}$

SKILL 30: *Subtracting Fractions and Mixed Numbers*

EXAMPLE

Subtract: $30\frac{1}{4} - 18\frac{2}{3}$

$$
\begin{array}{r}
30\frac{1}{4} = \quad 30\frac{3}{12} = \quad 29\frac{15}{12} \\
-18\frac{2}{3} = -18\frac{8}{12} = -18\frac{8}{12} \\
\hline
11\frac{7}{12}
\end{array}
$$

Subtract. Express in simplest form.

1. $\frac{4}{5} - \frac{2}{5}$ **2.** $\frac{7}{12} - \frac{5}{12}$ **3.** $\frac{7}{15} - \frac{2}{5}$

4. $\frac{5}{8} - \frac{2}{9}$ **5.** $21\frac{7}{10} - 3\frac{1}{10}$ **6.** $12\frac{2}{9} - 9\frac{5}{9}$

7. $34\frac{12}{27} - 28\frac{12}{27}$ **8.** $11\frac{19}{30} - 7$ **9.** $9 - 4\frac{3}{4}$

10. $30\frac{9}{16} - 16\frac{1}{2}$ **11.** $9\frac{2}{3} - 5\frac{7}{10}$ **12.** $58\frac{4}{9} - 32\frac{7}{15}$

SKILL 31: *Multiplying Fractions and Mixed Numbers*

EXAMPLE

Multiply: $3\frac{1}{2} \times 4\frac{2}{5}$

$$3\frac{1}{2} \times 4\frac{2}{5} = \frac{7}{\overset{\;}{\underset{1}{2}}} \times \frac{\overset{11}{22}}{5} = \frac{77}{5} = 15\frac{2}{5}$$

Multiply.

1. $\frac{3}{7} \times \frac{2}{3}$ 　　　　**2.** $\frac{2}{10} \times \frac{3}{4} \times \frac{4}{5}$ 　　　　**3.** $\frac{1}{2} \times \frac{13}{15} \times \frac{1}{4}$ 　　　　**4.** $1\frac{1}{2} \times \frac{2}{3}$

5. $\frac{3}{4} \times 2\frac{1}{5}$ 　　　　**6.** $3\frac{1}{3} \times 2\frac{1}{2}$ 　　　　**7.** $6\frac{1}{8} \times 7\frac{2}{5}$ 　　　　**8.** $12\frac{1}{3} \times 6$

9. $8 \times 9\frac{1}{3}$ 　　　　**10.** $12\frac{2}{3} \times 10\frac{1}{4}$ 　　　　**11.** $25 \times \frac{1}{6} \times \frac{2}{3}$ 　　　　**12.** $2\frac{3}{8} \times 3\frac{5}{6} \times 4\frac{1}{2}$

SKILL 32: *Dividing Fractions and Mixed Numbers*

EXAMPLE

Divide: $5\frac{5}{6} \div 1\frac{1}{3}$ 　　　　$5\frac{5}{6} \div 1\frac{1}{3} = \frac{35}{6} \div \frac{4}{3} = \frac{35}{\underset{2}{6}} \times \frac{\overset{1}{3}}{4} = \frac{35}{8} = 4\frac{3}{8}$

Divide.

1. $\frac{8}{9} \div \frac{1}{2}$ 　　　　**2.** $\frac{3}{4} \div \frac{2}{3}$ 　　　　**3.** $\frac{10}{12} \div \frac{1}{4}$ 　　　　**4.** $8 \div \frac{1}{2}$

5. $\frac{9}{10} \div 3$ 　　　　**6.** $4\frac{3}{4} \div \frac{2}{3}$ 　　　　**7.** $8\frac{1}{2} \div 1\frac{1}{4}$ 　　　　**8.** $12\frac{3}{5} \div 4\frac{1}{2}$

9. $10\frac{1}{8} \div 2\frac{1}{8}$ 　　　　**10.** $6\frac{4}{5} \div 2$ 　　　　**11.** $4\frac{3}{4} \div \frac{3}{4}$ 　　　　**12.** $15\frac{1}{3} \div \frac{1}{3}$

SKILL 33: *Expressing Fractions as Decimals*

EXAMPLE

Express $\frac{5}{12}$ as a decimal.
To express a fraction as a decimal, divide.

$$\begin{array}{r} 0.4166 \rightarrow 0.41\overline{6} \\ 12\overline{)5.00} \\ \underline{4\;8} \\ 20 \\ \underline{12} \\ 80 \\ \underline{72} \\ 80 \\ \underline{72} \\ 8 \end{array}$$

Use an overbar to show that the 6 repeats.

Express each fraction as a decimal.

1. $\frac{4}{25}$ 　　　　**2.** $\frac{7}{10}$ 　　　　**3.** $\frac{29}{50}$

4. $\frac{4}{5}$ 　　　　**5.** $\frac{3}{4}$ 　　　　**6.** $\frac{11}{20}$

7. $\frac{9}{40}$ 　　　　**8.** $\frac{5}{8}$ 　　　　**9.** $\frac{1}{3}$

10. $\frac{5}{6}$ 　　　　**11.** $\frac{11}{16}$ 　　　　**12.** $\frac{7}{15}$

SKILL 34: *Equivalent Ratios*

EXAMPLE

Are $\frac{5}{12}$ and $\frac{15}{36}$ equivalent?

Cross multiply: $\frac{5}{12} \diagdown\diagup \frac{15}{36}$

$\left.\begin{array}{l} 5 \times 36 = 180 \\ 12 \times 15 = 180 \end{array}\right\}$ Cross products are equal.

Yes, $\frac{5}{12}$ and $\frac{15}{36}$ are equivalent.

Are the ratios in each pair equivalent? Write *yes* or *no*.

1. $\frac{2}{3}, \frac{6}{9}$

2. $\frac{3}{4}, \frac{15}{20}$

3. $\frac{3}{8}, \frac{12}{24}$

4. $\frac{4}{9}, \frac{9}{27}$

5. $\frac{3}{6}, \frac{8}{16}$

6. $\frac{7}{9}, \frac{11}{13}$

7. $\frac{6}{7}, \frac{3}{4}$

8. $\frac{9}{21}, \frac{6}{14}$

9. $\frac{8}{3}, \frac{16}{7}$

10. $\frac{5}{9}, \frac{30}{54}$

11. $\frac{48}{56}, \frac{6}{7}$

12. $\frac{48}{90}, \frac{12}{30}$

SKILL 35: *Solving Proportions*

EXAMPLE

Solve: $\dfrac{5}{7} = \dfrac{15}{n}$

$5 \times n = 7 \times 15$

$5 \times n = 105$

$n = \dfrac{105}{5}$

$n = 21$

Check: $\dfrac{5}{7} \stackrel{?}{=} \dfrac{15}{21}$

$5 \times 21 = 105$

$7 \times 15 = 105$ ✔

Solve.

1. $\dfrac{2}{3} = \dfrac{4}{n}$

2. $\dfrac{2}{4} = \dfrac{m}{20}$

3. $\dfrac{3}{5} = \dfrac{d}{35}$

4. $\dfrac{12}{m} = \dfrac{3}{8}$

5. $\dfrac{a}{7} = \dfrac{30}{42}$

6. $\dfrac{12}{50} = \dfrac{f}{100}$

7. $\dfrac{7}{10} = \dfrac{70}{c}$

8. $\dfrac{5}{k} = \dfrac{15}{18}$

9. $\dfrac{9}{7} = \dfrac{n}{21}$

10. $\dfrac{56}{8} = \dfrac{s}{1}$

11. $\dfrac{4.8}{5.7} = \dfrac{4.8}{b}$

12. $\dfrac{2}{r} = \dfrac{0.8}{10}$

SKILL 36: *Expressing Decimals as Percents*

EXAMPLE

Write 0.235 as a percent.

$0.235 = 0.235\% = 23.5\%$ Move the decimal point 2 places to the right and add a percent sign.

Express each decimal as a percent.

1. 0.65

2. 0.31

3. 0.85

4. 0.06

5. 0.08

6. 0.127

7. 0.866

8. 0.0009

9. 1.78

10. 2.07

11. 5

12. 2.1

SKILL 37: *Expressing Percents as Decimals*

EXAMPLE

Express 175% as a decimal.

175% = 175. = 1.75   Move the decimal point 2 places to the left and
                              drop the percent sign.

Express each percent as a decimal.

1. 28%	**2.** 79%	**3.** 40%	**4.** 3%
5. 12.9%	**6.** 7.26%	**7.** 0.6%	**8.** 0.19%
9. 230%	**10.** 116%	**11.** 180.4%	**12.** 500%

SKILL 38: *Finding the Fractional Part of a Percent*

EXAMPLE

Find $\frac{2}{3}$ of 15%.

$$\frac{2}{3} \times 15\% = \frac{2}{\cancel{3}_{1}} \times \frac{\cancel{15}^{5}}{1} = \frac{10}{1} = 10\%$$

Find each product.

1. $\frac{1}{2}$ of 18%	**2.** $\frac{1}{21}$ of 28%	**3.** $\frac{2}{3}$ of 27%	**4.** $\frac{1}{2}$ of 15%
5. $\frac{3}{5}$ of 80%	**6.** $\frac{3}{4}$ of 9%	**7.** $\frac{5}{8}$ of 40%	**8.** $\frac{11}{12}$ of 120%
9. $\frac{7}{9}$ of 81%	**10.** $\frac{1}{5}$ of 92%	**11.** $\frac{7}{8}$ of 100%	**12.** $\frac{2}{3}$ of 0.6%

SKILL 39: *Adding Percents*

EXAMPLE

Find the sum: 8.5% + 13% + 20%

$$\begin{array}{r} 8.5\% \\ 13.0\% \\ +20.0\% \\ \hline 41.5\% \end{array}$$ Align decimal points.

Find each sum.

1. 6% + 11%	**2.** 29% + 15%	**3.** 41% + 17%
4. 32% + 15% + 8%	**5.** 2.1% + 3.8%	**6.** 17.9% + 18.6%
7. 25.5% + 73.4%	**8.** 16.1% + 23.4% + 7%	**9.** 11.4% + 21% + 16%
10. $8\frac{1}{2}\%$ + 14%	**11.** $6\frac{1}{2}\%$ + $8\frac{1}{2}\%$	**12.** $18\frac{2}{3}\%$ + $7\frac{1}{4}\%$ + $8\frac{1}{2}\%$

SKILL 40: *Finding a Percent of a Number*

EXAMPLE

Find 5½% of $680.50.
Think: 5½% = 5.5% = 0.055

$$\begin{array}{r} \$680.50 \\ \times\ \ 0.055 \\ \hline 3\ 40250 \\ 34\ 0250 \\ \hline 37.42750 \\ \$37.43 \end{array}$$ Round to nearest cent.

Find the number. Round to the nearest cent.

1. 7% of $35.50

2. 5% of $245.35

3. 15% of $495.50

4. 2.5% of $230.75

5. 4.7% of $525.95

6. 6.25% of $940.62

7. 12.75% of $2,468.93

8. 4.225% of $1,364.75

9. 0.8% of $586.93

10. 0.75% of $4,890.50

11. 54.6% of $8,950.75

12. 110% of $7,500

SKILL 41: *Finding What Percent One Number Is of Another*

EXAMPLE

What percent is 45 of 75?

$$\begin{array}{r} 0.6 = 60\% \\ 75\overline{)45.0} \\ \underline{45\ 0} \\ 0 \end{array}$$ To find what percent 45 is of 75, divide.

45 is 60% of 75.

$$\text{Check:}\quad \begin{array}{r} 75 \\ \times\,0.6 \\ \hline 45.0\checkmark \end{array}$$

Find what percent the first number is of the second.

1. 24, 48

2. 9, 36

3. 25, 150

4. 72, 90

5. 19, 57

6. 60, 300

7. 8, 32

8. 12, 240

9. 5, 500

10. 40, 50

11. 37.5, 300

12. 650, 400

SKILL 42: *Finding the Whole When a Percentage Is Known*

EXAMPLE

54 is 18% of what number?

$$\begin{array}{r} 3\ 00 \\ 0.18\overline{)54.00} \\ \underline{54} \\ 0 \end{array}$$ To find the whole given a percentage, divide the percentage by the percent.

54 is 18% of 300.

$$\text{Check:}\quad \begin{array}{r} 300 \\ \times\,0.18 \\ \hline 24\ 00 \\ 30\ 0 \\ \hline 54.00\checkmark \end{array}$$

Solve.

1. 20 is 40% of what number?

2. 3 is 75% of what number?

3. 36 is 90% of what number?

4. 15 is 25% of what number?

5. 8 is 5% of what number?

6. 12 is 2% of what number?

7. 75 is 7.5% of what number?

8. $25.95 is 8.5% of what number?

9. $250 is 15.75% of what number?

10. $650 is 125% of what number?

SKILL 43: *Converting Customary Measures*

EXAMPLE

Express 2 lb 5 oz as ounces.

2 lb 5 oz = (2 × 16) + 5   1 lb = 16 oz
      = 32   + 5 = 37 oz

3. Express 1 yd 2 ft in feet.

5. Express 2 qt 1 pt in pints.

Solve.

1. Express 8 lb 2 oz in ounces.

2. Express 5 ft 7 in. in inches.

4. Express 2 h 30 min in minutes.

6. Express $3\frac{1}{2}$ lb in ounces.

SKILL 44: *Adding Customary Measures*

EXAMPLE

Find the sum: 3 ft 7 in. + 5 ft 9 in.

  3 ft 7 in.
+5 ft 9 in.
  8 ft 16 in.   16 in. = 1 ft. 4 in.
  9 ft 4 in.   8 ft + 1 ft 4 in. = 9 ft 4 in.

Find each sum.

1. 8 ft 3 in. + 12 ft 7 in.

2. 3 yd 1 ft + 2 yd 2 ft

3. 2 gal 3 qt + 5 gal 2 qt

4. 1 ft 2 in. + 3 ft 9 in. + 2 ft 8 in.

SKILL 45: *Elapsed Time*

EXAMPLE

Compute the time from 10:15 A.M. to 3:20 P.M.

10:15 A.M. → 12 noon = 1 h 45 min
12 noon → 3:20 P.M. = 3 h 20 min
                4 h 65 min   65 min = 1 h 5 min
                5 h 5 min

5. noon to 4:30 A.M.

Compute the elapsed time.

1. 9 A.M. to 3 P.M.

2. 7 P.M. to 6 A.M.

3. 6:20 A.M. to 10:45 A.M.

4. 11:50 A.M. to 9:10 P.M.

6. midnight to 7:25 P.M.

SKILL 46: *Finding Mean, Mode, and Median*

EXAMPLE

Find the mean, the mode, and the median.
      8, 4, 5, 5, 5, 8, 14

Mean (average):
$$\frac{8 + 4 + 5 + 5 + 5 + 8 + 14}{7} = \frac{49}{7} = 7$$

Mode (most frequent number): 5
Median (middle number): 14 8 8 <u>5</u> 5 5 4

Find the mean, mode, and median.

1. 3, 3, 4, 4, 4, 5, 6, 6, 10

2. 10, 12, 14, 14, 18, 20, 24

3. 250, 300, 275, 250, 325

4. 70, 70, 75, 80, 90, 80, 70, 65

5. 27, 62, 38, 57, 40, 38, 50, 38, 38, 60

SKILL 47: *Finding Perimeter*

EXAMPLE

Find the perimeter of a rectangle with a
length of 3 meters and a width of 4 meters.

$P = 2l + 2w$
$P = (2 \times 3) + (2 \times 4)$
$P = 14$ m

Find the perimeter of each.

1. Rectangle: $l = 5$ cm, $w = 2$ cm

2. Rectangle: $l = 12$ mm, $w = 15$ mm

3. Square: $s = 6$ km

4. Square: $s = 3.75$ cm

5. Triangle: 2 m, 4 m, 5 m

6. Rectangle: $l = 0.8$ mi, $w = 1.2$ mi

7. Square: $s = 0.75$ cm

8. Rectangle: $l = 0.72$ m, $w = 0.64$ m

9. Equilateral triangle: $s = 6.75$ cm

10. Regular pentagon: $s = 9.23$ m

11. Regular octagon: $s = 10.2$ ft

12. Rectangle: $l = 0.05$ m, $w = 0.005$ m

SKILL 48: *Finding Area*

EXAMPLE

Formulas for finding area:
Rectangle: $A = l \times w$
Square: $A = s^2$
Triangle: $A = \frac{1}{2}bh$

Find the area of a triangle with a base of 10
centimeters and a height of 6 centimeters.
$A = \frac{1}{2}bh$
$A = \frac{1}{2} \times 10 \times 6$
$A = 30$ cm^2

Find the area of each rectangle.

1. $l = 5$m, $w = 8$m   **2.** $l = 0.23$ cm, $w = 1.35$ cm   **3.** $l = 2{,}468$ mi, $w = 3{,}571$ mi

Find the area of each square.

4. $s = 18$ in.   **5.** $s = 20$ m   **6.** $s = 2\frac{1}{2}$ ft

Find the area of each triangle.

7. $b = 8$ m, $h = 12$ m   **8.** $b = 3.6$ cm, $h = 6.4$ cm   **9.** $b = 0.25$ m, $h = 0.8$ m

---

SKILL 49: *Constructing Central Angles*

EXAMPLE

Make a circle graph that shows a central
angle of 45°.

Draw circle R.
Mark point X.
Draw a radius RX.
Use a protractor to
draw a 45° central angle.

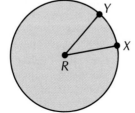

Make a circle graph that shows each
central angle.

1. 30°   **2.** 60°   **3.** 120°

4. 90°   **5.** 25°   **6.** 10°

7. 18°   **8.** 103°   **9.** 152°

10. $27\frac{1}{2}°$ **11.** $5\frac{1}{2}°$ **12.** $36\frac{1}{2}°$

Glossary

Add-on plan *(page 120)* A loan repayment plan in which simple interest is added to the amount borrowed and the total is repaid in equal installments.

Adjust *(page 150)* To make changes in.

Amortizing *(page 355)* Paying back the money borrowed for a loan.

Annual percentage rate (APR) *(page 180)* The yearly rate of interest charged on a credit plan.

Annual rate of interest *(page 110)* The rate paid when money is on deposit for 1 year.

Annual yield *(page 419)* The rate of simple interest a bank would have to offer to yield a specified rate of compound interest.

Assessed value *(page 360)* The value of a house for tax purposes; could be the market value or a percentage of the market value.

Average daily balance method *(page 176)* A plan for charging interest on the average daily balance of a charge account.

Average monthly expense *(page 134)* The average amount spent each month on a particular item.

Balance *(page 98)* The amount existing in a checking or savings account.

Balanced diet *(page 197)* A diet that includes a variety of food to ensure that nutritional requirements are met.

Bank *(page 98)* A financial institution that offers a full range of savings, checking, and lending services.

Bank credit card *(page 173)* A card that enables you to charge purchases at participating businesses such as stores, restaurants, or hotels.

Bar graph *(page 524)* A graph using bars to show data.

Base price *(page 256)* The price of a new car with only standard equipment.

Batting average *(page 514)* A decimal fraction that tells how often a baseball player gets a hit.

Beneficiary *(page 454)* The person to whom the face value of life insurance is paid in the event of the insured person's death.

Biweekly *(page 49)* Every two weeks.

Bond *(page 422)* A promise by the borrower (federal, state, or local governments or corporations) to repay a loan at a specified rate of interest.

Budget *(page 134)* A plan to manage income.

Byte *(page 486)* A single unit of computer memory.

Calorie *(page 194)* A unit of measure for the energy supplied by food.

Car pool *(page 308)* A group of co-workers who share driving to and from work.

CCF (100 cubic feet) *(page 333)* A measure of natural gas consumption.

Certificate of deposit *(page 418)* A type of savings account that requires the money be on deposit for a fixed period of time.

Check register *(page 98)* A form used to keep a record of checks you have written.

Checking account *(page 98)* A bank account against which checks may be written.

Circle graph *(page 143)* A circle divided into parts to show data.

Closing costs *(page 356)* Extra fees paid at the time a house is purchased.

Collision insurance *(page 262)* Insurance that will pay you for damages to your car caused by collision with another object or overturning.

Commission *(page 52)* The specified amount of money a salesperson receives for making a sale.

Commission rate *(page 52)* The percent of total sales paid as commission to a salesperson.

Compound interest *(page 114)* Interest paid on both the principal and the interest accumulated on the principal.

Condominium *(page 352)* An individually owned apartment in a multifamily structure.

Consumer price index (CPI) *(page 242)* An index number that measures the change in costs of consumer goods and services compared to a base year.

Convenience foods *(page 207)* Foods that have been prepared, cooked, and packaged by the manufacturer to save time for the consumer.

Corporate bonds *(page 426)* Bonds issued by corporations borrowing money.

Credit card *See* Bank credit card.

Credit union *(page 259)* A cooperative association that offers loans at low rates and other banking services to its members.

Current yield (of a bond) *(page 426)* The interest rate divided by the cost.

Daily log *(page 55)* A record of the time a worker begins and ends work each day.

Deductible (for insurance) *(page 450)* A specific dollar amount paid each year by the insured before the insurer has any liability.

Deductions *(page 70)* Amounts withheld on a paycheck for taxes or other purposes.

Depreciation *(page 270)* The decrease in value of an item due to such factors as age and use.

Discount *(page 224)* The amount saved by buying an item on sale.

Discount (bond) *(page 426)* A bond with a quoted price lower than its face value.

Down payment *(page 259)* The amount of money required as partial payment for an item bought on credit.

Driver rating factor *(page 262)* A means for determining a driver's automobile insurance premium, based on such factors as age and driving record.

Earnings statement *(page 70)* A record of earnings and deductions usually attached to a paycheck.

Exemption *(page 394)* The standard deduction from gross income for a taxpayer's dependents.

Expenditure *(page 134)* The amount of money spent on an item.

Expenses *(page 134)* The amount of money you can expect to spend on an item.

Face value (bond) *(page 422)* The value printed on the bond itself.

Face value (life insurance) *(page 454)* The value of the policy paid to the beneficiary in the event of the insured person's death.

Federal income tax *(page 386)* A tax imposed by the federal government on the income of a person or business.

FICA *(page 80)* The Federal Insurance Contributions Act, more commonly known as social security.

Fielding average *(page 514)* A decimal fraction that tells how well a baseball player fields the ball.

Filing status *(page 394)* Classification for taxpayers (for example, single, head of household, or married filing jointly).

Finance charge *(page 170)* The interest charged in connection with an installment plan or credit card purchase.

Fixed expense *(page 138)* A monthly expense that remains the same.

Frequency table *(page 520)* A table showing how often something occurs.

Gross pay *(page 70)* The total pay earned for a pay period.

Hardware *(page 485)* A computer and its supporting equipment.

Health insurance *(page 450)* Insurance to cover medical expenses.

Homeowner's policy *(page 364)* An insurance policy that covers a home against such perils as theft, fire, and vandalism.

Hourly rate *(page 42)* The fixed rate at which a worker is paid for a job.

Income tax return *(page 390)* The form a person is required to file with the government listing taxable income, deductions, and taxes paid or owed.

Inflation *(page 242)* An increase in prices and costs.

Installment plan *(page 170)* A method of making a purchase in which the purchaser pays a certain amount down and the remainder in regular installments.

Insurance *(page 262)* Protection against financial losses.

Interest *(page 110)* Money charged or paid for the use of money.

Interest formula (simple) *(page 110)* $i = prt$, where i is simple interest, p is principal, r is rate, and t is time.

Interest period *(page 114)* The time between interest payments.

Itemize *(page 399)* To list your tax-deductible expenses for such items as interest, medical payments, and charitable contributions.

Keogh plan *(page 467)* A plan that allows self-employed workers to save money for retirement.

Kilobyte *(page 486)* A unit of computer memory equal to 1,024 bytes.

Kilowatt-hours *(page 332)* A measure of electric power consumption; 1 kilowatt-hour is the amount of electricity needed to light ten 100-watt bulbs for 1 hour.

Lease (apartment) *(page 325)* A written agreement between an owner and a renter listing the rental terms.

Lease (automobile) *(page 275)* To rent on a long-term basis.

Liability insurance *(page 262)* Insurance against claims arising from injury to other people or damage to property.

Life insurance *(page 454)* Insurance designed to provide financial security for the family of the person insured.

Limited-payment life insurance *(page 458)* Life insurance that is fully paid for within a limited period of time, such as 20 or 30 years.

Line graph *(page 242)* A graph using lines to show data.

Long-distance call *(page 338)* A telephone call made to someone outside your local calling area.

Margin of profit *(page 256)* The amount of profit a dealer makes on a new car.

Markdown *(page 224)* The amount discounted from regular price to sale price.

Market value *(page 360)* The worth of a house or other commodity on the market.

Maturity *(page 418)* The date on which an obligation, such as a bond, must be paid.

Mean *(page 517)* The arithmetical average of a group of numbers; the sum of data divided by the number of data.

Median *(page 517)* The middle number in a group of numbers. (For an even number of data, the median is the average of the two middle numbers.)

Mill *(page 360)* One tenth of a cent.

Mode *(page 517)* The most frequently occuring number or numbers in a group of numbers.

Monthly installment plan *(page 120)* A loan repayment plan in which interest is charged on the unpaid part of the loan and the loan is repaid in equal monthly installments.

Mortgage *(page 355)* A loan for buying a home.

Mutually exclusive events *(page 515)* Two events that cannot happen at the same time.

Net pay *(page 70)* Take-home pay.

Nutrients *(page 194)* Substances the body needs to survive.

Odds *(page 513)* The ratio of successes to failures for an event.

Options *(page 256)* Optional equipment available on a new car.

Ordinary-life insurance *See* whole-life insurance.

Overtime *(page 42)* The hours a worker works in addition to regular hours.

Overtime rate *(page 42)* The amount a worker is paid for overtime.

Par value *(page 426)* The face value of a bond.

Pay period *(page 49)* The period of time between paychecks.

Payroll savings plan *(page 435)* A savings plan for an employee in which a portion of earnings is deposited automatically in savings.

Permutation *(page 371)* An ordered arrangement of a group of things.

Piecework *(page 45)* Work that is produced and paid for by the piece or unit.

Points *(page 356)* Percentages charged by a bank for granting a loan for purchasing a house.

Premium *(page 262)* The annual cost of insurance protection.

Premium (bond) *(page 426)* A bond with a quoted price higher than its face value.

Principal *(page 110)* The amount deposited or borrowed, upon which interest is based.

Probability *(page 510)* A measure of the likelihood that an event will occur.

Property damage insurance *(page 262)* Insurance against liability for damage to the property of another, such as a car, house, or storefront.

Property tax *(page 360)* A tax levied on all property within a city.

Quarterly *(page 114)* Four times a year.

Quoted price *(page 426)* The selling price of a bond.

Rate of assessment *(page 360)* The percentage rate at which property is assessed for real estate taxes.

Rate of interest *(page 110)* The percent used to determine the interest.

Reconcile (a bank statement) *(page 102)* To show that your accounting of a checking or savings account agrees with the bank's.

Renter's insurance *(page 329)* A form of personal property insurance for apartment tenants.

Replacement value *(page 364)* The cost of replacing an item.

Salary *(page 49)* The fixed amount of money a worker is paid for a job.

Sale price *(page 224)* The discounted price of an item.

Sales receipt *(page 167)* A written or printed record of a purchase showing the amount paid.

Sales tax *(page 164)* A percentage of the total price of an item collected on behalf of the county, state, or local government.

Sample space *(page 510)* The set of all possible outcomes for an experiment.

Savings and loan *(page 259)* A financial institution usually owned by its depositors, originally designed to specialize in home mortgages; it now offers most banking services.

Schedule *(page 297)* A listing of bus, train, or plane travel routes, times, and distances.

Security deposit *(page 325)* A cash deposit made by renter to owner to cover any damage that the renter may cause.

Semiannual *(page 423)* Twice a year.

Semimonthly *(page 49)* Twice a month.

Simple interest *(page 110)* Money paid only on the principal (amount deposited or borrowed) and not on accumulated interest.

Single-payment plan *(page 120)* A loan repayment plan in which the loan (interest plus principal) is repaid in one payment.

Social security benefits *(page 462)* Payments made to a person as retirement income by the social security system.

Social security card *(page 462)* A card that shows an individual's social security number.

Software *(page 485)* Sets of instructions that tell a computer what to do.

State income tax *(page 403)* A tax imposed by a state on the income of a person or business.

Sticker price *(page 256)* The total price of a car, including base price, options, and destination charges.

Stock *(page 430)* A share in the ownership of a corporation.

Stock market *(page 430)* A central location where stocks are bought and sold.

Stockbroker *(page 431)* A person who makes a living buying and selling stocks.

Tax schedule *(page 394)* A table of tax rates.

Tax table *(page 394)* A table that gives amounts of tax owed for various incomes.

Taxable income *(page 394)* The income upon which you pay taxes, determined by subtracting your deductions and exemptions from your gross earnings.

Term insurance *(page 454)* Life insurance that is valid for a specified period of time only, such as 5 years.

Time zone *(page 292)* A longitudinal division of the earth's surface in which a standard time is kept.

Timecard *See* weekly timecard.

Tips *(page 45)* Money given to a worker by a customer for good service.

Uninsured motorist coverage *(page 262)* Insurance coverage that pays you or someone riding in your car for injuries when your car is hit by an uninsured or hit-and-run driver.

Unit price *(page 200)* The cost of an item per unit (such as ounce or pound).

Unit rate *(page 45)* The amount paid to a worker per unit produced.

Unpaid balance method *(page 173)* A credit plan in which interest is charged only on the balance remaining to be paid.

U.S. Recommended Daily Allowance (U.S. R.D.A.) *(page 194)* The approximate amounts of proteins, vitamins, and minerals a person needs each day.

Utilities *(page 332)* Power, gas, and water services provided by a public utility.

Variable cost *(page 271)* The depreciation cost plus the cost of repairs and maintenance for a used car.

Variable expense *(page 138)* A monthly expense that can fluctuate in amount.

W-2 form *(page 386)* A form provided by an employer for an employee showing the total amount of earnings and taxes withheld during the past year.

Weekly timecard *(page 55)* A weekly tally of the daily logs for each working day of the week.

Whole-life insurance *(page 458)* Insurance with fixed premiums that covers the insured for his or her life and develops a cash value as premiums are paid.

Withhold *(page 73)* To hold back taxes or other deductions from a paycheck.

Index

Selected Answers

Chapter 1

Lesson 1-1, pages 43–44
Class Exercises
1. $30 *4.* $432 *7.* $256.80 *10.* $152.21
13. $7 \times 4 = $28; $.50 \times 4 = $2;
$28 + $2 = $30
Exercises
1. $395.20 *4.* $330 *7.* $209.89 *10.* $213.75
13. $12.75 *16.* $154

Lesson 1-2, pages 46–47
Class Exercises
1. $220.74 *4.* $301.20
Exercises
1. $855.96 *4.* $269.20 *7.* $273.85 *10.* $246.39
13. $188.05 *16.* $190.80 *19.* $222.70

Lesson 1-3, pages 50–51
Class Exercises
1. 12 *4.* $1,101.81 *7.* 24 *10.* 12 *13.* $20,400
Exercises
1. 26 *4.* $646.67 *7.* $20,499.44
10. Semimonthly *13.* Biweekly
16. Daphne earns $74.21 more than Jim each week.

Lesson 1-4, pages 53–54
Class Exercises
1. $76.48 *4.* $509
Exercises
1. $425 *4.* $1,021 *7.* $601.72 *10.* $651.92
13. $52,488

Lesson 1-5, pages 57–58
Class Exercises
1. $8\frac{1}{4}$ h *4.* $8\frac{3}{4}$ h *7.* $248.88
Exercises
1. $7\frac{3}{4}$ h *4.* $8\frac{1}{2}$ h *7.* $336.19 *10.* $40\frac{1}{3}$ h
13. $265.94

Chapter 1 Review, pages 64–65
1. overtime rate *4.* piecework *7.* salary *10.* tips
13. $300 *16.* $20.25 *19.* 14 *22.* $387.54
25. $10\frac{1}{12}$ *28.* $348.65 *31.* $215.50
34. $11,358.10 *37.* $228.36

Chapter 2

Lesson 2-1, pages 71–72
Class Exercises
1. $135.16 *4.* $184.05
Exercises
1. $314.76 *4.* $107.95 *7.* $2,613

Lesson 2-2, pages 74–75
Class Exercises
1. $31 *4.* $4
Exercises
1. $20 *4.* $31 *7.* $15
10. John: $29 withheld weekly; Margaret: $18 withheld weekly

Lesson 2-3, pages 78–79
Class Exercises
1. $5.62 *4.* $9.16
Exercises
1. $30 *4.* $19.63 *7.* $17.31 *10.* $16,200
13. Ex. 11; Ex. 10; Ex. 9

Lesson 2-4, pages 81–82
Class Exercises
1. $31.48 *4.* $36.60

7. Key: $\boxed{C_E^C}$ 642.37 $\boxed{\times}$ 15.02
$\boxed{\%}$ 96.483974

Exercises
1. $28.66 *4.* $67.86 *7.* $43.11 *10.* $1,865;
$140.06 *13.* November

Lesson 2-5, pages 85–86
Class Exercises
1. $376.29 *4.* $465.18
Exercises
1. $237.54 *4.* $192.57 *7.* $155.23 *10.* $120

Chapter 2 Review, pages 92–93
1. net pay *4.* deductions *7.* $144.61 *10.* F
13. 0.18 *16.* $34.03 *19.* $12.19 *22.* $298.50
25. $25 *28.* $202.36 *31.* $85.83 *34.* $1,474.59
37. $15,603.75

Chapter 3

Lesson 3-1, pages 99–101
Class Exercises
4. $305.56
Exercises
4. $368.92 *7.* $80.08 *10.* $230 *13.* $73.46

Lesson 3-2, pages 104–105
Class Exercises
1. $180.82 *4.* $659.05
Exercises
1. $750.99 *4.* $124.75 *7.* $539.03 *10.* $161.84

Lesson 3-3, pages 107–109

Class Exercises
1. $162.16
4. Quicker and easier than keying in data.
Exercises
1. $306.13   **4.** $802.34   **7.** Total deposit: $211.14
10. $114.27   **13.** Current balance: $637.60
16. Current balance: $822.88

Lesson 3-4, pages 111–112
Class Exercises
1. $28   **4.** $51
7. 7% = 0.07. When multiplying by a 2-place
decimal, move decimal point 2 places to the left.
0.07 × 200 = 14.00 × 2 y = $28.
Exercises
1. $60   **4.** $47.50   **7.** $14.99   **10.** $597.50
13. Ex. 1, 9; Ex. 2, 8; Ex. 3–7, 10–12
16. $157.50; $1,837.50

Lesson 3–5, pages 115–116
Class Exercises
1. $824.18   **4.** $20.40   **7.** $688.50   **10.** $55.86
13. $2,293.15
Exercises
1. $10   **4.** $520.20   **7.** $18.27   **10.** $2,050
13. $67.42   **16.** $2,431.99   **19.** $7.06; $922.30

Lesson 3-6, pages 118–119
Class Exercises
1. $56.20   **4.** $85
Exercises
1. $43.20   **4.** $22.80   **7.** $386.50   **11.** Think:
1,000 + 75 = 1,075; 1,075 ÷ 107.5 = 10

Lesson 3-7, pages 121–22
Class Exercises
1. $79.50   **4.** $45.09
Exercises
1. $32.38   **4.** $51.55   **7.** $650

Chapter 3 Review, pages 128–129
1. interest   **4.** single-payment plan   **7.** compound
interest   **10.** $330.50   **13.** $3,581.70   **16.** 0.1975
19. 0.857   **22.** $472.02   **25.** $488.26
28. $515.11

Chapter 4

Lesson 4-1, pages 136–137
Class Exercises
1. $250.98   **4.** $143.27   **7.** $129.59   **10.** $859.21
13. $1,024.49

Exercises
1. $372.41   **4.** $252.85   **7.** $192.93
10. $2,277.55   **13.** $2,068.02   **16.** $467

Lesson 4-2, pages 140–141
Class Exercises
1. $307.67   **4.** $500   **7.** $645.93   **10.** It would
take longer to key data than to compute mentally.
Exercises
1. $550   **4.** $305   **7.** $285   **10.** $451.29
13. $700   **16.** Mentally add $400 + $250 = $650.
Then add $100: $650 + $100 = $750

Lesson 4-3, pages 144–145
Class Exercises
1. 22%   **4.** 5%   **7.** 22%   **10.** 6%   **13.** 3%
Exercises
1. 13%   **4.** 83°   **7.** 17%   **10.** 43°   **13.** 12%

Lesson 4-4, pages 148–149
Class Exercises
1. $42   **4.** $138.84
7. $3.77 less than amount budgeted
Exercises
1. $30   **4.** $124.32   **7.** $167.18   **10.** $3,600

Lesson 4-5, pages 151–152
Class Exercises
1. $80   **4.** $84
Exercises
1. $12   **4.** $79.63   **7.** Yes; $100

Chapter 4 Review, pages 158–159
1. expenditure   **4.** fixed expense   **7.** 18.4   **10.** 806
16. $130.07   **19.** 19.5%   **22.** $194.08   **25.** $845
28. 72°   **31.** 43°   **34.** $300   **37.** $180
40. $31.25

Chapter 5

Lesson 5-1, pages 165–166
Class Exercises
1. $10   **4.** $12   **7.** $67.32
10. Ex. 1, 4, 5; Ex. 2, 8, 9; Ex. 3, 6, 7
Exercises
1. $11   **4.** $7.35   **7.** $2   **10.** $15.36   **13.** $7.65
16. $13.13   **19.** 6.24%

Lesson 5-2, pages 168–169
Class Exercises
1. $2.85   **4.** $8.36
Exercises
1. $1.78   **4.** $.83   **7.** $3.57   **10.** $2.78

13. $19.26   **16.** $5.35; $5.80, $4.20
19. Total: $57.01

Lesson 5-3, pages 171–172
Class Exercises
1. $80   **4.** $20
Exercises
1. $20   **4.** $11   **7.** $20   **10.** $35   **13.** $100

Lesson 5-4, pages 174–175
Class Exercises
1. $1.50   **4.** $363.05   **7.** $4.62
Exercises
1. $1.50   **4.** $118.23   **7.** $1.87   **10.** $1.76
13. 1% of $250 is $2.50; 0.5% of $250 is $1.25;
1.5% of $250 is $3.75

Lesson 5-5, pages 177–178
Class Exercises
1. $150   **4.** $1,016.33   **7.** $1,624.60
10. $178.18
Exercises
1. $130   **4.** $1,062.48   **7.** $1,114.16
10. $181.71   **13.** $3.01

Lesson 5-6, pages 181–182
Class Exercises
1. 24%   **4.** 15%
Exercises
1. 12%   **4.** 21%   **7.** credit union

Chapter 5 Review, pages 188–189
1. Sales tax   **4.** finance charge   **7.** average daily
balance method   **10.** $151   **13.** $12.25   **16.** $9.19
19. $31.05   **22.** $147.60   **25.** $50   **28.** $1.45
31. $6.91

Chapter 6

Lesson 6-1, pages 195–196
Class Exercises
1. 282   **4.** 1,450   **7.** 17.9%
Exercises
1. 280   **4.** 102.5   **7.** 15%   **10.** 53.8%
13. 29.2%   **16.** Because of different size, different
growth patterns, and the like; activity level, age, and
weight might affect calorie requirements.

Lesson 6-2, pages 198–199
Class Exercises
1. 585 calories   **4.** 51.3%
Exercises
1. 34.5 g of fat   **4.** 78%   **7.** 24   **10.** 60 ÷ 3 =
20; 20 × 4 = 80; 80 ÷ 800 = 10%

13.	2 toast	140
	2 eggs	170
	orange juice	90
	1 tbsp butter	100
		500
	3 oz chicken	140
	milk	160
	beans	30
	potato	145
		475

Lesson 6-3, pages 201–202
Class Exercises
1. $.046   **4.** $.70   **7.** 8-oz bottle ($.069/oz)
Exercises
1. $.05/oz   **4.** $.917/lb   **7.** 7 oz   **10.** 1 lb 2 oz
13. $.292 per serving   **16.** 2-qt bottle   **19.** Size C,
16 servings

Lesson 6-4, pages 204–-205
Class Exercises
1. $.10 on generic   **4.** $.21 on generic
Exercises
1. $.30 on generic   **4.** no savings   **7.** $2.79

Lesson 6-5, pages 208–209
Class Exercises
1. $.06   **4.** $.77   **7.** $.59
Exercises
1. $.95   **4.** $.24   **7.** $.80   **10.** $.10

Lesson 6-6, pages 211–212
Class Exercises
1. $7   **4.** $7
Exercises
1. $7   **4.** $7   **7.** 72   **10.** Convenient, saves time

Chapter 6 Review, pages 218–219
1. U.S. RDA   **4.** convenience foods   **7.** 7,155
10. 7 pt   **13.** $.64   **16.** about $16   **19.** 32.1%
22. 22.3%   **25.** 8 oz   **28.** $1.30   **31.** 90

Chapter 7

Lesson 7-1, pages 225–226
Class Exercises
1. $10   **4.** $9.60   **7.** $41.56
10. Ex. 1, 2, 8, 9; Ex. 4, 5; Ex. 3, 6, 7
Exercises
1. $10   **4.** $13.78   **7.** $2.96   **10.** $2   **13.** $3.98
16. no, she spent $41.14   **19.** $20.08

Lesson 7-2, pages 228–230
Class Exercises
1. $3.59 **4.** 4 lb 6 oz **7.** $77.83 **10.** $2.45
Exercises
1. 13 lb 10 oz **4.** $1.62 **7.** 17 lb 6 oz
10. $107.01 **13.** $2.45 **16.** $108.54 **19.** $27.88
22. $19.50, $11.52, $25.18, $56.20, $2.81, $1.76

Lesson 7-3, pages 232–233
Class Exercises
1. $.65 **4.** $.25 **7.** $1.75
Exercises
1. $1.05 **4.** $1.25 **7.** $2.75 **10.** $1.49
13. $1.66 **16.** $1.77 **19.** $2.39 **22.** $2.04
25. yes, $2.55 **28.** $2.99

Lesson 7-4, pages 236–237
Class Exercises
1. $6.19 **4.** $11.01 **7.** $12.25 **10.** $3
Exercises
1. $5 **4.** $8.73 **7.** $9 **10.** $7 **13.** $12.10
16. a. He wrote $3\frac{7}{8}$ as a decimal and multiplied by
cost per yard. **b.** change 7 to 1; change 3 to 2

Lesson 7-5, pages 240–241
Class Exercises
1. $22.26 **4.** $18.01
Exercises
1. $13.77 **4.** $65.17 **7.** $60.40 **10.** $50.33
13. Discount store; cheaper by $.62

Lesson 7-6, pages 243–244
Class Exercises
1. 115 **4.** 1.26
Exercises
1. 200 **4.** 1980 **7.** $1.28 **10.** $12.39
13. $13.20

Chapter 7 Review, pages 250–251
1. discount, or markdown **4.** 0.16 **7.** 12 lb 2 oz
10. $\frac{69}{8}$ **13.** $27.33 **16.** $10.39 **19.** 7 lb, $2.01
22. $.85 **25.** $5.82 **28.** $37.48 **31.** $25.11
34. 239

Chapter 8

Lesson 8-1, pages 257–258
Class Exercises
1. $7,380 **4.** $600 **7.** $1,400 **10.** $1,800
13. $8,100 + $1,100 = $9,200; $9,200 + $200 =
$9,400
Exercises
1. $6,750 **4.** $500 **7.** $3,000 **10.** $4,000
13. No. His cost is $8,400

Lesson 8-2, pages 260–261
Class Exercises
1. $1,079.50 **4.** $4,538.14
Exercises
1. $1,414.38 **4.** $7,331.70 **7.** $1,092.96 **10.** If
30% is down payment, then 70% is the rest of total
cost. 0.7 × $9,000 = $6,300 **13.** $4,621.88

Lesson 8-3, pages 264–265
Class Exercises
1. $106 **4.** $425
Exercises
1. $126.50 **4.** $340 **7.** $250 + $75 = $325; $13
+ $16 = $29; $205.05 + $53 = $258.05. Then use
paper and pencil to add. **10.** $2.15 **13.** 25/50/10,
50/100/5, or 10/20/25

Lesson 8-4, pages 268–269
Class Exercises
1. $5.51 **4.** $13.32 **7.** $48
Exercises
1. $9.95 **4.** $2.32 **7.** $240 **10.** $158.50
13. $358.32

Lesson 8-5, pages 271–273
Exact values have been used for the answers but your
answers will vary depending on how accurately you
read the graphs.
Class Exercises
1. $1,005 **4.** $956 **7.** $689
10. $1,776 **13.** $3,519
Exercises
1. $1,059 **4.** $1,105 **7.** $548 **10.** $350
13. $1,545 **16.** $655 **19.** $1,005 **22.** $1,401
25. $4,221 **28.** $1,863 **31.** $2,009 **34.** $3,439;
$.287 per mile

Lesson 8-6, pages 276–277
Class Exercises
1. $13,392 **4.** Ex. 2; Ex. 3; Ex. 1 **7.** $10,000
Exercises
1. $16,512 **4.** $18,780 **7.** $10,785

Lesson 8-7, pages 279–280
Class Exercises
1. 77 mi **4.** 3 h 59 min
Exercises
1. 30 mi **4.** 308 mi **7.** $425\frac{1}{4}$ mi **10.** 48 mi
13. 300 mi

Chapter 8 Review, pages 286–287
1. base price **4.** premium **7.** 1,140 **10.** $n = 2$
13. $12,519.33 **16.** $8,608.08 **19.** $33.54
22. $2,036 **25.** $4\frac{1}{2}$ h

Chapter 9

Lesson 9-1, pages 293–295
Class Exercises
1. 4 h 42 min   **4.** 7:15 to 9:15 = 2 h; 9:15 to 9:45 = $\frac{1}{2}$ h; add 1 h for time zone
Exercises
1. 4 h 31 min   **4.** 3 h 25 min   **7.** $168   **10.** $147
13. $73.80   **16. a.** First class 130% of coach so multiply coach by 1.3   **b.** 82 would be 147   **c.** 0.90 × 82 = 73.80

Lesson 9-2, pages 299–300
Class Exercises
1. 1,653 mi   **4.** 379 mi
Exercises
1. 542 mi   **4.** 2,756 mi   **7.** 399 mi   **10.** 3 h 4 min; 50.5 mi/h   **13.** $71.16   **16.** 2 h 20 min; 26 h 43 min (excluding layover time)

Lesson 9-3, pages 302–304
Class Exercises
1. $2.30   **4.** $41.63
Exercises
1. $10.50   **4.** $18.75   **7.** $15.40   **10.** $31.11
13. Taxi; $33 (car, $33)   **16.** $6.12   **19.** $6\frac{1}{8}$¢

Lesson 9-4, pages 306–307
Class Exercises
1. $226.21
Exercises
1. $1,070.40   **4.** 18¢   **10.** $105   **13.** 12¢

Lesson 9-5, pages 309–310
Class Exercises
1. $260   **4.** Ex. 1; Ex. 3; Ex. 2
Exercises
1. $111.20   **4.** $44   **7.** $7.25   **10.** $43.85

Chapter 9 Review, pages 316–317
1. time zone   **4.** 5 h 25 min   **7.** $44\frac{4}{5}$ **10.** $29.12
13. $114.40   **16.** 428 mi   **19.** $.15   **22.** $132.82
25. $.162, or 16.2¢ per mile   **28.** $5.61

Chapter 10

Lesson 10-1, pages 323–324
Class Exercises
1. $300   **4.** $6,000   **7.** $4,956
Exercises
1. $350   **4.** $4,800   **7.** Apt. 4   **10.** $425
13. $5,760   **16.** for example, commuting

Lesson 10-2, pages 326–328
Class Exercises
1. $575   **4.** $332.64

Exercises
1. $450   **4.** $1,124.15   **7.** $28   **10.** $9,318
13. $7,762.08   **16.** $350

Lesson 10-3, pages 330–331
Class Exercises
1. $1,200; $600   **4.** $79
Exercises
1. $2,000; $1,000   **4.** $9,200; $4,600   **7.** $77
10. $6,750

Lesson 10-4, pages 334–335
Class Exercises
1. 518 kWh   **4.** $75.75
Exercises
1. 182 kWh   **4.** $22.20   **7.** $24.38   **10.** $.06
13. $89.32

Lesson 10-5, pages 339–340
Class Exercises
1. $84.45   **4.** $2.14
Exercises
1. $64.50   **4.** $10.75   **7.** $2.57   **10.** Economy
13. 153 and over   **16.** $.32 initial, $.18 each additional minute

Chapter 10 Review, pages 346–347
1. lease   **4.** kilowatt-hours   **7.** $308.64   **10.** $970
13. $875   **16.** 0.963   **19.** $63.80   **22.** $6,000
25. $4,000   **28.** limited   **31.** $20.52

Chapter 11

Lesson 11-1, pages 353–354
Class Exercises
1. $9,552   **4.** $8,556.25
Exercises
1. $5,000   **4.** $9,552   **7.** $50,000   **10.** $128,300
13. $96,590

Lesson 11-2, pages 357–358
Class Exercises
1. $50,300   **4.** $142,912
Exercises
1. $900   **4.** $2,000   **7.** Ex. 4; Ex. 1, 5, 6; Ex. 2, 3
10. $1,910   **13.** $46,029.60

Lesson 11-3, pages 361–363
Class Exercises
1. $30,000   **4.** $2,520.21
Exercises
1. $20,000   **4.** $71,804   **7.** $1,640.21
10. $1,843.16   **13.** 58%   **16.** $1,260.53

Lesson 11-4, pages 365–367
Class Exercises

1. $72,000 *4.* $61,200
Exercises
1. $64,000 *4.* 0.8 × $80,000 = $64,000
7. $36,000 *10.* $81 more · *13.* $35,325 *16.* $35
19. $85,000

Lesson 11-5, pages 370–371
Class Exercises
1. $289.77 *4.* 1 gal
Exercises
1. $147.30 *4.* $504.90 *7.* $41.20 *10.* $189.62
13. How many quarts in a gallon? 500 ÷ 2 = 250
and 250 ÷ 2 = 125

Lesson 11-6, pages 373–374
Class Exercises
1. $630 *4.* $545
Exercises
1. $336 *4.* $413.49 *7.* $913.97 *10.* $804.45
13. $153

Chapter 11 Review, pages 380–381
1. mortgage *4.* Points *7.* $114.75 *10.* 0.85625
13. $3,675 *16.* 144 ft² *19.* $107,860
22. $71,250 *25.* $62,530 *28.* $64,000 *31.* $225

Chapter 12

Lesson 12-1, pages 388–389
Class Exercises
1. 542-54-5260 *4.* $1,321.30
Exercises
1. $29,356.80 *4.* $2,245.80 *7.* $2,446.40
10. $1,673.50 *13. a.* He stores his earnings in
memory and subtracts the amounts withheld. Then he
finds the percent that the remainder is of his original
salary. *b.* 21352 becomes 22352
c. [C$_E^C$] 29356.80 [M+] [−] 4967.88 [−] 2054.98
[−] 2245.80 [÷] [M$_C^R$] [×] 100 [=] 68.42755

Lesson 12-2, pages 392–393
Class Exercises
1. $23,819 *4.* $15,090
Exercises
1. $15,902 *4.* $41,871.09 *7.* $1,848.50
10. owed $87.60

Lesson 12-3, pages 396–397
Class Exercises
1. $10,820 *4.* $53,095
Exercises
1. $5,000 *4.* $39,300 *7.* $5,656.44
10. $982.80 *13.* owe, $6,249.74; refund, $753.05

Lesson 12-4, pages 400–402
Class Exercises
1. $625 *4.* $9,109
Exercises
1. $7,772 *4.* $1,360 *7.* Ex. 2, 4; Ex. 3, 5; Ex. 1,
6 *10.* $0 *13.* $1,805

Lesson 12-5, pages 404–406
Class Exercises
1. $1,300 *4.* $590 *7.* Ex. 1, 4; Ex. 2; Ex. 3, 5, 6
Exercises
1. $1,040 *4.* $1,500 *7.* $11,190 *10.* $1,224.60
13. $883.44 *16.* $1,269; $1,209; save $60 filing
separately

Chapter 12 Review, pages 412–413
1. W-2 form *4.* tax schedule *7.* $301.64
10. 0.03 *13.* $1,395 *16.* $41.85 *19.* $4,049.50
22. $540.05 *25.* $1,300

Chapter 13

Lesson 13-1, pages 420–421
Class Exercises
1. $1,327.59 *4.* 8.87%
Exercises
1. $173.47 *4.* $1,862.54 *7.* 9.96% *10.* 8198.19
[÷] 1.26162 [=] 6498.1452

Lesson 13-2, pages 424–425
Class Exercises
1. $50 *4.* $29.72 *7.* $135.45
Exercises
1. $25 *4.* $250 *7.* $579.80 *10.* $23.94
13. $215.66 *16.* $300

Lesson 13-3, pages 428–429
Class Exercises
1. 10.4% *4.* 12.5%
Exercises
1. $1,000 *4.* $1,020 *7.* $662.50 *10.* $796.25
13. $1,043.75 *16.* $645 *19.* $923.75
22. AmMot, EnCot, Foley *25.* more than 9.7%

Lesson 13-4, pages 432–433
Class Exercises
1. BaChefs *4.* $18,075 *7.* $30,855.50
Exercises
1. AlumCo; AaFunCo; Araln; BritOil *4.* AFG;
AaFunCo *7.* $6,225 *10.* 2.7% *13.* $2,106.13
16. $361.50 *19.* $1,453.60 profit

Lesson 13-5, pages 436–438
Class Exercises
1. $100 *4.* $12,141.88 *7.* $60.39

Exercises
1. $100   **4.** $156.92   **7.** $132,048.80   **10.** $29.69
13. $66.90   **16.** $15,301.74

Chapter 13 Review, pages 444–445
1. certificate of deposit   **4.** par value   **7.** stock
10. $6,350   **13.** 8%   **16.** 0.5   **19.** $51.92
22. $8.33%   **25.** $100   **28.** $8,450   **31.** $57.78

Chapter 14
Lesson 14-1, pages 452–453
Class Exercises
1. $300   **4.** $32.50   **7.** $1,850
Exercises
1. $400   **4.** $827   **7.** $53.33   **10.** $975
13. $9.25   **16.** $1,180

Lesson 14-2, pages 456–457
Class Exercises
1. $68.80   **4.** $1,190
Exercises
1. $65.50   **4.** $228.57   **7.** $85.15   **10.** $827.50
13. $146.40   **16.** $3,086.25   **19.** $16,000
22. 0.008

Lesson 14-3, pages 460–461
Class Exercises
1. $129.80   **4.** $2,320
Exercises
1. $247.50   **4.** $2,190   **7.** $9,984   **10.** $2,070

Lesson 14-4, pages 464–465
Class Exercises
1. 12 quarters   **4.** $275.40   **7.** $761.60
Exercises
1. 32   **4.** 34   **7.** $506.20   **10.** $1,110.60
13. $27,390.81

Lesson 14-5, pages 468–469
Class Exercises
1. $4,860.80   **4.** $1,053.78
Exercises
1. $3,600   **4.** $5,390.84   **7.** $663.70
10. $12,202.88

Chapter 14 Review, pages 476–477
1. health insurance   **4.** beneficiary   **7.** $2,235
10. $34   **13.** $2,871.67   **16.** $4.81   **19.** $721.60
22. 14   **25.** $14,454.55

Chapter 15
Lesson 15-1, pages 483–484

Class Exercises
1. $905.50   **4.** $1,129.70   **7.** $30
Exercises
1. $650   **4.** $868.84   **7.** $269.50
10. AM/FM tuner $226.96   **13.** $165
    Turntable $100.87
    Tape player $126.09
    Speakers $210.15
    Disc player $176.53

Lesson 15-2, pages 486–487
Class Exercises
1. CPU, monitor, extra disk drive, printer   **4.** 4
Exercises
1. Changes can be made easily   **4.** keyboard, disk
drive   **7.** 7   **10.** $2,287.50   **13.** $762.50

Lesson 15-3, pages 490–491
Class Exercises
1. $131   **4.** $405
Exercises
1. $92   **4.** $52   **7.** $98   **10.** 14   **13.** $1,303

Lesson 15-4, pages 494–495
Class Exercises
1. $184   **4.** $4.33
Exercises
1. $200   **4.** $24   **7.** 100   **10.** 2,016 ft   **13.** annual
fee of $75, $5 per visit; $30

Lesson 15-5, pages 497–498
Class Exercises
1. 90   **4.** 74
Exercises
1. 80   **4.** 79.75 or 80   **7.** 85   **10.** $250   **13.** 73.5
16. $1,062.50

Chapter 15 Review, pages 504–505
1. hardware   **4.** kilobyte   **7.** $1,089   **10.** $8,100
13. 206.67   **16.** $243   **19.** $225   **22.** $3\frac{1}{2}$ **25.** 31
28. $1.60   **31.** 87.5

Chapter 16
Lesson 16-1, pages 511–513
Class Exercises
1. $\frac{1}{3}$ **4.** 300
Exercises
1. $\frac{2}{5}$ **4.** 200   **7.** 420   **10.** Ex. 1–5, 9; Ex. 6; Ex. 7,
8   **13.** 11 h 40 min   **16.** 0.26 lb

Lesson 16-2, pages 515–516
Class Exercises
1. .250   **4.** $\frac{12}{35}$

Exercises
1. .250 **4.** .287 **7.** 4 **10.** $\frac{38}{135}$

Lesson 16-3, pages 518–519
Class Exercises
1. 36.8 **4.** median
Exercises
1. $25,900 **4.** median **7.** 1 (Talk show)
10. 17.5%

Lesson 16-4, pages 521–523
Class Exercises
4. 19
Exercises
4. $11,000 **7.** 32.9 **10.** mean **13.** 18.9 **19.** 17
22. mode **25.** $\frac{1}{10}$

Lesson 16-5, pages 525–527
Class Exercises
1. $1,800 **4.** $2\frac{1}{4}$
Exercises
1. 49.5 **4.** 79.5 **7.** 400,000 **10.** 2 **13.** 10%
16. 4 **19.** Because the scale begins at 30, not 0.

Chapter 16 Review, pages 534–535
1. mean **4.** batting average **7.** 0.18 **10.** 417
13. 18.67 **16.** 26 h 15 min **22.** 80 **25.** 12 lb
31. Include only months school is in session or graph by school week.

Acknowledgments

Photo Credits

Cover, John Martucci

2, Susan Van Etten 3, Dave Schaefer 4, Susan Van Etten 5, Dave Schaefer 6, John Coletti/Stock Boston 7, Dave Schaefer 8, John Martucci Studios 9, 10, Susan Van Etten 11, 12, Dave Schaefer 13, 14, 15, 16, Susan Van Etten 17, Dave Schaefer 18, 19, 20, 21, 22, 23, Susan Van Etten 24, 25, Dave Schaefer 26, Chuck Fishman/Woodfin Camp Inc. 27, 28, 29, Susan Van Etten 30, Dave Schaefer 31, Stacy Pick/Stock Boston 32, 34, 35, 36, Dave Schaefer 37, Bob Daemmrich/Stock Boston 38, 39, Susan Van Etten 40, 41, Julie Houck 42, Michal Heron/Monkmeyer Press 44, Eric Roth/The Picture Cube 45, Dave Schaefer 47, top, Joan Menschenfreund/Taurus Photos 47, bottom, Susan Van Etten 48, David Hiser/The Image Bank 49, Betsy Cole/The Picture Cube 50, Dave Schaefer 51, Paul Slaughter/The Image Bank 53, David Conklin 54, Pam Hasegawa/Taurus Photos 55, Alvis Upitis/The Image Bank 58, Michal Heron/Woodfin Camp and Associates 59, John Martucci Studios 60, 61, 62, 63, 68, 69, Julie Houck 70, Susan Van Etten 71, Paul Conklin 72, David Conklin 74, Carol Palmer/The Picture Cube 75, David Conklin 76, Rick Friedman/The Picture Cube 77, Susan Van Etten 79, Janice Fullman/The Picture Cube 80, Sobel Klonsky/The Image Bank 82, Susan Van Etten 83, Lawrence Fried/The Image Bank 84, Miro Vintoniv/The Picture Cube 86, Susan Van Etten 88, Dave Schaefer 91, Don Spiro/The Stock Shop 96, 97, Bill Leatherman 99, David Conklin 101, David York/Stock Shop 102, Peter Chapman 103, Susan Van Etten 106, Bob Daemmrich/Stock Boston 109, Susan Van Etten 110, Murray Alcosser/The Image Bank 113, Paul Conklin 117, 118 Susan Van Etten 121, David Conklin 124, 125, 127, Bill Leatherman 132, 133, Julie Houck 134, Donald Dietz/Stock Boston 137, Renate Hiller/Monkmeyer Press 139, Stacy Pick/Stock Boston 141, Andrew Brilliant/The Picture Cube 143, Susan Van Etten 145, Erdoes/Taurus Photos 146, Susan Van Etten 149, Dave Schaefer 152, Peter Menzel/Stock Boston 154, 155, 157, 162, 163, Julie Houck 164, Raoul Hackel/Stock Boston 168, Paul Conklin 170, Dave Schaefer 172, Tom Tracy/The Stock Shop 173, Susan Van Etten 177, Dave Schaefer/The Picture Cube 179, Charles Gupton/Southern Light 181, David York/The Stock Shop 184, 186, 187, Julie Houck 192, 193, Ken O'Donoghue 195, Frank Siteman/The Picture Cube 196, 199, Susan Van Etten 201, Ted Kawalerski/The Image Bank 203, Ellis Herwig/Stock Boston 205, David Conklin 206, Joan Menschenfreund/Taurus Photos 208, Walter Bibikow/The Image Bank 211, Mike Mazzachi/Stock Boston 212, Owen Franken/Stock Boston 214, 215 Ken O'Donoghue 217, Obremski/The Image Bank 222, David York/The Stock Shop 223, Ralph Mercer 225, R.P. Kingston/The Picture Cube 226, Paul Conklin 229, Michal Heron/Woodfin Camp and Associates 230, James Knowles/Stock Boston 232, Dave Schaefer 233, Susan Van Etten 234, Freda Leinwand/Monkmeyer Press 236, B.I. Ullmann/Taurus Photos 237, Hasegawa/Taurus Photos 239, Michal Heron/Woodfin Camp and Associates 241, Cary Wolinsky/Stock Boston

243, Mike Maple/Woodfin Camp and Associates 244, Susan Van Etten 246, 249, Ralph Mercer 254, 255, Bill Leatherman 257, Richard Hirnelson/The Stock Shop 259, Jose Fernandez/Woodfin Camp and Associates 262, John Coletti/Stock Boston 265, Dave Schaefer 267, David Conklin 268, Mike L. Wanamacker/Taurus Photos 272, Betsy Cole/The Picture Cube 273, Susan Van Etten 274, Betsy Cole/The Picture Cube 276, Audrey Gottlieb/Monkmeyer Press 279, Dallas & John Heaton/The Stock Shop 282, John Coletti/Stock Boston 283, Susan Van Etten 290, 291, Bill Leatherman 292, Ira Block/The Image Bank 294, Summer Productions/Taurus Photos 296, 297, L.L.T. Rhodes/Taurus Photos 299, 300, Bill Gallery/Stock Boston 302, Bill Anderson/Monkmeyer Press 303, Bryce Flynn/Stock Boston 304, Susan Van Etten 306, Sepp Seitz/Woodfin Camp and Associates 308, Bohdan Hrynewych/Stock Boston 309, Robert J. Capece/Monkmeyer Press 312, Bill Leatherman 313, Paul Conklin 315, Bill Leatherman 320, 321, Ken O'Donoghue 323, Michael Hayman/Stock Boston 326, Owen Franken/Stock Boston 327, Bruce Roberts 328, Susan Van Etten 329, Dave Schaefer 330, Martha Bates/Stock Boston 331, Susan Van Etten 332, David Conklin 333, Daniel Brody/Stock Boston 335, Frank Siteman/Stock Boston 336, Nancy Bates/The Picture Cube 339, David Conklin 340, Mike Mazzaschi/Stock Boston 342, Ida Wyman/Monkmeyer Press 343, 345, Ken O'Donoghue 350, 351, Bill Leatherman 352, Ellis Herwig/Stock Boston 353, Paul Von Stroheim/The Stock Shop 355, Frank Siteman/Stock Boston 356, Comstock 359, Bob Daemmrich/Stock Boston 361, John Coletti/Stock Boston 363, Dave Schaefer 364, John Coletti/Stock Boston 365, 366, 367, Susan Van Etten 369, Phaneuf/Gurdziel/The Picture Cube 370, Janice Fullman/The Picture Cube 373, Dave Schaefer 376, 378, Bill Leatherman 384, 385, Ken O'Donoghue 387, Bill Pasley/Stock Boston 392, Susan Van Etten 395, top, Pam Hasegawa/Taurus Photos 395, middle, Leonore Weber/Taurus Photos 395, bottom, Mark A. Mitteman/Taurus Photos 396, Susan Van Etten 397, Michael Heron/Woodfin Camp and Associates 398, Susan Van Etten 400, Billy E. Barnes 402, Billy E. Barnes/Stock Boston 405, Susan Van Etten 406, Paul Conklin 408, 410, Ken O'Donoghue 416, 417, Bill Leatherman 418, Susan Van Etten 420, Dave Schaefer 422, Brett Froomer/The Image Bank 424, The Granger Collection 425, Susan Van Etten 427, Robert McElroy/Woodfin Camp and Associates 428, Dick Luria/The Stock Shop 429, Chuck Fishman/Woodfin Camp and Associates 430, Stacy Pick/Stock Boston 432, Joe Azzara/The Stock Shop 434, Billy E. Barnes 436, Andrew Brilliant/The Picture Cube 438, Susan Van Etten 440, Bill Leatherman 441, 442, Susan Van Etten 448, 449, Bill Leatherman 451, Charles Gupton/Stock Boston 453, Milton Feinberg/Stock Boston 456, Tom Doody/The Picture Cube 462, Dave Schaefer 465, Billy E. Barnes 467, Mike Mazzaschi/Stock Boston 468, Lisl Dennis/The Image Bank 470, Martin Rogers/Stock Boston 472, 473, 475,

Bill Leatherman **480, 481,** Ralph Mercer **483, 485,** Susan Van Etten **486,** Dick Durrance II/Woodfin Camp and Associates **489,** Susan Van Etten **491,** Dave Schaefer **492,** Bob Daemmrich/Stock Boston **494,** Jon Feingersh/Stock Boston **496,** Susan Van Etten **500, 501, 503, 508, 509,** Ralph Mercer **510,** Michael L. Abramson/Woodfin Camp and Associates **513,** Mike Yamashita/ Woodfin Camp and Associates **514,** Bruce Roberts **516,** Mike Yamashita/The Stock Shop **517,** Bohdan Hrynewych/Stock Boston **519,** Susan Van Etten **521,** Dave Schaefer **523,** Bill Gallery/Stock Boston **525,** Susan Van Etten **527,** Edward L. Miller/Stock Boston **528,** Susan Van Etten **530, 532, 533,** Ralph Mercer

Illustration Credits

Michael Blaser: **pp 200, 235**

Boston Graphics, Inc.: **pp 26, 27, 29, 32, 33, 34, 114, 115, 140, 175, 263, 324, 338, 360, 539, 553**

Michael C. Burggren: **pp 124, 126, 142, 246, 247, 260, 261, 273, 284, 344, 377, 473, 501, 502, 532**

Sanderson Associates: **pp 278, 280**

Vantage Art, Inc.: **pp 48, 49, 55, 56, 57, 60, 61, 62, 63, 66, 70, 71, 72, 73, 74, 83, 84, 85, 89, 93, 94, 98, 99, 101, 103, 104, 105, 106, 107, 129, 135, 138, 143, 147, 150, 167, 168, 194, 198, 199, 202, 207, 210, 211, 212, 224, 227, 228, 231, 238, 242, 252, 256, 266, 267, 268, 269, 270, 271, 275, 276, 285, 295, 297, 298, 305, 313, 314, 322, 325, 329, 330, 333, 336, 337, 339, 368, 386, 388, 390, 391, 393, 394, 398, 399, 400, 403, 404, 409, 413, 414, 419, 423, 427, 430, 431, 435, 482, 485, 487, 488, 524, 525, 526, 527, 531, 536**